M

21/,

m/z

CALCULUS

CALCULUS

BY

EDWARD S. SMITH, M.E., Ph.D.
Professor of Mathematics, University of Cincinnati

MEYER SALKOVER, Ph.D.
Assistant Professor of Mathematics, University of Cincinnati

HOWARD K. JUSTICE, C.E., Ph.D.
Assistant Dean, University of Cincinnati

FIFTEENTH PRINTING

NEW YORK
JOHN WILEY & SONS, Inc.
London: CHAPMAN & HALL, Limited

PREFACE

This book is planned as a first course in calculus, and for the most part presupposes a knowledge of the mathematics generally taught in the freshman year.

The fundamental ideas and applications of both differential and integral calculus are presented as soon as possible in connection with polynomial functions, and are reconsidered as the other elementary functions are studied. This arrangement offers the following advantages. In the first place, we are firmly convinced that a student learns by repetition. Secondly, too many students form the impression that calculus is primarily a body of formulas and a technique for using them; this impression is not so likely to arise if the central problems of calculus are introduced at a stage when manipulation is comparatively simple. Thirdly, many students take calculus and physics concurrently, and whether or not these courses are correlated, an early acquaintance with integration will facilitate the understanding of mechanics and other branches of physics.

Every teacher of mathematics realizes that the average student is incapable of grasping the full significance of the subject unless moderate or even abundant emphasis is placed on applications. Whether an undergraduate course in mathematics be preparatory to pure research or constitute the basis for advanced technical training, constant attention to concrete aspects is a pedagogical necessity. However, this necessity should not be met at the expense of a reasonable standard of mathematical rigor. In addition to being inherently unsound, such a sacrifice would breed disrespect for the subject.

Imbued with these convictions, we have striven to prepare a book sufficiently practical, and at the same time adequately rigorous, for both technical and non-technical schools. In this connection we may cite the fact that, although Duhamel's Theorem is used in the development of formulas relating to applications of integration, the illustrative examples are, with one or two exceptions, free from refinements involving the theorem. This is because of our belief that the student, once having seen the justification for neglecting infinitesimals of higher order, should be trained to acquire facility in setting up directly definite integrals representing geometrical and physical quantities. As for the use

v

of Duhamel's Theorem in the solution of problems, the teacher may of course impose his own requirements.

An effort has been made to be honest with the student. Where a delicate question, too abstruse for thorough consideration, is not treated completely, a definite admission is made of the fact, in the hope that the better student may be stimulated to further study.

UNIVERSITY OF CINCINNATI,   EDWARD S. SMITH
January, 1938.   MEYER SALKOVER
                                                 HOWARD K. JUSTICE

CONTENTS

vii

CHAPTER IV

DIFFERENTIATION OF ALGEBRAIC FUNCTIONS

CHAPTER V

DIFFERENTIATION OF TRANSCENDENTAL FUNCTIONS

CHAPTER VI

FURTHER APPLICATIONS OF DERIVATIVES

CONTENTS

CHAPTER VII

PLANE CURVES—RECTANGULAR COÖRDINATES

CHAPTER VIII

INTEGRATION

CHAPTER IX

DEFINITE INTEGRALS

CHAPTER X

APPLICATIONS OF INTEGRATION

CHAPTER XI

APPROXIMATE INTEGRATION

CHAPTER XII

INDETERMINATE FORMS

CHAPTER XIII

INFINITE SERIES

A. General Discussion

B. Series of Constant Terms

C. Series of Variable Terms

CHAPTER XIV

EXPANSION OF FUNCTIONS

CHAPTER XV

HYPERBOLIC FUNCTIONS

CHAPTER XVI

PARTIAL DIFFERENTIATION

CHAPTER XVII

MULTIPLE INTEGRALS

CHAPTER XVIII

TABLE OF INTEGRALS

CALCULUS

CHAPTER I

VARIABLES, FUNCTIONS, AND LIMITS

1. Variables and Constants. Mathematical problems involve two kinds of quantities: **constants** and **variables**. In any given problem, a constant has a fixed value, while a variable may assume any of a set of values. The set of the permissible values of a variable in a given problem is called the **range** of the variable.

The slope-intercept form, $y = mx + b$, of the equation of a straight line will serve to bring out the distinction between constants and variables. This equation may refer to any line not parallel to the y-axis; but once a definite line is chosen, m and b are constants characterizing the line. The quantities x and y, the coördinates of any point of the line, are variables; their values change as we pass from one point to another. If the line is oblique with respect to the coördinate axes, the ranges of both variables, x and y, are unlimited.

Again, in the equation $x^2 + y^2 = r^2$ of a circle with center at the origin, the radius r is constant for a particular circle, while x and y are variables each having a range from $-r$ to r.

In the given examples the constants m, b, and r differ from line to line, or from circle to circle, as the case may be. Thus, according to the direction of the line, m may have any positive or negative value. Similarly, since there are no limitations on the size of a circle, r may have any positive value. Constants, like m, b, and r, whose values are arbitrary previous to being specified are called **arbitrary constants** or **parameters**. Numbers, such as 2, $\sqrt{3}$, and π, whose values are the same in all problems are called **absolute constants**.

2. Functions. Let us consider once more the equation $y = mx + b$; for the sake of definiteness, let the constants m and b have the values 2 and 3, respectively. Then we have

$$y = 2x + 3.$$

For any value assigned to x, a corresponding value of y is determined.

1

Thus, if $x = 1$, $y = 5$; if $x = 4$, $y = 11$.   A variable, such as y in this example, whose value depends on the value assigned to another variable (here x) is said to be a **function** of the other variable.

A function of a variable x is said to be **single-valued** for $x = a$ if only one value of the function corresponds to $x = a$.   Thus, in the equation $y = 2x + 3$, y is single-valued for every value of x.   A function of a variable x is said to be **multiple-valued** for $x = a$ if two or more values of the function correspond to $x = a$.   To illustrate a simple case of a multiple-valued function, let us consider y defined as a function of x by the equation $x^2 + y^2 = r^2$.   Here to every value of x numerically less than r, there correspond two real values of y, namely, the positive and negative square roots of $r^2 - x^2$.   We may, however, decompose this double-valued function into a pair of functions, namely $\sqrt{r^2 - x^2}$ and $- \sqrt{r^2 - x^2}$, each of which is single-valued; these are called **branches** of the original function.

In this book we shall be concerned primarily with single-valued functions.

The idea of function, far from being confined to abstract mathematics, occurs frequently in science and even in ordinary experience.   Thus, for a fixed electromotive force (E), the current (I) passing through a circuit is a function of the resistance (R), according to the simple formula known as Ohm's Law: $I = \dfrac{E}{R}.$ If, by use of a standard cell, E is fixed say at 2 volts, and we put in succession various resistances into the circuit, the value of the current will be determined by the resistance used.   If R is, for instance, 5 ohms, then I is $\frac{2}{5}$ ampere.   If we are free to change cells as well as resistances, that is, if E as well as R is variable, then I is a function of the two variables E and R.   Functions of more than two variables also exist.

3. Independent and Dependent Variables.   We have seen that the equation $y = 2x + 3$ expresses y as a function of x.   In obtaining pairs of values of x and y that satisfy this equation, values were freely assigned to x, and the corresponding values of y depended on the substitutions made for x.   On account of this fact, it is customary to call x the **independent variable** and y the **dependent variable**.   The rôles of dependent and independent variables are often interchangeable.   Thus, if we solve $y = 2x + 3$ for x, we obtain

$$x = \tfrac{1}{2}(y - 3),$$

and here x is represented as a function of y, or, to use our new terms y is the independent and x the dependent variable.

A symbol commonly used to denote a function of x alone is $f(x)$, read " f-function of x," or " f of x." The function designated as $f(x)$ may have a definite mathematical expression, while again it may be quite arbitrary except for satisfying conditions of a general nature. If in the same discussion reference must be made to two or more functions of x, separate functional symbols $f(x)$, $F(x)$, $g(x)$, etc., may be introduced to denote them.

The functional symbol $f(x)$ affords a convenient means of indicating substitutions for x. Thus, the result of substituting a for x in $f(x)$ is denoted by $f(a)$; the result of substituting 3 for x, by $f(3)$.

For example, if

$$f(x) = x^2 + x - 6,$$

then

$$f(a) = a^2 + a - 6,$$

and

$$f(3) = 3^2 + 3 - 6 = 6.$$

PROBLEMS

1. If $f(x) = x^3 - 2x^2 + 2x - 4$, show that $f(0) = -4, f(1) = -3, f(-1) = -9$, and $f(2) = 0$.

2. Find $f(0)$, $f(2)$, $f(-2)$, and $f(14)$ if $f(x) = \dfrac{8}{4 + x^2}$.

3. If $f(x) = \log_{10}(x + 2)$, find $f(98)$.

4. If $f(x) = \sin^2 x$, find $f(x) + f(90° - x)$. (See Formulas 15(c) and 16(a), p. 508.)

5. If $f(x) = 2^{1-x}$, find $f(0), f(1)$, and $f(-3)$.

6. If $f(x) = x^x$, find $f(1), f(-2)$, and $f(\frac{3}{2})$.

7. If $f(x) = \dfrac{1}{x}$, show that $f(x + a) - f(x - a) = \dfrac{2a}{a^2 - x^2}$.

8. If $f(x) = \dfrac{1}{\sqrt{x + 1}}$, show that $f(x - 1) - f(x) = \dfrac{1}{x\sqrt{x + 1} + (x + 1)\sqrt{x}}$.

9. If $f(x) = \log x$, show that $f(yz) = f(y) + f(z)$. (See Formula 4(a), p. 507.)

10. If $f(x) = \log \dfrac{x}{x - 1}$, show that $f(y + 1) + f(y) = \log \dfrac{y + 1}{y - 1}$.

4. Limit of a Variable. If a variable x approaches more and more closely a constant value a, so that $|a - x|$ * eventually becomes and remains less than any preassigned number, however small, the constant a is said to be the **limit** of the variable x.

---

* The essentially positive quantity $|N|$, read " **numerical value** of N " or " **absolute value** of N," N being real, is N if N is a positive number and $-N$ if N is negative. Thus $|5| = |-5| = 5$. Hence $|a - x|$ means the result of subtracting x from a with the sign changed to plus if the difference should be negative.

Consider, for instance, a variable that assumes the sequence of values $\frac{1}{2}$, $\frac{1}{4}$, $\frac{1}{8}$, $\frac{1}{16}$, $\cdots$, $\frac{1}{2^n}$, $\cdots$. This variable is approaching zero as a limit because the numerical value of the difference between zero and the variable eventually becomes and remains less than any preassigned number, however small. For definiteness, let the assigned number be $\frac{1}{100,000}$. It is easily seen that the sixteenth value of the variable is $\frac{1}{65,536}$; the next value differs numerically from zero by less than $\frac{1}{100,000}$, and so do all subsequent values. If the variable is called x, then, by definition, the limit of x is zero, or, in the customary notation, $\lim x = 0$.

5. Theorems on Limits. We shall require several fundamental theorems on limits. Although these theorems are apparently self-evident, rigorous proofs could be given. However, as the proofs are too abstract for a beginning student, we shall merely state the theorems.

THEOREM 1. *The limit of the sum of a finite number of variables is the sum of their respective limits.*

THEOREM 2. *The limit of the product of a finite number of variables is the product of their respective limits.*

THEOREM 3. *The limit of the product of a variable by a constant is the constant times the limit of the variable.*

THEOREM 4. *The limit of the quotient of two variables is the quotient of the limits of the variables, if the divisor has a limit other than zero.*

THEOREM 5. *If a variable never decreases and never becomes greater than a fixed number, then it approaches a limit which is not greater than the number.*

THEOREM 6. *If a variable never increases and never becomes less than a fixed number, the variable approaches a limit which is not less than the number.*

Example 1. Let a variable assume the sequence of values 2, $2\frac{1}{2}$, $2\frac{2}{3}$, $2\frac{3}{4}$, $2\frac{4}{5}$, $\cdots$. It never exceeds 3. Then, by Theorem 5, it approaches a limit which is not greater than 3. As a matter of fact, the limit is exactly 3, as may be shown by the following argument:

The values successively assumed by the variable may be expressed by the formula $2 + \frac{n}{n+1}$ ($n = 0, 1, 2, \cdots$). With increasing n, the fraction $\frac{n}{n+1}$ approaches unity so that for sufficiently large n the difference $1 - \frac{n}{n+1}$ becomes, and for larger n

remains, less than any assigned positive constant, however small. Thus, if the assigned constant is $\dfrac{1}{1{,}000{,}000}$, then for any $n \geqq 1{,}000{,}000$, $1 - \dfrac{n}{n+1} < \dfrac{1}{1{,}000{,}000}$.

Hence, by definition, $\lim \dfrac{n}{n+1} = 1$ and $\lim \left(2 + \dfrac{n}{n+1} \right) = 3$; this limit is approached but never attained.

Example 2. Let a variable assume the sequence of values 2, $1\frac{9}{10}$, $1\frac{10}{12}$, $1\frac{11}{14}$, $1\frac{12}{16}$, $1\frac{13}{18}$, $\cdots$. The variable never increases—in fact, it steadily decreases—and it is never less than $1\frac{1}{2}$. By Theorem 6, therefore, the variable approaches a limit which is not less than $1\frac{1}{2}$. It can be shown that the limit is exactly $1\frac{1}{2}$.

6. Limiting Value of a Function. A function of a variable may or may not approach a limit as the variable approaches a limit.   If, when x approaches a, $f(x)$ approaches a limit l, we express this fact thus:

$$\lim_{x \to a} f(x) = l,$$

read " the limit, as x approaches a, of $f(x)$ is l." When we use the symbol $\lim\limits_{x \to a} f(x)$, we imply that the variable x is allowed to approach a in any manner whatever. In case the function approaches two different limits according as x approaches a through values larger than a or through values smaller than a, we designate them, respectively, by $\lim\limits_{x \to a^+} f(x)$ and $\lim\limits_{x \to a^-} f(x)$, where $x \to a^+$ may be read " as x approaches a from the right " and $x \to a^-$, " as x approaches a from the left." But since under such circumstances no unique limit is approached, we may say that $\lim\limits_{x \to a} f(x)$ does not then exist.

To illustrate a function for which $\lim\limits_{x \to a} f(x)$ exists, let us take $f(x) = x^2 + \dfrac{1}{x}$ and $a = 2$.   Since $\lim\limits_{x \to 2} x = 2$, it follows from Theorems 1, 2, and 4 of the preceding article that

$$\lim_{x \to 2} f(x) = \lim_{x \to 2} \left(x^2 + \frac{1}{x} \right) = \lim_{x \to 2} (x^2) + \lim_{x \to 2} \left(\frac{1}{x} \right) = \left(\lim_{x \to 2} x \right)^2 + \tfrac{1}{2} = 4\tfrac{1}{2}.$$

Four cases will be considered in connection with the limit of a function.

Case 1: $\lim\limits_{x \to a} f(x)$ exists and equals $f(a)$. This case has just been illustrated for $f(x) = x^2 + \dfrac{1}{x}$ and $a = 2$.

Case 2: $\lim\limits_{x \to a} f(x)$ exists but $f(a)$ is not defined. Consider, for instance, $f(x) = \dfrac{x^2 - 1}{x - 1}$ and $a = 1$. Since for all values of x except

$x = 1$, $\dfrac{x^2 - 1}{x - 1} = x + 1$, and as x approaches 1, this reduction continues to be valid, we have

$$\lim_{x \to 1} f(x) = \lim_{x \to 1} (x + 1) = 2.$$

Nevertheless, $f(1)$ is not defined, because the denominator of $\dfrac{x^2 - 1}{x - 1}$ becomes zero when $x = 1$.*

Case 3: $f(a)$ is defined but $\lim\limits_{x \to a} f(x)$ does not exist. As an example, we may cite $f(x) = (x + 1) \sqrt{(x - 2)(x + 2)}$, for which we at once find that $f(-1)$ exists; in fact, $f(-1) = 0$.

If, however, we restrict $f(x)$ to real values, then $\lim\limits_{x \to -1} f(x)$ is without meaning. For $f(x)$ is imaginary for values of x numerically less than 2, with the single exception of $x = -1$. Hence if we restrict ourselves to the domain of real numbers, $f(x)$ cannot be regarded as approaching a limit as x approaches -1.†

Case 4: $\lim\limits_{x \to a} f(x)$ does not exist and $f(a)$ is not defined. Consider, for example, $f(x) = x^2 + \dfrac{1}{x}$ and let $a = 0$. As x approaches 0, $f(x)$ increases indefinitely in numerical value on account of the term $\dfrac{1}{x}$, and therefore $\lim\limits_{x \to 0} f(x)$ does not exist; moreover, $f(0)$ is not defined because division by zero is excluded.

7. Continuity. A single-valued function $f(x)$ is said to be **continuous** for $x = a$ if $f(a)$ is defined and if $\lim\limits_{x \to a} f(x) = f(a)$. The latter condition implies that $f(x)$ is defined also for a range of values extending on either side of $x = a$; that is, if b is any value of x belonging to the range, the substitution of b for x leads to the determinate real value $f(b)$.

If $f(x)$ is continuous for every value of x in a range (or interval) of values of x, it is said to be continuous throughout the range (or interval).

Of the four cases treated in the preceding article, the first is that of a function continuous for $x = a$, while the remaining three cases deal with functions **discontinuous** for $x = a$. Thus the functions $x^2 + \dfrac{1}{x}$, which was cited under Cases 1 and 4, is discontinuous for $x = 0$ but continuous for all other values of x.

---

* This example will be further discussed in the next article.

† The graph of the equation $y = (x + 1) \sqrt{(x - 2)(x + 2)}$ is said to have an **isolated point** at $(-1, 0)$.

If a single-valued function $f(x)$ is continuous for every value of x in the range or interval $a < x < b$,* the corresponding portion of the graph of the equation $y = f(x)$ will be unbroken. For there will be a point of the curve for any value of x, say c, belonging to the interval. Moreover, since $\lim\limits_{x \to c} f(x) = f(c)$, it follows that for values of x sufficiently close to c we may obtain points on the curve whose ordinates differ from $f(c)$ by arbitrarily small amounts. Hence the curve has no break in the neighborhood of the point $(c, f(c))$. We thus see that functions which are continuous according to the formal mathematical definition of the term have graphs that are continuous in the ordinary sense of the word.

While a function having the properties described under Case 2 of the preceding article is discontinuous for $x = a$, it is possible by a supplementary definition to remove this discontinuity. For example, consider again the function $f(x) = \dfrac{x^2 - 1}{x - 1}$. Although $f(1)$ is originally undefined, $f(x)$ can be rendered continuous for $x = 1$ by defining $f(1)$ to be 2, for then $\lim\limits_{x \to 1} f(x) = f(1)$.

The situation will be made clearer by considering the graph of the equation $y = \dfrac{x^2 - 1}{x - 1}$ (Fig. 7). Since, for all values of x except unity, we have the identity $\dfrac{x^2 - 1}{x - 1} = x + 1$, the graph, save for the lack of a point corresponding to $x = 1$, is simply the straight-line locus of the equation $y = x + 1$. The supplementary definition serves to insert the

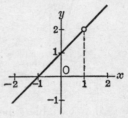

Fig. 7

missing point of this line and to render the graph of $y = \dfrac{x^2 - 1}{x - 1}$ continuous.

8. Infinity. If, as x approaches a, $f(x)$ becomes and remains greater than any assigned positive constant, however large, then $f(x)$ is said to *increase without limit*, or to *become positively infinite*. In symbols this is often expressed as

$$\lim_{x \to a} f(x) = \infty,$$

where ∞ is read "infinity." The notation, however, is objectionable, because $f(x)$ is in reality not approaching a limit, and infinity is not a number. We therefore prefer the statement that $f(x)$ increases without limit, or becomes positively infinite, as x approaches a.

* Read " x greater than a but less than b."

Similarly, if, as x approaches a, $f(x)$ becomes and remains less than any assigned negative number of arbitrarily large absolute value, $f(x)$ is said to *decrease without limit*, or to *become negatively infinite*. In symbols this is often expressed as

$$\lim_{x \to a} f(x) = -\infty,$$

though likewise in this case the limit does not exist.

A function $f(x)$ which becomes either positively or negatively infinite as x approaches a is obviously discontinuous for $x = a$, because neither $f(a)$ nor $\lim_{x \to a} f(x)$ exists (cf. Case 4, Art. 6).

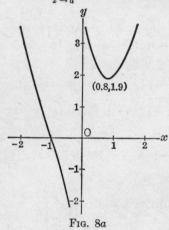

Fig. 8a

Example 1. Discuss the discontinuity of $f(x) = x^2 + \dfrac{1}{x}$. As has been noted in the preceding article, $f(x)$ is discontinuous for $x = 0$ alone. To determine the nature of the discontinuity, we note that, if x is allowed to approach zero through positive values, $f(x)$ eventually becomes and remains greater than any arbitrarily large positive constant which may be assigned, for instance 10^9. For $f(x) > 10^9$ when $0 < x < 10^{-9}$. Hence, by definition, $f(x)$ becomes positively infinite as x approaches zero from the positive side. Similarly, it can be shown that $f(x)$ becomes negatively infinite as x approaches zero from the negative side.

The graph of the equation $y = x^2 + \dfrac{1}{x}$ is shown in Fig. 8a.

As a variable x becomes positively infinite, a function $f(x)$ may or may not approach a limit. If it does approach a limit l, we may express this fact by means of the equation

$$\lim_{x \to \infty} f(x) = l.$$

In using the symbol $\lim_{x \to \infty} f(x)$ we must clearly understand that x is increasing indefinitely and not approaching a limit.

Similarly, if $f(x)$ approaches a limit l as x becomes negatively infinite, we may write

$$\lim_{x \to -\infty} f(x) = l.$$

As instances of functions which do not approach limits as the independent variable becomes infinite, we may cite $x^2 + \dfrac{1}{x}$ and $\sin x$. The first of these becomes positively infinite (cf. Fig. 8a) as x becomes either positively or negatively infinite; the second function, sin x, continues to oscillate between the values 1 and -1, approaching no limit as x becomes either positively or negatively infinite.

Example 2. Discuss the discontinuity of $f(x) = 2 + \dfrac{1}{(x-1)^2}$; also determine $\lim\limits_{x \to \pm\infty} f(x)$.

The function is discontinuous for $x = 1$, because then the denominator of the fraction vanishes. As x approaches unity from either direction, $f(x)$ becomes positively infinite.

As x becomes infinite in either sense, the fraction $\dfrac{1}{(x-1)^2}$ tends to zero and $f(x)$ approaches 2 as a limit. That is, $\lim\limits_{x \to \pm\infty} f(x) = 2$.

The graph of the equation $y = 2 + \dfrac{1}{(x-1)^2}$ is shown in Fig. 8b.

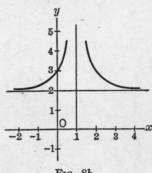

Fig. 8b

As a more complicated illustration of the ideas of limit, continuity, and infinity, let us consider

Example 3. Discuss the discontinuity of $f(x) = \dfrac{2^{\frac{1}{x-3}} + 1}{2^{\frac{1}{x-3}} - 1}$.

For convenience we reduce the fraction to a mixed expression, obtaining

$$f(x) = 1 + \frac{2}{2^{\frac{1}{x-3}} - 1}.$$

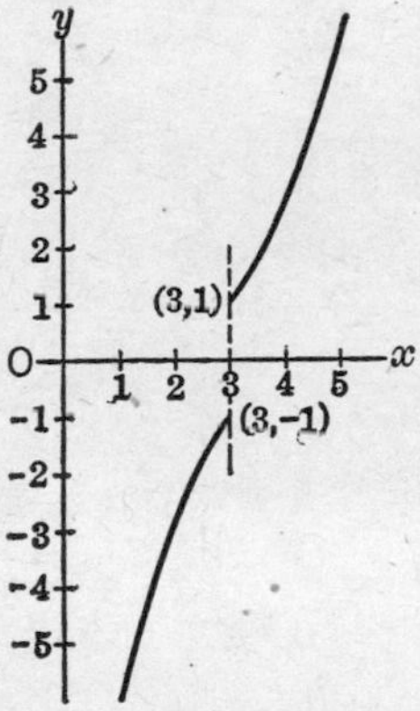

Since division by zero is excluded, the exponent, and therefore the function $f(x)$, is not defined for $x = 3$. Hence $f(x)$ is discontinuous for this value of x.

As x approaches 3 from the right, $2^{\frac{1}{x-3}} - 1$ becomes positively infinite. Consequently

$$\lim_{x \to 3^+} \frac{2}{2^{\frac{1}{x-3}} - 1} = 0$$

and

$$\lim_{x \to 3^+} f(x) = 1.$$

As x approaches 3 from the left, $2^{\frac{1}{x-3}} - 1$ approaches -1. Hence

$$\lim_{x \to 3^-} f(x) = 1 - 2 = -1.$$

Fig. 8c

Thus as x increases through 3, the value of the function jumps suddenly from -1 to $+1$. Accordingly, we say that $f(x)$ has a finite discontinuity for $x = 3$.

In Fig. 8c is shown the graph of the equation $y = \dfrac{2^{\frac{1}{x-3}} + 1}{2^{\frac{1}{x-3}} - 1}$.

PROBLEMS

Verify the limits given in Problems 1 to 10, inclusive:

1. $\lim_{x \to 2} (x^2 - x + 1) = 3.$

2. $\lim_{h \to 0} \dfrac{x^2 - h^2}{x^2 + 2hx + h^2} = 1.$

3. $\lim_{x \to \infty} \dfrac{x^2 - 3x + 2}{x^2 - 4x + 3} = 1.$

HINT: Divide numerator and denominator by x^2, the highest power of x present, and use the fact that $\lim_{x \to \infty} \dfrac{1}{x} = 0.$

4. $\lim_{x \to \infty} \dfrac{x^3 - 5x + 1}{2x^3 - 4x^2 + 3x - 2} = \dfrac{1}{2}.$

5. $\lim_{x \to 0} (a^x + a^{-x}) = 2.$

6. $\lim_{x \to 0} \dfrac{a^x - a^{-x}}{a^x + a^{-x}} = 0.$

7. $\lim_{x \to \infty} \dfrac{6 - x}{x^2 + x - 2} = 0.$

8. $\lim_{h \to 0} \dfrac{\sqrt{x + h} - \sqrt{x}}{h\sqrt{x(x + h)}} = \dfrac{1}{2x\sqrt{x}}.$

HINT: Multiply numerator and denominator by $\sqrt{x + h} + \sqrt{x}.$

9. $\lim_{h \to 0} \dfrac{\sqrt{x + h} - \sqrt{x}}{h} = \dfrac{1}{2\sqrt{x}}.$

10. $\lim_{x \to \infty} \dfrac{\sqrt[3]{2x^4 - x^3 + 5}}{\sqrt[6]{x^8 - x^4 + 1}} = \sqrt[3]{2}.$

11. If $f(x) = \dfrac{1}{2x}$, find $\lim_{h \to 0} \dfrac{f(x + h) - f(x)}{h}.$

12. If $f(x) = 2x - x^2$, find $\lim_{h \to 0} \dfrac{f(x + h) - f(x)}{h}.$

13. Find $\lim_{x \to 3} \dfrac{x^2 - 9}{x^2 - 4x + 3}.$

14. Find $\lim_{x \to 2} \dfrac{x - 2}{x^2 - 3x + 2}.$

15. Find $\lim_{x \to 1^+} \dfrac{\sqrt{(x^2 - 1)^3}}{x^2 - x}.$

16. Show that $\lim\limits_{x \to 3^+} \dfrac{\sqrt{x-3}}{x^2-9}$ does not exist, the function becoming infinite.

17. Show that $\lim\limits_{x \to -2} \dfrac{x^2-4}{x^2+4x+4}$ does not exist.

18. Show that $\lim\limits_{x \to 0} \sin \dfrac{1}{x}$ does not exist.

19. Show that $\lim\limits_{x \to 0} \tan \dfrac{1}{x}$ does not exist.

20. Show that $\lim\limits_{x \to 0} x \sin \dfrac{1}{x} = 0$.

Find the values of x for which the following functions are discontinuous and discuss the discontinuity.

21. $\dfrac{x+1}{x+2}$.

22. $\dfrac{x}{x^2-5x+6}$.

23. $\dfrac{x^2+1}{x^2}$.

24. $\sqrt{x^4-x^2}$.

25. $\dfrac{x+1}{x^2-4}$.

26. $\dfrac{x^2-9}{x^2+2x-3}$.

27. $\dfrac{1}{(x+2)^2}$.

28. $\tan 2x$.

29. $\sec 3x$.

30. $\dfrac{1}{1-\cos x}$.

31. $\dfrac{\sin^2 x}{1+\cos x}$.

32. $\csc x - \cot \dfrac{x}{2}$.

CHAPTER II

DIFFERENTIATION AND APPLICATIONS

9. Increment of a Function. In Chapter I, a variable $f(x)$ whose value depends on the value assigned to the independent variable x was defined to be a function of x. It follows that a change in the value of x, called an **increment** of x, will, in general, give rise to an increment of the function; the latter increment may be calculated if $f(x)$ has, as will be assumed, a definite mathematical expression. In this chapter we shall study a fundamental operation of calculus, known as **differentiation,** which develops from a comparison of the corresponding increments of a function and its independent variable.

10. Increment Notation. Let y be a continuous, single-valued function of x, defined by the equation

$$(1) \qquad\qquad y = f(x).$$

In (1) we may regard x as an initial value of the independent variable, in which case y will denote the initial value of the function. Let Δx, read " delta x," represent an increment of the independent variable. If the variable x increases, Δx is positive; if it decreases, Δx is negative. The corresponding increment of the function, whether positive or negative, will be denoted by Δy, or $\Delta f(x)$. Since the final value of x is $x + \Delta x$, (1) shows that the final value of the function is given by

$$(2) \qquad\qquad y + \Delta y = f(x + \Delta x).$$

Subtracting (1) from (2), we obtain for the increment of y or $f(x)$

$$(3) \qquad \Delta y = \Delta f(x) = f(x + \Delta x) - f(x).$$

It should be clearly understood that Δx and Δy are not the products of a quantity Δ and the respective variables, but are merely symbols for the increments of these variables.

Example. If $y = x + x^2$, find the increment of y when x changes from 2 to 2.1.
First Method. Since $x + \Delta x = 2.1$, it follows from (2) that

$$y + \Delta y = 2.1 + (2.1)^2 = 6.51;$$

and since

$$y = 2 + 2^2 = 6,$$

12

we find

$$\Delta y = 6.51 - 6 = 0.51.$$

Second Method. Using (3), we have

$$\Delta y = x + \Delta x + (x + \Delta x)^2 - (x + x^2)$$
$$= x + \Delta x + x^2 + 2x \cdot \Delta x + (\Delta x)^2 - x - x^2$$
$$= \Delta x + 2x \cdot \Delta x + (\Delta x)^2.$$

This is a general expression for the increment of $y = x + x^2$ for arbitrary values of x and Δx. Substituting $x = 2$ and $\Delta x = 0.1$, we find

$$\Delta y = 0.1 + 0.4 + 0.01 = 0.51.$$

11. Average Rate of Change. On dividing the increment of y, given by (3) of the preceding article, by Δx, we obtain

(1) $$\frac{\Delta y}{\Delta x} = \frac{f(x + \Delta x) - f(x)}{\Delta x}.$$

This represents the average change of y per unit change of x, or *the average rate of change of y with respect to x* in the interval Δx.

Thus, if $y = x + x^2$, and we place $x = 2$ and $\Delta x = 0.1$, so that $\Delta y = 0.51$, as in the example above, we have

$$\frac{\Delta y}{\Delta x} = 5.1;$$

hence, as x changes from 2 to 2.1, y is changing, on the average, at the rate of 5.1 units per unit change of x. The significance of the phrase " on the average " will become clear when we subdivide the interval from 2 to 2.1; then it is found by computation that, as x increases from 2 to 2.05, y increases 0.2525 unit, while as x increases from 2.05 to 2.1, y increases 0.2575 unit. As these increments of y, corresponding to equal increments of x, are different, y does not maintain a uniform rate of change with respect to x within the interval from $x = 2$ to $x = 2.1$.

In the same example, we found, for any x and any Δx,

$$\Delta y = \Delta x + 2x \cdot \Delta x + (\Delta x)^2.$$

Hence

$$\frac{\Delta y}{\Delta x} = 1 + 2x + \Delta x,$$

and this is a general expression for the average rate of change of $y = x + x^2$ with respect to x in the interval from x to $x + \Delta x$.

This illustrates the fact that $\dfrac{\Delta y}{\Delta x}$ depends, in general, on x (i.e., the initial value of the independent variable) and on Δx.

12. Derivative; Rate of Change. Since the initial value of x, once assigned, is fixed, $\dfrac{\Delta y}{\Delta x}$ may be regarded as a function of Δx alone. As Δx approaches zero, $\dfrac{\Delta y}{\Delta x}$ may or may not approach a limit. If it does, the limit in question may be interpreted as the rate of change of y with respect to x for the initial value of x.

From (1) of the preceding article, we obtain

$$(1) \qquad \lim_{\Delta x \to 0} \frac{\Delta y}{\Delta x} = \lim_{\Delta x \to 0} \frac{f(x + \Delta x) - f(x)}{\Delta x},$$

provided that this limit exists. Since $f(x)$ has been assumed continuous (Art. 7), $\lim\limits_{\Delta x \to 0} f(x + \Delta x) = f(x)$. Hence both Δy and Δx are approaching zero; but their quotient may approach a finite limit, even though $\dfrac{\Delta y}{\Delta x}$ is not defined for $\Delta x = 0$. We have already encountered situations of this sort under Case 2, Art. 6.

The limit (1) is called **the derivative of y with respect to x,** and will for the present usually be denoted by the symbol $D_x y$. Other symbols in common use are

$$D_x f(x),\ y',\ f'(x),\ \frac{dy}{dx},\ \text{and}\ \frac{d}{dx} f(x).$$

The last two of these imply a point of view which will be given in Art. 24.

By definition, then, we have, when $y = f(x)$,

$$(2) \qquad D_x y = \lim_{\Delta x \to 0} \frac{\Delta y}{\Delta x} = \lim_{\Delta x \to 0} \frac{f(x + \Delta x) - f(x)}{\Delta x}.$$

The process of finding $D_x y$ from an equation defining y as a function of x is called **differentiation.** Functions for which the limit constituting the derivative exists are said to be **differentiable.** The functions with which we shall deal are differentiable except possibly for particular values of the independent variable.

It follows from (2) that no function of x can possess a derivative for values of x for which the function is discontinuous. However, the continuity of a function is not sufficient to guarantee the existence of a derivative; in fact, functions may be cited which are continuous for every value of the independent variable and yet possess no derivatives.

Example 1. If $y = x + x^2$, find $D_x y$ (a) for any value of x; (b) for $x = 2$.
In the preceding article, we found, for this function,

$$\frac{\Delta y}{\Delta x} = 1 + 2x + \Delta x.$$

Hence, by (2),

$$D_x y = \lim_{\Delta x \to 0} \frac{\Delta y}{\Delta x} = \lim_{\Delta x \to 0} (1 + 2x + \Delta x) = 1 + 2x,$$

for any value of x. In particular, for $x = 2$,

$$D_x y = 5.$$

Since differentiation is of fundamental importance in calculus, it is desirable to summarize the procedure involved in differentiating a function.

We start from the relation

$$y = f(x)$$

and give x the increment Δx; whereupon y becomes

$$y + \Delta y = f(x + \Delta x).$$

Subtracting y from $y + \Delta y$, we obtain

$$\Delta y = f(x + \Delta x) - f(x).$$

Next we divide Δy by Δx; the quotient,

$$\frac{\Delta y}{\Delta x} = \frac{f(x + \Delta x) - f(x)}{\Delta x},$$

is the average rate of change of y with respect to x in the interval from x to $x + \Delta x$. Finally, passing to the limit as Δx approaches zero, we obtain the derivative of y with respect to x:

$$D_x y = \lim_{\Delta x \to 0} \frac{\Delta y}{\Delta x} = \lim_{\Delta x \to 0} \frac{f(x + \Delta x) - f(x)}{\Delta x}.$$

This result represents **the rate of change of y with respect to x** at the beginning of the interval.

Example 2. Find $D_x y$ for $y = x^3$.
Performing the steps listed above, we have

$$y + \Delta y = (x + \Delta x)^3 = x^3 + 3x^2 \cdot \Delta x + 3x(\Delta x)^2 + (\Delta x)^3,$$

whence

$$\Delta y = 3x^2 \cdot \Delta x + 3x(\Delta x)^2 + (\Delta x)^3,$$

$$\frac{\Delta y}{\Delta x} = 3x^2 + 3x \cdot \Delta x + (\Delta x)^2,$$

and

$$D_x y = \lim_{\Delta x \to 0} \frac{\Delta y}{\Delta x} = \lim_{\Delta x \to 0} (3x^2 + 3x \cdot \Delta x + (\Delta x)^2) = 3x^2.$$

Example 3. If $y = \dfrac{x}{x-1}$, find $D_x y$ (a) for any value of x; (b) for $x = 3$.

Proceeding as above, we obtain

$$y + \Delta y = \frac{x + \Delta x}{x + \Delta x - 1}$$

and

$$\Delta y = \frac{x + \Delta x}{x + \Delta x - 1} - \frac{x}{x - 1}$$

$$= \frac{(x + \Delta x)(x - 1) - x(x + \Delta x - 1)}{(x + \Delta x - 1)(x - 1)}$$

$$= - \frac{\Delta x}{(x + \Delta x - 1)(x - 1)} \, ;$$

whence

$$\frac{\Delta y}{\Delta x} = - \frac{1}{(x + \Delta x - 1)(x - 1)} \, ,$$

and

$$D_x y = \lim_{\Delta x \to 0} \frac{\Delta y}{\Delta x} = - \frac{1}{(x - 1)^2}$$

for any value of x.   In particular, for $x = 3$,

$$D_x y = -\tfrac{1}{4}.$$

Example 4.   The altitude of a right circular cone is always equal to the diameter of the base.   If the cone expands, what is the rate of change of the volume with respect to the radius of the base?   Interpret the result for a radius of 5 in.

Denoting the radius of the base by r and the volume by V, we have, since the altitude is equal to the diameter,

$$V = \tfrac{2}{3}\pi r^3.$$

Here r is the independent variable (corresponding to x in the previous examples), while V is the function (corresponding to y).   Giving r the increment Δr, we obtain

$$V + \Delta V = \tfrac{2}{3}\pi (r + \Delta r)^3,$$

$$\Delta V = \tfrac{2}{3}\pi [(r + \Delta r)^3 - r^3]$$

$$= \tfrac{2}{3}\pi [3r^2 \cdot \Delta r + 3r(\Delta r)^2 + (\Delta r)^3],$$

$$\frac{\Delta V}{\Delta r} = \tfrac{2}{3}\pi [3r^2 + 3r \cdot \Delta r + (\Delta r)^2],$$

and

$$D_r V = \lim_{\Delta r \to 0} \frac{\Delta V}{\Delta r} = 2\pi r^2.$$

Hence the rate of change of the volume with respect to the radius is 2π times the square of the instantaneous value of the radius.

For $r = 5$ in., $D_r V = 50\pi$.   The volume is therefore increasing instantaneously at the rate of 50π cu. in. per in. of increase in the radius.

PROBLEMS

Find $D_x y$ for the following functions:

1. $y = \dfrac{1}{x}.$

2. $y = \dfrac{1}{1-x}.$

3. $y = \dfrac{1-x}{x}.$

4. $y = 2x^3.$

5. $y = x^2 - \dfrac{1}{x}.$

6. $y = \dfrac{1}{x^2}.$

7. $y = \dfrac{1}{(1-x)^2}.$

8. $y = \sqrt{x}.$

HINT: $\Delta y = \sqrt{x+\Delta x} - \sqrt{x} = \dfrac{\Delta x}{\sqrt{x+\Delta x} + \sqrt{x}}$, on multiplication and division by $\sqrt{x+\Delta x} + \sqrt{x}$.

9. $y = \dfrac{1}{\sqrt{x}}.$

10. $y = x^{\frac{3}{2}}.$

11. $y = \sqrt{9 - x^2}.$

12. $y = \dfrac{x}{\sqrt{x+1}}.$

13. Find the rate at which the lateral surface of a right circular cone is changing with respect to the altitude, if the radius is constantly 3 ft.

14. The volume V (in cubic inches) of a certain weight of a gas at a certain temperature varies with the pressure p (in pounds per square inch) according to the law

$$V = \frac{240}{p}.$$

Find the rate of change of V with respect to p at the instant when p attains the value 20.

15. Find the rate at which the volume of a spherical soap-bubble changes with respect to the radius when the radius is 2 in.

13. Slope. There is a simple geometric interpretation of the derivative which underlies many important applications of calculus.

Let the curve of Fig. 13a represent the graph of the function $y = f(x)$. As in Arts. 10–12, let x and $x + \Delta x$ be the initial and final values of the independent variable, and consider the two points of the curve corresponding to these values, namely, the points $P(x, y)$ and $Q(x + \Delta x, y + \Delta y)$. From the figure, we see that $\Delta x = PR$ and $\Delta y = RQ$.

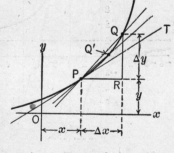

Fig. 13a

Since $\dfrac{RQ}{PR}$ is the slope of the secant line through P and Q, it follows that

(1) $\dfrac{\Delta y}{\Delta x}$ = slope of secant line through $P(x, y)$ and $Q(x + \Delta x, y + \Delta y)$.

Now let Q move along the curve toward P, through positions such as Q' in the figure; the secant line then rotates about P, its slope always being given by (1).   But as Q approaches P, the position of the secant approaches that of the line PT, called the **tangent** to the curve at P. Therefore the slope of the secant approaches the slope of the tangent as a limit.   Since, as Q approaches P, Δx approaches zero, we have, using (1),

(2) $\displaystyle\lim_{\Delta x \to 0} \dfrac{\Delta y}{\Delta x}$ = slope of tangent at $P(x, y)$.

Hence, by (2) of the preceding article,

(3) $D_x y$ = **slope of tangent at** $P(x, y)$.

For brevity, we shall designate the slope of a tangent line of a curve as the slope of the curve at the point of tangency.   We may accordingly restate (3) as follows:

The derivative of a function $f(x)$, for a given value of x, is equal to the slope of the curve $y = f(x)$ at the point having as abscissa the given value of x.

Example 1.   What is the slope of the curve $y = \dfrac{x + 2}{x - 2}$ at the point $(3,5)$?   Construct the corresponding tangent.

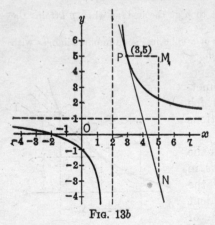

Differentiating as in the preceding article, we obtain

$$D_x y = -\dfrac{4}{(x - 2)^2}.$$

The required slope is therefore

$$-\dfrac{4}{(3 - 2)^2} = -4.$$

The tangent to the curve at $P(3,5)$ may be constructed (Fig. 13b) by laying off an arbitrary distance PM to the right, also a distance $MN = 4PM$ vertically downward from M, and drawing the line through P and N.

FIG. 13b

Example 2.   At what point of the curve $y = 2x - x^2$ is the slope equal to 4? By the method of the preceding article, we obtain

$$D_x y = 2 - 2x.$$

This is the formula for the slope of the curve at any point. To find the point at which the slope is 4, we equate the expression for $D_x y$ to 4 and solve for x. The root of the equation

$$2 - 2x = 4$$

is

$$x = -1.$$

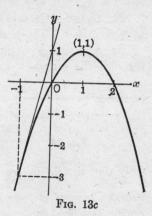

FIG. 13c

This is the abscissa of the required point; the ordinate,

$$y = -3,$$

is found by substituting $x = -1$ in the equation of the curve. (See Fig. 13c.)

PROBLEMS

1. Given the point $P(1,1)$ on the curve $y = x^2$, verify the following table of the slopes of secant lines PQ:

Location of Q	Slope of Secant
(1.4, 1.96)	2.4
(1.3, 1.69)	2.3
(1.1, 1.21)	2.1
(1.01, 1.0201)	2.01
(1.001, 1.002001)	2.001.

From these data infer the slope of the curve at (1,1); then prove the inference to be correct by the use of equation (3).

In Problems 2 to 10, inclusive, find the slope of the curve at the given point. Sketch the curve in the neighborhood of the point, and construct the tangent to the curve at the point.

2. $y = 1 - x^2$, $(2, -3)$.

3. $y = \dfrac{1}{x}$, $(\tfrac{1}{2}, 2)$.

4. $y = \dfrac{1}{1 - x}$, $(-1, \tfrac{1}{2})$.

5. $y = \dfrac{4}{x^2}$, $(-2, 1)$.

6. $y = x^3 - 2x^2 + x - 9$, $(2, -7)$.

7. $y = \dfrac{x}{2 - x}$, $(4, -2)$.

8. $y = \sqrt{3x}$, $(3, 3)$.

9. $y = \sqrt{2 - x}$, $(-2, 2)$.

10. $y = \dfrac{1}{\sqrt{4 + x}}$, $(-3, 1)$.

11. At what point does the curve $y = \sqrt{4 - x}$ have a slope of $-\tfrac{1}{2}$?

12. At what point does the curve $y = 4x - x^2$ have a horizontal tangent?

13. What is the angle between the line $y = x + 2$ and the curve $y = \dfrac{4 - x}{x}$ (i.e., the tangent to the curve) at each point of intersection of the line and the curve?

14. Speed. Certain important physical concepts can be formulated as derivatives. The simplest of these is *speed*.

Suppose that a particle moves along the line OS (Fig. 14) and passes through the points P and Q at the times t and $t + \Delta t$, respectively.

FIG. 14

Choose as an origin a fixed point (say O) on the line, and designate by s and Δs the segments OP and PQ, considering them positive or negative according as they extend from left to right, or from right to left. Then, since the particle undergoes the displacement Δs in the time Δt, $\dfrac{\Delta s}{\Delta t}$ is the average rate of change of s with respect to t, or the **average speed**, during the time-interval Δt.

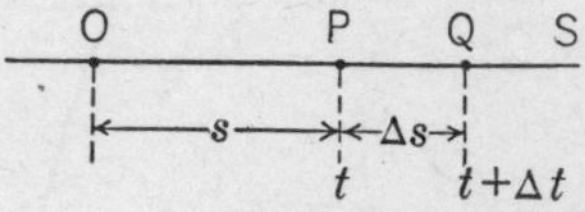

If the motion is uniform, so that $\dfrac{\Delta s}{\Delta t}$ is constant, this constant will represent the actual speed at any time.

If, however, the motion is not uniform, then $\dfrac{\Delta s}{\Delta t}$ will for sufficiently small Δt approximate the instantaneous rate of change of s with respect to t, or the **instantaneous speed** of the particle as it passes through P. The smaller Δt is taken, the better the approximation becomes. In fact, if we denote the instantaneous speed by v, we have

$$v = \lim_{\Delta t \to 0} \frac{\Delta s}{\Delta t}.$$

Hence, by the definition of a derivative (Art. 12), the speed at any time is

(1) $$v = D_t s.$$

While in the above discussion it was for definiteness assumed that the path of the particle is a straight line, the fact is that (1) is likewise true when the path is an arbitrary curve. In this general case, s is measured along the curve from a fixed point O on the curve to the position P occupied by the particle at the time t.

In order that the speed along either a straight or curved path may be found from (1), it is necessary that s be given as a function of t.

Example 1. If $s = 2t^2 + 8t$, where s is in feet and t in seconds, find the speed at any time, and, in particular, when $t = 2$.

Proceeding as in Art. 12, we obtain

$$\Delta s = 4t \cdot \Delta t + 2(\Delta t)^2 + 8\Delta t,$$

$$\frac{\Delta s}{\Delta t} = 4t + 2\Delta t + 8,$$

and, by (1),

$$v = D_t s = \lim_{\Delta t \to 0} \frac{\Delta s}{\Delta t} = 4t + 8.$$

For $t = 2$,

$$v = 16 \text{ ft. per sec., or } 16 \text{ ft./sec.}$$

Example 2. If a body is thrown vertically upward with an initial speed of 64 ft. per sec., its distance from the starting-point is known to be expressed in terms of the time by the formula

$$s = 64t - 16t^2,$$

where s is in feet and t in seconds. Find s and v at intervals of one second up to $t = 5$, and interpret these results.

The speed at any time is

$$v = D_t s = 64 - 32t.$$

Substituting the designated values of t in this and in the given equation, we obtain the following table:

t	0	1	2	3	4	5
s	0	48	64	48	0	−80
v	64	32	0	−32	−64	−96

The result $s = 0$ for $t = 4$ signifies that at this instant the body has returned to the starting-point. The negative value of s for $t = 5$ shows that at this time the body is below the starting-point; thus s is positive for positions above the starting-point and negative for positions below it. It would appear that the maximum height is 64 ft., attained when $t = 2$; this inference is confirmed by observing that $v = 0$, and hence the body is instantaneously at rest when, and only when, $t = 2$. The fact that v is positive for $t < 2$ is then correlated with upward motion, that is, motion in the direction specifying positive s. Similarly, the negative sign of v for $t > 2$ indicates motion in the negative, or downward, direction. The question of the sign of v will be reconsidered in Art. 18.

PROBLEMS

1. The distance fallen by a body dropped from a height is given by the approximate formula

$$s = 16t^2,$$

where s is in feet and t in seconds. Find the speed at any time, and the speed when $t = 4$.

2. A body moves on a curve so that its distance s (in feet) at time t (in seconds) from a fixed point on the curve is

$$s = t^2 - 4t + 5.$$

Find (a) the speed at any time; (b) the values of t and s when the body is instantaneously at rest.

3. For the body which moves in accordance with the equation $s = \dfrac{2}{t}$, find the speed when $t = 2$.

4. A stone which is thrown vertically upward from the top of a building 96 ft. high, and which finally strikes the ground, moves so that at time t (seconds) its height s (feet) above the ground is given by

$$s = 80t - 16t^2 + 96.$$

Find (a) the speed at any time; (b) the initial speed; (c) the time when the speed is instantaneously zero; (d) the time when the stone strikes the ground; (e) the speed just before striking.

5. Two particles, starting from the same position at the same time and moving on the same line, are at time t at distances

$$s_1 = t^2 - 3t$$

and

$$s_2 = 9t - 2t^2$$

from the starting-point, where distance and time are expressed in feet and seconds, respectively. When will the particles be moving with the same speed? What are their speeds at the instants when they have the same position?

6. If $s = 1 + 6t^2 - t^3$, at what instants will the speed be zero? Determine the direction of motion just before and after the later of these instants.

7. For the body discussed in Example 2, find the speed corresponding to a position 336 ft. below the starting-point.

15. Acceleration. Suppose that a particle moves along the line OS (Fig. 15), and passes through the points P and Q at the times t and $t + \Delta t$, respectively. Let the speed of the particle for the position P be v, and for the position Q, $v + \Delta v$. Then $\dfrac{\Delta v}{\Delta t}$ is the average rate of change of the

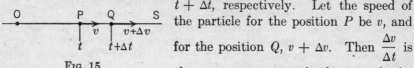

Fig. 15

speed with respect to the time during the interval Δt. For rectilinear motion, the rate of change of the speed with respect to the time is called the **acceleration.** By virtue of this definition, $\dfrac{\Delta v}{\Delta t}$ is the **average acceleration** of the particle during the interval from t to $t + \Delta t$.

If the speed changes at a uniform rate, so that $\dfrac{\Delta v}{\Delta t}$ is constant, this constant will represent the actual acceleration at any time.

If, however, the speed changes at a variable rate, then $\dfrac{\Delta v}{\Delta t}$ will for sufficiently small Δt approximate the **instantaneous acceleration** of the particle as it passes through P. The smaller Δt is taken, the better the approximation becomes.   In fact, if we denote this instantaneous acceleration by a, we have

$$a = \lim_{\Delta t \to 0} \frac{\Delta v}{\Delta t}.$$

Hence, by the definition of a derivative (Art. 12), the acceleration at any time is

(1) $a = D_t v.$

It should be emphasized that (1) is valid only in the case of straight-line motion.   For motion on a curve, $D_t v$ represents only part of the acceleration.   (See Art. 63.)

Example.   A particle moves on a straight line according to the equation

$$s = t^3 + t^2 + 5t,$$

where s is in feet and t in seconds.   Find the acceleration at any time, and, in particular, when $t = 2$.

On differentiation, we obtain

$$v = D_t s = 3t^2 + 2t + 5.$$

To find the acceleration we take the derivative of v with respect to t.   The result is

$$a = D_t v = 6t + 2.$$

In particular, when $t = 2$,

$$a = 14.$$

Since for rectilinear motion acceleration is the time rate of change of the speed its units are those of speed/time.   Hence in the last result $a = 14$ (ft./sec.)/sec., or more briefly, 14 ft./sec.^{2}

PROBLEMS

In all these problems the path is understood to be a straight line; moreover, distance is in feet and time in seconds.

1. If $s = \sqrt{1 + t}$, find the speed and the acceleration.

2. If $v = \dfrac{8}{2 + t}$, find the acceleration when the speed is 2 ft./sec.

3. If $s = t^3 - 6t^2 + 9t - 5$, find the acceleration when the speed is zero.

4. At what time will the acceleration of a particle moving according to the law

$$s = 2t^3 - 6t^2 + 8t + 9$$

be 12 ft./sec.^{2}?   What is the corresponding speed?

5. Two particles move according to the laws

$$s_1 = t^3 + 12t^2 + 5t$$

and

$$s_2 = 3t^3 + 6t^2 - 7t.$$

Find their speeds and positions when they have the same acceleration.

16. Differentiation of Polynomials by Formula. In finding slope, speed, and acceleration, we repeatedly had to differentiate polynomials in x or t. The work was laborious; it may be much simplified by the use of a formula which we shall proceed to derive. Later on we shall develop formulas for differentiating other types of functions.

Let $y = x^n$, where the exponent is a positive whole number. Then

$$y + \Delta y = (x + \Delta x)^n,$$

so that

$$\Delta y = (x + \Delta x)^n - x^n.$$

Factoring this on the principle that

$$a^n - b^n = (a - b)(a^{n-1} + a^{n-2}b + a^{n-3}b^2 + \cdots + ab^{n-2} + b^{n-1}),$$

we obtain

$$\Delta y = [(x + \Delta x) - x][(x + \Delta x)^{n-1} + (x + \Delta x)^{n-2}x + \cdots$$
$$+ (x + \Delta x)x^{n-2} + x^{n-1}]$$

$$= \Delta x[(x + \Delta x)^{n-1} + (x + \Delta x)^{n-2}x + \cdots + (x + \Delta x)x^{n-2} + x^{n-1}].$$

Next, we divide by Δx:

$$\frac{\Delta y}{\Delta x} = (x + \Delta x)^{n-1} + (x + \Delta x)^{n-2}x + \cdots + x^{n-1}.$$

Observing that there are n terms on the right side, each of which approaches x^{n-1} as $\Delta x \to 0$, we find

$$D_x y = \lim_{\Delta x \to 0} \frac{\Delta y}{\Delta x} = nx^{n-1}.$$

We have therefore proved that

(1) $$D_x(x^n) = nx^{n-1}.$$

It will be shown later (Art. 56) that this formula applies when n is any real number.

The same result could have been obtained by expanding $(x + \Delta x)^n$ by the binomial theorem (Formula 1, p. 507).

Example 1. If $y = x^7$, then $D_x y = 7x^6$.

The student may readily establish the more general formula

$$(2) \qquad D_x(ax^n) = anx^{n-1},$$

where a is a constant and n is, as before, a positive integer.

Example 2. If $y = 5x^4$, $D_x y = 20x^3$.

From (2), if $n = 1$, we obtain

$$(3) \qquad D_x(ax) = a.$$

Example 3. If $y = 6x$, $D_x y = 6$.

Considering now the derivative of a constant a, we note that Δa is always zero; hence $\dfrac{\Delta a}{\Delta x} = 0$, and

$$(4) \qquad D_x a = 0.$$

That is, *the derivative of a constant is zero.*

In view of Art. 12, (4) merely states the obvious fact that the rate of change of a constant is zero.

Since $a = ax^0$, we thus see that (2) holds also for $n = 0$.

Example 4. If $y = 10$, $D_x y = 0$.

By the method used in deriving (1), we may show that $D_x(x^n + x^m) = nx^{n-1} + mx^{m-1}$, or more generally that

$$(5) \qquad D_x(a_0 x^n + a_1 x^{n-1} + \cdots + a_{n-1}x + a_n)$$

$$= a_0 n x^{n-1} + a_1(n-1)x^{n-2} + \cdots + a_{n-1}.$$

Thus *the derivative of a polynomial is the sum of the derivatives of the terms.* It will develop that this is a particular case of Theorem 1, Art. 41.

Example 5. If $y = x^4 - 3x^2 + 4x - 6$, then

$$D_x y = 4x^3 - 6x + 4.$$

Example 6. Find the general expressions for the speed and acceleration of a particle moving in a straight line according to the law $s = 8t^3 - 21t^2 + 5t - 7$.

By means of (5) we obtain

$$v = D_t s = 24t^2 - 42t + 5$$

and

$$a = D_t v = 48t - 42.$$

PROBLEMS

Write down the derivative of each of the polynomials in Problems 1–8, regarding a, b, c, and d as constants.

1. $x^2 + 5x - 6$.

2. $t^3 - 6t^2 + 5t - 7$.

3. $\frac{1}{2}t^2 - \frac{1}{4}t + \frac{1}{3}$.

4. $7 - \dfrac{x}{2} + \dfrac{2x^2}{3} - 8x^4 + x^5$.

5. $at^3 - bt^2 + ct - d$.

6. $\dfrac{x^3}{a^3} + \dfrac{3x^2}{a^2} + \dfrac{9x}{a} + b$.

7. $\dfrac{x^4 - b^2x^2}{b^4} - cx$.

8. $\dfrac{x^3}{\sqrt{(a^2 - b^2)^3}} - \dfrac{x^2}{\sqrt{b}} + 2x\sqrt{a}$.

9. Find the general expression for the acceleration of a particle moving in a straight line according to the law

$$s = \tfrac{1}{6}t^3 - \tfrac{1}{2}t^2 + t - 4.$$

10. Find the points at which the slope of the curve

$$y = x^4 - 4x^3 - 8x^2 + 48x - 20$$

is zero.

17. Tangent and Normal. In Art. 13 it was shown that the slope of the line tangent to a curve $y = f(x)$ at the point (x_1, y_1) is the value of $D_x y$ for $x = x_1$. Hence, by Formula 23(b), p. 509, the equation of the tangent is

$$(1) \qquad y - y_1 = f'(x_1)(x - x_1),$$

where (cf. Arts. 3 and 12) $f'(x_1)$ denotes the value of the derivative $f'(x) = D_x y$ for $x = x_1$. The notation $f'(x_1)$ is here more convenient than other possible notations, such as $(D_x y)_{x=x_1}$ or $(D_x y)_1$.

The **normal line,** or **normal,** to the curve $y = f(x)$ at (x_1, y_1) is defined as the line through (x_1, y_1) perpendicular to the tangent at this point. Hence the slope of the normal (by Formula 22(c), p. 509) is the negative reciprocal of the slope of the tangent, and the equation of the normal is

$$(2) \qquad y - y_1 = -\frac{1}{f'(x_1)} (x - x_1).$$

Example 1. What are the equations of the tangent and normal lines to the curve

$$y = x^3 - 4x^2 + 7$$

at $(2, -1)$?

Denoting $x^3 - 4x^2 + 7$ by $f(x)$, we obtain

$$f'(x) = 3x^2 - 8x.$$

Hence

$$f'(2) = -4.$$

The equation of the required tangent is therefore

$$y + 1 = -4(x - 2)$$

or

$$4x + y - 7 = 0.$$

Since $-\dfrac{1}{f'(2)} = \dfrac{1}{4}$, the equation of the required normal is

$$y + 1 = \tfrac{1}{4}(x - 2)$$

or

$$x - 4y - 6 = 0.$$

Example 2. What are the equations of those tangent lines to the curve $y = 2x^3 - 3x^2 - 6x + 7$ which have a slope of 6?

Since $D_x y = 6x^2 - 6x - 6$, the abscissas of the points of tangency satisfy the equation

$$6x^2 - 6x - 6 = 6,$$

whence

$$x = -1, 2.$$

From the equation of the curve, the corresponding values of y are

$$y = 8, -1.$$

Therefore the points of tangency are $(-1, 8)$ and $(2, -1)$, and the equations of the required tangent lines are

$$y - 8 = 6(x + 1) \quad \text{or} \quad 6x - y + 14 = 0$$

and

$$y + 1 = 6(x - 2) \quad \text{or} \quad 6x - y - 13 = 0.$$

The curve and its tangents are shown in Fig. 17a.

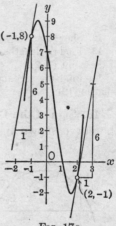

FIG. 17a

PROBLEMS

1. Find the equations of the tangent and normal to the curve $y = x^2 - x + 5$ at the point $(1, 5)$.

2. Find the equations of the tangent and normal to the curve $y = x^3 - 3x^2 + 2x - 7$ at the point for which $x = 2$.

3. Find the equations of the tangents to the curve $y = x^2 - 5x + 4$ at the points for which $y = 10$.

4. Find the equations of the normals to the curve $y = x^3 - 3x^2 - 4x + 10$ at the points for which $y = -2$.

5. At what points of the curve $y = x^3 - 6x^2 + 6x - 8$ are the tangents parallel to the line $3x + y + 4 = 0$? What are the equations of these tangents?

6. At what point of the curve $y = x^2 - 6x + 8$ is the normal parallel to $x + 2y - 3 = 0$? What is the equation of the normal?

7. Find the angle between the curve $y = x^3 - 2x^2 + x + 1$ and the line $y = 2x - 1$ at each point of intersection. (Formula 22(a), p. 509.)

8. Find the angle between the curves $y = x^2 - 6$ and $y = x^3 + x^2 + 2$ at their point of intersection.

9. Show that the length of the tangent PT, Fig. 17b, is $\dfrac{y_1}{f'(x_1)}\sqrt{1+[f'(x_1)]^2}$.

10. Show that the length of the normal PN, Fig. 17b, is $y_1\sqrt{1+[f'(x_1)]^2}$.

11. Show that the **subtangent** TA, Fig. 17b, is $\dfrac{y_1}{f'(x_1)}$.

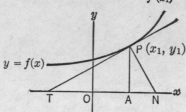

Fig. 17b

12. Show that the **subnormal** AN, Fig. 17b, is $y_1 f'(x_1)$.

13. Find the lengths of the tangent and the normal to the curve $y = x^3 + 3x^2 - 8x + 6$ at the point $(1, 2)$.

14. Find the subtangent and subnormal to the curve $y = x^3 - 3x - 40$ at the point $(4, 12)$.

18. Sign of the Derivative. Let P_1 be a point at which the slope of the curve shown in Fig. 18 is positive. Since the inclination of the tangent line at this point is an acute angle ϕ_1, so that the tangent line extends upward toward the right, the curve necessarily rises from left to right through P_1. That is, when the slope is positive y increases as x increases. On the other hand, if we take a point such as P_2 at which the slope is negative ($\tan \phi_2 < 0$), the tangent line extends downward toward the right, and the curve falls from left to right through P_2. That is, when the slope is negative y decreases as x increases. Since the slope of a curve at any point is the value of $D_x y$ at the point, we have the following

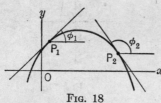

Fig. 18

Theorem. *If x is assumed to be increasing, then when $D_x y$ is positive y increases; but when $D_x y$ is negative y decreases.*

Conversely, for increasing x, if y increases, $D_x y$ is generally positive; and if y decreases, $D_x y$ is generally negative. In either case, however, $D_x y$ may be zero for exceptional values of x. (See Art. 22.)

The above theorem can be established also by using, instead of the geometric meaning of $D_x y$, its interpretation as the rate of change of y with respect to x. For if x increases and y has a positive rate of change with respect to x, y must also increase. But if y has a negative rate of change with respect to x, y must be changing in a sense opposite to that in which x changes, so that if x increases y must decrease.

Example 1. If x is understood to be increasing, for what range of values of x does $y = 2x^3 - 3x^2 - 36x + 6$ increase, and for what range does it decrease?

On differentiating, we obtain

$$D_x y = 6x^2 - 6x - 36 = 6(x + 2)(x - 3).$$

If $x < -2$ both parentheses are negative, so that the product, and therefore $D_x y$, is positive. If $-2 < x < 3$, the first parenthesis is positive, but the second negative, so that $D_x y$ is negative. If $x > 3$ both parentheses are positive, and $D_x y$ is also positive. Hence, by the theorem, y increases for $x < -2$ and $x > 3$; y decreases for $-2 < x < 3$.

Example 2. If a particle moves along a straight line so that its displacement at time t is $s = t^3 - 9t^2 + 15t - 7$, find when the speed is positive and when it is negative, and interpret the results.

We have

$$v = D_t s = 3t^2 - 18t + 15$$
$$= 3(t - 1)(t - 5).$$

From the factored form of the derivative we conclude by reasoning analogous to that given in Example 1 that v is positive for $t < 1$, negative for $1 < t < 5$, and positive for $t > 5$. Hence s increases until $t = 1$, decreases from $t = 1$ to $t = 5$, and increases thereafter. The motion thus undergoes a reversal of direction when $t = 1$ and when $t = 5$.

Whenever v is positive, the particle moves in the direction of increasing s, and when v is negative, in the direction of decreasing s (cf. Example 2, Art. 14).

PROBLEMS

In Problems 1–5, determine the ranges of values of x for which, as x increases, (a) y increases; (b) y decreases.

1. $y = x^3 - 12x$.   **3.** $y = x^4 + 4x^2 - 7$.

2. $y = 2x^3 + 3x^2 - 12x + 5$.   **4.** $y = 3x^4 + 4x^3 - 96x^2 - 192x$.]

5. $y = 3x^4 + 44x^3 + 210x^2 + 300x - 500$.

In Problems 6–10, s represents the displacement of a moving particle. Find when the speed is positive and when it is negative.

6. $s = t^2 - 4t + 2$.

7. $s = t^3 - \frac{7}{2}t^2 + 2t - 5$.

8. $s = t^3 - 3t^2 + 3t + 2$.

9. $s = t^4 - \dfrac{40t^3}{3} + 4t^2 - 80t + 28$.

10. $s = t^4 - 12t^3 + 48t^2 - 80t + 28$.

19. Higher Derivatives. The derivative of a function is, as we have found, in general also a function of the same variable that occurs in the original function, and hence may be differentiable. If it is, its derivative is called the **second derivative** of the original function.

Similarly the derivative of the second derivative is called the **third derivative**, and so on for still higher derivatives.

Symbols for the second derivative, $D_x(D_xy)$, of $y = f(x)$ with respect to x are

$$D_x{}^2y,\ y'',\ f''(x),\ \frac{d^2y}{dx^2},\ \frac{d^2f(x)}{dx^2},\ \text{and}\ \frac{d^2}{dx^2}f(x).$$

The corresponding symbols for the third derivative are

$$D_x{}^3y,\ y''',\ f'''(x),\ \frac{d^3y}{dx^3},\ \frac{d^3f(x)}{dx^3},\ \text{and}\ \frac{d^3}{dx^3}f(x),$$

and, in general, for the nth derivative are

$$D_x{}^ny,\ y^{(n)},\ f^{(n)}(x),\ \frac{d^ny}{dx^n},\ \frac{d^nf(x)}{dx^n},\ \text{and}\ \frac{d^n}{dx^n}f(x).$$

Example. Find the successive derivatives of $y = 2x^3 - 3x^2 - 36x + 6$.
Since $D_xy = 6x^2 - 6x - 36$, we obtain

$$D_x{}^2y = D_x(D_xy) = 12x - 6,$$

$$D_x{}^3y = D_x(D_x{}^2y) = 12,$$

and

$$D_x{}^4y = D_x(D_x{}^3y) = 0;$$

the fifth and all subsequent derivatives are also zero.

20. Sign of the Second Derivative. Since $D_x{}^2y$ is found from D_xy in the same manner as D_xy is found from y, it follows by analogy with the theorem of Art. 18 that

If x is assumed to be increasing, then when $D_x{}^2y$ is positive D_xy increases; but when $D_x{}^2y$ is negative D_xy decreases.

Conversely, for increasing x, if D_xy increases, $D_x{}^2y$ is generally positive; and if D_xy decreases, $D_x{}^2y$ is generally negative. In either case, however, $D_x{}^2y$ may be zero for exceptional values of x. (See Art. 22.)

Example 1. If $y = 2x^3 - 6x^2 + 24x - 8$, where x is understood to be increasing, for what range of values of x does D_xy increase and for what range does it decrease?
We obtain

$$D_xy = 6x^2 - 12x + 24$$

and

$$D_x{}^2y = 12x - 12 = 12(x - 1).$$

Since $D_x{}^2y$ is negative for $x < 1$ and positive for $x > 1$, we conclude that if $x < 1$, D_xy decreases as x increases, while if $x > 1$, D_xy increases as x increases.

Acceleration (Art. 15) is an instance of a second derivative. For, in the case of rectilinear motion, $a = D_tv$, and since $v = D_ts$, it follows that $a = D_t^2 s$. Therefore, as t increases, v increases algebraically when a is positive, and decreases when a is negative.

Example 2. If a particle moves on a straight line so that $s = t^3 - 9t^2 + 15t - 7$, find when the acceleration is positive and when it is negative. Corresponding to these results, determine the sense in which v changes.

The first and second derivatives of s are

$$v = D_t s = 3t^2 - 18t + 15$$

and

$$a = D_t v = D_t^2 s = 6t - 18 = 6(t - 3).$$

Hence, for $t < 3$, a is negative and v is decreasing; while for $t > 3$, a is positive and v is increasing.

It may be helpful to tabulate corresponding values of v and a at intervals of a second, as follows:

t	0	1	2	3	4	5	6
v	15	0	-9	-12	-9	0	15
a	-18	-12	-6	0	6	12	18

We note, for instance, that the acceleration is positive for $t = 4$ and that the speed is increasing algebraically though decreasing numerically. If we keep clearly in mind the algebraic sense of the words "increase" and "decrease," we readily see that the entries of the table are in complete agreement with the connection pointed out in this article between the sign of the second derivative (here a) and the increase or decrease of the first derivative (v).

PROBLEMS

1. If $y = x^5$, find y', y'', y''', y^{iv}, and y^v.

2. If $y = x^4 + 2x^3 - 36x^2 + 120x - 36$, find for what values of x the first derivative increases with x and for what values it decreases.

3. If $y = \dfrac{1 - x}{1 + x}$, find $D_x^2 y$ by the use of increments.

(For the sake of convenience in notation, designate the first derivative by y'; then $D_x^2 y = \lim\limits_{\Delta x \to 0} \dfrac{\Delta y'}{\Delta x}$.)

4. Find the equation of the tangent to the curve $y = x^3 - 6x^2 + 18x - 6$ at the point for which $D_x^2 y = 0$.

5. For the same curve, find for what values of x the slope increases with x, and for what values it decreases.

6. If $s = t^4 - 8t^3 + 4t$, find the speed at a time half way between the instants for which $a = 0$. Is the speed then increasing or decreasing? Is the numerical value of the speed increasing or decreasing?

21. Concavity; Points of Inflection. Let us consider an arc of the curve $y = f(x)$ at every point of which $D_x^2 y$ is positive. By the preceding article, $D_x y$ (the slope) increases as the arc is traversed from left to right. Such an arc is shown in Fig. 21a. It will be noticed that the arc lies wholly above the tangent line at every one of its points and is *concave upward*. We conclude that

A curve $y = f(x)$ is concave upward at any point for which $D_x^2 y$ is positive.

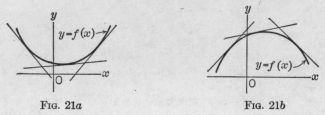

FIG. 21a FIG. 21b

In Fig. 21b is shown an arc at every point of which $D_x^2 y$ is negative so that the slope, or $D_x y$, decreases as the arc is traversed from left to right. This arc lies wholly below the tangent line at every one of its points and is *concave downward*. We conclude that

A curve $y = f(x)$ is concave downward at any point for which $D_x^2 y$ is negative.

It should be remarked that a curve may be concave upward or downward at a point for which $D_x^2 y = 0$, for concavity depends directly on the sense in which $D_x y$ is changing, and it was pointed out in Art. 20 that an increasing or decreasing $D_x y$ is not incompatible with a vanishing $D_x^2 y$.

Consider the curve $y = f(x)$ and suppose that y, $D_x y$, and $D_x^2 y$ are continuous for a certain range of values of x. Moreover, suppose that $D_x^2 y$ changes in sign as x passes through a certain value $x = a$ within the range, so that by the continuity of $D_x^2 y$

$$(1) \qquad\qquad D_x^2 y = 0 \text{ for } x = a.$$

When these conditions are fulfilled, the point on the curve corresponding to $x = a$ is called **a point of inflection.**

By the connection pointed out in this article between the sign of the second derivative and the sense of concavity, a point of inflection, such as A, B, or C (Fig. 21c), separates two arcs of opposite concavity.* Hence at a point of inflection a

FIG. 21c

---

* But not every point which separates two arcs of opposite concavity satisfies our definition of a point of inflection. Thus, the curve $x = y^3$ is concave upward to the left of the origin and concave downward to the right; at the origin, $D_x^2 y$ is infinite, not zero. However, many writers regard a change in the sense of concavity at a point of a curve as defining a point of inflection; from this point of view, $x = y^3$ has a point of inflection at the origin.

curve crosses the line there tangent to it. This tangent line may be horizontal, as at C; such special points of inflection will be studied further in the next article.

It must be emphasized that the property (1) does not completely characterize a point of inflection. For even though (1) is satisfied at a point of a curve $y = f(x)$, we cannot be sure that the point is a point of inflection unless, as the point is passed, the sign of $D_x^2 y$ changes either from minus to plus (as at A and C) or from plus to minus (as at B).

Example. Find the point of inflection of the curve $y = x^3 - 3x^2 + 6$.

On differentiating twice we obtain

$$D_x^2 y = 6x - 6.$$

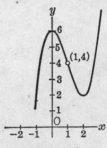

FIG. 21d

To find a possible point of inflection we set

$$6x - 6 = 0,$$

whence

$$x = 1.$$

Thus there may be a point of inflection at (1, 4). This is actually a point of inflection, for when $x < 1$, $D_x^2 y < 0$, and when $x > 1$, $D_x^2 y > 0$.

The curve is shown in Fig. 21d.

PROBLEMS

1. Find the points of inflection of the curve $y = \dfrac{1}{x^2 + 3}$.

2. Find the equation of the line tangent to the curve $y = x^3 - 3x^2 + 24x - 18$ at its point of inflection.

3. Show that (0,12) is not a point of inflection of the curve $y = x^4 + 24x + 12$.

Find the points of inflection of the following curves, and the corresponding slopes.

4. $y = x^5$.

5. $y = x^4 - 6x^2 + 24x - 12$.

6. $y = x^4 + 4x^3 - 12x - 24$.

7. $y = x^4 - 2x^3 - 72x^2 + 24x - 60$.

8. $y = 2x^6 - 45x^4 + 20x - 15$.

9. $y = 2x^6 + 5x^4 + 30x^2 + 120x + 60$.

10. $y = 10x^7 + 21x^5 - 60x - 20$.

22. Critical Points; Maxima and Minima. Let $f(x)$ be a single-valued function of x having a first and a second derivative which are continuous for a range of values of x including $x = a$. Then if $f'(a) = 0$, the point $(a, f(a))$ will be called a **critical point** of the curve $y = f(x)$, provided that $f(x)$ is not a constant. It follows that the tangent to a curve at a critical point is horizontal. The behavior of a curve near a critical point may be studied with reference to the slope of the curve; and since the slope must be either positive or negative on each side of the critical point, one of the following four cases will arise:

Case 1. $f'(x) > 0$ for $x < a, f'(x) < 0$ for $x > a$;

Case 2. $f'(x) < 0$ for $x < a, f'(x) > 0$ for $x > a$;

Case 3. $f'(x) > 0$ for $x < a$ and $x > a$;

Case 4. $f'(x) < 0$ for $x < a$ and $x > a$.

In the above inequalities x is restricted to intervals throughout which $f(x)$ and $f'(x)$ remain continuous and $f'(x)$ does not vanish.

We shall consider these cases in detail.

Under the conditions of Case 1, a point tracing the curve from left to right rises before the position of the critical point is reached, and then falls. Such a critical point (as A, Fig. 22a) is called a **maximum point**; it is higher than the points of its neighborhood on either side. A sufficiently short arc containing a maximum point is concave downward, since as it is traced from left to right $D_x y$ is decreasing; hence at maximum points $D_x^2 y$ is generally negative, but sometimes zero (cf. Art. 20). An instance of a maximum point at which $D_x^2 y = 0$ is given in Example **1**.

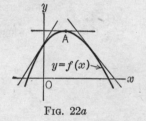

FIG. 22a FIG. 22b

When the curve $y = f(x)$ has a maximum point at $x = a$, the function $f(x)$ is said to have a **maximum value**, or to be a **maximum**, for $x = a$.

Under the conditions of Case 2, a point tracing the curve from left to right falls before the position of the critical point is reached, and then rises. Such a critical point (as B, Fig. 22b) is called a **minimum point**; it is lower than the points of its neighborhood on either side. A sufficiently short arc containing a minimum point is concave upward, since as it is traced from left to right $D_x y$ is increasing; hence at minimum points $D_x^2 y$ is generally positive, but sometimes zero.

When the curve $y = f(x)$ has a minimum point at $x = a$, the function $f(x)$ is said to have a **minimum value**, or to be a **minimum**, for $x = a$.

A maximum or minimum value of a function is sometimes called an **extreme** of the function.

Under the conditions of Case 3, a point tracing the curve from left to right rises both before and after the position of the critical point is reached. Therefore $D_x y$, which by hypothesis is continuous, decreases steadily to zero, its value at the critical point, and then increases. Hence

$D_x{}^2y$ is negative * just to the left of the critical point and positive * to the right, and since it is by hypothesis continuous, it follows that at the critical point $D_x{}^2y = 0$. The critical point under discussion is therefore a point of inflection with a horizontal tangent (abbreviated H.P.I.) on a rising curve. Such a point is shown at C, Fig. 22c.

In Art. 18 it was stated that a function $y = f(x)$ increases with x when D_xy is positive, but that conversely, when y increases with x, D_xy, while usually positive, may for certain values of x be zero. Now we find that the latter exceptional situation occurs at a critical point such as C (Fig. 22c), since y is increasing and yet for the value of x corresponding to the critical point $D_xy = 0$.

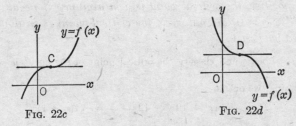

FIG. 22c   FIG. 22d

It is left to the student to show that a critical point of the type described under Case 4 is a point of inflection, with a horizontal tangent, on a falling curve. This is illustrated in Fig. 22d.

If a curve has a critical point at $x = a$, the following table, in which the results of this article are summarized, indicates how the critical point may be classified:

	Maximum Point	Minimum Point	H.P.I. (Rising curve)	H.P.I. (Falling curve)
$x < a$	$D_xy > 0$	$D_xy < 0$	$D_xy > 0$	$D_xy < 0$
$x = a$	$D_xy = 0$	$D_xy = 0$	$D_xy = 0$	$D_xy = 0$
$x > a$	$D_xy < 0$	$D_xy > 0$	$D_xy > 0$	$D_xy < 0$
$x = a$	$D_x{}^2y \leqq 0$	$D_x{}^2y \geqq 0$	$D_x{}^2y = 0$	$D_x{}^2y = 0$

The following procedure, based on this table, is recommended for the purpose of locating and classifying all the critical points of a curve $y = f(x)$.

Find D_xy, or $f'(x)$, set $f'(x) = 0$, and solve for x. The roots are the

---

* It is unnecessary to consider the possible existence of exceptional points for which $D_x{}^2y = 0$, for we may so restrict the intervals on either side of the critical point that $D_x{}^2y$ does not vanish within them.

abscissas of the critical points of the curve, the ordinates being found by substituting in the equation $y = f(x)$. Two tests will be given for classifying the critical points thus found:

TEST 1. *Corresponding to each real root x_i $(i = 1, 2, \cdots)$ of $f'(x)$ $= 0$, evaluate $f'(x)$ for $x < x_i$ and for $x > x_i$, where the interval between x and x_i does not include another root of $f'(x) = 0$ or any value of x for which $f(x)$ or $f'(x)$ is discontinuous; according as the results of these substitutions have the signs $+-$, $-+$, $++$, or $--$, the critical point is a maximum point, a minimum point, an H.P.I. on a rising curve, or an H.P.I. on a falling curve.*

TEST 2. *Evaluate the second derivative $D_x^2 y$, or $f''(x)$, for $x = x_i$. If $f''(x_i)$ is positive, the critical point is a minimum; if negative, a maximum. If $f''(x_i) = 0$, the nature of the critical point is in doubt but may be established by Test 1.*

Example 1. Locate and classify the critical point of the curve $y = -x^4 + 4x^3 -6x^2 + 4x - 3$.

Differentiating, we obtain

$$D_x y = -4x^3 + 12x^2 - 12x + 4 = -4(x - 1)^3.$$

Hence $D_x y = 0$ when $x = 1$, and we have a critical point at $(1, -2)$.

To classify this critical point, we apply Test 1.

It is clear from the factored form of $D_x y$ that for $x < 1$, $D_x y > 0$, and for $x > 1$, $D_x y < 0$. Hence $(1, -2)$ is a maximum point.

In this example, Test 2 fails, since the second derivative

$$D_x^2 y = -12x^2 + 24x - 12 = -12(x - 1)^2$$

vanishes for $x = 1$.

The curve is shown in Fig. 22e.

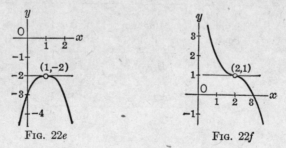

FIG. 22e   FIG. 22f

Example 2. Locate and classify the critical point of the curve $y = 9 - 12x + 6x^2 - x^3$ and determine its nature.

Since $D_x y = -12 + 12x - 3x^2 = -3(x - 2)^2$ there is a critical point at $x = 2$, the corresponding ordinate being 1.

From the factored form of $D_x y$, it is evident that $D_x y$ is negative on both sides of the critical point. Hence, by Test 1, $(2, 1)$ is a point of inflection with a horizontal tangent.

The curve is shown in Fig. 22f.

The work of determining the graph of an equation $y = f(x)$ is facilitated by plotting the maximum and minimum points and points of inflection.

Example 3. Locate and classify all critical points of the curve

$$y = \frac{x^5}{5} - x^4 + \frac{2}{3}x^3 + 2x^2 - 3x.$$

Also find any remaining points of inflection. Using these points, sketch the curve.

On differentiation, we obtain

$$D_x y = x^4 - 4x^3 + 2x^2 + 4x - 3 = (x + 1)(x - 1)^2(x - 3).$$

The critical points are therefore $(-1, \frac{47}{15})$, $(1, -\frac{17}{15})$, and $(3, -\frac{27}{5})$.

For the ranges of x suggested by the factored form of $D_x y$, we find:

$$
\begin{aligned}
x &< -1, & D_x y &> 0, \\
-1 &< x < 1, & D_x y &< 0, \\
1 &< x < 3, & D_x y &< 0, \\
x &> 3, & D_x y &> 0.
\end{aligned}
$$

Hence by Test 1, $(-1, \frac{47}{15})$ is a maximum point, $(1, -\frac{17}{15})$ a point of inflection with a horizontal tangent, and $(3, -\frac{27}{5})$ a minimum point.

The same conclusions with regard to the first and third of these critical points may be reached alternatively by applying Test 2, for the second derivative

$$D_x^2 y = 4x^3 - 12x^2 + 4x + 4 = 4(x - 1)(x^2 - 2x - 1)$$

is negative for $x = -1$ and positive for $x = 3$.

Since the roots of the equation obtained by setting $D_x^2 y$ equal to zero include the abscissas of all points of inflection, and one root $(x = 1)$ corresponds to the H.P.I. already determined, all other possible points of inflection are found by solving the quadratic equation

$$x^2 - 2x - 1 = 0.$$

The roots of this equation are

$$x = 1 \pm \sqrt{2},$$

or, approximately,

$$x = 2.41 \text{ and } -0.41.$$

The corresponding ordinates are approximately -3.77 and 1.51. Since $D_x^2 y$ has opposite signs to the left and right of each of these points, the latter are points of inflection.

From the above results, we readily obtain the graph shown in Fig. 22g.

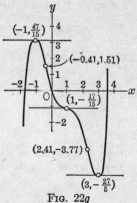

Fig. 22g

PROBLEMS

Find the maximum and minimum points and points of inflection of each of the following curves, and use these results in sketching the curve.

1. $y = x + \dfrac{4}{x}.$

2. $y = x^3 - 4x^2 + 4x.$

3. $y = x^3 - 3x + 2.$

4. $y = x^3 - 3x^2 + 3x - 1.$

5. $y = x^3 + 3x^2 - 9x + 5.$

6. $y = x^4 - 2x^3 - 8x + 3.$

7. $y = x^4 + 12x^3 + 54x^2 + 108x + 85.$

8. $y = \dfrac{x^5}{10} - 3x^3 + \dfrac{81x}{2}.$

9. $y = x^4 + 2x^3 - 72x^2 - 216x + 2000.$

10. $y = x^5 - 10x^3 + 20x^2 - 15x - 10.$

23. Applications of Maxima and Minima. The conclusions of the preceding article as regards the maximum or minimum values (extremes) of a function may be stated thus:

Given a function $f(x)$ and a value a of the variable x such that $f'(a) = 0$, it follows from Test 1 that $f(a)$ is a maximum or a minimum value of $f(x)$ according as $f'(x)$ changes from plus to minus, or from minus to plus, as x increases through the *critical value a*. Or, alternatively, by Test 2, $f(a)$ is a maximum if $f'(a) = 0$ and $f''(a)$ is negative; $f(a)$ is a minimum if $f'(a) = 0$ and $f''(a)$ is positive.

In a large variety of problems, many of them arising in geometry, mechanics, or physics, a maximum or minimum whose existence is known in advance is sought. In such a case, should only one critical value be found, it is unnecessary to apply either of the tests described above. If several critical values should be found, from the nature of the problem it is often possible to rule out some of them as meaningless. The significance of these remarks will come to light in the following examples.

Example 1. A triangle has a base of 12 ft. and an altitude of 6 ft. Find the largest rectangle that can be inscribed in the triangle so that the base of the rectangle falls on the base of the triangle.

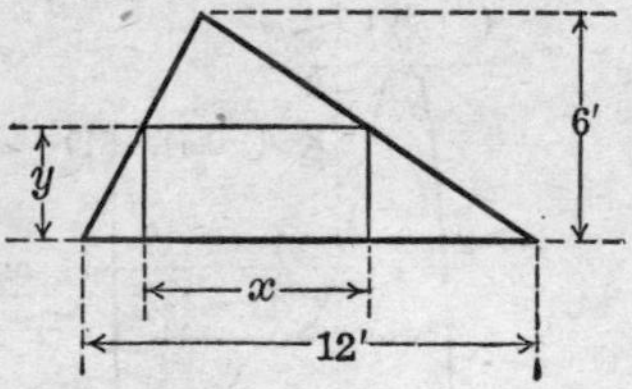

FIG. 23a

Call the dimensions of a variable inscribed rectangle x and y. (See Fig. 23a.) The function to be made a maximum is $A = xy$. This function apparently depends on two variables, whereas in the preceding article the functions whose maximum and minimum values were investigated depended on only one variable. It is possible, however, to express y in terms of x, so that A will depend only on x, for from similar triangles we have

$$\frac{x}{12} = \frac{6 - y}{6}$$

or

$$y = 6 - \frac{x}{2}.$$

Then

$$A = x\left(6 - \frac{x}{2}\right) = 6x - \frac{x^2}{2},$$

and

$$D_xA = 6 - x.$$

Setting $6 - x$ equal to zero, we find

$$x = 6.$$

Since this is the only critical value, and since it is evident that, as x increases from zero to 12, the area increases from zero to a maximum and then decreases to zero, it is clear that A is a maximum for $x = 6$. The same conclusion would be reached by applying either of the tests.

Therefore the rectangle we seek has the dimensions $x = 6$ ft. and $y = 6 - \dfrac{x}{2} = 3$ ft.

The maximum area is 18 sq. ft.

Example 2. A box with square base and open top is to have a total inner surface of 432 sq. in. What are its dimensions if the volume is a maximum?

Calling each side of the base x (Fig. 23b), and the height y, we have for the volume

$$V = x^2y,$$

where x and y are related by the equation

$$x^2 + 4xy = 432,$$

or

$$y = \frac{108}{x} - \frac{x}{4}.$$

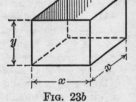

Fig. 23b

Substituting for y, we obtain V as a function of x alone:

$$V = 108x - \frac{x^3}{4}.$$

Hence

$$D_xV = 108 - \frac{3x^2}{4}.$$

Equating this derivative to zero, we find

$$x = \pm 12.$$

The negative solution is, of course, rejected. Although it is geometrically evident that a maximum volume exists and hence must correspond to $x = 12$, the same conclusion may be reached by applying either test. In particular, since the second derivative,

$$D_x^2V = -\tfrac{3}{2}x,$$

is negative when $x = 12$, V is, by Test 2, a maximum for this value of x. The corresponding height of the box is 6 in. and the maximum volume itself is 864 cu. in

PROBLEMS

1. Find two numbers whose sum is 12 and whose product is a maximum.

2. Find two numbers whose sum is 12 and the sum of whose squares is a minimum.

3. Find two numbers whose sum is 12 and the sum of whose cubes is a minimum.

4. Find two numbers whose sum is 12, such that the product of one number by the square of the other is a maximum.

5. Find two numbers whose sum is 12, such that the product of one number by the cube of the other is a maximum.

6. One side of a rectangular field is adjacent to a river; for the other three sides 240 yd. of fence are available. What are the dimensions of the field when the area is a maximum?

7. A rectangular plot of perimeter 160 ft. is to contain a rectangular flower bed surrounded by a walk 2 ft. wide along the sides of the plot and 3 ft. wide along the ends. Find the dimensions of the plot if the area of the flower bed is a maximum.

8. A closed box, whose base is a rectangle twice as long as wide, is to have a surface of 432 sq. in. What are its dimensions, if the volume is a maximum?

9. A square box is to be made from a piece of cardboard 18 in. on a side by cutting out a square from each corner and turning up the sides. Find the volume of the largest box which can be so constructed.

10. A rectangular box is to be made from a piece of cardboard 24 in. long and 9 in. wide by cutting out a square from each corner and turning up the sides. Find the volume of the largest box which can be so constructed.

11. The sum of the lateral area and the area of the base of a cylindrical pail is 12π sq. in. Find the base-radius and the altitude if the volume is a maximum.

12. A wire of length l is cut into two parts one of which is bent into a circle and the other into a square. Find the diameter of the circle and the side of the square if the sum of the areas of the figures is a minimum.

13. A wire of length l is cut into two parts one of which is bent into a square and the other into an equilateral triangle. Find the sides of the square and the triangle if the sum of the areas of the figures is a minimum.

14. Find the volume of the largest right circular cylinder which can be inscribed in a right circular cone of base-radius 6 in. and altitude 6 in.

15. The perimeter of a sector of a circle is 12 in. Find the radius, if the area of the sector is a maximum. (Area $= \frac{1}{2}$ radius $\times$ arc.)

16. The sum of the bases and the altitude of a trapezoid is 20 in., and one base is 4 in. longer than the other. Find all three dimensions if the area is a maximum.

17. A right circular cone is inscribed in a sphere of radius 6 in. Find the altitude of the cone if the volume is a maximum.

18. A figure consists of a rectangle surmounted by a semicircle, the diameter of the semicircle coinciding with the upper base of the rectangle. If the perimeter of the figure is $8 + 2\pi$ in., and the area is a maximum, find the altitude of the rectangle and the radius of the semicircle.

19. A figure consists of a rectangle surmounted by an equilateral triangle, the base of the triangle coinciding with the upper base of the rectangle. If the perimeter of the figure is 33 in., and the area is a maximum, find the dimensions of the rectangle.

20. The sum of the length and the girth of a parcel of square cross-section is 72 in. Find the maximum volume of the parcel.

21. The cost per hour of fuel for running a train is proportional to the square of the speed and is $20 an hour when the speed is 20 mi./hr. In addition, other charges aggregate

$80 an hour regardless of the speed. Set up an expression for the cost per mile as a function of the speed and find the speed for which this cost is a minimum.

22. The strength of a rectangular beam is proportional to the width and the square of the depth. Find the width and depth of the strongest beam which can be cut from a circular log $6\sqrt{3}$ in. in diameter.

23. At a certain time, a ship A was 150 mi. south of another ship B; it then sailed east at the constant rate of 9 mi./hr. In the meantime B was sailing south at the rate of 12 mi./hr. Express the square of the distance between the ships as a function of the time that elapsed after the initial moment, and find the time at which the squared distance, and hence the distance itself, was a minimum.

24. A printer contracts to print 4000 circulars or less at the rate of $1 per hundred. If the number of circulars exceeds 4000, he will deduct 1¢ per hundred on the whole contract for each hundred printed in excess of 4000. For what number of circulars would the printer realize maximum receipts, and what would these receipts be?

24. Differentials; Approximations. It will now be shown that the derivative $D_x y$ or $f'(x)$ of the function $y = f(x)$, besides being the limit of the fraction $\dfrac{\Delta y}{\Delta x}$, may itself be regarded as a fraction and denoted by a fractional symbol, $\dfrac{dy}{dx}$, the meanings of the numerator and denominator of which will be established by the following geometrical discussion.

Let $P(x, y)$ and $Q(x + \Delta x, y + \Delta y)$ be two points (Fig. 24a) on

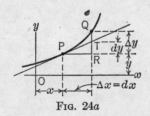

FIG. 24a

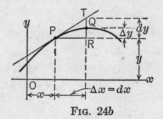

FIG. 24b

the curve $y = f(x)$, so that $\Delta x = PR$ and $\Delta y = RQ$. Then, if the tangent to the curve at P intersects RQ at T, the slope of the tangent is

$$\frac{RT}{\Delta x} = f'(x),$$

whence

(1) $$RT = f'(x)\Delta x.$$

Therefore, since

(2) $$\Delta y = RT + TQ,*$$

* In Fig. 24b, TQ is negative.

we obtain

$$\frac{\Delta y}{\Delta x} = f'(x) + \frac{TQ}{\Delta x} = f'(x) + \eta,$$

where

$$\eta = \frac{TQ}{\Delta x}.$$

Since

$$\lim_{\Delta x \to 0} \frac{\Delta y}{\Delta x} = f'(x),$$

it follows that

$$\lim_{\Delta x \to 0} \eta = 0.$$

Hence, writing (2) as

$$(3) \qquad \Delta y = RT + \eta \Delta x = f'(x)\Delta x + \eta \Delta x = (f'(x) + \eta)\Delta x,$$

we note that, if $f'(x)$ is not zero and Δx is numerically so small that η may be neglected in comparison with $f'(x)$, then $RT = f'(x)\Delta x$ is an approximation to Δy.

Regardless of the value of Δx, we shall call $f'(x)\Delta x$ the **differential** of y, and denote it by the symbol dy. Thus, by definition, for any differentiable function $y = f(x)$,

$$(4) \qquad dy = f'(x)\Delta x.$$

It is clear that for any value of x for which $f'(x)$ exists, dy depends on the value of this derivative and also on the arbitrary increment Δx. By virtue of the preceding paragraph we may state that, *if Δx is sufficiently small in numerical value and $f'(x) \neq 0$, dy is an approximation to Δy.*

If in particular $f(x) = x$, so that the equation of the curve $y = f(x)$ becomes $y = x$, then

$$f'(x) = 1$$

and

$$dy = dx.$$

Substituting in (4), we find

$$(5) \qquad dx = \Delta x.$$

Thus *the differential of the independent variable is the same as its increment.* *

From (4) and (5) we obtain

$$(6) \qquad dy = f'(x)\,dx.$$

---

* Some writers dispense with the argument leading to (5), and give this equation as the *definition* of dx.

That is, *the differential of the function $y = f(x)$ is its derivative multiplied by the differential of the independent variable x.*

In Figs. 24a and 24b, dx and dy are shown as line segments. In accordance with (5) and (6)

$$dx = PR, \qquad dy = RT.$$

Dividing both sides of (6) by dx, we have

(7) $$\frac{dy}{dx} = f'(x) = D_x y.$$

· In the future we shall employ the symbol $\dfrac{dy}{dx}$ or $\dfrac{d}{dx} f(x)$ instead of $D_x y$ or $D_x f(x)$. Similarly, we shall usually denote the second derivative of y with respect to x as $\dfrac{d^2 y}{dx^2}$, a contraction of $\dfrac{d\left(\dfrac{dy}{dx}\right)}{dx}$ or $\dfrac{d}{dx}\left(\dfrac{dy}{dx}\right)$, and, in general, the nth derivative as $\dfrac{d^n y}{dx^n}$.

Example 1. If $y = x^4 - 3x^2 + 5x + 6$, find dy.
On differentiating, we obtain

$$\frac{dy}{dx} = \frac{d}{dx}(x^4 - 3x^2 + 5x + 6) = 4x^3 - 6x + 5,$$

and on multiplying by dx

$$dy = (4x^3 - 6x + 5)dx.$$

Or alternatively, if we denote the given function by $f(x)$, then $f'(x) = 4x^3 - 6x + 5$ and, by (6),

$$dy = f'(x)dx = (4x^3 - 6x + 5)dx.$$

Example 2. If A is the area of a square of side x, so that $A = x^2$, and x is increased by Δx, find ΔA, dA, and $\Delta A - dA$ for any x and Δx, and in particular for $x = 10$ in. and $\Delta x = 0.0003$ in.
Evidently

$$A + \Delta A = (x + \Delta x)^2 = x^2 + 2x\Delta x + (\Delta x)^2,$$

and therefore

$$\Delta A = 2x\Delta x + (\Delta x)^2.$$

This result is likewise obtainable from Fig. 24c, where

$$A = \text{area } OBCD$$

and

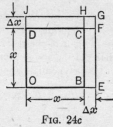

FIG. 24c

$$\Delta A = \text{area } BEFC + \text{area } DCHJ + \text{area } CFGH$$

$$= x\Delta x + x\Delta x + (\Delta x)^2$$

$$= 2x\Delta x + (\Delta x)^2.$$

We find dA as follows:

$$\frac{dA}{dx} = 2x,$$

whence

$$dA = 2x\,dx.$$

Since $dx = \Delta x$, the difference between ΔA and dA is

$$\Delta A - dA = (\Delta x)^2.$$

In Fig. 24c this is the area of the square $CFGH$.

In particular for $x = 10$ in. and $\Delta x = 0.0003$ in.,

$$\Delta A = 0.00600009 \text{ sq. in.,}$$

$$dA = 0.006 \text{ sq. in.,}$$

and

$$\Delta A - dA = 0.00000009 \text{ sq. in.}$$

Thus, because Δx is small, dA is a close approximation to ΔA.

Example 3. By the use of differentials, find an approximation to the value of $x^4 - 7x^3 + 25x^2 - 17x + 8$ when $x = 2.998$.

We may regard the value 2.998 as the result of applying an increment of -0.002 to an original value 3. That is, $x = 3$ and $dx = \Delta x = -0.002$. Calling the given function y we have

$$\frac{dy}{dx} = 4x^3 - 21x^2 + 50x - 17$$

and

$$dy = (4x^3 - 21x^2 + 50x - 17)dx.$$

Substituting $x = 3$ and $dx = -0.002$, we find

$$dy = 52(-0.002) = -0.104,$$

and this is approximately the change in y caused by changing x from 3 to 2.998. When $x = 3$, $y = 74$. Hence

$$y + dy = 74 - 0.104 = 73.896,$$

and this is approximately the value of the polynomial for $x = 2.998$.

To determine the degree of accuracy of the approximation, let us calculate the exact value of the polynomial for $x = 2.998$. This involves considerably more labor than did the above computation of $y + dy$, even if instead of substituting $x = 2.998$ in the polynomial, we evaluate the increment

$$\Delta y = 4x^3\Delta x + 6x^2(\Delta x)^2 + 4x(\Delta x)^3 + (\Delta x)^4 - 21x^2\Delta x - 21x(\Delta x)^2$$

$$-7(\Delta x)^3 + 50x\Delta x + 25(\Delta x)^2 - 17\Delta x$$

for $x = 3$ and $\Delta x = -0.002$, and add the result to $y = 74$. We find $y + \Delta y = 73.896063960016$. Thus we see that the approximation by differentials holds to within three decimal places, and this is satisfactory since there are only three decimal places in 2.998, the given value of x.

Example 4. The altitude of a certain right circular cone is the same as the radius of the base, and is measured as 5 in., with a possible error of 0.02 in.   Find approximately the greatest possible error in the calculated value of the volume.

A possible error of 0.02 in. in the measured value of the altitude h signifies that this value is subject to a correction (or change) which may amount to as much as 0.02 in. in either sense; that is, the error to which h is subject may be taken as $\Delta h = dh = \pm 0.02$.   Then since Δh is small, the computed value of the volume $V = \frac{1}{3}\pi h^3$ is subject to an error approximately given by

$$dV = \pi h^2 dh$$

which, for $h = 5$ and $dh = \pm 0.02$, is $\pm 0.5\pi$.   Thus the computed value of V, namely $\frac{125\pi}{3}$ cu. in., may be too great or too small by as much as 0.5π cu. in., approximately.

Relative Error and Percentage Error.   If Δy is the error in y, then $\dfrac{\Delta y}{y}$ is called the **relative error** in y, and $100\,\dfrac{\Delta y}{y}$ the **percentage error.** These may be approximated by $\dfrac{dy}{y}$ and $100\,\dfrac{dy}{y}$, respectively, if the increment of the variable on which y depends is sufficiently small numerically.

Thus, taking for convenience the error in the volume of the cone of the preceding example as positive, we have

$$\frac{dV}{V} = \frac{0.5\pi}{\dfrac{125\pi}{3}} = 0.012;$$

hence the volume is subject to a relative error of approximately 0.012, or 1.2 per cent.

PROBLEMS

1. If $y = 4x^3 - 9x^2 + 7x - 5$, find dy.

2. If $y = \frac{3}{5}x^5 - \frac{7}{4}x^4 - \frac{2}{3}x^3 + \frac{5}{2}x^2 - 10$, find dy.

3. If $y = \dfrac{2x}{3 - x}$, find $\dfrac{dy}{dx}$ by the increment process, and thence obtain dy.

4. If $y = \sqrt{1 - 2x}$, find $\dfrac{dy}{dx}$ by the increment process, and thence obtain dy.

5. If $y = x^3$, find Δy, dy, and $\Delta y - dy$.   Interpret the results geometrically. (Cf. Example 2.)

6. If $y = 2x^3 - 2x^2 + 3x - 5$, find Δy and dy for $x = 2$ and $\Delta x = 0.1$.

7. If $y = x^3 + 4x^2 - 10x - 3$, find Δy and dy for $x = 3$ and $\Delta x = -0.2$.

8. Find the approximate value of $3x^4 - 4x^3 + 8x^2 - 5x - 8$ for $x = 2.02$; for $x = 1.98$.

9. Find the approximate value of $x^5 - 12x^4 + 2x^3 - 9x^2 - 4x - 18$ for $x = 3.04$; for $x = 2.97$.

10. The side of a square is, by measurement, 3 ft. long.   If this length is subject to an error of $\frac{1}{2}$ in., find approximately the greatest error in the calculated value of the area of the square.

11. The side of a cube is, by measurement, 6 in. long.   If this length is subject to an error of 0.05 in., find approximately the greatest error in the calculated value of the volume of the cube.

12. The circumference of a great circle of a sphere is, by measurement, 10 in., with a possible error of 0.1 in.   Find approximately the greatest error in the calculated value of (a) the surface of the sphere, and (b) its volume.

13. The altitude of a right circular cylinder is the same as the diameter of the base and is measured as 8 in., with a possible error of 0.01 in.   Find approximately the greatest error in the calculated value of (a) the lateral surface of the cylinder, (b) its total surface, and (c) its volume.

14. The acute angles of an isosceles trapezoid are each 45°.   If the shorter base, which is assumed exactly equal to the altitude, is measured as 4 in. long, with a possible error of 0.03 in., what is (approximately) the greatest error in the calculated value of the area?

15. Find approximately the relative error and the percentage error to which the area of the preceding problem is subject.

16. If the diameter of a circle is measured as 4 in., with a possible error of 0.02 in., find approximately the relative error to which the area of the circle is subject.

17. Show that the relative error in the nth power of a measurement is approximately n times the relative error in the measurement.

18. By means of differentials, compute the allowable percentage error in the diameter of a sphere if the volume is to be correct to within 3 per cent.

25. Infinitesimals.   In calculus and in more advanced mathematics the concept of an *infinitesimal* plays a vital rôle.   We shall develop this concept now because of its close connection with the preceding article and its importance for the next chapter.

As the term is employed in mathematics, an **infinitesimal** is a variable which approaches zero as a limit.   Thus, contrary to common usage, a constant, however small in numerical value, is not an infinitesimal.   Moreover, an infinitesimal need not be restricted to values in the immediate neighborhood of zero.   For example Δx and Δy are infinitesimals in the sense in which they appear in the definition of the derivative

$$\frac{dy}{dx} = \lim_{\Delta x \to 0} \frac{\Delta y}{\Delta x},$$

but they may initially have large absolute values.   These increments are infinitesimals only because their limit is zero—that is, because ultimately they become and remain less in numerical value than any preassigned constant, however small.

Corresponding to an infinitesimal increment of a variable x, the differential of a function y of the variable is an infinitesimal; for by (3) and (4) of the preceding article

$$(1) \qquad\qquad dy = \Delta y - \eta \Delta x,$$

so that, as Δx (and consequently Δy) approaches zero, dy also approaches zero. Moreover, since $\lim_{\Delta x \to 0} \eta = 0$, η too is an infinitesimal.

Suppose that, for two infinitesimals α and β,

$$\lim \frac{\beta}{\alpha} = c,$$

where c is a constant. Then, if c is not zero, β is said to be an infinitesimal of the **same order** as α. If, on the contrary, $c = 0$, then β is said to be an infinitesimal of **higher order** than α. If $\lim \frac{\beta}{\alpha}$ fails to exist because the ratio becomes infinite, then

$$\lim \frac{\alpha}{\beta} = 0$$

and consequently α is of higher order than β, or equivalently β is of lower order than α.

Thus if y is a function of x and x has a value for which $\lim_{\Delta x \to 0} \frac{\Delta y}{\Delta x}$ exists and is not zero, then the corresponding increments Δx and Δy are infinitesimals of the same order. On the other hand, $(\Delta x)^2$ is an infinitesimal of higher order than Δx since

$$\lim_{\Delta x \to 0} \frac{(\Delta x)^2}{\Delta x} = \lim_{\Delta x \to 0} \Delta x = 0.$$

In this case $(\Delta x)^2$ is said to be an infinitesimal of the second order with respect to Δx.

More generally, if α is an infinitesimal, then α^2, α^3, α^4, $\cdots$ are infinitesimals of higher order than α, their orders with respect to α being the second, third, fourth, $\cdots$. Moreover, if

$$\lim_{\alpha \to 0} \frac{\beta}{\alpha^n}$$

exists and is not zero, then β is an infinitesimal of the nth order with respect to α.

If an infinitesimal consists of two or more terms of different orders, the term of lowest order is said to be the **principal part** of the infinitesimal.   Clearly the order of such an infinitesimal is the same as that of its principal part.   Thus, if α is an infinitesimal, the principal part of

$$\beta = \alpha^2 - 2\alpha^3 + 5\alpha^4$$

is α^2, and β is of the second order with respect to α.

THEOREM 1.   *If for the infinitesimals α and β, $\lim \dfrac{\alpha}{\beta} = 1$, the difference $\beta - \alpha$ is an infinitesimal of higher order than α or β.*

To show this we form the ratio $\dfrac{\beta - \alpha}{\beta}$ and evaluate its limit:

$$\lim \frac{\beta - \alpha}{\beta} = 1 - \lim \frac{\alpha}{\beta} = 1 - 1 = 0.$$

Hence $\beta - \alpha$ is an infinitesimal of higher order than β; and since the hypothesis implies that β and α are of the same order, it follows that $\beta - \alpha$ is also of higher order than α.

This theorem affords a means of comparing the infinitesimals dy and Δy occurring in (1); for if $\lim\limits_{\Delta x \to 0} \dfrac{\Delta y}{\Delta x}$ is not zero, so that $\lim\limits_{\Delta x \to 0} \dfrac{\Delta x}{\Delta y}$ exists, we obtain from (1)

$$\lim_{\Delta x \to 0} \frac{dy}{\Delta y} = 1 - \lim_{\Delta x \to 0} \eta \cdot \lim_{\Delta x \to 0} \frac{\Delta x}{\Delta y} = 1,$$

since $\lim\limits_{\Delta x \to 0} \eta = 0$.   Hence, by Theorem 1, $\Delta y - dy = \eta \Delta x$ is an infinitesimal of higher order than Δy, dy, or Δx, all three of which are of the same order.

Since, for $y = f(x)$,

$$dy = f'(x)dx = f'(x)\Delta x,$$

so that dy involves no term of higher order than Δx, and since it has just been shown that in

$$\Delta y = dy + \eta \Delta x$$

the term $\eta \Delta x$ is of higher order than Δx, we conclude that, for infinitesimal Δx, *dy is the principal part of Δy, when $f'(x) \neq 0$.*

Example 1.   If $y = x^3$, $\Delta y = 3x^2 \Delta x + 3x(\Delta x)^2 + (\Delta x)^3$; for infinitesimal Δx, the principal part of Δy is $3x^2 \Delta x$, and this is the same as dy.

THEOREM 2.   *If α, β, γ, and δ are infinitesimals so related that $\lim \dfrac{\alpha}{\gamma} = 1$ and $\lim \dfrac{\beta}{\delta} = 1$, and if $\lim \dfrac{\alpha}{\beta}$ and $\lim \dfrac{\gamma}{\delta}$ exist, then*

$$\lim \frac{\alpha}{\beta} = \lim \frac{\gamma}{\delta}.$$

For since

$$\frac{\alpha}{\beta} = \frac{\gamma \dfrac{\alpha}{\gamma}}{\delta \dfrac{\beta}{\delta}},$$

it follows that

$$\lim \frac{\alpha}{\beta} = \left(\lim \frac{\gamma}{\delta} \right) \frac{\lim \dfrac{\alpha}{\gamma}}{\lim \dfrac{\beta}{\delta}}$$

$$= \lim \frac{\gamma}{\delta}.$$

In other words, in finding the limit of a ratio of infinitesimals, we may replace the given infinitesimals by others differing from them by infinitesimals of higher order.

By Theorem 2, the limit of the ratio of two infinitesimals is equal to the limit of the ratio of their principal parts.

Example 2. Show that, as θ approaches zero, $\sin \theta$ and $\tan \theta$ are infinitesimals of the same order.

Since

$$\lim_{\theta \to 0} \sin \theta = 0$$

and

$$\lim_{\theta \to 0} \tan \theta = 0,$$

it follows that $\sin \theta$ and $\tan \theta$ are infinitesimals. Since

$$\lim_{\theta \to 0} \frac{\sin \theta}{\tan \theta} = \lim_{\theta \to 0} \cos \theta = 1,$$

and this result is different from zero, $\sin \theta$ and $\tan \theta$ are, by definition, infinitesimals of the same order. The same conclusion may be reached by observing that, since the last limit is 1, $\sin \theta$ and $\tan \theta$ differ by an infinitesimal of higher order (Theorem 1).

Example 3. Show that $\displaystyle \lim_{x \to 0} \frac{3x^2 - x^3 + 4x^4}{4x^2 - 3x^3 + 5x^4} = \frac{3}{4}.$

Replacing, in accordance with Theorem 2, the infinitesimal numerator and denominator by their principal parts, we obtain

$$\lim_{x \to 0} \frac{3x^2 - x^3 + 4x^4}{4x^2 - 3x^3 + 5x^4} = \lim_{x \to 0} \frac{3x^2}{4x^2} = \frac{3}{4}.$$

Example 4. Find the principal part of the volume of a hollow right circular cylinder whose thickness is infinitesimal.

Let us denote the altitude by h, the inner radius by r, and the thickness by t. Then the volume is

$$\pi(r + t)^2 h - \pi r^2 h = 2\pi r h t + \pi h t^2,$$

in which the second term of the last expression is an infinitesimal of higher order than the first term.   Hence the principal part of the volume is $2\pi rht$.

If we write $dr = t$, and hold h constant, $2\pi rht$ is identical with the differential of the volume of a right circular cylinder encased in the given hollow cylinder.

PROBLEMS

In each of Problems 1–6, find the order of the designated infinitesimal with respect to the independent variable which is made to approach zero.

1. The circumference of a circle of radius r, as r approaches zero.

2. The area of a circle of radius r, as r approaches zero.

3. The volume of a right circular cone, of base-radius r and altitude h, (a) as r approaches zero, h remaining constant, and (b) as r approaches zero, h varying so that $h = 2r$.

4. The volume of a right circular cylinder of base-radius r and altitude $h = r^2$, as r approaches zero.

5. The total surface of the right circular cylinder of Problem 4.   Find also the principal part of this infinitesimal.

6. The volume of a frustum of a right circular cone, whose altitude is equal to the radius of the smaller base, as this radius approaches zero.   Find also the principal part of the volume.

7. If α and β are infinitesimals, β being of the second order with respect to α, determine the orders with respect to α of $\alpha + \beta$, $\dfrac{\beta}{\alpha}$, $\alpha\beta$, and $\dfrac{\alpha^3}{\beta}$.

8. If α and β are infinitesimals of the same order and $\lim \dfrac{\alpha}{\beta}$ is not ± 1, determine the orders with respect to α or β of $\alpha + \beta$, $\alpha^2 + \beta^2$, $\alpha - \beta$, and $\alpha^2 - \beta^2$.

Find the differential of each of the following functions by taking the principal part of its increment, assumed infinitesimal.

9. $y = 2x - x^2$.

10. $y = (x - 1)^4$.

CHAPTER III

INTEGRATION AND APPLICATIONS

26. Integration. The inverse process of differentiation, that is, the process of finding the function whose derivative, or whose differential, is given, is known as **integration.** Integration provides the means of solving many important problems in geometry, physics, chemistry, astronomy, and other fields.

27. Definitions. In the problem of differentiation treated in the preceding chapter, we were given a function of a variable and were asked to find the rate of change, or the derivative, of the function with respect to its variable. In the problem of integration, however, we are given the derivative of a function with respect to its variable and are asked to determine the function.

If, for example,
$$\frac{dy}{dx} = 4x^3,$$

we should be able to find y as a function whose derivative will equal $4x^3$, or whose differential will equal $4x^3dx$. Clearly $y = x^4$ is such a function, as are also $y = x^4 + 2$, $y = x^4 - 3$, $y = x^4 + C$, where C is any constant. The last of these, of which the others are only special cases, is the general function whose derivative is $4x^3$. It is customary to express such a function by means of the symbol $\int$, called the **integral sign,** which symbol is placed before the differential and not the derivative.* Using this symbol in the present example, we have

$$\int 4x^3dx = x^4 + C.$$

The above may be generalized as

THEOREM 1. *If $F(x)$ is a function whose derivative is $f(x)$ (or whose differential is $f(x)dx$), then $F(x) + C$ is a whole class of functions having the same derivative (or differential).*

The question now arises as to whether $F(x) + C$ is the most general function whose derivative is $f(x)$. To show that it is, let

$$F_1(x) = F(x) + C,$$

* This convention will be justified in Art. 33.

and now suppose that $F_2(x)$ is another function having $f(x)$ as its derivative.   Then if we set

$$u = F_1(x) - F_2(x),$$

and observe that

$$\frac{d}{dx} F_1(x) = \frac{d}{dx} F_2(x) = f(x),$$

we have

$$\frac{du}{dx} = 0,$$

for any value of x.   Thus the rate of change of u is zero, and u, or $F_1(x) - F_2(x)$, is therefore a constant.   Recalling now that $F_1(x) = F(x) + C$, where C is an arbitrary constant, we conclude that $F_2(x)$ is necessarily one of the functions of the class $F(x) + C$.

This fact we state as

THEOREM 2.   *If $F(x)$ is a function having $f(x)$ as its derivative, then $F(x) + C$ is the most general function having this derivative.*

Understanding $f(x)$ and $F(x)$ to be related as in the theorems, and using the integral sign defined above, we may write

$$\int f(x)dx = F(x) + C.$$

This equation is read, "The integral of $f(x)dx$ is equal to $F(x) + C$." We now explicitly define **integration** as the general process of finding a function of x, namely $F(x)$, whose derivative $f(x)$, or whose differential $f(x)dx$, is given.   It is customary to call $f(x)$ the **integrand**, $F(x)$ a **particular integral**, $F(x) + C$ the **general** or **indefinite integral** of $f(x)dx$, and C the **constant of integration**.

28. Integration of Polynomial Functions.   If the integrand is a polynomial,

$$a_0x^n + a_1x^{n-1} + a_2x^{n-2} + \cdots + a_{n-1}x + a_n,$$

where n is a positive integer and the a's are constants, we apply the formula

(1) $$\int ax^n dx = a \int x^n dx = \frac{ax^{n+1}}{n+1} + C$$

to the successive terms of the polynomial and obtain

(2) $$\int (a_0x^n + a_1x^{n-1} + a_2x^{n-2} + \cdots + a_{n-1}x + a_n)\, dx$$

$$= \frac{a_0x^{n+1}}{n+1} + \frac{a_1x^n}{n} + \frac{a_2x^{n-1}}{n-1} + \cdots + \frac{a_{n-1}x^2}{2} + a_nx + C,$$

where C here represents the sum of the constants arising in the integration of the separate terms.

These formulas can be verified by differentiation. They will be treated more generally in Chapter VIII, which is devoted to formulas and methods suitable for the integration of a variety of elementary functions. There we shall see that (1) holds also when n has any real value other than -1.

Formula (1) shows that *a constant factor can be transferred from one side of the integral sign to the other.* The student is warned never to treat a variable factor in this manner.

Example 1. $\int x\, dx = \dfrac{x^2}{2} + C.$

Example 2. $\int (x + 2)dx = \dfrac{x^2}{2} + 2x + C.$

Example 3. $\int (x^3 + 2x^2 + 5)dx = \dfrac{x^4}{4} + \dfrac{2x^3}{3} + 5x + C.$

Example 4. $\int (a + bx^2)^2 dx = \int (a^2 + 2abx^2 + b^2 x^4)dx = a^2x + \dfrac{2abx^3}{3} + \dfrac{b^2 x^5}{5} + C.$

PROBLEMS

1. $\int 3\, dx.$

2. $\int (x - 2)dx.$

3. $\int (3 - x)dx.$

4. $\int (5x - 2)dx.$

5. $\int (a + bx)dx.$

6. $\int (3x^2 - 3x + 2)dx.$

7. $\int (2x + 3)^2 dx.$

8. $\int (2x + 3)^2 x\, dx.$

9. $\int (3x + 1)^2 5\, dx.$

10. $\int (x^2 - 2)^2 dx.$

11. $\int (2x^3 - 1)^2 x\, dx.$

12. $\int x^2(3 - 4x)dx.$

13. $\int (a^2 - x^2)dx.$

14. $\int (1 - 2x)(2 + x)dx.$

15. $\int (2 - 7x)^4 dx.$

16. $\int (a_0 x^3 + a_1 x^2 + a_2 x + a_3)dx.$

17. $\int \sqrt{8}\, x\, dx.$

18. $\int x^2(1 - 2x)dx.$

19. $\int (3x - 4)^2 x^2 dx.$

20. $\int (2x^4 - 3x^2 - x + 4)dx.$

21. $\int (3x^{10} - 4x^7 - 3x^6 - 12x^3 + 3)dx.$

22. $\int (3x^4 - 3x^2 + 4x + 2)dx.$

23. $\int (3x^5 - 4x^3 - 7x + 2)dx.$

24. $\int (2x - 1)^2 x\, dx.$

29. Constant of Integration. Since the result of an integration, that is, the indefinite integral, includes a constant C, the value of the indefinite integral, for a particular value of the independent variable, depends on the value of C. This can be determined only if additional data are given, as in the following illustrative example.

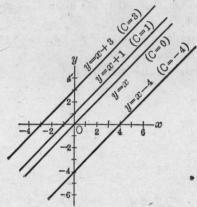

FIG. 29

Example. If $\dfrac{dy}{dx} = 1$, then

$$y = \int dx,$$

or

(1)
$$y = x + C.$$

For different values of C this equation represents different straight lines, each making an angle of $45°$ with the x-axis (Fig. 29).

In order to establish the equation of a particular line of this set we must have additional information regarding the position of the line. Thus for the line passing through the point $(-2, 1)$, we obtain from (1)

$$1 = -2 + C,$$

whence

$$C = 3,$$

so that the equation of the required line is

$$y = x + 3.$$

PROBLEMS

1. Find the equation of the curve passing through the point $(1, 3)$, and having the slope $2x$.

2. If a curve passes through the point $(-1, -2)$, and its slope at any point (x, y) is $3x^2 + 2x - 3$, find its equation.

3. If a curve passes through the point $(0, 2)$, and its slope at any point (x, y) is $2x - 3$, find its equation.

4. If $ds = t\, dt$, and $s = 2$ when $t = 0$, find s as a function of t.

5. If $dy = (3x + 2)dx$, and $y = 3$ for $x = 2$, find y as a function of x.

30. Area. We shall now see that integration is applicable to the determination of areas bounded by curves and lines whose equations are known.

In Fig. 30a, $ABCD$ represents an area bounded by a curve whose equation is $y = f(x)$, the x-axis, and the vertical lines $x = a$ and $x = b$. This area is also called the area under the curve from $x = a$ to $x = b$.

In Fig. 30b, $EFGH$ represents an area bounded by a curve whose equation is $x = g(y)$, the y-axis, and the horizontal lines $y = c$ and $y = d$.

Either of these areas is readily formulated in terms of an integral. The necessary procedure will be given in connection with the area $BCDE$

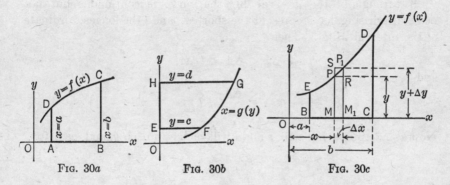

FIG. 30a   FIG. 30b   FIG. 30c

of Fig. 30c, which area will be regarded as generated by an ordinate of the curve as it moves from $x = a$ to $x = b$. As the ordinate moves it gives rise to a growing or variable area A, bounded on the left by the line BE, above by the curve $y = f(x)$, below by the x-axis, and on the right by the moving ordinate. This area A is a function of x, the variable abscissa of the generating line. In order to find the area $BCDE$ it will be necessary to determine $\dfrac{dA}{dx}$.

In Fig. 30c, $BMPE$ represents an instantaneous value of A. If x increases by an amount $\Delta x = MM_1$, A increases by a corresponding amount ΔA = area MM_1P_1P. If, as shown in the figure, y increases continuously with x, MP is the shortest, and M_1P_1 the longest, ordinate in the interval from M to M_1. Hence the area of the rectangle MM_1RP is less than the increment of area, ΔA, while the area of the rectangle MM_1P_1S is greater than ΔA. That is,

$$\text{area } MM_1RP < \Delta A < \text{area } MM_1P_1S,$$

or

$$y\Delta x < \Delta A < (y + \Delta y)\Delta x.$$

Dividing each term of this inequality by Δx, we have

$$y < \frac{\Delta A}{\Delta x} < (y + \Delta y).$$

Now let Δx approach zero; then Δy also approaches zero, and therefore

$$\lim_{\Delta x \to 0} \frac{\Delta A}{\Delta x} = \frac{dA}{dx} = y.$$

Thus we see that *the rate of change of the area A with respect to the abscissa x is equal to the ordinate y.*

If throughout the interval BC the curve is continuous but not necessarily rising, let s represent the shortest, and l the longest, ordinate of the interval MM_1. Then

$$s \cdot \Delta x < \Delta A < l \cdot \Delta x,$$

and

$$s < \frac{\Delta A}{\Delta x} < l.$$

Now as Δx approaches zero, s and l will each approach y, and, as before,

$$\frac{dA}{dx} = y.$$

The area is now found by integration:

(1) $$A = \int y\, dx = \int f(x)\, dx = F(x) + C,$$

where $F(x)$ is a function whose derivative is $f(x)$.

In order to evaluate C we note that $A = 0$ when $x = a$. Substituting these values of A and x in (1) we have

$$0 = F(a) + C,$$

whence

$$C = -F(a).$$

Hence

(2) $$A = F(x) - F(a).$$

This equation gives the variable area bounded by the curve $y = f(x)$, the x-axis, the fixed line $x = a$, and the variable line. If b is substituted for x in equation (2), the required area, bounded by the curve $y = f(x)$, the x-axis, and the lines $x = a$ and $x = b$, is found to be

(3) $$\text{area } BCDE = F(b) - F(a).$$

For the present, we shall not be concerned with any area for which the boundary curve $y = f(x)$ has negative ordinates within the horizontal extent of the area, that is, within the interval from $x = a$ to $x = b$. This restriction will be removed in Art. 34. We do not, however, exclude zero ordinates. Thus $f(a)$ or $f(b)$, or both, may be zero; likewise the boundary curve may touch the x-axis at any number of points between $(a, 0)$ and $(b, 0)$.

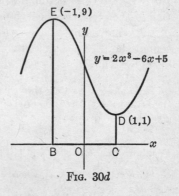

Example. Find the area bounded by the curve $y = 2x^3 - 6x + 5$, the x-axis, and the maximum and minimum ordinates of the curve.

By Art. 22 the maximum and minimum ordinates correspond to $x = -1$ and $x = 1$, respectively. Hence the required area is $BCDE$ of Fig. 30d.

Fig. 30d

By (1) we have

$$A = \int (2x^3 - 6x + 5)dx$$

$$= \frac{x^4}{2} - 3x^2 + 5x + C.$$

Since $A = 0$ for $x = -1$, it follows that $C = \frac{15}{2}$. Hence

$$A = \frac{x^4}{2} - 3x^2 + 5x + \frac{15}{2}$$

is the area under the curve from $x = -1$ to an arbitrary value of x. Setting $x = 1$ we obtain

$$\text{area } BCDE = \tfrac{1}{2} - 3 + 5 + \frac{15}{2} = 10 \text{ square units.}$$

Alternatively if we use equation (3) with $F(x) = \frac{x^4}{2} - 3x^2 + 5x$, $a = -1$, and $b = 1$, we find that

$$\text{area } BCDE = F(1) - F(-1)$$
$$= [(\tfrac{1}{2} - 3 + 5) - (\tfrac{1}{2} - 3 - 5)]$$
$$= 10.$$

31. Interpretation of Areas. The determination of areas by integration will be treated from another point of view in the next article. The reason for placing so much emphasis on the calculation of areas by integration is that many quantities of geometrical, mechanical, and physical importance are conveniently formulated as areas. For instance, if the speed of a moving particle is plotted against the time, the area under a portion of the speed-time graph thus obtained represents the distance between the initial and final positions of the particle. This will be illustrated in the example below. Moreover, if a particle moves under the action of forces and the resultant force in the direction of motion is plotted against the displacement along the path, the area under the force-displacement graph represents the work done on the particle. Likewise if cross-sectional areas of a solid are plotted against the position of the cross-sections, the area under the graph represents the volume of the solid. Such illustrations can be multiplied, but those just presented should be sufficient to give the student an idea of the importance of the area problem.

Example. A particle thrown vertically downward with an initial speed of 16 ft./sec. moves so that its speed v (in feet per second) at any time t (in seconds) is given by the equation

$$v = 32t + 16.$$

Find how far the particle will fall in the time from $t = 1$ to $t = 4$.

Since $v = \dfrac{ds}{dt}$ (Art. 14), where s is the distance from a fixed point of the path to the position of the particle at the time t, we have

$$\frac{ds}{dt} = 32t + 16,$$

and therefore

$$s = \int (32t + 16)dt$$

$$= 16t^2 + 16t + C.$$

Since, when $t = 1$, none of the required distance has been traversed, we set $s = 0$ when $t = 1$, and find $C = -32$. Therefore the distance from the position occupied by the particle when $t = 1$ to its position at any later time t is

$$s = 16t^2 + 16t - 32.$$

In particular, if $t = 4$, we obtain

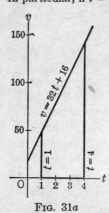

Fig. 31a

required distance $= 16(4)^2 + 16(4) - 32$

$$= 288 \text{ ft.}$$

If v is plotted against t (Fig. 31a), the area under this speed-time curve, from a fixed ordinate at $t = 1$ to a variable ordinate, is, by the preceding article,

$$A = \int (32t + 16)dt$$

$$= 16t^2 + 16t - 32.$$

The right member is identical with the above expression for s, and therefore for $t = 4$ yields the same result, namely 288. Consequently the required distance is represented by the area under the speed-time curve from $t = 1$ to $t = 4$.

In general if a particle moves in such a way that the displacement s, measured along the path, increases with the time, the distance traversed by the particle during any interval of time is equal to the corresponding area under the speed-time curve.

PROBLEMS

In all problems requiring an area, the area is to be found by integration; every boundary curve should be sketched.

1. Find the area bounded by the line $y = 2x - 3$, the x-axis, and the lines $x = 2$ and $x = 5$.

2. Find the area bounded by the line $y = x + 4$, the x-axis, and the lines $x = -2$ and $x = 3$.

3. Find the area bounded by the line $x - 2y + 12 = 0$, the x-axis, and the lines $x = -4$ and $x = -2$.

4. Find the area bounded by the line $x - y + 2 = 0$, the x-axis, and the line $x = 0$.

5. Find the area bounded by the line $x - 3y + 18 = 0$, the x-axis, the y-axis, and the line $x = 3$.

6. Find the area bounded by the line $y = 2x - 6$, the x-axis, and the lines $x = 4$ and $x = 6$.

7. Find the area bounded by the curve $y = \frac{1}{2}x^2$, the x-axis, and the lines $x = 2$ and $x = 4$.

8. Find the area bounded by the curve $x^2 - 2y + 3 = 0$, the x-axis, and the lines $x = 1$ and $x = 4$.

9. Find the area bounded by the curve $x^2 - 2y - 5 = 0$, the x-axis, and the lines $x = 3$ and $x = 5$.

10. Find the area bounded by the curve $y = x^2 + 3$, the x-axis, and the lines $x = 0$ and $x = 1$.

11. Find the area bounded by the curve $x^2 + y - 4 = 0$, and the x-axis.

12. Find the area bounded by the curve $x^2 - 4x + y = 0$, the x-axis, the maximum ordinate to the curve, and the line $x = 3$.

13. Find the area bounded by the curve $y = 5 + 4x - x^2$ and the x-axis.

14. Find the area bounded by the curve $x^2 - y - 9 = 0$, the x-axis, and the lines $x = 4$ and $x = 5$.

15. Find the closed area bounded by the curve $x^2 + 4x - y + 4 = 0$ and the coördinate axes.

16. Find the area under the curve $y = x^3$, from $x = 1$ to $x = 4$.

17. Find the area lying in the second quadrant bounded by the curve $y = x^3 - 4x$ and the x-axis.

18. Find the area under the curve $x^3 - 12x - y = 0$ from the maximum ordinate to $x = 0$.

19. Find the area bounded by the curve $y = x^3 - 3x + 3$, the x-axis, and the maximum and minimum ordinates of the curve.

20. Find the area bounded by the curve $y = x^4 - 8x^2 + 16$ and the x-axis.

21. Find the closed area bounded by the curve $y = x^2$ and the line $y = x$.

22. Find the closed area bounded by the curves $y = x^2$ and $y = x^3$.

23. Find the closed area bounded by the curve $x^2 - 4y = 0$ and the line $x - 2y + 4 = 0$.

24. If A is the area bounded by the curve $x = g(y)$, the y-axis, the line $y = c$, and the horizontal line through the point (x, y) of the curve, show that

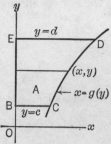

$$\frac{dA}{dy} = x = g(y),$$

and deduce a formula analogous to (3), Art. 30, for finding the area $BCDE$ of Fig. 31b.

25. Find the area bounded by the line $2x - y + 1 = 0$, the y-axis, and the lines $y = 2$ and $y = 5$.

26. Find the area bounded by the line $x - 2y + 2 = 0$, the y-axis, and the line $y = 4$.

Fig. 31b

27. Find the area bounded by the line $x - 2y + 4 = 0$, the y-axis, and the lines $y = 3$ and $y = 5$.

28. The slope of a curve at any point (x, y) is $2x - 3$, and the curve passes through the point $(3, 2)$.

(a) Find the equation of the curve.

(b) Find the area under this curve from $x = 2$ to $x = 4$.

29. The slope of a curve at any point (x, y) is $3x^2 - 12x + 9$, and the intercept of the curve on the y-axis is 4.

(a) Find the equation of the curve.

(b) Find the area bounded by this curve, the coördinate axes, and the minimum ordinate.

30. The speed v (in feet per second) of a body moving in a straight line is given in terms of the time t (in seconds) by the equation $v = 256 - 32t$.

(a) How far will the body move from $t = 0$ to $t = 4$?

(b) How far will the body move from $t = 0$ until the speed is zero?

31. The speed v of a particle moving along a straight line is proportional to the square of the time t, and is 16 ft./sec. when $t = 2$ sec. How far will the particle move in the first 5 sec.?

32. The acceleration of a falling particle is approximately 32 ft./sec.[2] If a particle is dropped, find:

(a) Its speed at the end of 3 sec.

(b) The distance it moves in the first 4 sec.

(c) Its speed at the end of 4 sec.

(d) The distance it moves in the fourth second.

33. A particle is thrown downward with an initial speed of 40 ft./sec.; its acceleration is approximately 32 ft./sec.[2] Find:

(a) Its speed 5 sec. after it is thrown.

(b) The distance it moves in the sixth second.

(c) The distance the particle moves in the first 2 sec.

34. A particle is thrown upward from a point 256 ft. above the ground with an initial speed of 96 ft./sec. Its acceleration is -32 ft./sec.[2] Find:

(a) A formula for the height (s) of the particle above its starting-point at any time (t).

(b) The height of the particle above its starting-point when $t = 2$.

(c) The time required for the particle to reach its highest point.

(d) The maximum height of the particle above its starting-point.

(e) The value of t when the particle reaches the ground.

35. Using the same data as in Problem 34, find:

(a) A formula for the height (y) of the particle above the ground after t seconds of motion.

(b) The height of the particle above the ground when $t = 2$.

(c) The time required for the particle to reach its highest point.

(d) The maximum height of the particle above the ground.

(e) The value of t when the particle reaches the ground.

Compare the results of Problems 34 and 35.

32. Summation. An area, or any quantity which may be interpreted as an area, is readily expressed as the limit of a sum. This point of view will be developed by considering anew the area under a curve.

Let the base BC of the area $BCDE$ (Fig. 32a), whose upper boundary is the curve $y = f(x)$, where $f(x)$ is continuous and increases with x, be divided into n parts which we shall call **intervals.** For convenience, these

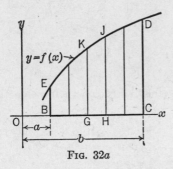

FIG. 32a

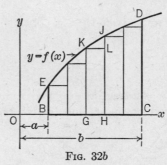

FIG. 32b

intervals will be taken as equal; their common length will be denoted by Δx, so that $\Delta x = \dfrac{b-a}{n}.$ If at each point of division an ordinate is drawn to the curve, the area will be divided into n parts, called **increments of area,** such as $GHJK$. Each of these increments may be approximated by an inscribed rectangular strip whose altitude is the minimum ordinate of the corresponding interval, as in Fig. 32b, or by a circumscribed rectangular strip whose altitude is the maximum ordinate, as in Fig. 32c. Such rectangular strips, whether inscribed or circumscribed, will be called **elements of area.**

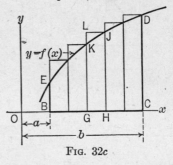

FIG. 32c

Letting $x_0 = a$, $x_1 = a + \Delta x$, $x_2 = a + 2\Delta x$, $\cdots$, $x_n = b$, and observing that the sum of the inscribed rectangular areas (Fig. 32b) is less than the area $BCDE$, we have the inequality

(1) $f(x_0)\Delta x + f(x_1)\Delta x + \cdots + f(x_{n-1})\Delta x < \text{area } BCDE,$

or, using the summation sign Σ, we may write (1) more compactly as

(2) $$\sum_{i=0}^{i=n-1} f(x_i)\Delta x < \text{area } BCDE.$$

Since the sum of the circumscribed rectangular areas (Fig. 32c) is greater than the area $BCDE$, and their respective altitudes are $f(x_1)$, $f(x_2), \cdots, f(x_n)$, we have

(3) $$f(x_1)\Delta x + f(x_2)\Delta x + \cdots + f(x_n)\Delta x > \text{area } BCDE,$$

or

(4) $$\sum_{i=1}^{i=n} f(x_i)\Delta x > \text{area } BCDE.$$

From (2) and (4) we obtain

(5) $$\sum_{i=0}^{i=n-1} f(x_i)\Delta x < \text{area } BCDE < \sum_{i=1}^{i=n} f(x_i)\Delta x.$$

On subtracting the two sums appearing in (5), or their respective equivalents in (1) and (3), we find

(6) $$\sum_{i=1}^{i=n} f(x_i)\Delta x - \sum_{i=0}^{i=n-1} f(x_i)\Delta x = [f(x_n) - f(x_0)]\Delta x = [f(b) - f(a)]\Delta x.$$

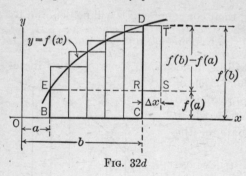

FIG. 32d

The last member of (6) is represented geometrically in Fig. 32d by the rectangle $RSTD$ whose altitude is $f(b) - f(a)$ and whose base is Δx.

If now we allow n, the number of intervals, to become infinite, so that Δx approaches zero, the right members of (6) approach zero. Therefore

$$\lim_{n \to \infty} \left[\sum_{i=1}^{i=n} f(x_i)\Delta x - \sum_{i=0}^{i=n-1} f(x_i)\Delta x \right] = 0,$$

or

(7) $$\lim_{n \to \infty} \sum_{i=1}^{i=n} f(x_i)\Delta x = \lim_{n \to \infty} \sum_{i=0}^{i=n-1} f(x_i)\Delta x.$$

That is, the first and third members of the inequality (5) approach a common limit, and this limit must be the area $BCDE$, since the latter, for any finite n, however large, is intermediate in value between the two sums.

Hence

(8)
$$\lim_{n \to \infty} \sum_{i=0}^{i=n-1} f(x_i)\Delta x = \text{area } BCDE$$

and

(9)
$$\lim_{n \to \infty} \sum_{i=1}^{i=n} f(x_i)\Delta x = \text{area } BCDE.$$

Thus *the area under a continuous curve between two fixed ordinates may be approximated to any desired degree of accuracy by summing the areas of a sufficiently large number, n, of rectangular elements, either inscribed or circumscribed; and the exact area under the curve is the limit of this sum as n becomes infinite.*

While this conclusion was reached on the assumption that $f(x)$ increases with x, so that the curve $y = f(x)$ rises from left to right, the assumption may be abandoned without altering the conclusion, for if $f(x)$ decreases as x increases, the inequality signs in (5) will be reversed, but (8) and (9) will continue to hold. It follows immediately therefore that the conclusion is valid likewise when $f(x)$ alternately increases and decreases.

In this article we have assumed that $f(x)$ is positive throughout the range from $x = a$ to $x = b$. In Art. 34 this restriction will be removed.

33. The Definite Integral. In (3), Art. 30, we found that the area $BCDE$ (Fig. 30c), bounded by the curve $y = f(x)$, the x-axis, and the lines $x = a$ and $x = b$, is given by

(1)
$$\text{area } BCDE = F(b) - F(a),$$

where $F(x)$ is a particular integral of $f(x)dx$. The right member of (1) is the difference between the values of this integral for $x = b$ and $x = a$, and is denoted by the symbol $\int_a^b f(x)dx$, read "the **definite integral** from a to b of $f(x)dx$." Thus by definition

(2)
$$\int_a^b f(x)dx = F(b) - F(a).$$

If $f(x)$ is a given function, then $\int_a^b f(x)dx$ has a definite value which depends only on a and b; this accounts for the term *definite integral*.

From (1) and (2) it follows that

$$(3) \qquad \text{area } BCDE = \int_a^b f(x)dx.$$

Comparing (3) with (8) and (9) of the preceding article, we see that

$$(4) \qquad \lim_{n \to \infty} \sum_{i=0}^{i=n-1} f(x_i)\Delta x = \lim_{n \to \infty} \sum_{i=1}^{i=n} f(x_i)\Delta x = \int_a^b f(x)dx.$$

It thus appears that *the limit of the sum of the elementary rectangular areas* $f(x_i)\Delta x$ *(Fig. 32b or 32c) is represented by the definite integral* $\int_a^b f(x)dx$.

From these considerations the reason becomes apparent for giving the integral sign $\int$ the form of a modified letter S, for as used with a definite integral it signifies the limit of the sum denoted by the corresponding Greek letter Σ. Moreover, the product $f(x)dx$ appearing in the symbol

$$\int_a^b f(x)dx$$

is merely a typical one of the elements of summation. This fact justifies the use of the integral sign with $f(x)dx$ rather than with $f(x)$ alone in the corresponding indefinite integral

$$\int f(x)dx.$$

Though we have introduced the definite integral in connection with areas, we shall see that definite integrals have many other important uses. Accordingly we shall now discuss them from a purely formal point of view.

In the definite integral $\int_a^b f(x)dx$, a and b are called the **limits of integration**, a the **lower limit** and b the **upper limit**. If $b > a$, and $f(x)$ is positive throughout the range from $x = a$ to $x = b$, then it follows from (4) that $\int_a^b f(x)dx$ is positive.

If $y = f(x)$ we may write

$$\int_a^b f(x)dx = \int_a^b y\, dx$$

without ambiguity as to the variable to which the limits refer, for, in general, if a definite integral involves two or more variables, the limits will, unless otherwise specified (as, for example, in $\int_{y=c}^{y=d} y\,dx$), be understood to refer to the **variable of integration,** that is, to the variable whose differential appears with the integrand.

The definite integral $\int_{a}^{b} y\,dx$, where $y = f(x)$, may be evaluated in two ways. We may either substitute $f(x)$ for y, and apply (2), or we may express dx in terms of y and dy, say,

$$dx = g(y)dy,$$

so that, if $y = c$ when $x = a$, $y = d$ when $x = b$, and $G(y)$ is a function whose differential is $y\,g(y)dy$,

$$\int_{a}^{b} y\,dx = \int_{c}^{d} y\,g(y)dy = G(d) - G(c).$$

Though no proof of this fact will be given, it will be illustrated in Example 4 below.

It is customary to denote the difference $F(b) - F(a)$, occurring in (2), by the symbol $[F(x)]_{a}^{b}$, so that

$$(5) \qquad \int_{a}^{b} f(x)\,dx = [F(x)]_{a}^{b} = F(b) - F(a).$$

Since

$$[F(x) + C]_{a}^{b} = [F(b) + C] - [F(a) + C]$$
$$= F(b) - F(a)$$
$$= [F(x)]_{a}^{b},$$

it is clearly unnecessary to introduce a constant of integration in evaluating a definite integral.

If the limits of a definite integral are interchanged the result undergoes a change of sign; for

$$(6) \qquad \int_{b}^{a} f(x)dx = F(a) - F(b) = -[F(b) - F(a)] = -\int_{a}^{b} f(x)dx.$$

Example 1. $\int_{2}^{4} dx = [x]_{2}^{4} = 4 - 2 = 2.$

Example 2. $\int_{0}^{3} x\,dx = \left[\dfrac{x^2}{2}\right]_{0}^{3} = \tfrac{9}{2} - 0 = \tfrac{9}{2}.$

Example 3. $\int_{-1}^{3}(x^2 + 4)dx = \left[\dfrac{x^3}{3} + 4x\right]_{-1}^{3} = [(\tfrac{27}{3} + 12) - (-\tfrac{1}{3} - 4)] = \tfrac{76}{3}.$

Example 4. If $y = 12 - 3x$, evaluate

$$\int_1^3 y\, dx.$$

First Solution.

$$\int_1^3 y\, dx = \int_1^3 (12 - 3x)dx = \left[12x - \frac{3x^2}{2} \right]_1^3 = 12.$$

Second Solution. Since $y = 9$ when $x = 1$, and $y = 3$ when $x = 3$, and since $x = -\frac{1}{3}y + 4$, so that $dx = -\frac{1}{3}dy$, we have

$$\int_1^3 y\, dx = \int_{x=1}^{x=3} y(-\tfrac{1}{3}dy) = -\tfrac{1}{3}\int_9^3 y\, dy = \tfrac{1}{3}\int_3^9 y\, dy = \tfrac{1}{6}[y^2]_3^9 = 12.$$

PROBLEMS

Evaluate the definite integrals in Problems 1–16.

1. $\int_1^4 3\, dx.$

9. $\int_2^4 \tfrac{1}{2}x^2 dx.$

2. $\int_2^5 (2x - 3)dx.$

10. $\int_0^2 (256 - 32t)dt.$

3. $\int_{-3}^1 (2 - x)dx.$

11. $\int_1^3 t(256 - 32t)dt.$

4. $\int_1^2 (x^2 - 1)^2 dx.$

12. $\int_3^4 (s^2 - 4)ds.$

5. $\int_0^2 (x^2 + x)dx.$

13. $\int_1^4 (4\theta - 3)d\theta.$

6. $\int_{-2}^0 (x + 2)dx.$

14. $\int_0^4 (4x - x^2)dx.$

7. $\int_{-1}^2 x^2(2 - x)dx.$

15. $\int_1^3 (x - 1)(2x + 1)dx.$

8. $\int_3^4 (2t - 6)dt.$

16. $\int_0^5 (x^2 - 25)dx.$

Evaluate each of the following definite integrals in two ways:

17. $\int_0^1 y\, dx$, where $y = x + 2$.

20. $\int_0^2 x^2 dy$, where $x = 2y + 6$.

18. $\int_0^4 y\, dx$, where $2x + y - 8 = 0$.

21. $\int_{-6}^{-1} y^4\, dx$, where $y = \sqrt{3 - x}$.

19. $\int_0^8 x\, dy$, where $2x + y - 8 = 0$.

22. $\int_0^1 (x - 2)dy$, where $x + 2y = 4$.

34. Area. We shall now illustrate the application of the definite integral to problems in area.

Example 1. Find the area under the curve $y = x^3 - 4x + 4$ from $x = -2$ to $x = 2$.

· We divide the interval on the x-axis from $x = -2$ to $x = 2$ into n equal parts, and through each point of division pass a line parallel to the y-axis, thus dividing the area into n increments such as $GHJK$, Fig. 34a. An element of area corresponding to this increment is $GHLK$, and its area is $y\Delta x$, where y is the ordinate of the point K on the curve. If we sum the n elements corresponding to the n increments of area we obtain an approximation to the area bounded by the curve, the x-axis, and the lines $x = -2$ and $x = 2$. The exact area, that is, the limit of this sum as n becomes infinite, is the definite integral $\int_{-2}^{2} y\, dx$. Hence

$$\text{area } BCDE = \int_{-2}^{2} y\, dx = \int_{-2}^{2} (x^3 - 4x + 4)dx = \left[\frac{x^4}{4} - 2x^2 + 4x\right]_{-2}^{2}$$

$$= [(\tfrac{16}{4} - 8 + 8) - (\tfrac{16}{4} - 8 - 8)] = 16.$$

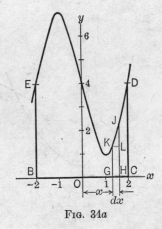

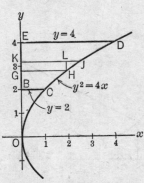

FIG. 34a FIG. 34b

Example 2. Find the area bounded by the curve $y^2 = 4x$, the y-axis, and the lines $y = 2$ and $y = 4$.

For this area we use horizontal strips. Dividing the interval on the y-axis from $y = 2$ to $y = 4$ into n parts, and through each point of division passing a line parallel to the x-axis, we obtain n increments of area such as $GHJK$, Fig. 34b. Corresponding to this increment we shall choose as element the strip $GHLK$, whose area is $x\Delta y$, where x is the abscissa of the point H on the curve. Since the limit of the sum of n such elements as n becomes infinite is the required area, we have

$$\text{area } BCDE = \int_{2}^{4} x\, dy = \int_{2}^{4} \frac{y^2}{4}\, dy - \frac{1}{4}\left[\frac{y^3}{3}\right]_{2}^{4} = \frac{14}{3}.$$

Example 3. Find the area bounded by the parabola $x^2 - 4y + 4 = 0$ and the line $x - 2y + 6 = 0$.

Solving the two equations simultaneously we see that the line and the curve intersect in the points $P_1(-2, 2)$ and $P_2(4, 5)$. We are required to find the area $P_1VP_2RP_1$. (See Fig. 34c.)

This area could be computed by subtracting the area $M_1M_2P_2VP_1$ from the area $M_1M_2P_2RP_1$, each of the latter two areas being found as in Example 1. We prefer, however, to find the required area directly. For this purpose we divide the area into n parts, or increments, such as $GHJKG$, by drawing lines parallel to the y-axis spaced at equal intervals Δx (or dx) from $x = -2$ to $x = 4$. As corresponding elements we shall take rectangular strips such as $GNLKG$ whose area we shall denote by dA. Whence

$$dA = [(y \text{ of the line}) - (y \text{ of the curve})]\, dx.$$

Expressed in terms of x this becomes

$$dA = \left[\frac{x+6}{2} - \frac{x^2+4}{4}\right] dx = \tfrac{1}{4}[-x^2 + 2x + 8]dx.$$

The sum of the n elements is an approximation to the required area; and the limit of this sum, which is found by integration, is the exact value of the area. Hence

$$\text{area } P_1VP_2RP_1 = \tfrac{1}{4}\int_{-2}^{4}(-x^2 + 2x + 8)dx$$

$$= \tfrac{1}{4}\left[-\frac{x^3}{3} + x^2 + 8x\right]_{-2}^{4}$$

$$= 9.$$

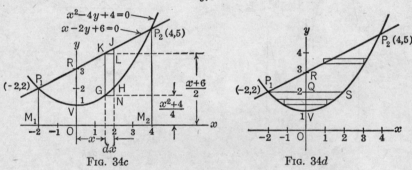

FIG. 34c   FIG. 34d

Before starting to solve an area problem the student should give some consideration to the choice of area element. He will find that a sketch will be of assistance. It should be observed that the use of horizontal strips in Example 3 would require two integrations and therefore should be avoided, for one integration would be required to find the area P_1VSQP_1 (Fig. 34d) and another to find the area $P_1QSP_2RP_1$, since only above the horizontal line P_1S does a strip extend from the line $x - 2y + 6 = 0$ to the curve $x^2 - 4y + 4 = 0$.

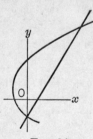

FIG. 34e

By similar reasoning we see that horizontal strips should be used in finding the area shown in Fig. 34e, whereas, for areas such as those in Figs. 34f, 34g, 34h, either horizontal or vertical strips may be used, preference being given to that choice in each case which yields the simpler integral.

The area of a strip, whether horizontal or vertical, should be so formulated as to be positive in order that the computed value of the required area shall be positive. This was accomplished in Example 3

by subtracting the ordinate of the lower boundary curve from that of
the upper, and by selecting -2 (the smaller of the two limits of integration) as the lower limit.   From Examples 4 and 5 it will become clear
that when such precautions are taken the computed value of an area

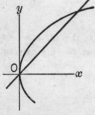

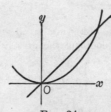

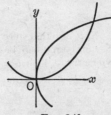

Fig. 34*f*   Fig. 34*g*   Fig. 34*h*

between two curves will be positive regardless of the position of the
area with respect to the coördinate axes.

Example 4..   Find the area bounded by the two parabolas $x^2 + 8x + 2y + 20 = 0$
and $x^2 + 8x - 2y + 4 = 0$.

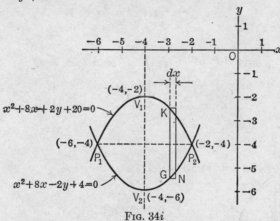

Fig. 34*i*

These curves, together with the coördinates of their points of intersection and
vertices, are shown in Fig. 34*i*.
   Writing

$$dA = [(y \text{ of upper curve}) - (y \text{ of lower curve})]dx$$
$$= [-\tfrac{1}{2}(x^2 + 8x + 20) - \tfrac{1}{2}(x^2 + 8x + 4)]dx$$
$$= -[x^2 + 8x + 12]dx,$$

we find

$$\text{area } P_1V_2P_2V_1P_1 = -\int_{-6}^{-2} (x^2 + 8x + 12)dx$$

$$= -\left[\frac{x^3}{3} + 4x^2 + 12x\right]_{-6}^{-2}$$

$$= \tfrac{32}{3}.$$

This result is positive because the height GK of the elementary strip is obtained by subtracting the ordinate of the lower curve from that of the upper and is therefore positive; and likewise the width $GN = dx$ is positive since the limits of the definite integral are taken so that x increases from the lower limit -6 to the upper limit -2.

Note that by (6), Art. 33, we may evaluate the definite integral thus:

$$-\int_{-6}^{-2} (x^2 + 8x + 12)dx = \int_{-2}^{-6} (x^2 + 8x + 12)dx = \tfrac{32}{3}.$$

Note also that since the area sought is symmetrical with respect to the line $x = -4$ the total area can be found by doubling the area on either side of this axis of symmetry. That is

$$\text{area } P_1V_2P_2V_1P_1 = 2\left\{ -\int_{-4}^{-2} (x^2 + 8x + 12)dx \right\}$$

$$= -2\left[\frac{x^3}{3} + 4x^2 + 12x \right]_{-4}^{-2}$$

$$= \tfrac{32}{3}.$$

Example 5. Find the area bounded by the parabola $y^2 + 16x + 6y - 71 = 0$ and the line $4x + y + 7 = 0$. (See Fig. 34*j*.)

Writing
$$dA = [(x \text{ of curve}) - (x \text{ of line})]dy$$
$$= [\tfrac{1}{16}(-y^2 - 6y + 71) - \tfrac{1}{4}(-y - 7)]dy$$
$$= \tfrac{1}{16}[-y^2 - 2y + 99]dy,$$

we obtain
$$\text{area } P_1P_2VP_1 = \tfrac{1}{16}\int_{-11}^{9} [-y^2 - 2y + 99]dy$$

$$= \tfrac{1}{16}\left[-\frac{y^3}{3} - y^2 + 99y \right]_{-11}^{9}$$

$$= \tfrac{250}{3}.$$

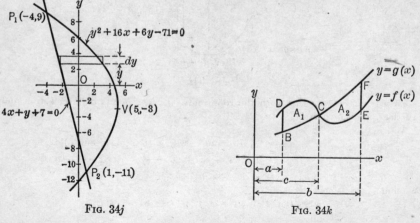

FIG. 34*j*   FIG. 34*k*

If an area consists of two or more parts, it may be necessary to find each part by a separate integration. For example, two integrations are needed to find the area in Fig. 34*k* between the curves $y = f(x)$ and

$y = g(x)$ and bounded on the left by the line $x = a$ and on the right by the line $x = b$. Thus if A_1 represents the area BCD and A_2 the area CEF we obtain for the required area

$$(1) \qquad A_1 + A_2 = \int_a^c [f(x) - g(x)]dx + \int_c^b [g(x) - f(x)]dx.$$

It should be observed that the definite integral

$$\int_a^b [f(x) - g(x)]dx$$

represents the area $A_1 - A_2$; for the area element $[f(x) - g(x)]dx$ is positive for values of x from $x = a$ to $x = c$ and negative from $x = c$ to $x = b$.

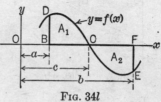

FIG. 34*l*

The area shown in Fig. 34*l*, between the x-axis and the curve $y = f(x)$ from $x = a$ to $x = b$, differs essentially from the area just treated only in the fact that the x-axis $(y = 0)$ replaces the boundary curve $y = g(x)$. It follows therefore from (1), in which we set $g(x) = 0$, that

$$(2) \qquad A_1 + A_2 = \int_a^c f(x)dx - \int_c^b f(x)dx,$$

where A_1 and A_2 denote, respectively, the parts of the area to the left and right of the point C where the curve $y = f(x)$ crosses the x-axis.

Evidently the area A_2 is expressed as a positive quantity by

$$-\int_c^b f(x)dx,$$

since $f(x) < 0$ for $c < x < b$. In general, an area, such as that shown in Fig. 34*m*, bounded above by the x-axis, below by a curve $y = f(x)$, and on the left and right by vertical lines, is given as a positive quantity by

FIG. 34*m*

$$\text{area } BCDE = -\int_a^b f(x)dx,$$

where $b > a$.

Thus it becomes clear that the definite integral

$$\int_a^b f(x)dx, \qquad b > a,$$

when interpreted as an area between the curve $y = f(x)$, the x-axis, and the vertical lines $x = a$ and $x = b$, yields this area as a positive or a negative quantity according as the curve $y = f(x)$ from $x = a$ to $x = b$ lies wholly above or wholly below the x-axis; and in case the curve crosses the x-axis between $x = a$ and $x = b$, it yields the algebraic sum of the areas above and below the x-axis.

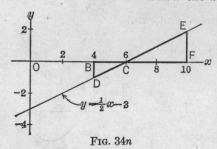

FIG. 34n

Example 6. Find the total area bounded by the line $y = \frac{1}{2}x - 3$, the x-axis, and the lines $x = 4$ and $x = 10$ (Fig. 34n).

Since the line $y = \frac{1}{2}x - 3$ crosses the x-axis at C (6, 0), the required area is the sum of the two triangular areas BDC and CFE, of which the first is below, and the second above, the x-axis. Both these areas may be computed as positive quantities by geometry; their sum is 5.

To obtain this result by integration, we have from the general considerations preceding this example

$$\text{area } BDC = -\int_4^6 (\tfrac{1}{2}x - 3)dx = 1,$$

and

$$\text{area } CFE = \int_6^{10} (\tfrac{1}{2}x - 3)dx = 4,$$

whence the required area is 5.

PROBLEMS

With each problem draw a figure showing all curves and boundary lines. Show an element of area, and express it in such a way that the computed area will be a positive quantity.

1. Find the area bounded by the parabola $y = x^2$, the x-axis, and the lines $x = -1$ and $x = 3$.

2. Find the area bounded by the curve $x^2 - 4y + 3 = 0$, the x-axis, and the lines $x = 3$ and $x = 4$.

3. Find the area bounded by the parabola $y = x^2 - 4$, the x-axis, and the lines $x = 3$ and $x = 5$.

4. Find the area bounded by the parabola $y = x^2 - 4$ and the x-axis.

5. Find the area bounded by the parabola $y = x^2 - 4x$ and the x-axis.

6. Find the area bounded by the parabola $x^2 - 2x + y - 8 = 0$ and the x-axis.

7. Find the total area between the line $y = 2x - 6$ and the x-axis from $x = 2$ to $x = 4$.

8. Find the total area between the curve $x^2 - y - 9 = 0$ and the x-axis from $x = 1$ to $x = 4$.

9. Find the area between the curve $y = x^3 - 1$ and the x-axis from $x = 0$ to $x = 2$.

10. Find the total area bounded by the curve $x^3 - 4x - y = 0$ and the x-axis.

11. Find the area bounded by the parabola $x^2 - 2x + y - 8 = 0$ and the line $2x - y + 4 = 0$.

12. Find the area bounded by the parabola $x^2 - 2x + y - 8 = 0$ and the line $y = 4x$.

13. Find the area bounded by the parabola $x^2 - 2x + y - 8 = 0$ and the line $2x - y - 1 = 0$.

14. Find the area under the parabola $x^2 - 8x - 4y + 24 = 0$ from $x = 1$ to $x = 3$.

15. Find the area bounded by the parabola $x^2 - 8x - 4y + 24 = 0$ and the line $x - 2y + 4 = 0$.

16. Find the area bounded by the parabola $y^2 = x$, the y-axis, and the lines $y = 1$ and $y = 5$.

17. Find the area bounded by the parabola $y^2 + x - 6y + 5 = 0$ and the y-axis.

18. Find the area bounded by the parabola $y^2 + x - 6y + 5 = 0$ and the line $y - x - 5 = 0$.

19. Find the closed area bounded by the two parabolas $4x^2 - y = 0$ and $x^2 - y + 12 = 0$.

20. Find the area in the first quadrant bounded by the parabola $y = 3x^2$ and the cubic curve $y = 4x - x^3$.

21. Find the total area bounded by the cubic curve $y = x^3 - 3x^2 + 3x + 1$ and the line $x - y + 1 = 0$.

22. Find the total area bounded by the cubic curve $y = x^3 - 7x^2 + 8x + 17$, the x-axis, and the maximum and minimum ordinates to the curve.

23. Find the total area bounded by the two curves in Problem 20.

24. Find the total area bounded by the curve $y + 1 = (x - 2)^3$ and the line $y = 7x - 9$.

35. Fundamental Theorem; Duhamel's Theorem.   In Art. 33 we defined the definite integral by the equation

$$(1) \qquad \int_a^b f(x)dx = F(b) - F(a),$$

where $F(x)$ is a particular integral of $f(x)dx$, and found that it represents the area under the curve * $y = f(x)$ from $x = a$ to $x = b$. Moreover (cf. (4), Art. 33), we showed that

$$(2) \qquad \lim_{n \to \infty} \sum_{i=0}^{i=n-1} f(x_i)\Delta x = \lim_{n \to \infty} \sum_{i=1}^{i=n} f(x_i)\Delta x = \int_a^b f(x)dx,$$

where $f(x_i)\Delta x$ is the area of an elementary rectangular strip. Clearly (2) may be divorced completely from the concept of area, and any limit of the type

$$\lim_{n \to \infty} \sum_{i=0}^{i=n-1} f(x_i)\Delta x, \text{ or } \lim_{n \to \infty} \sum_{i=1}^{i=n} f(x_i)\Delta x,$$

* It developed in the last article that if the curve crosses the x-axis between $x = a$ and $x = b$, then $\int_a^b f(x)dx$ gives the algebraic sum of the areas above and below the x-axis.

may at once be replaced by $\int_a^b f(x)dx$ and evaluated by (1), regardless of the geometrical or physical interpretation of $f(x)$, provided, of course, that the limit exists.   This important point of view we now state as the

FUNDAMENTAL THEOREM ON DEFINITE INTEGRALS.   *If, by taking n sufficiently large, an arbitrarily close approximation to a required quantity Q in any problem is given by* *

$$\sum_{i=1}^{i=n} f(x_i)\Delta x,$$

so that

$$Q = \lim_{n \to \infty} \sum_{i=1}^{i=n} f(x_i)\Delta x,$$

where $x_0 = a$, $x_1 = a + \Delta x$, $x_2 = a + 2\Delta x, \cdots, x_n = a + n\Delta x = b$, then

$$Q = \int_a^b f(x)dx,$$

provided that $f(x)$ is single-valued and continuous from $x = a$ to $x = b$.

In applications of this theorem the question arises as to how, after the quantity Q has been divided into n parts, or increments, ΔQ_i, each ΔQ_i being merely approximated by $f(x_i)\Delta x$, we may be sure that

$$Q = \lim_{n \to \infty} \sum_{i=1}^{i=n} f(x_i)\Delta x;$$

for it will develop that ΔQ_i is often an expression of the form

$$\Delta Q_i = [f(x_i) + \eta_i]\Delta x,$$

where the η_i are infinitesimals of at least the same order as Δx, and *a priori* it is not clear that the terms $\eta_i \cdot \Delta x$ may be neglected.   However, it follows from a theorem known as *Duhamel's Theorem*, which we shall state presently, that

$$\lim_{n \to \infty} \sum_{i=1}^{i=n} [f(x_i) + \eta_i]\Delta x = \lim_{n \to \infty} \sum_{i=1}^{i=n} f(x_i)\Delta x.$$

This fact enables us to find Q by a direct application of the Fundamental Theorem; for, since

$$Q = \sum_{i=1}^{i=n} \Delta Q_i,$$

---

* For convenience, we omit the first formulation of the sum in (2).

regardless of the number of increments ΔQ_i, we may write

$$(3) \qquad Q = \lim_{n \to \infty} \sum_{i=1}^{i=n} \Delta Q_i$$

$$= \lim_{n \to \infty} \sum_{i=1}^{i=n} [f(x_i) + \eta_i]\Delta x$$

$$= \lim_{n \to \infty} \sum_{i=1}^{i=n} f(x_i)\Delta x,$$

so that by the Fundamental Theorem

$$(4) \qquad Q = \int_a^b f(x)dx.$$

Thus, if it is possible to formulate every increment ΔQ_i as $f(x_i)\Delta x$ plus an infinitesimal of higher order than Δx, we may discard the latter infinitesimal term and evaluate Q exactly by the Fundamental Theorem.

If in (4) we replace the upper limit b by the variable x then Q becomes a function of x which by Art. 33 may be written in the form

$$Q = F(x) - F(a),$$

where

$$\frac{d}{dx} F(x) = f(x).$$

Therefore

$$\frac{dQ}{dx} = f(x),$$

and

$$dQ = f(x)dx.$$

In problems requiring the determination of a quantity Q by the Fundamental Theorem it will be convenient to use this notation, that is, to designate $f(x)dx$, the element of integration, by dQ, even though Q is a definite invariable quantity.

DUHAMEL'S THEOREM. *If for all values of n all the elements of the two sequences*

$$\alpha_1(n), \ \alpha_2(n), \cdots, \alpha_n(n),$$

$$\beta_1(n), \ \beta_2(n), \cdots, \beta_n(n),$$

have the same sign, and each one approaches zero as n becomes infinite (i.e., is an infinitesimal), and further if

(5) $$\lim_{n \to \infty} \frac{\alpha_i(n)}{\beta_i(n)} = 1, \ (i = 1, 2, \cdots, n),$$

then

$$\lim_{n \to \infty} \sum_{i=1}^{i=n} \alpha_i(n) = \lim_{n \to \infty} \sum_{i=1}^{i=n} \beta_i(n),$$

provided that these limits exist.

The student should be informed that the conditions of this theorem are not complete; hence no proof can be given. The theorem as stated, however, is believed to be adequate for a first course in calculus, for the omitted conditions are such as to be automatically fulfilled in all elementary applications.

The condition (5) may, by Art. 25, be alternatively written

(6) $$\alpha_i(n) = \beta_i(n) + \zeta_i(n), \ (i = 1, 2, \cdots, n),$$

where $\zeta_i(n)$ is an infinitesimal of higher order than $\alpha_i(n)$ or $\beta_i(n)$.

We are now in a position to justify the last member of (3); for ΔQ_i, $f(x_i)\Delta x$, and $\eta_i \cdot \Delta x$ may be identified, respectively, with the infinitesimals $\alpha_i(n)$, $\beta_i(n)$, and $\zeta_i(n)$ in Duhamel's Theorem and in (6).

Since in the ensuing applications requiring the use of definite integrals Duhamel's Theorem will be extensively employed, it may be helpful to illustrate this theorem in connection with a simple area problem.

Example. Applying Duhamel's Theorem and the Fundamental Theorem, find the area under the line $y = 2x + 1$ from $x = 0$ to $x = 1$.

Dividing the interval from $x = 0$ to $x = 1$ into n equal parts Δx, and designating the required area by A and the increment of area shown ($GHJK$, Fig. 35) by ΔA_i, we have

$$A = \sum_{i=0}^{i=n-1} \Delta A_i,$$

regardless of the value of n.   Hence

$$A = \lim_{n \to \infty} \sum_{i=0}^{i=n-1} \Delta A_i.$$

From the figure this evidently becomes

$$A = \lim_{n \to \infty} \sum_{i=0}^{i=n-1} (y_i + \tfrac{1}{2}\Delta y_i)\Delta x$$

$$= \lim_{n \to \infty} \sum_{i=0}^{i=n-1} [y_i \Delta x + (\Delta x)^2],$$

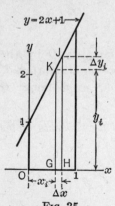

FIG. 35

the last step being a consequence of the fact that $\Delta y_i = 2\Delta x$ which we readily obtain from the equation of the line.

Now by Duhamel's Theorem we may disregard the second-order infinitesimal $(\Delta x)^2$ and write

$$A = \lim_{n \to \infty} \sum_{i=0}^{i=n-1} y_i \Delta x,$$

whence by the Fundamental Theorem

$$A = \int_0^1 y \, dx = \int_0^1 (2x + 1)dx = 2.$$

Thus it is apparent that Duhamel's Theorem and the Fundamental Theorem lead to the same definite integral for the area as would be obtained by the method of the preceding article.

36. Volume. Consider a solid (Fig. 36a) whose cross-section in a plane perpendicular to the x-axis is a known function (say $A(x)$) of the distance x from the origin to the cutting plane. If the solid is bounded on the left and right by the planes $x = a$ and $x = b$, respectively, and its volume V is divided by equally spaced planes $x = x_i$ ($i = 0, 1, \cdots, n - 1$; $x_0 = a$) into n increments ΔV_i of thickness $\Delta x = \dfrac{b - a}{n}$, and if $A(x)$ is an increasing* func-

Fig. 36a

tion of x, then each ΔV_i is intermediate in value between the volumes of two laminas of common thickness Δx and of respective face-areas $A(x_i)$ and $A(x_{i+1})$. That is, ΔV_i is equal to $A(x_i)\Delta x$ plus a fractional part of the difference between the volumes of the laminas. Therefore,

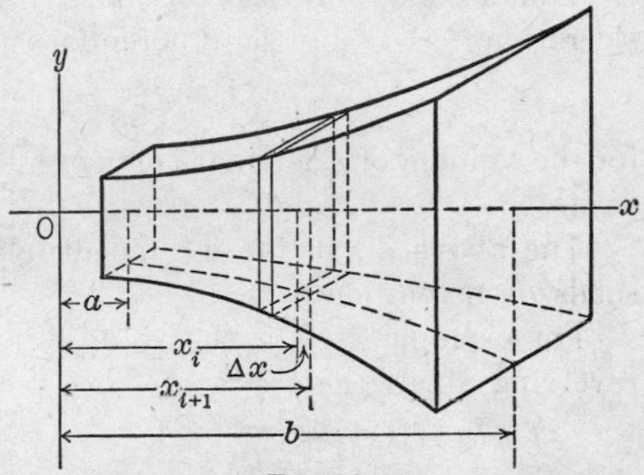

$$\Delta V_i = A(x_i)\Delta x + k_i[A(x_{i+1}) - A(x_i)]\Delta x$$

where the fraction k_i (whose value in general depends on i) satisfies the condition $0 < k_i < 1$. Since

$$V = \sum_{i=0}^{i=n-1} \Delta V_i,$$

regardless of the value of n, we may allow n to become indefinitely large, and write

$$V = \lim_{n \to \infty} \sum_{i=0}^{i=n-1} \Delta V_i$$

$$= \lim_{n \to \infty} \sum_{i=0}^{i=n-1} \{A(x_i)\Delta x + k_i[A(x_{i+1}) - A(x_i)]\Delta x\}$$

* This restriction is imposed merely for simplicity of exposition.

Now $A(x_{i+1}) - A(x_i)$ approaches zero as Δx approaches zero; hence the product of this difference by Δx is an infinitesimal of higher order than $A(x_i)\Delta x$, and may therefore by Duhamel's Theorem be neglected in taking the limit of the sum. Thus we obtain

$$V = \lim_{n \to \infty} \sum_{i=0}^{i=n-1} A(x_i)\Delta x,$$

and by the Fundamental Theorem

(1)
$$V = \int_a^b A(x)\,dx.$$

Thus to determine the volume of a solid such as the one under consideration, we set up the differential expression

$$dV = A(x)dx$$

for the volume of a laminar element and integrate this between proper limits.

The above discussion is immediately applicable to the volumes of solids of revolution.

For example, if V is the volume of the solid (Fig. 36b) formed by revolving about the x-axis the area bounded by the x-axis, the curve

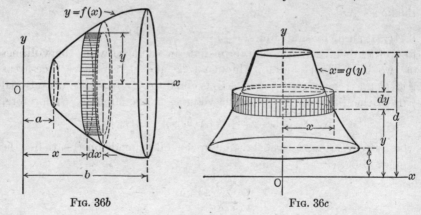

FIG. 36b   FIG. 36c

$y = f(x)$, and the lines $x = a$ and $x = b$, then the volume element is a cylindrical disc of volume

$$dV = \pi y^2 dx,$$

and hence

(2)
$$V = \pi \int_a^b y^2 dx = \pi \int_a^b [f(x)]^2 dx.$$

Similarly, for the volume of the solid (Fig. 36c) formed by revolving about the y-axis the area bounded by the y-axis, the curve $x = g(y)$, and the lines $y = c$ and $y = d$, we have

$$(3) \qquad V = \pi \int_c^d x^2 dy = \pi \int_c^d [g(y)]^2 dy.$$

Example 1. Find by integration the volume of the cone (Fig. 36d) generated by revolving about the x-axis the right triangular area whose vertices are $(0, 0)$, $(6, 0)$, and $(6, 2)$.

Since the equation of the line joining the origin to the point $(6, 2)$ is $y = \frac{1}{3}x$ we have, by (2),

$$V = \pi \int_0^6 y^2 dx = \frac{\pi}{9} \int_0^6 x^2 dx = 8\pi.$$

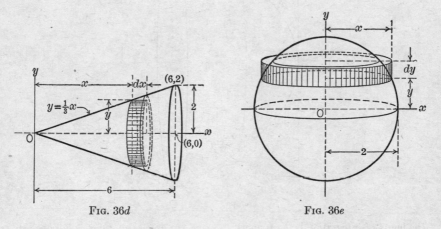

FIG. 36d   FIG. 36e

Example 2. Find by integration the volume of a sphere of radius 2. (See Fig. 36e.)

Regarding this sphere as generated by revolving about the y-axis the area bounded by the y-axis and the right half of the circle $x^2 + y^2 = 4$, we have, by (3),

$$V = \pi \int_{-2}^2 x^2 dy = \pi \int_{-2}^2 (4 - y^2) dy = \pi \left[4y - \frac{y^3}{3} \right]_{-2}^2 = \frac{32\pi}{3}.$$

Alternatively, taking advantage of the symmetry of the generating area with respect to the x-axis, we obtain

$$V = 2\pi \int_0^2 x^2 dy = 2\pi \int_0^2 (4 - y^2) dy = \frac{32\pi}{3}.$$

Example 3. Find the volume of the solid generated by revolving about the x-axis the area bounded by the parabolas $y^2 = 8x$ and $8y = x^2$. (See Fig. 36f.)

The cross-section of the solid in a plane perpendicular to the x-axis and at distance x from the origin is an annular ring whose outer and inner radii are the ordinates

$y = \sqrt{8x}$ and $y = \dfrac{x^2}{8}$ to the respective curves $y^2 = 8x$ and $8y = x^2$. That is, the area of the cross-section is

$$A(x) = \pi(\sqrt{8x})^2 - \pi\left(\frac{x^2}{8}\right)^2 = \pi\left(8x - \frac{x^4}{64}\right).$$

Hence, by (1),

$$V = \pi\int_0^8\left(8x - \frac{x^4}{64}\right)dx,$$

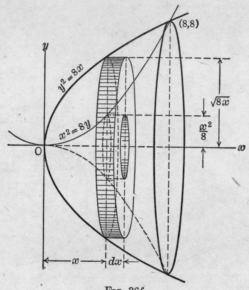

FIG. 36f

the limits of integration being found by solving the given equations simultaneously. Thus

$$V = \pi\left[4x^2 - \frac{x^5}{320}\right]_0^8 = \frac{768\pi}{5}.$$

It should be observed that this volume may be regarded as the limit of the sum of washer-shaped elements (one of which is shown in the figure) of face-area $A(x)$, thickness dx, and volume

$$dV = A(x)dx = \pi\left(8x - \frac{x^4}{64}\right)dx.$$

Example 4.   Find the volume of the solid generated by revolving about the line $y = 2$ the area in the first quadrant bounded by the parabola $8y = x^2$, the y-axis, and the line $y = 2$.   (See Fig. 36g.)

Choosing as an element of volume a disc having as its axis the line $y = 2$ we obtain, by analogy with (2),

$$V = \pi\int_0^4 r^2dx,$$

where r is the radius of the disc, and the upper limit of integration is the positive value of x found by substituting $y = 2$ in the equation $8y = x^2$.

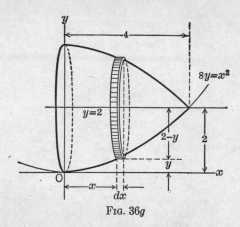

Fig. 36g

In order to evaluate this definite integral we must express r in terms of x. But clearly

$$r = 2 - y = 2 - \frac{x^2}{8}.$$

Hence

$$V = \pi \int_0^4 \left(2 - \frac{x^2}{8}\right)^2 dx$$

$$= \pi \int_0^4 \left(4 - \frac{x^2}{2} + \frac{x^4}{64}\right) dx = \pi \left[4x - \frac{x^3}{6} + \frac{x^5}{320}\right]_0^4$$

$$= \frac{128\pi}{15}.$$

Example 5. Find the volume of the wedge-shaped solid cut from a right circular cylinder of radius 2 ft. by a plane passing through a diameter of the base and making an angle of 45° with the axis of the cylinder.

For convenience let us take the plane of the base of the cylinder as the xy-plane, the center of the base as the origin, and the edge of the dihedral angle of the wedge as the y-axis. (See Fig. 36h.)

Since the cross-section of the wedge in a plane perpendicular to the y-axis and at a distance y from the origin is a triangle of base x and equal altitude, and the equation of the base-circle is $x^2 + y^2 = 4$, we have, for the cross-section area,

$$A = \tfrac{1}{2}x^2 = \tfrac{1}{2}(4 - y^2),$$

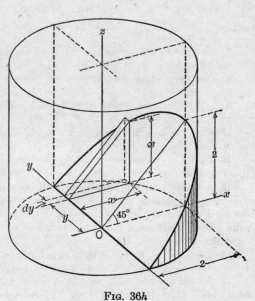

Fig. 36h

and for the volume of a laminar element,

$$dV = \tfrac{1}{2}(4 - y^2)dy.$$

Hence the required volume is

$$V = \tfrac{1}{2}\int_{-2}^{2}(4 - y^2)dy = \tfrac{16}{3}.$$

PROBLEMS

1. In Fig. 36i the equation of the curve is $y^2 = 4x$.

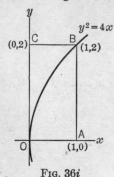

Fig. 36i

(*a*) Find the volume generated by revolving about the x-axis the area OAB.

(*b*) Find the volume generated by revolving about the line AB the area OAB.

(*c*) Find the volume generated by revolving about the y-axis the area OBC.

(*d*) Find the volume generated by revolving about the y-axis the area OAB.

2. Find the volume generated by revolving about the x-axis the area bounded by the curve $y = x^3$, the x-axis, and the lines $x = 2$ and $x = 3$.

3. Find the volume generated by revolving about the x-axis the area in the first quadrant bounded by the curve $y^2 = 2x^3$, the x-axis, and the lines $x = 1$ and $x = 3$.

4. Find the volume generated by revolving about the x-axis the area bounded by the curve $y = x^3 - 3x + 4$, the x-axis, and the lines $x = 1$ and $x = 2$.

5. Find by integration the volume of the cone generated by revolving about the x-axis the area of the right triangle whose vertices are $(2, 0)$, $(2, 2)$, and $(5, 0)$.

6. Find the volume generated by revolving about the x-axis the area enclosed by the ellipse $\dfrac{x^2}{9} + \dfrac{y^2}{4} = 1$.

7. Find the volume generated by revolving about the y-axis the area bounded by the curve $x = y^2 - y^3$ and the y-axis.

8. Find the volume generated by revolving about the y-axis the area bounded by the curve $x = 2y - y^2$ and the y-axis.

9. Find the volume generated by revolving about the x-axis the area enclosed by the loop of the curve $y^2 = 4x^2 - x^3$.

10. Find the volume generated by revolving about the y-axis the area bounded by the parabolas $y^2 = x$ and $y = x^2$.

11. Find the volume generated by revolving about the y-axis the area bounded by the parabola $y^2 = 4x - 4$, the line $y = x$, and the x-axis.

12. A variable rectangle remains parallel to a fixed plane as one vertex moves on a line perpendicular to the plane. One dimension is always twice the distance from the fixed plane and the other the square of the distance. Find the volume of the solid generated as the rectangle moves from a distance zero to a distance 4 from the fixed plane.

13. The axes of two equal right circular cylinders intersect at right angles. The radius of each cylinder is 3. Find the volume common to the two cylinders.

14. A solid has a circular base of radius 6. The x-axis coincides with a diameter of the base. Find the volume of a solid if every section by a plane perpendicular to the x-axis is:

(a) A square.

(b) An isosceles right triangle with its hypotenuse in the plane of the base.

(c) An isosceles right triangle with one leg in the plane of the base.

15. Two circles have a common diameter of 4 in. and the circles lie in perpendicular planes. A square moves in such a way that its plane is perpendicular to the common diameter and its diagonals are chords of the circles. Find the volume of the solid generated.

16. Consider a volume such as that described at the beginning of this article, whose cross-section in two planes perpendicular to the x-axis at distances x and $x + \Delta x$ from the origin are $A(x)$ and $A(x + \Delta x)$. Designating by $\Delta V(x)$ the volume included between these cross-sections, and noting that, for a solid such as that shown in Fig. 36a,

$$A(x)\Delta x < \Delta V(x) < A(x + \Delta x)\Delta x,$$

show that

$$\frac{dV(x)}{dx} = A(x),$$

and hence infer that

$$V(x) = \int A(x)dx,$$

where $V(x)$ is the volume included between an arbitrary plane such as $x = a$ and a variable plane at distance x from the origin. Thence deduce formula (1).

37. Pressure. In the design of dams, locks, reservoirs, water-towers, ships, and any other structures that must withstand liquid pressure, it is necessary to calculate the total force exerted by the liquid on the wetted area. The problem of finding this force in some special cases is considered here as an interesting application of integration.

Consider a point P within a liquid at rest. Pass any plane through P, and in this plane draw a closed curve surrounding P. Let ΔA be the area enclosed by the curve, and ΔF the force exerted by the liquid on one side of ΔA. Then $\dfrac{\Delta F}{\Delta A}$ is the average force per unit area of ΔA, or the **average pressure** on ΔA. As the area ΔA shrinks indefinitely but in such a manner as always to contain the point P, the average pressure $\dfrac{\Delta F}{\Delta A}$ approaches a limit, say p, which in hydrostatics is shown to be independent of the orientation of the plane through P, and which we shall call the **pressure** at the point P. That is

$$(1) \qquad p = \lim_{\Delta A \to 0} \frac{\Delta F}{\Delta A}.$$

It is further shown in hydrostatics that

$$(2) \qquad p = wh,$$

where w is the (constant) weight of the liquid per unit volume and h is the depth of the point P below the surface of the liquid.

By (2) the pressure is the same at all points of a submerged area A situated in a horizontal plane, at depth h; then p may be regarded as the force exerted by the liquid on every unit of this area, and the total force on one side of the area is

$$F = whA.$$

Let us now consider the more difficult problem of determining the total force F exerted by a liquid on one side of a submerged area in a vertical plane. (See Fig. 37a.)

Let h be the depth of any point of the area, and suppose that h ranges from a value a at the top of the area to a value b at the bottom. Divide

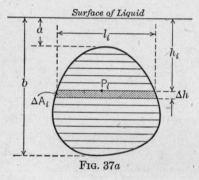

Fig. 37a

the area into n increments ΔA_i ($i = 0$, $1, 2, \cdots, n - 1$) of width $\Delta h = \dfrac{b - a}{n}$ by means of the horizontal lines $h = h_i$, and denote by ΔF_i the force exerted by the liquid on ΔA_i. Then if P_i is a point on the upper edge of ΔA_i, the pressure at P_i is, by (2), wh_i. Since the depths of the other points of ΔA_i range between h_i and $h_i + \Delta h$, it follows that

$$wh_i \Delta A_i < \Delta F_i < w(h_i + \Delta h)\Delta A_i.$$

Hence ΔF_i differs from $wh_i \Delta A_i$ by a quantity which is less than $w\Delta h \Delta A_i$; calling this difference $w\eta_i \Delta A_i$, we have

$$\Delta F_i = w(h_i + \eta_i)\Delta A_i,$$

where $\eta_i < \Delta h$.

The total force exerted by the liquid on the area A is therefore

$$F = \sum_{i=0}^{i=n-1} \Delta F_i = \sum_{i=0}^{i=n-1} w(h_i + \eta_i)\Delta A_i,$$

or, since n may be taken as indefinitely large,

$$F = \lim_{n \to \infty} \sum_{i=0}^{i=n-1} w(h_i + \eta_i)\Delta A_i.$$

Now if l_i is the length of the upper edge of ΔA_i, we may write

$$\Delta A_i = (l_i + \zeta_i)\Delta h,$$

where ζ_i is an infinitesimal of at least the same order as Δh.   Hence

$$F = \lim_{n \to \infty} \sum_{i=0}^{i=n-1} w(h_i + \eta_i)(l_i + \zeta_i)\Delta h.$$

By Duhamel's Theorem we may discard infinitesimals of higher order than Δh; therefore

$$F = \lim_{n \to \infty} \sum_{i=0}^{i=n-1} w\, h_i l_i \Delta h,$$

whence, by the Fundamental Theorem,

(3) $$F = \int_a^b whl\, dh,$$

where the variable l denotes the width of the submerged area at the depth h.

Thus (3) states that the force F is the limit of the sum of the products obtained by multiplying the area $dA = l\,dh$ of each of the rectangular strips shown in Fig. 37b by the pressure wh at any point of the strip, and may be found by expressing dA in terms of h and dh and integrating

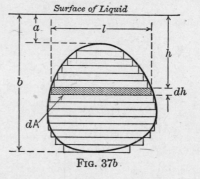

Fig. 37b

(4) $$dF = wh\, dA$$

between limits specifying the range of the variable h.

If, as is advantageous in many problems, we express dF in terms of a variable other than h, the limits of integration must be taken as the values of the new variable corresponding to $h = a$ and $h = b$, respectively.

For convenience we shall often refer to the force F, exerted by a liquid on a submerged area, as the **total pressure** on the area.

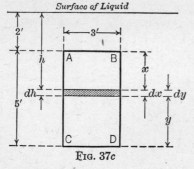

Fig. 37c

Example 1. A rectangular plate is submerged in a liquid weighing 50 lb./cu. ft., as shown in Fig. 37c. If the edges AC and BD are vertical find the force exerted by the liquid on one side of the plate.

We shall solve this problem in three ways, using the respective variables h, x, and y, shown in the figure as variables of integration.

First Solution. Evidently

$$dA = 3 \, dh,$$

$$dF = (50h)(3 \, dh) = 150h \, dh,$$

and

$$F = 150 \int_2^7 h \, dh = 150 \left[\frac{h^2}{2} \right]_2^7 = 3375 \text{ lb.}$$

Second Solution. Using x as the variable of integration, and observing that the depth of the upper edge of the strip is $2 + x$, we obtain

$$dA = 3 \, dx,$$

$$dF = 50(2 + x)(3 \, dx) = 150(2 + x)dx,$$

whence

$$F = 150 \int_0^5 (2 + x)dx = 150 \left[2x + \frac{x^2}{2} \right]_0^5 = 3375 \text{ lb.}$$

Third Solution. Using y as the variable of integration, and observing that the depth of the lower edge of the strip is $7 - y$, we obtain

$$dA = 3 \, dy,$$

$$dF = 50(7 - y)(3 \, dy) = 150(7 - y)dy,$$

and therefore

$$F = 150 \int_0^5 (7 - y)dy = 150 \left[7y - \frac{y^2}{2} \right]_0^5 = 3375 \text{ lb.}$$

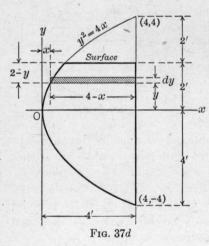

FIG. 37d

Example 2. A plate in the form of a parabolic segment of base 8 ft. and altitude 4 ft. is partially submerged in a liquid weighing 60 lb./cu. ft. in such a way that the base is vertical and the axis is 2 ft. below the surface. Find the total pressure on one side of the plate.

Choosing coördinate axes as in Fig. 37d, and observing that the equation of the parabola is then of the form $y^2 = kx$ and that the curve passes through the point $(4, -4)$, we readily find that $k = 4$. Hence the equation of the parabola is $y^2 = 4x$.

Clearly the area of the rectangular strip shown is

$$dA = (4 - x)dy,$$

and since for any position of the strip the depth of its lower edge is $2 - y$, we obtain

$$dF = 60(2 - y)(4 - x)dy$$

$$= 60(2 - y) \left(4 - \frac{y^2}{4} \right) dy$$

$$= 60 \left(8 - 4y - \frac{y^2}{2} + \frac{y^3}{4} \right) dy.$$

Therefore

$$F = 60 \int_{-4}^{2} \left(8 - 4y - \frac{y^2}{2} + \frac{y^3}{4} \right) dy$$

$$= 60 \left[8y - 2y^2 - \frac{y^3}{6} + \frac{y^4}{16} \right]_{-4}^{2}$$

$$= 2700 \text{ lb.}$$

Example 3. The sloping face of a dam is a rectangle the lengths of whose sides are 82 ft. and 20 ft. If one of the longer sides is at the water level and each of the shorter sides has a slope of $\frac{40}{9}$, find the total pressure on the dam. The weight of water per cubic foot is approximately 62.5 lb. or $\frac{1}{32}$ ton.

Although formula (4) was derived on the supposition that the submerged area lay in a vertical plane, the derivation may readily be modified to show that the

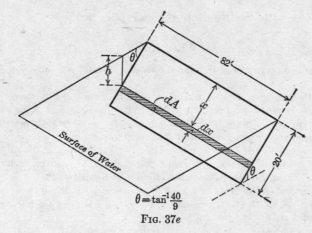

$$\theta = \tan^{-1}\frac{40}{9}$$

FIG. 37e

formula holds for any orientation of a plane area, and is therefore adapted to the solution of the present problem.

Denoting by x the distance along an inclined edge of the dam from the surface of the water to the upper horizontal side of a rectangular strip lying in the face of the dam, we have (Fig. 37e)

$$h = x \sin \theta = \tfrac{40}{41} x,$$

$$dA = 82 \, dx,$$

and

$$dF = wh(82 \, dx)$$

$$= 80 \, wx \, dx.$$

Hence

$$F = 80w \int_{0}^{20} x \, dx = 80w \left[\frac{x^2}{2} \right]_{0}^{20} = 16,000 \, w = 500 \text{ tons.}$$

This force is, of course, normal to the face of the dam.

38. Pressure and Geometrical Center.

If an area A submerged in a liquid of weight w per unit volume has a geometrical center whose depth below the surface of the liquid is $\bar{h}$, then it can be shown that the force exerted by the liquid on the area is*

(1) $$F = w\bar{h}A.$$

Since it is desirable that the student acquire facility in solving problems in liquid pressure by integration, it is recommended that (1) be used only as a check in those problems to which it applies.

For instance, in the case of the rectangular dam of Example 3 of the preceding article,

$$\bar{h} = 10 \sin \theta = \tfrac{400}{41},$$

so that, by (1),

$$F = \tfrac{1}{32} \left(\tfrac{400}{41}\right) (1640) = 500 \text{ tons},$$

in agreement with the result previously obtained.

PROBLEMS

In problems on water pressure take the weight of water per cubic foot as 62.5 lb. or $\tfrac{1}{32}$ ton.

1. A rectangular gate in a vertical dam is 12 ft. wide and 8 ft. deep. Find the total pressure when the level of the water is 10 ft. above the top of the gate.

2. Find how far the water level must fall in order that the total pressure on the gate of Problem 1 may be reduced to half of its original value.

3. A vertical gate 4 ft. square closes the end of a millrace. If the surface of the water is just level with the top of the gate, find the total pressure on each of the two portions into which the square is divided by one of its diagonals.

4. The vertical end of a water trough is an isosceles triangle 6 ft. across the top and 4 ft. deep. Find the total pressure on one end if the trough is filled with water to a depth of 3 ft.

5. A triangular plate whose plane is vertical is submerged in water as shown in Fig. 38a. Find in three ways the total pressure on one side of the plate, using x, y, and z in turn as variables of integration.

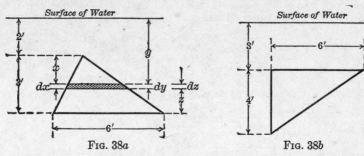

Fig. 38a   Fig. 38b

6. A triangular plate whose plane is vertical is submerged in water as shown in Fig. 38b. Find in three ways the total pressure on one side of the plate.

* In reality (1) holds for any submerged area provided that we regard $\bar{h}$ as the depth of a point known as the *centroid* of the area. (Cf. Problem 23, p. 303.) The centroid of an area coincides with the geometrical center when the latter exists.

7. The vertical end of a trough is an isosceles trapezoid with dimensions as shown in Fig. 38c. Find the pressure on the end when the trough is filled to a depth of 1 ft. with a liquid that weighs 60 lb./cu. ft.

8. A vertical dam is in the form of a trapezoid with its parallel sides horizontal. If these sides have lengths of 300 ft. and 200 ft. respectively, the longer side being at the top, and if the height of the dam is 16 ft., find the total pressure on the dam when the water is level with its top.

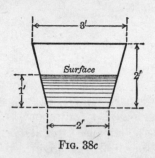

FIG. 38c

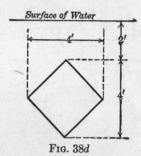

FIG. 38d

9. A square plate whose diagonal is 4 ft. long is submerged in water in a vertical plane as shown in Fig. 38d. Find the total pressure on one of its faces.

10. A cylindrical water-tower whose inner radius is 10 ft. contains water to a depth of 16 ft. Find the total pressure on the lateral surface.

11. The area $OBCO$ (Fig. 38e) lies in a vertical plane and is symmetrical with respect to the vertical line AC. With the axes as shown, the equation of the curve OC is $y^2 = 4x$. A portion of this area is subject to water pressure, the surface being at DF. Find the total pressure on the area $OBFEDO$.

12. A portion of the sloping face of a dam is a rectangle the lengths of whose sides are 320 ft. and 25 ft. If one of the longer sides is at the water level and each of the shorter sides has a slope of $\frac{2.4}{7}$, find the total pressure on the rectangle.

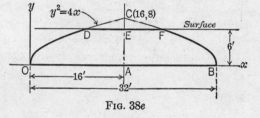

FIG. 38e

13. Find the pressure on the rectangular area of Problem 12 when the water has risen 12 ft.

39. Work. If the point of application of a constant force f moves a distance s along the fixed line of action of the force, then the force is said to do the **work**

$$w = \pm fs,$$

the sign being $+$ or $-$ according as the point of application moves in the direction of f or in the opposite direction.

In the British system of units, the unit of work commonly employed is the *foot-pound* (abbreviated ft-lb.), defined as the work done by a force of one pound acting through a distance of one foot. In the C.G.S. system the unit of work is the *erg*; an erg is the work done by a force of one dyne acting through a distance of one centimeter.

For example, if a 10-lb. horizontal force f' moves a block 3 ft. along a horizontal plane, and a 2-lb. force of friction, f'', resists the motion, the work done by f' is

$$w' = 10 \times 3 = 30 \text{ ft-lb.},$$

and that done by f'' is

$$w'' = -2 \times 3 = -6 \text{ ft-lb.}$$

Consider now the work done by a variable force.

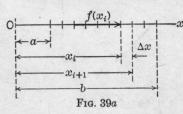

FIG. 39a

Let a variable force be directed along the positive x-axis, and assume that the force is a continuous function $f(x)$ of the distance x of its point of application from the origin. It is required to find the work w done by the force $f(x)$ as its point of application is displaced along the x-axis from $x = a$ to $x = b$, where $b > a$. (See Fig. 39a.)

Divide the segment of the x-axis from $x = a$ to $x = b$ into n parts, or increments, of common length $\Delta x = \dfrac{b-a}{n}$, and designate the abscissas of the points of division by x_i $(i = 0, 1, \cdots, n-1; \; x_0 = a)$. If $f(x)$ increases with x, and Δw_i denotes the work done by the force while the point of application undergoes the displacement $x_{i+1} - x_i$, then clearly

(1) $$f(x_i)\Delta x < \Delta w_i < f(x_i + \Delta x)\Delta x.$$

Letting

$$\eta_i = f(x_i + \Delta x) - f(x_i),$$

we see from (1) that there exists a proper fraction k_i such that

$$\Delta w_i = [f(x_i) + k_i\eta_i]\Delta x.$$

Therefore since the total work w done by the force is given by $\displaystyle\sum_{i=0}^{i=n-1} \Delta w_i$, we have

$$w = \sum_{i=0}^{i=n-1} [f(x_i) + k_i\eta_i]\Delta x,$$

whence, allowing n to increase indefinitely, we obtain

$$w = \lim_{n \to \infty} \sum_{i=0}^{i=n-1} [f(x_i) + k_i\eta_i]\Delta x.$$

Now by Duhamel's Theorem we may neglect the infinitesimal $\eta_i \Delta x$ which is of higher order than Δx, so that

$$w = \lim_{n \to \infty} \sum_{i=0}^{i=n-1} f(x_i)\Delta x.$$

Hence by the Fundamental Theorem

(2) $$w = \int_a^b f(x)dx.$$

It can be shown that (2) is true even if the restriction that $f(x)$ increases with x is removed.

Thus the work done over a specified displacement along the x-axis by a variable force $f(x)$ having this axis as its line of action may be obtained by integrating, between suitably chosen limits, the element of work

(3) $$dw = f(x)dx.$$

Example 1. A helical spring (Fig. 39*b*) has a modulus of 30 lb./in.; this means that if one end of the spring is fixed and if the free end is displaced longitudinally x inches, then the force needed to maintain this deformation is $30x$ pounds. Find the work done in compressing the spring 4 in.

Since the variable compressive force is

$$f(x) = 30x,$$

FIG. 39*b*

the element of work corresponding to a displacement dx of the free end of the spring is, by (3),

$$dw = 30x \, dx.$$

Hence the total work of compression is

$$w = \int_0^4 30x \, dx = 240 \text{ in-lb.} = 20 \text{ ft-lb.}$$

Example 2. A cable weighing 3 lb./ft. is unwound from a cylindrical drum (Fig. 39*c*). If the lower end of the cable is initially 100 ft. below the drum how much work is done by gravity as an additional 200 ft. are unwound?

Let s (in feet) be the length of cable which hangs from the drum at any time. Then the force of gravity (in pounds) operating to unwind the cable, being the weight of the suspended part, is

FIG. 39*c*

$$f(s) = 3s;$$

hence the element of work corresponding to a displacement ds is, by (3),

$$dw = 3s \, ds.$$

The initial and final positions of the lower end of the cable being given, respectively, by $s = 100$ and $s = 300$, the total work done by gravity is

$$w = \int_{100}^{300} 3s \; ds = 120,000 \text{ ft-lb.}$$

Example 3. A right circular cylindrical tank of depth 10 ft. and radius 2 ft. is full of water. Find the work done in pumping the water to the top of the tank.

First Solution. Imagine that a piston, placed at the bottom of the tank, is forced upward, and thus causes the water to spill over the top of the tank. The lifting force exerted by the piston at any time is evidently equal to the weight of the water then remaining in the tank. Hence if y (Fig. 39d) is the height of the piston above the bottom of the tank, the lifting force is

$$f(y) = 4\pi(62.5)(10 - y),$$

the density of water being taken as 62.5 lb./cu. ft. The element of work corresponding to a displacement dy of the piston is, by (3),

$$dw = 4\pi(62.5)(10 - y)dy;$$

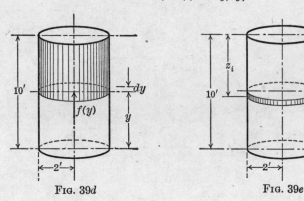

FIG. 39d   FIG. 39e

whence the total work done in emptying the tank is

$$w = \int_{0}^{10} 4\pi(62.5)(10 - y)dy = 12,500\pi \text{ ft-lb.}$$

Second Solution. Imagine the water originally in the tank to be divided into n layers or discs of common thickness Δz and let z_i (Fig. 39e) be the depth of the bottom of the ith disc below the top of the tank. Then, since the weight of this disc is $4\pi(62.5)\Delta z$, the work done in lifting its center to the top of the tank is

$$\Delta w_i = 4\pi(62.5)\Delta z \left(z_i - \frac{\Delta z}{2} \right).$$

The total work done in emptying the tank is therefore

$$w = \lim_{n \to \infty} \sum_{i=1}^{i=n} \Delta w_i = 250\pi \lim_{n \to \infty} \sum_{i=1}^{i=n} z_i \Delta z,$$

since, by Duhamel's Theorem, infinitesimals of higher order than Δz may be neglected. Hence by the Fundamental Theorem

$$w = 250\pi \int_0^{10} z \, dz = 12,500\pi \text{ ft-lb.}$$

PROBLEMS

1. The natural length of a helical spring is 15 in. The modulus of the spring in tension is 8 lb./in. How much work is done in stretching this spring from a length of 16 in. to a length of 18 in.?

2. The modulus of the spring on a bumping post in a freight-yard is 480,000 lb./ft. How much work is done in compressing the spring $\frac{1}{2}$ in.?

3. A helical spring whose modulus is 5 lb./in. is 12 in. long. Find the work required to compress it from a length of 10 in. to a length of 8 in.

4. A cable 100 ft. long and weighing 2 lb./ft. hangs from a windlass. Find the work done in winding it up.

5. A cable 100 ft. long and weighing 4 lb./ft. supports a weight of 1000 lb. Find the work done in winding the cable on a drum until the weight is at the level of the drum.

6. By means of a cable wound on a drum, a weight of 1200 lb. is drawn upward from a depth of 400 ft. below the drum to a depth of 200 ft. If the cable weighs 5 lb./ft., find the work done.

7. A right circular cylindrical tank of depth 12 ft. and radius 3 ft. is full of water. Find the work done in pumping the water to the top of the tank.

8. A right circular cylindrical tank of depth 16 ft. and radius 5 ft. is half full of water. Find the work done in pumping the water to the top of the tank.

9. A right circular cylindrical tank of depth 12 ft. and radius 3 ft. is full of water. Find the work done in pumping the water to a height of 10 ft. above the top of the tank.

10. A right circular cylindrical tank is 20 ft. deep and 10 ft. in diameter. Find the work done in filling the tank if water is pumped in through the bottom of the tank from a depth of 40 ft. below the bottom of the tank.

11. A reservoir in the form of an inverted right circular cone of altitude 18 ft. and radius 9 ft. is full of water. Find the work done in pumping the water to the top of the reservoir.

12. The inner surface of a tank has the form of a paraboloid of revolution whose axis is vertical. The depth of the tank is 4 ft., and the diameter of the circular top is 4 ft. If the tank is originally full of water, find the work done in pumping the water to the top of the tank.

CHAPTER IV

DIFFERENTIATION OF ALGEBRAIC FUNCTIONS

40. Algebraic Functions. The definition of a derivative,

$$\frac{dy}{dx} = \lim_{\Delta x \to 0} \frac{\Delta y}{\Delta x},$$

provides us with the general method of differentiating functions of one variable. To save labor, however, we have in Art. 16 derived a formula for differentiating a specific kind of function, namely a polynomial.

In this chapter we shall derive formulas enabling us to differentiate **algebraic functions.** Though it is not necessary to give here a general definition * of an algebraic function of a variable x, it may be stated that an important class of such functions are those which are obtained from x by the application of a finite number of algebraic operations: addition, subtraction, multiplication, division, raising to powers, and extracting roots. Any polynomial is an algebraic function; so are also

$$(x^2 + 1)^{\frac{3}{2}}, \ (x^4 + 2)\sqrt[3]{x + 5}, \text{ and } \frac{x^2 - 5}{(x^3 + 1)^4}.$$

41. Theorems on Derivatives. It should be remarked that the proofs of the following theorems pertaining to the differentiation of sums (or differences), powers, products, and quotients do not require that the functions u, v, and w be algebraic, although they will be so assumed in the examples and problems of the present chapter. In subsequent chapters, however, these theorems will often be applied to other types of functions.

THEOREM 1. *The derivative of the algebraic sum of a finite number of functions is the sum of the derivatives of the functions.*

For if $y = u + v - w$, where u, v, and w are differentiable functions of x, then

$$\Delta y = \Delta u + \Delta v - \Delta w,$$

and

$$\frac{\Delta y}{\Delta x} = \frac{\Delta u}{\Delta x} + \frac{\Delta v}{\Delta x} - \frac{\Delta w}{\Delta x}.$$

---

* For a general definition of an algebraic function, the student is referred to the remarks immediately following (3), Art. 75.

Passing to the limit, we have by Theorem 1, Art. 5,

$$\frac{dy}{dx} = \lim_{\Delta x \to 0} \frac{\Delta y}{\Delta x} = \lim_{\Delta x \to 0} \frac{\Delta u}{\Delta x} + \lim_{\Delta x \to 0} \frac{\Delta v}{\Delta x} - \lim_{\Delta x \to 0} \frac{\Delta w}{\Delta x}$$

$$= \frac{du}{dx} + \frac{dv}{dx} - \frac{dw}{dx}.$$

The extension of this result to the algebraic sum of any finite number of differentiable functions is obvious.

A special case of this theorem occurred in (5), Art. 16, where the functions in the sum were the terms of a polynomial.

THEOREM 2. *The derivative of the product of a function by a constant is the product of the derivative of the function by the constant.*

That is, if $y = cu$, where c is a constant and u is a differentiable function of x,

$$\frac{dy}{dx} = c \frac{du}{dx}.$$

The proof is immediate if Theorem **3**, Art. 5, is used.

A special case of this theorem occurred in (2), Art. 16, where the function u was x^n.

THEOREM 3. *The derivative of a constant is zero.*

That is, for a constant c,

$$\frac{dc}{dx} = 0.$$

This was proved in Art. 16.

THEOREM 4. *The derivative of the product of two functions is the sum of the products obtained by multiplying each function by the derivative of the other.*

Let $y = uv$, where u and v are differentiable functions of x.

When x receives the increment Δx, then u, v, and y become $u + \Delta u$, $v + \Delta v$, and $y + \Delta y$, respectively, so that

$$y + \Delta y = (u + \Delta u)(v + \Delta v) = uv + u\Delta v + v\Delta u + \Delta u\Delta v,$$

whence

$$\Delta y = u\Delta v + v\Delta u + \Delta u\Delta v,$$

and

$$\frac{\Delta y}{\Delta x} = u \frac{\Delta v}{\Delta x} + v \frac{\Delta u}{\Delta x} + \Delta u \frac{\Delta v}{\Delta x}.$$

Passing to the limit as Δx approaches zero, and using Theorems 1–3, Art. 5, we obtain

$$\frac{dy}{dx} = u\frac{dv}{dx} + v\frac{du}{dx},$$

since $\lim\limits_{\Delta x \to 0} \left(\Delta u\, \frac{\Delta v}{\Delta x} \right) = 0$. This completes the proof of the theorem.

To differentiate the product of any finite number of functions, we need only make successive applications of this theorem. Thus if $y = uvw$, where $u, v,$ and w are differentiable functions of x, we may write

$$y = (uv)w,$$

whence

$$\frac{dy}{dx} = uv\frac{dw}{dx} + w\frac{d(uv)}{dx}$$

$$= uv\frac{dw}{dx} + uw\frac{dv}{dx} + vw\frac{du}{dx}.$$

Example 1. Find the derivative of $(x^2 + 4)(x^3 - x^2 - 8)$.
Let $y = (x^2 + 4)(x^3 - x^2 - 8)$; then

$$\frac{dy}{dx} = (x^2 + 4)\frac{d}{dx}(x^3 - x^2 - 8) + (x^3 - x^2 - 8)\frac{d}{dx}(x^2 + 4)$$

$$= (x^2 + 4)(3x^2 - 2x) + (x^3 - x^2 - 8)2x$$

$$= 5x^4 - 4x^3 + 12x^2 - 24x.$$

Here the derivative could have been found by multiplying out the factors of y and differentiating the resulting polynomial; but in many examples that will arise later it will be necessary to differentiate products by the method just illustrated.

Theorem 5. *The derivative of the quotient of two functions is the denominator times the derivative of the numerator minus the numerator times the derivative of the denominator, all divided by the square of the denominator.*

For if

$$y = \frac{u}{v},$$

where u and v are differentiable functions of x, and x is given the increment Δx, it follows that

$$y + \Delta y = \frac{u + \Delta u}{v + \Delta v},$$

whence

$$\Delta y = \frac{u + \Delta u}{v + \Delta v} - \frac{u}{v}$$

$$= \frac{v(u + \Delta u) - u(v + \Delta v)}{(v + \Delta v)v} = \frac{v\Delta u - u\Delta v}{(v + \Delta v)v},$$

and

$$\frac{\Delta y}{\Delta x} = \frac{v\dfrac{\Delta u}{\Delta x} - u\dfrac{\Delta v}{\Delta x}}{(v + \Delta v)v}.$$

Passing to the limit as Δx approaches zero, and using Theorems 1, 3, and 4, Art. 5, we obtain

$$\frac{dy}{dx} = \frac{v\dfrac{du}{dx} - u\dfrac{dv}{dx}}{v^2}.$$

This completes the proof of the theorem.

Example 2.   Find the derivative of $\dfrac{x^2 - x}{x^3 + 1}$.

Let $y = \dfrac{x^2 - x}{x^3 + 1}$; then

$$\frac{dy}{dx} = \frac{(x^3 + 1)(2x - 1) - (x^2 - x)3x^2}{(x^3 + 1)^2}$$

$$= \frac{-x^4 + 2x^3 + 2x - 1}{(x^3 + 1)^2}.$$

THEOREM 6.   *If y is a function of u and u is a function of x, so that y may be considered as a function of x, then the derivative of y with respect to x is the product of the derivative of y with respect to u by the derivative of u with respect to x.*

Let x be given an increment Δx, the corresponding increments of u and y being Δu and Δy, respectively.   Obviously

$$\frac{\Delta y}{\Delta x} = \frac{\Delta y}{\Delta u} \cdot \frac{\Delta u}{\Delta x}.$$

Passing to the limit as Δx approaches zero, we have, by Theorem 2, Art. 5,

$$\frac{dy}{dx} = \frac{dy}{du} \cdot \frac{du}{dx},$$

provided that y and u are differentiable functions of their respective variables.

Example 3. If $y = u^3$ and $u = x^2 + 5x - 6$, find $\dfrac{dy}{dx}$.

Since

$$\frac{dy}{du} = 3u^2$$

and

$$\frac{du}{dx} = 2x + 5,$$

we have, by Theorem 6,

$$\frac{dy}{dx} = 3u^2(2x + 5) = 3(x^2 + 5x - 6)^2(2x + 5).$$

THEOREM 7.   *The derivative of the nth power of a function, where n is a constant, is n times the product of the $(n - 1)$th power of the function by the derivative of the function.*

That is, if

$$y = u^n$$

where u is a differentiable function of x, then

$$\frac{dy}{dx} = nu^{n-1}\frac{du}{dx}.$$

This theorem holds for any constant value of n. We are, however, interested at this stage in rational exponents only, and shall consider the two cases that arise according as n is a positive or a negative rational number. In Art. 56 a proof will be given in which the constant n may be any real number, whether rational or irrational.

Case 1. Let n be a positive rational number, so that we may write $n = \dfrac{p}{q}$, where p and q are positive integers. Thus we have

$$y = u^{\frac{p}{q}},$$

whence

$$\Delta y = (u + \Delta u)^{\frac{p}{q}} - u^{\frac{p}{q}}.$$

Then

$$\frac{\Delta y}{\Delta u} = \frac{(u + \Delta u)^{\frac{p}{q}} - u^{\frac{p}{q}}}{\Delta u} = \frac{(u + \Delta u)^{\frac{p}{q}} - u^{\frac{p}{q}}}{(u + \Delta u) - u}.$$

On factoring the numerator and denominator of the last fraction, we obtain

$$\frac{\Delta y}{\Delta u} = \frac{[(u + \Delta u)^{\frac{1}{q}} - u^{\frac{1}{q}}]\,[(u + \Delta u)^{\frac{p-1}{q}} + (u + \Delta u)^{\frac{p-2}{q}} u^{\frac{1}{q}} + \cdots + u^{\frac{p-1}{q}}]}{[(u + \Delta u)^{\frac{1}{q}} - u^{\frac{1}{q}}]\,[(u + \Delta u)^{\frac{q-1}{q}} + (u + \Delta u)^{\frac{q-2}{q}} u^{\frac{1}{q}} + \cdots + u^{\frac{q-1}{q}}]},$$

where the second bracket in the numerator contains p terms and that in the denominator q terms. Canceling the common factor and passing to the limit as Δu approaches zero, we find

$$\frac{dy}{du} = \frac{pu^{\frac{p-1}{q}}}{qu^{\frac{q-1}{q}}} = \frac{p}{q} u^{\frac{p}{q}-1} = nu^{n-1},$$

whence, by Theorem 6,

$$\frac{dy}{dx} = nu^{n-1}\frac{du}{dx}.$$

Case 2. Let n be a negative rational number. Writing $n = -\frac{p}{q}$, where p and q are positive integers, we have

$$y = u^{-\frac{p}{q}}.$$

Therefore

$$\frac{\Delta y}{\Delta u} = \frac{(u + \Delta u)^{-\frac{p}{q}} - u^{-\frac{p}{q}}}{\Delta u}.$$

Multiplying the numerator and denominator of the right member by $(u + \Delta u)^{\frac{p}{q}} u^{\frac{p}{q}}$, we find that

$$\frac{\Delta y}{\Delta u} = -\frac{1}{(u + \Delta u)^{\frac{p}{q}} u^{\frac{p}{q}}} \cdot \frac{(u + \Delta u)^{\frac{p}{q}} - u^{\frac{p}{q}}}{\Delta u}.$$

Allowing Δu to approach zero, and observing that the last fraction has, in Case 1, been shown to have $\frac{p}{q} u^{\frac{p}{q}-1}$ as its limit, we obtain

$$\frac{dy}{du} = -\frac{1}{u^{\frac{2p}{q}}} \cdot \frac{p}{q} u^{\frac{p}{q}-1} = -\frac{p}{q} u^{-\frac{p}{q}-1} = nu^{n-1},$$

whence, by Theorem 6,

$$\frac{dy}{dx} = nu^{n-1}\frac{du}{dx}.$$

Thus the theorem has been proved for positive and negative rational values of n; it holds likewise if $n = 0$ (Art. 16).

If in the result

$$\frac{d}{dx} u^n = nu^{n-1} \frac{du}{dx},$$

we set $u = x$, so that $\dfrac{du}{dx} = 1$, we obtain

$$\frac{d}{dx} x^n = nx^{n-1}.$$

This formula is an extension of (1), Art. 16, where n was restricted to positive integral values.

Example 4. Work Example 3 by the use of Theorem **7**.
Evidently

$$y = (x^2 + 5x - 6)^3.$$

Hence

$$\frac{dy}{dx} = 3(x^2 + 5x - 6)^2 \frac{d}{dx} (x^2 + 5x - 6)$$

$$= 3(x^2 + 5x - 6)^2(2x + 5),$$

in agreement with the previous solution.

Example 5. If $y = \dfrac{1}{\sqrt[3]{7 - x^2 + x^4}}$, find $\dfrac{dy}{dx}$.

Writing

$$y = (7 - x^2 + x^4)^{-\frac{1}{3}},$$

we obtain, by Theorem 7,

$$\frac{dy}{dx} = -\frac{1}{3} (7 - x^2 + x^4)^{-\frac{4}{3}} \frac{d}{dx} (7 - x^2 + x^4)$$

$$= \frac{2x - 4x^3}{3(7 - x^2 + x^4)^{\frac{4}{3}}}.$$

Example 6. If $y = \sqrt[3]{\dfrac{x^2 - 1}{x^2 + 1}}$, find $\dfrac{dy}{dx}$.

First Solution.

$$y = \left(\frac{x^2 - 1}{x^2 + 1}\right)^{\frac{1}{3}}$$

$$\frac{dy}{dx} = \frac{1}{3} \left(\frac{x^2 - 1}{x^2 + 1}\right)^{-\frac{2}{3}} \frac{d}{dx} \left(\frac{x^2 - 1}{x^2 + 1}\right) \qquad \text{(Theorem 7)}$$

$$= \frac{1}{3} \left(\frac{x^2 + 1}{x^2 - 1}\right)^{\frac{2}{3}} \frac{(x^2 + 1)(2x) - (x^2 - 1)(2x)}{(x^2 + 1)^2} \qquad \text{(Theorem 5)}$$

$$= \frac{1}{3} \frac{(x^2+1)^{\frac{2}{3}}}{(x^2-1)^{\frac{2}{3}}} \frac{4x}{(x^2+1)^2}$$

$$= \frac{4x}{3(x^2-1)^{\frac{2}{3}}(x^2+1)^{\frac{4}{3}}}.$$

Second Solution. Writing

$$y = \frac{(x^2-1)^{\frac{1}{3}}}{(x^2+1)^{\frac{1}{3}}},$$

we obtain, by Theorems 5 and 7,

$$\frac{dy}{dx} = \frac{(x^2+1)^{\frac{1}{3}} \cdot \frac{1}{3}(x^2-1)^{-\frac{2}{3}}(2x) - (x^2-1)^{\frac{1}{3}} \cdot \frac{1}{3}(x^2+1)^{-\frac{2}{3}}(2x)}{(x^2+1)^{\frac{2}{3}}}$$

$$= \frac{2x[(x^2+1)-(x^2-1)]}{3(x^2+1)^{\frac{2}{3}}(x^2-1)^{\frac{2}{3}}(x^2+1)^{\frac{2}{3}}}$$

$$= \frac{4x}{3(x^2-1)^{\frac{2}{3}}(x^2+1)^{\frac{4}{3}}}.$$

Third Solution. Writing

$$y = (x^2-1)^{\frac{1}{3}}(x^2+1)^{-\frac{1}{3}},$$

we have, by Theorems 4 and 7,

$$\frac{dy}{dx} = (x^2-1)^{\frac{1}{3}}(-\frac{1}{3})(x^2+1)^{-\frac{4}{3}}(2x) + (x^2+1)^{-\frac{1}{3}} \cdot \frac{1}{3}(x^2-1)^{-\frac{2}{3}}(2x)$$

$$= \frac{4x}{3(x^2-1)^{\frac{2}{3}}(x^2+1)^{\frac{4}{3}}}.$$

THEOREM 8. *The derivative of y with respect to x is the reciprocal of the derivative of x with respect to y.*

That is,

$$\frac{dy}{dx} = \frac{1}{\dfrac{dx}{dy}}.$$

Let x and y be two related variables either of which may be regarded as a function of the other. Then if x changes by Δx, y changes by Δy, and we have

$$\frac{dy}{dx} = \lim_{\Delta x \to 0} \frac{\Delta y}{\Delta x} = \lim_{\Delta x \to 0} \frac{1}{\dfrac{\Delta x}{\Delta y}}$$

$$= \lim_{\Delta y \to 0} \frac{1}{\dfrac{\Delta x}{\Delta y}} = \frac{1}{\dfrac{dx}{dy}},$$

provided that x is a differentiable function of y and that we exclude values of y for which $\dfrac{dx}{dy}$ vanishes.

Here we have used Theorem 4, Art. 5, together with the fact that when Δx approaches zero Δy does likewise.

This theorem may be applied to problems requiring $\dfrac{dy}{dx}$ when the expression for x in terms of y is simpler than that for y in terms of x.

Example 7. If $x = \sqrt[3]{1 - y^2 + y^4}$, find $\dfrac{dy}{dx}$.

We have, by Theorem 7,

$$\frac{dx}{dy} = \tfrac{1}{3}(1 - y^2 + y^4)^{-\frac{2}{3}}(-2y + 4y^3)$$

$$= \frac{4y^3 - 2y}{3(1 - y^2 + y^4)^{\frac{2}{3}}}.$$

Then, by Theorem 8,

$$\frac{dy}{dx} = \frac{3(1 - y^2 + y^4)^{\frac{2}{3}}}{4y^3 - 2y}.$$

THEOREM 9. *If x and y are both functions of a variable u, then*

$$\frac{dy}{dx} = \frac{\dfrac{dy}{du}}{\dfrac{dx}{du}}.$$

This theorem is a consequence of Theorems 6 and 8, for if x and y are both differentiable functions of u, and if we exclude values of u for which $\dfrac{dx}{du}$ vanishes, we have

$$\frac{dy}{dx} = \frac{dy}{du} \cdot \frac{du}{dx} = \frac{dy}{du} \cdot \frac{1}{\dfrac{dx}{du}} = \frac{\dfrac{dy}{du}}{\dfrac{dx}{du}}.$$

Example 8. If $x = \dfrac{u^3 - 1}{u^3 + 1}$ and $y = \dfrac{u^2 - 1}{u^2 + 1}$, find $\dfrac{dy}{dx}$.

In this example, we may obtain $\dfrac{dy}{dx}$ by differentiating the expression for y in terms of x which arises when u is eliminated from the given equations. Such a procedure would, however, be quite laborious; the following method is therefore preferable.

We have, by Theorem 5,

$$\frac{dy}{du} = \frac{4u}{(u^2 + 1)^2}$$

and

$$\frac{dx}{du} = \frac{6u^2}{(u^3 + 1)^2}.$$

Hence, by Theorem 9,

$$\frac{dy}{dx} = \frac{2(u^3 + 1)^2}{3u(u^2 + 1)^2}.$$

Example 9. If $x = \dfrac{u}{1 + u^2}$ and $y = \dfrac{u^2}{1 + u^2}$, find $\dfrac{d^2y}{dx^2}$.

We readily obtain

$$\frac{dx}{du} = \frac{1 - u^2}{(1 + u^2)^2}$$

and

$$\frac{dy}{du} = \frac{2u}{(1 + u^2)^2},$$

whence, by Theorem 9,

$$\frac{dy}{dx} = \frac{2u}{1 - u^2}.$$

To find the second derivative we note that, by Theorem 6,

$$\frac{d^2y}{dx^2} = \frac{d}{dx}\left(\frac{dy}{dx}\right) = \frac{d}{du}\left(\frac{dy}{dx}\right)\frac{du}{dx}.$$

But by Theorem 8, $\dfrac{du}{dx}$ is the reciprocal of $\dfrac{dx}{du}$; therefore

$$\frac{d^2y}{dx^2} = \frac{d}{du}\left(\frac{2u}{1 - u^2}\right) \cdot \frac{(1 + u^2)^2}{1 - u^2} = \frac{2u^2 + 2}{(1 - u^2)^2} \cdot \frac{(1 + u^2)^2}{1 - u^2}$$

$$= \frac{2(1 + u^2)^3}{(1 - u^2)^3}.$$

42. Summary of Formulas. For convenience, we assemble as formulas the results of the theorems proved in the last article. The student should memorize these formulas and be prepared to apply them to problems in which the variables and functions are denoted by letters other than those here used.

I
$$\frac{d}{dx}(u + v) = \frac{du}{dx} + \frac{dv}{dx}.$$

II
$$\frac{d}{dx}(cu) = c\frac{du}{dx}.$$

III
$$\frac{dc}{dx} = 0.$$

IV
$$\frac{d}{dx}(uv) = u\frac{dv}{dx} + v\frac{du}{dx}.$$

V
$$\frac{d}{dx}\left(\frac{u}{v}\right) = \frac{v\dfrac{du}{dx} - u\dfrac{dv}{dx}}{v^2}.$$

VI
$$\frac{dy}{dx} = \frac{dy}{du} \cdot \frac{du}{dx}.$$

VII
$$\frac{d}{dx}u^n = nu^{n-1}\frac{du}{dx}.$$

VIII
$$\frac{dy}{dx} = \frac{1}{\dfrac{dx}{dy}}.$$

IX
$$\frac{dy}{dx} = \frac{\dfrac{dy}{du}}{\dfrac{dx}{du}}.$$

For reference we write the first five and the seventh of these formulas in differential form.

I'
$$d(u + v) = du + dv.$$

II'
$$d(cu) = c\,du.$$

III'
$$dc = 0.$$

IV'
$$d(uv) = u\,dv + v\,du.$$

V'
$$d\left(\frac{u}{v}\right) = \frac{v\,du - u\,dv}{v^2}.$$

VII'
$$d(u^n) = nu^{n-1}\,du.$$

PROBLEMS

In problems 1–25, find $\dfrac{dy}{dx}$ and simplify the results.

1. $y = (1 - 2x)^3.$

2. $y = (10x^4 - 11x^2 + 1)^5.$

3. $y = 2\sqrt[5]{x} - \dfrac{3}{\sqrt[5]{x}}.$

4. $y = 2x^{\frac{5}{4}} - x^{\frac{3}{4}} - 6x^{\frac{1}{4}} + \dfrac{2}{x^{\frac{1}{4}}} + \dfrac{5}{x^{\frac{3}{4}}}.$

5. $y = \sqrt[3]{x^2} - \dfrac{1}{\sqrt[3]{x}} + \dfrac{3}{\sqrt[3]{x^2}} - \dfrac{4}{x\sqrt[3]{x}}.$

6. $y = (1 - 2x)^{\frac{1}{3}}$.

7. $y = \dfrac{1}{(1 - 2x)^{\frac{3}{5}}}$.

8. $y = \sqrt{1 - 4x^2}$.

9. $y = \sqrt[3]{8 + 5x + 2x^2 - 7x^3}$.

10. $y = x\sqrt{2x + 1}$.

11. $y = x^2\sqrt[3]{1 - 2x}$.

12. $y = \dfrac{x}{4 - 9x^2}$.

13. $y = \dfrac{(x - 2)^2}{8 - 27x^3}$.

14. $y = \dfrac{x}{\sqrt{4 - 9x^2}}$.

15. $y = \dfrac{\sqrt{16 + x^2}}{x^2}$.

16. $y = (2 - 3x)^4\sqrt{5 - x^2}$.

17. $y = \dfrac{\sqrt{3x - 1}}{(2 - x)^2}$.

18. $y = \dfrac{x}{(4 - x^2)^{\frac{3}{2}}}$.

19. $y = x^3\sqrt[3]{(8 - x^3)^2}$.

20. $y = \dfrac{x}{\sqrt{7x^2 - 6x - 1}}$.

21. $y = (x - 2)^3\sqrt{9x^4 + 1}$.

22. $y = \sqrt{\dfrac{1 - x}{1 + x}}$.

23. $y = \sqrt{\dfrac{1 + x^2}{1 - x^2}}$.

24. $y = \dfrac{1}{x + \sqrt{4 + x^2}}$.

25. $y = \dfrac{x}{x - \sqrt{4 - x^2}}$.

26. Find $\dfrac{dy}{dx}$ and $\dfrac{d^2y}{dx^2}$, if $x = \dfrac{3u}{1 + u^3}$ and $y = \dfrac{3u^2}{1 + u^3}$.

27. Find $\dfrac{dy}{dx}$ and $\dfrac{d^2y}{dx^2}$ if $x = \dfrac{2t}{1 + t^2}$ and $y = \dfrac{1 - t^2}{1 + t^2}$.

28. Find $\dfrac{dy}{dx}$ and $\dfrac{d^2y}{dx^2}$ if $x = 2t$ and $y = 2\sqrt{1 - t^2}$.

29. Find $\dfrac{dy}{dx}$ if $x = a(1 + 2t - 2t^2)$ and $y = 2a\sqrt{1 - t^2}(1 - t)$.

30. Find $\dfrac{dy}{dx}$ if $x = \sqrt{\dfrac{1 - y^3}{1 + y^3}}$.

31. Find $\dfrac{dy}{dx}$ if $x = 2y + \sqrt{1 - 4y^2}$.

32. Find $\dfrac{dy}{dx}$ if $x = \dfrac{\sqrt{1 + y} - \sqrt{1 - y}}{\sqrt{1 + y} + \sqrt{1 - y}}$.

33. Find the equations of the tangent and the normal to the curve $y = \dfrac{8}{x^2 + 1}$ at the point $(1, 4)$.

34. Find the angle between the curve $2y^2 = x^3$ and the line $2x + y = 6$ at their point of intersection.

35. Find the equations of those tangent lines to the curve $y = \dfrac{1}{2x - 3}$ which have a slope of -2.

36. At what angle do the curves $y = \dfrac{x}{4 - x^2}$ and $y = \dfrac{1}{3x}$ intersect each other?

37. Find the slope of the curve $y = x\sqrt{4 - x}$ at each point of intersection with the curve $y = \dfrac{3}{\sqrt{4 - x}}$.

38. Find the points of inflection of the curve $y = \dfrac{4}{x^2 + 3}$, and the slope of the curve at each point of inflection.

39. Find and classify the critical points of the curve $y = \dfrac{x^4 + 16}{x^2}$.

40. Find the maximum and minimum points, and points of inflection, of the curve $y = \dfrac{4x}{4 + x^2}$.

41. Find the maximum and minimum points of the curve $y = \dfrac{8 - 12x}{x(2 + x)}$.

42. Find the maximum and minimum points, and points of inflection, of the curve $y = \dfrac{2x}{\sqrt{(2 + x^2)^3}}$.

43. The capacity of a box with square base and open top is 256 cu. in. Find the inside dimensions, if the cost of lining the box is a minimum.

44. The capacity of a box with square base and open top is 54 cu. ft. If the lining for the bottom and for the sides costs 40¢ and 10¢ per sq. ft., respectively, and this cost is a minimum, find the inside dimensions of the box.

45. A right circular cylinder is to be designed so as to have a volume of 128π cu. in. and a minimum total surface. Find the base-radius and the altitude.

46. Show that, if the sum of the surfaces of a cube and a sphere is given, the sum of the volumes will be a minimum when the radius of the sphere is half as long as the edge of the cube.

47. Find the area of the smallest right triangle which can be drawn so as to circumscribe a rectangle 8 ft. long and 6 ft. wide, the right angle of the triangle coinciding with one of the angles of the rectangle.

48. Find the volume of the largest right circular cone whose slant height is $3\sqrt{3}$ in.

49. Find the dimensions of the largest rectangle which can be inscribed in the ellipse $4x^2 + y^2 = 8$.

50. A man at a point A on one shore of a lake having straight shorelines and a uniform width of $\dfrac{\sqrt{5}}{2}$ mi. wishes to reach a point B on the opposite shore and 6 mi. from the point C directly across the lake. If he can row 2 mi./hr. and walk 3 mi./hr., and if he sets out from A by boat, find how far from C he should land in order that the time required for the trip should be a minimum.

51. A town B is 250 mi. north of another town A. A car starts from A at noon, and travels toward B at a constant speed of 40 mi./hr. At the same time, another car starts from B and travels east at a constant speed of 30 mi./hr. When will the distance between the cars be least, and what is this distance?

43. Differentiation of Implicit Functions.
An equation of the form $y = f(x)$ is said to define y as an **explicit function** of x.

If, however, two variables x and y are connected by an equation in such a way that neither variable is expressed directly in terms of the other, then each of the variables is said to be an **implicit function** of the other, for the functional relation between the variables is implied and not expressed.   Thus, for instance, the equation $x^2 + 4y^2 = 4$ defines x and y as implicit functions of each other.

If an implicit relationship between two variables is solvable for one variable in terms of the other, this solution, of course, yields the former variable as an explicit function of the latter. For example, from the equation $x^2 + 4y^2 = 4$, we obtain

$$x = \pm\, 2\sqrt{1 - y^2}, \quad y = \pm\, \tfrac{1}{2}\sqrt{4 - x^2};$$

the first of these solutions expresses x as an explicit function of y, while the second expresses y as an explicit function of x.

Explicit functions may be differentiated directly by applying suitable formulas, such as those of the last article.

When, however, it is inconvenient or impossible to convert an implicit into an explicit function, the derivative of the function may be found by an indirect procedure known as **implicit differentiation.** This consists of differentiating the given equation by the use of appropriate formulas, and solving algebraically for the required derivative. We shall illustrate at once.

Example 1.   If $x^3 + 2x^2y + 4xy^2 + 8y^3 = 40$, find $\dfrac{dy}{dx}$.

Differentiating both sides of the given equation, we obtain

$$\frac{d}{dx}(x^3 + 2x^2y + 4xy^2 + 8y^3) = \frac{d}{dx}(40) = 0,$$

whence by I, II, IV, and VII, Art. 42,

$$3x^2 + 4xy + 2x^2\frac{dy}{dx} + 4y^2 + 8xy\frac{dy}{dx} + 24y^2\frac{dy}{dx} = 0.$$

Next we collect terms in $\dfrac{dy}{dx}$ and solve for $\dfrac{dy}{dx}$:

$$(2x^2 + 8xy + 24y^2)\frac{dy}{dx} = -\,3x^2 - 4xy - 4y^2,$$

$$\frac{dy}{dx} = -\,\frac{3x^2 + 4xy + 4y^2}{2x^2 + 8xy + 24y^2}.$$

Evidently the expression for $\dfrac{dy}{dx}$ which results from implicit differentiation may contain both x and y. If $\dfrac{dy}{dx}$, in turn, is differentiated, the resulting expression for the second derivative may contain x, y, and $\dfrac{dy}{dx}$; if $\dfrac{dy}{dx}$ occurs in the second derivative, it may be replaced by the result of the first differentiation.

Example 2. If $x^{\frac{2}{3}} + y^{\frac{2}{3}} = a^{\frac{2}{3}}$, find $\dfrac{dy}{dx}$ by implicit differentiation; then find $\dfrac{d^2y}{dx^2}$.

On differentiating, we obtain

$$\frac{2}{3}\,x^{-\frac{1}{3}} + \frac{2}{3}\,y^{-\frac{1}{3}}\frac{dy}{dx} = 0,$$

whence

$$\frac{dy}{dx} = -\frac{x^{-\frac{1}{3}}}{y^{-\frac{1}{3}}} = -\frac{y^{\frac{1}{3}}}{x^{\frac{1}{3}}}.$$

We differentiate again:

$$\frac{d^2y}{dx^2} = -\frac{x^{\frac{1}{3}}\cdot\dfrac{1}{3}y^{-\frac{2}{3}}\dfrac{dy}{dx} - y^{\frac{1}{3}}\cdot\dfrac{1}{3}x^{-\frac{2}{3}}}{x^{\frac{2}{3}}}$$

$$= -\frac{x\dfrac{dy}{dx} - y}{3x^{\frac{4}{3}}y^{\frac{2}{3}}}.$$

Substituting for $\dfrac{dy}{dx}$, we find

$$\frac{d^2y}{dx^2} = -\frac{x\left(-\dfrac{y^{\frac{1}{3}}}{x^{\frac{1}{3}}}\right) - y}{3x^{\frac{4}{3}}y^{\frac{2}{3}}}$$

$$= \frac{x^{\frac{2}{3}} + y^{\frac{2}{3}}}{3x^{\frac{4}{3}}y^{\frac{1}{3}}}$$

$$= \frac{a^{\frac{2}{3}}}{3x^{\frac{4}{3}}y^{\frac{1}{3}}}$$

where the final simplification arises from the given equation.

Example 3. Find the equation of the line tangent to the curve of Example 1 at the point $(-2, 2)$.

The slope of a tangent line is found by substituting the coördinates x_1 and y_1 of the point of tangency in the expression for $\dfrac{dy}{dx}$; denoting this result by $\left(\dfrac{dy}{dx}\right)_1$, we may write the equation of a tangent line (cf. (1), Art. 17) in the form

$$y - y_1 = \left(\frac{dy}{dx}\right)_1 (x - x_1).$$

Substituting the coördinates of the point of tangency $(-2, 2)$ in the derivative obtained in Example 1, we find

$$\left(\frac{dy}{dx}\right)_1 = -\frac{12 - 16 + 16}{8 - 32 + 96} = -\frac{1}{6}.$$

Therefore the equation of the tangent line is

$$y - 2 = -\frac{1}{6}(x + 2),$$

or

$$x + 6y - 10 = 0.$$

Implicit differentiation may be conveniently used in many problems on maxima and minima.

Example 4. The strength of a rectangular beam of given length varies jointly as the width and the square of the depth. Find the dimensions of the cross-section of the strongest rectangular beam which can be cut out of a cylindrical log whose diameter is 12 in.

Denoting the strength of a beam by S, the width by w, and the depth by h, we have

(1) $$S = kwh^2 \quad (k = \text{const.})$$

and

(2) $$w^2 + h^2 = 144.$$

Differentiating (1) with respect to w, and observing that by (2) h is a function of w, we obtain

(3) $$\frac{dS}{dw} = k\left(2wh\frac{dh}{dw} + h^2\right),$$

while by implicit differentiation of (2) we find

(4) $$\frac{dh}{dw} = -\frac{w}{h}.$$

Substituting the expression for $\frac{dh}{dw}$ from (4), we rewrite (3) as

$$\frac{dS}{dw} = k(-2w^2 + h^2).$$

If S is a maximum, $\frac{dS}{dw} = 0$; hence

$$h^2 = 2w^2,$$

and by (2)

$$w = 4\sqrt{3} \text{ in.},$$

$$h = 4\sqrt{6} \text{ in.}$$

PROBLEMS

In Problems 1–11 obtain $\dfrac{dy}{dx}$ by implicit differentiation; in the first four problems also find $\dfrac{d^2y}{dx^2}$.

1. $x^2 + y^2 = 16$.

2. $\dfrac{x^2}{9} + \dfrac{y^2}{4} = 1$.

3. $16x^2 - 9y^2 = 144$.
4. $x^3 + y^3 - 3axy = 0$.
5. $y^2 - 4x^2y^2 - 8x = 0$.
6. $(2a - x)y^2 - 4x^3 = 0$.

7. $x^3 + x^{\frac{3}{2}}y^{\frac{3}{2}} + y^3 = a^3$.

8. $x^2 + 2x\sqrt{y - x} - 2y^2 - 1 = 0$.

9. $\dfrac{y}{x} + \sqrt[3]{\dfrac{x}{y}} = 2$.

10. $(x^2 - y^2)^2 + a^2(x^2 + y^2) - b^2 = 0$.
11. $x^4 - 3x^3y + 5x^2y^2 - 6xy^3 + 3y^4 = 0$.

Find the equations of the tangent and the normal to each of the curves in Problems 12–16 at the point designated.

12. $\sqrt{x} + \sqrt{y} = 3$; $(4, 1)$.
13. $y^2 - 3xy - 2x^2 - 8 = 0$; $(2, -2)$.
14. $x^3 - 2axy - 4y^3 = 0$; $(2a, a)$.

15. $5ay^2 - 4xy^2 - 4ax^2 = 0$; $(a, 2a)$.
16. $y^2(4 - x) - x^3 = 0$; $(2, 2)$.

In Problems 17–20, find the angles of intersection of the given curves.

17. $\begin{cases} y^2 = 4x^3, \\ xy = 2. \end{cases}$

18. $\begin{cases} xy = -12, \\ x^2 + y^2 = 25. \end{cases}$

19. $\begin{cases} x^2 + y^2 + 2y - 24 = 0, \\ x^2 + 4y^2 + 8y - 48 = 0. \end{cases}$

20. $\begin{cases} y^2 = 2(x - 2), \\ 4y^2 = x(x - 2)^2. \end{cases}$

21. Find and classify the critical point of the curve $4x^2y - 8xy^2 + 5y^3 = 1$.

22. Find and classify those critical points of the curve $x^4 - 2x^2y^2 - 8y^4 + 8 = 0$ which have rational coördinates.

Use implicit differentiation in solving the following problems:

23. Find the base-radius and altitude of the largest right circular cone which can be inscribed in a sphere of radius 6 in.

24. If the convex surface of a right circular cone is given, find the ratio of the length of the altitude to that of the base-radius when the volume is a maximum.

25. Find the dimensions of the largest rectangle which can be inscribed in the curve $x^{\frac{2}{3}} + y^{\frac{4}{3}} = 24$.

26. Find the base-radius and altitude of the smallest right circular cone which can circumscribe a right circular cylinder of base-radius 4 in. and altitude 6 in.

CHAPTER V

DIFFERENTIATION OF TRANSCENDENTAL FUNCTIONS

44. Transcendental Functions. Thus far we have seen how to differentiate only algebraic functions (i.e., functions which arise from a variable by the application of a finite number of algebraic operations and also implicit functions such as those in the text and problems of Art. 43). Functions which are not algebraic are called **transcendental.** The simplest transcendental functions—trigonometric, inverse trigonometric, logarithmic, and exponential functions—will be studied in this chapter.

45. The Radian. In calculus and its applications, the radian is the most convenient unit angle. We recall from trigonometry that a radian is an angle which, when placed so that its vertex is at the center of a circle, intercepts an arc equal in length to the radius.

If r (Fig. 45a) denotes the radius of the circle, we have, from geometry,

$$\frac{360°}{1 \text{ radian}} = \frac{2\pi r}{r} = 2\pi.$$

Hence

$$360° = 2\pi \text{ radians,}$$

or

$$1 \text{ radian} = \frac{180°}{\pi} = 57.2958°.$$

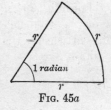

FIG. 45a

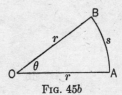

FIG. 45b

When angles are expressed in radians, it is customary to omit the unit. Thus an angle of 2 means an angle of 2 radians, or 114.5916°; similarly an angle of π means π radians, or 180°.

In Fig. 45b, let the central angle θ, intercepting the arc $AB = s$, be measured in radians. Then

$$\frac{s}{2\pi r} = \frac{\theta}{2\pi},$$

or

(1) $$s = r\theta,$$

111

a relation we shall have occasion to use. Also

$$\frac{\text{area of sector } AOB}{\pi r^2} = \frac{\theta}{2\pi},$$

or

(2) $$\text{area of sector } AOB = \frac{1}{2}r^2\theta.$$

The student will note that, if θ were measured in degrees, the right sides of (1) and (2) would contain the additional factor $\dfrac{\pi}{180}$.

46. Limit of $\dfrac{\sin \theta}{\theta}$. In deriving the formula for differentiating the sine function, we shall use the fact that, if θ is expressed in radians,

$$\lim_{\theta \to 0} \frac{\sin \theta}{\theta} = 1.$$

To establish this fact, compare the areas of the sector AOB (Fig. 46) and the triangles AOB and DOE, where DE is tangent to the circle at C,

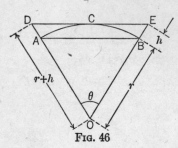

Fig. 46

the midpoint of the arc AB, and the angle AOB is θ radians. Evidently area of triangle AOB < area of sector AOB < area of triangle DOE. Denoting the radius by r, letting $h = AD = BE$, and using Formula 20(c), p. 509, for the areas of the triangles and (2) of the preceding article for the area of the sector, we obtain

$$\tfrac{1}{2}r^2 \sin \theta < \tfrac{1}{2}r^2\theta < \tfrac{1}{2}(r + h)^2 \sin \theta,$$

or, on division by $\tfrac{1}{2}r^2 \sin \theta$,

$$1 < \frac{\theta}{\sin \theta} < \frac{(r + h)^2}{r^2}.$$

Hence

$$1 > \frac{\sin \theta}{\theta} > \left(\frac{r}{r + h}\right)^2.$$

As θ approaches zero, h also approaches zero and $\left(\dfrac{r}{r + h}\right)^2$ approaches 1.

Therefore $\dfrac{\sin \theta}{\theta}$, which lies between $\left(\dfrac{r}{r+h}\right)^2$ and 1, must have 1 as its limit. That is,

(1)
$$\lim_{\theta \to 0} \frac{\sin \theta}{\theta} = 1.$$

47. Differentiation of Trigonometric Functions. Let

$$y = \sin u,$$

where the angle u is a differentiable function of x and is expressed in radians. We form

$$y + \Delta y = \sin (u + \Delta u),$$

whence

$$\Delta y = \sin (u + \Delta u) - \sin u.$$

Using Formula 18(b), p. 508, we obtain

$$\Delta y = 2 \cos \left(u + \frac{\Delta u}{2} \right) \sin \frac{\Delta u}{2} ,$$

whence

$$\frac{\Delta y}{\Delta u} = \cos \left(u + \frac{\Delta u}{2} \right) \frac{\sin \dfrac{\Delta u}{2}}{\dfrac{\Delta u}{2}} ,$$

and

$$\frac{\Delta y}{\Delta x} = \frac{\Delta y}{\Delta u} \cdot \frac{\Delta u}{\Delta x} = \cos \left(u + \frac{\Delta u}{2} \right) \frac{\sin \dfrac{\Delta u}{2}}{\dfrac{\Delta u}{2}} \cdot \frac{\Delta u}{\Delta x}.$$

As Δx approaches zero, Δu and $\dfrac{\Delta u}{2}$ also approach zero. Hence, by the definition of a derivative and by (1) of the preceding article

X
$$\frac{d}{dx} \sin u = \cos u \, \frac{du}{dx}.$$

We shall now find the derivatives of the other five trigonometric functions of u, where the angle u is a differentiable function of the independent variable x.

Letting

$$y = \cos u,$$

and, by Formula 16(a), p. 508, rewriting this as

$$y = \sin\left(\frac{\pi}{2} - u\right),$$

we obtain from X

$$\frac{dy}{dx} = \cos\left(\frac{\pi}{2} - u\right)\frac{d}{dx}\left(\frac{\pi}{2} - u\right)$$

$$= -\cos\left(\frac{\pi}{2} - u\right)\frac{du}{dx}$$

$$= -\sin u\,\frac{du}{dx}.$$

We have thus shown that

XII $\qquad\qquad \dfrac{d}{dx}\cos u = -\sin u\,\dfrac{du}{dx}.$

To differentiate $\tan u$, we let

$$y = \tan u = \frac{\sin u}{\cos u},$$

and use V, Art. 42, obtaining

$$\frac{dy}{dx} = \frac{\cos u\,\dfrac{d}{dx}\sin u - \sin u\,\dfrac{d}{dx}\cos u}{\cos^2 u}$$

$$= \frac{\cos^2 u + \sin^2 u}{\cos^2 u}\cdot\frac{du}{dx} \qquad \text{(by X and XI)}$$

$$= \sec^2 u\,\frac{du}{dx}.$$

Thus

XII $\qquad\qquad \dfrac{d}{dx}\tan u = \sec^2 u\,\dfrac{du}{dx}.$

Writing $\cot u = \dfrac{\cos u}{\sin u}$, we obtain similarly

XIII $\qquad\qquad \dfrac{d}{dx}\cot u = -\csc^2 u\,\dfrac{du}{dx}.$

The function $\sec u$ may be differentiated by writing

$$\sec u = \frac{1}{\cos u} = (\cos u)^{-1}$$

and applying VII, Art. 42.   Thus

$$\frac{d}{dx} \sec u = - (\cos u)^{-2} \frac{d}{dx} \cos u = - \frac{1}{\cos^2 u} \left(- \sin u \frac{du}{dx} \right).$$

The result in simplified form is

XIV $$\frac{d}{dx} \sec u = \sec u \tan u \frac{du}{dx}.$$

By similar procedure, if we put $\csc u = (\sin u)^{-1}$, we find that

XV $$\frac{d}{dx} \csc u = - \csc u \cot u \frac{du}{dx}.$$

Example 1.   If $y = 4 \cos (x^2 + 3)$, find $\dfrac{dy}{dx}$.

By XI we obtain

$$\frac{dy}{dx} = - 4 \sin (x^2 + 3) \frac{d}{dx} (x^2 + 3) = - 8x \sin (x^2 + 3).$$

Example 2.   If $y = \sin^3 2x$, find $\dfrac{dy}{dx}$.

Differentiating by VII, Art. 42, we obtain

$$\frac{dy}{dx} = 3 \sin^2 2x \frac{d}{dx} \sin 2x$$

$$= 3 \sin^2 2x (2 \cos 2x) \qquad\qquad \text{(by X)}$$

$$= 6 \sin^2 2x \cos 2x.$$

Note that the derivative of $\sin^3 2x$ is not the cube of the derivative of $\sin 2x$.

Example 3.   If $y = 3 \tan \dfrac{x}{2} + \tan^3 \dfrac{x}{2}$, find $\dfrac{dy}{dx}$.

$$\frac{dy}{dx} = 3 \left(\sec^2 \frac{x}{2} \right) \frac{1}{2} + 3 \tan^2 \frac{x}{2} \frac{d}{dx} \left(\tan \frac{x}{2} \right)$$

$$= \frac{3}{2} \left(\sec^2 \frac{x}{2} + \tan^2 \frac{x}{2} \sec^2 \frac{x}{2} \right)$$

$$= \frac{3}{2} \sec^2 \frac{x}{2} \left(1 + \tan^2 \frac{x}{2} \right) = \frac{3}{2} \sec^4 \frac{x}{2}.$$

Example 4.   If $x = \sqrt{4 + \cos y}$, find $\dfrac{dy}{dx}$.

First Solution.   We shall first find $\dfrac{dx}{dy}$; the reciprocal of this is $\dfrac{dy}{dx}$ (VIII, Art. 42).

$$\frac{dx}{dy} = \frac{1}{2} (4 + \cos y)^{-\frac{1}{2}} (-\sin y) = - \frac{\sin y}{2\sqrt{4 + \cos y}}.$$

Hence

$$\frac{dy}{dx} = - \frac{2\sqrt{4 + \cos y}}{\sin y}.$$

Second Solution. Squaring the given equation and differentiating implicitly with respect to x (cf. Art. 43) we obtain

$$x^2 = 4 + \cos y,$$

and

$$2x = -\sin y \frac{dy}{dx},$$

whence

$$\frac{dy}{dx} = -\frac{2x}{\sin y} = -\frac{2\sqrt{4 + \cos y}}{\sin y}.$$

Example 5. If $y = x^2 + x \sin 2x + \dfrac{\cos 2x}{2}$, find $\dfrac{dy}{dx}$.

Observing that the second term on the right side is a product, and therefore using IV, Art. 42, we obtain

$$\frac{dy}{dx} = 2x + 2x \cos 2x + \sin 2x - \sin 2x$$

$$= 2x(1 + \cos 2x)$$

$$= 4x \cos^2 x \qquad\qquad \text{(by Formula 19}(d)\text{, p. 509)}.$$

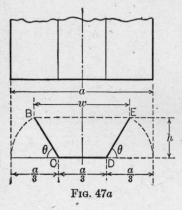

Some problems in maxima and minima may advantageously be formulated and solved in terms of trigonometric functions.

Example 6. A gutter with sloping sides of equal inclination is to be made from a long piece of sheet metal of width a by folding up one-third of the sheet on either side (Fig. 47a). Find the width across the top when the capacity is a maximum.

The capacity of the gutter varies as the area A of the trapezoid $BCDE$; therefore the problem resolves itself into finding the width $w = BE$ across the top when A is a maximum.

Fig. 47a

Since, in terms of the angle θ, the altitude h of the trapezoid is given by

$$h = \frac{a}{3} \sin \theta,$$

while

(1) $$w = \frac{a}{3}(1 + 2 \cos \theta),$$

we have

$$A = \frac{a^2}{9} \sin \theta (1 + \cos \theta),$$

whence

$$\frac{dA}{d\theta} = \frac{a^2}{9}(-\sin^2 \theta + \cos \theta + \cos^2 \theta)$$

$$= \frac{a^2}{9}(2 \cos^2 \theta + \cos \theta - 1).$$

The value of $\cos \theta$ for which A is a maximum must be a root of the equation obtained by setting $\dfrac{dA}{d\theta}$ equal to zero, that is, of

$$2 \cos^2 \theta + \cos \theta - 1 = 0.$$

Of the two roots,

$$\cos \theta = \tfrac{1}{2}, \quad \text{and} \quad \cos \theta = -1,$$

only the first can possibly correspond to maximum A; that it does, readily follows from geometrical considerations or from the tests of Art. 22. Substituting, then, $\cos \theta = \tfrac{1}{2}$ in (1), we find that for the capacity of the gutter to be a maximum

$$w = \frac{2a}{3}.$$

PROBLEMS

Differentiate each of the functions in Problems 1–30 with respect to its variable, and simplify.

1. $\sin (3x - 2)$.

2. $\cos (\sqrt{3x} - 2)$.

3. $\tan \dfrac{1}{x^2}$.

4. $\cot \left(\dfrac{2}{x} - 1 \right)$.

5. $\sec \sqrt{3 - x}$.

6. $\csc (x\sqrt{2 - x})$.

7. $\sin \dfrac{x^2}{4 - x^2}$.

8. $\cos^2 (5 - 2x)$.

9. $\tan^3 \left(\dfrac{\pi}{2} - 3x \right)$.

10. $\sec^2 (\pi - 2x)$.

11. $\tfrac{1}{2}\theta - \tfrac{1}{4} \sin 2\theta$.

12. $\tfrac{1}{2}\theta + \tfrac{1}{4} \sin 2\theta$.

13. $\tan x - \cot x - \tfrac{1}{3} \cot^3 x$.

14. $2 \tan \dfrac{x}{2} - x$.

15. $x - \tfrac{1}{3}(\csc 3x - \cot 3x)$.

16. $\tfrac{1}{2}(\sec 2x + \tan 2x) - x$.

17. $\dfrac{3x}{8} - \dfrac{3}{4} \sin x + \dfrac{3}{16} \sin 2x$.

18. $\dfrac{10}{3} \cos^3 \dfrac{x}{5} - 5 \cos \dfrac{x}{5} - \cos^5 \dfrac{x}{5}$.

19. $\tfrac{1}{7} \tan^7 x + \tfrac{1}{5} \tan^5 x$.

20. $\tfrac{1}{9} \sec^3 3t - \tfrac{1}{3} \sec 3t$.

21. $\tfrac{1}{12} \tan^3 4\theta - \tfrac{1}{4} \tan 4\theta + \theta$.

22. $\tfrac{1}{9} \sin 3\phi - \tfrac{1}{3}\phi \cos 3\phi$.

23. $\tfrac{1}{4} \cos 2x + \tfrac{1}{2}x \sin 2x$.

24. $\tfrac{1}{4}x^2 - \tfrac{1}{2}x \sin x - \tfrac{1}{2} \cos x$.

25. $\cos x \cos 3x + 3 \sin x \sin 3x$.

26. $\dfrac{\sin 2x}{1 + \cos 2x}$.

27. $\dfrac{\tan 2\theta}{\sec 2\theta + \tan 2\theta}$.

28. $\dfrac{\cos 2x + \sin 2x}{\cos 2x - \sin 2x}$.

29. $\sqrt{\dfrac{1 - \cos 3x}{1 + \cos 3x}}$.

30. $\sqrt{\dfrac{1 - \tan^2 2\phi}{2 \tan 2\phi}}$.

In each of Problems 31–34, find $\dfrac{dy}{dx}$ by implicit differentiation.

31. $y^2 \sin x - x^2 \sin y - 4 = 0$.
32. $y \sin x + x \cos y + x^2 - xy = 0$.
33. $y \sec x + x \tan y - xy + 9 = 0$.
34. $\cos (3x + y) + \sin (x + 3y) - \tfrac{1}{2} = 0$.

In each of Problems 35–38, find $\dfrac{dy}{dx}$ by the use of IX, Art. 42.

35. $x = \sin^2 t$, $y = 2 \sin^3 t \sec t$.

36. $x = a(1 - \cos t)$, $y = a(t + \sin t)$.

37. $x = 2 \sin t + \sin 2t$, $y = 2 \cos t - \cos 2t$.

38. $x = a \cos^3 t$, $y = a \sin^3 t$.

Solve the following problems by the use of trigonometric functions.

39. Find the base-radius and the altitude of the largest right circular cylinder which can be inscribed in a sphere of radius a.

40. Find the altitude of the right circular cone of least volume which can be circumscribed about a sphere of radius a.

41. Find the altitude of the right circular cone of greatest volume which can be inscribed in a sphere of radius a.

42. Find the altitude of the right circular cone of least lateral surface which can be circumscribed about a sphere of radius a.

43. Find the altitude of the right circular cone of least total surface which can be circumscribed about a sphere of radius a.

44. The strength of a rectangular beam varies jointly as the width and the square of the depth. Find the dimensions of the cross-section of the strongest rectangular beam which can be cut from a cylindrical log of diameter a.

45. Two corridors, of respective widths 4 ft. 6 in. and 10 ft. 8 in., meet at right angles. Find the length of the longest thin rod which can be moved in a horizontal position from one corridor to the other.

46. A corridor 8 ft. wide meets another at right angles. If the length of the longest thin rod which can be carried horizontally around the corner is 27 ft., what is the width of the second corridor?

47. The weight W which can be pulled with uniform speed along a rough horizontal surface by a force f directed obliquely upward and making an angle α with the horizontal is given by

$$W = \frac{f}{\mu}(\cos \alpha + \mu \sin \alpha),$$

where μ is the coefficient of friction. Find the value of α which renders W a maximum.

48. Three towns, A, B, C, are to be connected by three roads, AD, BD, CD, as shown in Fig. 47b. What should be the length of the road CD in order that the roads should have the least total length?

49. A ditch is to be dug to connect the points A and B (Fig. 47c). The earth to the left of DE is soft, and the cost of digging the portion AC is $5 per foot. The earth to the

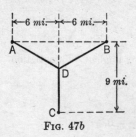

Fig. 47b

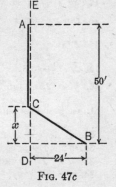

Fig. 47c

right of DE is hard, and the cost of digging the portion CB is \$13 per foot. Find the length AC if the total cost of excavation is a minimum.

48. Differentiation of Inverse Trigonometric Functions. The equation $y = \sin x$ defines y as a function of x; but it also defines x as a function of y. That is, if a value numerically less than or equal to 1 is assigned to y, a corresponding value of x can be found with the help of a table of sines.

The notation commonly used to express x as a function of y in the illustration just cited is

$$x = \sin^{-1} y,$$

where $\sin^{-1} y$ is read " inverse sine of y " or " an angle whose sine is y." It should be emphasized that the index -1 is part of the symbol, and is not an exponent.

The inverse sine function is multiple-valued, for if the sine is given there are infinitely many angles having this sine. Thus, $\sin^{-1} \frac{1}{2}$ may be 30°, or, as we prefer to express it, $\frac{\pi}{6}$; but it may also be $\frac{5\pi}{6}, \frac{13\pi}{6}, -\frac{7\pi}{6}$, etc.

Other inverse trigonometric functions, for instance, the inverse cosine and the inverse tangent, may be similarly defined; they too are multiple-valued. Thus the equation $y = \tan^{-1} u$ means that y is an angle whose tangent is u, or that $u = \tan y$. Some writers use the notation arc sin u, arc cos $u, \cdots$, in place of $\sin^{-1} u$, $\cos^{-1} u, \cdots$.

Supposing now that u is a differentiable function of x, let us develop the formulas for the derivatives of the inverse trigonometric functions of u.

To find the derivative of $\sin^{-1} u$, we write

$$y = \sin^{-1} u.$$

Differentiating the equivalent relation

$$u = \sin y$$

with respect to x, we obtain

$$\frac{du}{dx} = \cos y \frac{dy}{dx},$$

whence

$$\frac{dy}{dx} = \frac{d}{dx} \sin^{-1} u = \frac{1}{\cos y} \frac{du}{dx}.$$

Using the identity

$$\cos y = \pm \sqrt{1 - \sin^2 y},$$

and the fact that $\sin y = u$, we express the required derivative in the form

XVI $$\frac{d}{dx}\sin^{-1} u = \pm \frac{1}{\sqrt{1-u^2}}\frac{du}{dx}, \quad |u| < 1.$$

In this formula we use the plus sign when $\sin^{-1}u$ is in the first or fourth quadrant, and the minus sign when $\sin^{-1}u$ is in the second or third quadrant; for in the former case, $\cos y = \sqrt{1-u^2}$, and in the latter, $\cos y = -\sqrt{1-u^2}$.

To find the derivative of $\cos^{-1} u$, we write

$$y = \cos^{-1} u,$$

or, equivalently,

$$u = \cos y.$$

Differentiating the last equation with respect to x, we obtain

$$\frac{du}{dx} = -\sin y \frac{dy}{dx},$$

whence

$$\frac{dy}{dx} = \frac{d}{dx}\cos^{-1} u = -\frac{1}{\sin y}\frac{du}{dx}.$$

Using the identity

$$\sin y = \pm \sqrt{1 - \cos^2 y},$$

we find the required derivative in the form

XVII $$\frac{d}{dx}\cos^{-1} u = \mp \frac{1}{\sqrt{1-u^2}}\frac{du}{dx}, \quad |u| < 1.$$

From this derivation, it follows that the sign is minus when $\cos^{-1}u$ is in the first or second quadrant, and plus when $\cos^{-1} u$ is in the third or fourth quadrant.

To find the derivative of $\tan^{-1} u$, we write

$$y = \tan^{-1} u,$$

or, equivalently,

$$u = \tan y.$$

From this we obtain

$$\frac{du}{dx} = \sec^2 y \frac{dy}{dx},$$

whence

$$\frac{dy}{dx} = \frac{1}{\sec^2 y}\frac{du}{dx}.$$

Since $\sec^2 y = 1 + \tan^2 y = 1 + u^2$, we have the formula

XVIII $$\frac{d}{dx} \tan^{-1} u = \frac{1}{1 + u^2} \frac{du}{dx},$$

regardless of the quadrant in which $\tan^{-1} u$ lies.

Similarly, it may be proved that

XIX $$\frac{d}{dx} \cot^{-1} u = -\frac{1}{1 + u^2} \frac{du}{dx}$$

regardless of the quadrant in which $\cot^{-1} u$ lies. The proof is left to the student.

It will next be shown that

XX $$\frac{d}{dx} \sec^{-1} u = \pm \frac{1}{u\sqrt{u^2 - 1}} \frac{du}{dx}, \quad |u| > 1,$$

where the sign is plus if $\sec^{-1} u$ is in the first or third quadrant and minus if $\sec^{-1} u$ is in the second or fourth quadrant. Writing

$$y = \sec^{-1} u,$$

or, equivalently,

$$u = \sec y,$$

we find that

$$\frac{du}{dx} = \sec y \tan y \frac{dy}{dx},$$

whence

$$\frac{dy}{dx} = \frac{d}{dx} \sec^{-1} u = \frac{1}{\sec y \tan y} \frac{du}{dx}.$$

Replacing $\sec y$ by u, and observing that $\tan y = +\sqrt{u^2 - 1}$ when y (i.e., $\sec^{-1} u$) is in the first or third quadrant, and $\tan y = -\sqrt{u^2 - 1}$ when $\sec^{-1} u$ is in the second or fourth quadrant, we immediately obtain XX.

It is left to the student as an exercise to prove that

XXI $$\frac{d}{dx} \csc^{-1} u = \mp \frac{1}{u\sqrt{u^2 - 1}} \frac{du}{dx}, \quad |u| > 1$$

the minus sign holding when $\csc^{-1} u$ is in the first or third quadrant and the plus sign when $\csc^{-1} u$ is in the second or fourth quadrant.

For the sake of completeness, we have derived the formulas for differentiating all six of the inverse trigonometric functions, though it is always possible, and frequently advantageous, to change a given inverse trigonometric function into another before differentiating (cf. Example 2).

Owing to this fact and the special importance of the integral formulas arising from XVI and XVIII, the problems that follow will be devoted principally to the differentiation of the inverse sine and inverse tangent functions.

Example 1. If $y = \sin^{-1} 2x$, where y is in the first quadrant, find $\dfrac{dy}{dx}$.

From XVI we obtain

$$\frac{dy}{dx} = \frac{1}{\sqrt{1 - 4x^2}} \frac{d}{dx} (2x) = \frac{2}{\sqrt{1 - 4x^2}}.$$

Example 2. If $y = \sec^{-1} \sqrt{1 + x^2}$, where y is in the first quadrant, find $\dfrac{dy}{dx}$.

From XX we obtain

$$\frac{dy}{dx} = \frac{1}{\sqrt{1 + x^2} \sqrt{(1 + x^2) - 1}} \frac{d}{dx} \sqrt{1 + x^2} = \frac{1}{1 + x^2}.$$

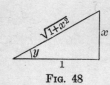

FIG. 48

The same result could have been found more easily by writing $\sec^{-1} \sqrt{1 + x^2} = \tan^{-1} x$, a fact which is readily seen from Fig. 48, and then using XVIII.

Example 3. If $y = (9 + x^2) \tan^{-1} \dfrac{x}{3} - 3x$, find $\dfrac{dy}{dx}$ and simplify.

Observing that the first term in the right member is a product, we obtain

$$\frac{dy}{dx} = (9 + x^2) \frac{d}{dx} \tan^{-1} \frac{x}{3} + \tan^{-1} \frac{x}{3} \frac{d}{dx} (9 + x^2) - 3$$

$$= (9 + x^2) \frac{3}{9 + x^2} + 2x \tan^{-1} \frac{x}{3} - 3$$

$$= 2x \tan^{-1} \frac{x}{3}.$$

PROBLEMS

Differentiate each of the functions in Problems 1–34 with respect to x, and simplify. Assume every inverse trigonometric function to be an angle in the first quadrant, so that in formulas XVI, XVII, XX, and XXI the upper sign applies.

1. $\sin^{-1}\dfrac{x}{2}$.

2. $\tan^{-1} 3x$.

3. $\cos^{-1}\dfrac{1}{x}$.

4. $\sec^{-1}\dfrac{1}{x^2}$.

5. $\csc^{-1}\sqrt{x}$.

6. $\cot^{-1}\sqrt{2x + x^2}$.

7. $\sin^{-1}\sqrt{1 - x^2}$.

8. $\tan^{-1}\dfrac{x}{\sqrt{1 - x^2}}$.

9. $\cos^{-1}\dfrac{1}{\sqrt{1 + x^2}}$.

10. $\sec^{-1}\sqrt{x^2 + 2x + 2}$.

11. $\sin^{-1}(x\sqrt{2x - x^2})$.

12. $\tan^{-1}\sqrt{x^2 - 1}$.

13. $\dfrac{\sin^{-1} x}{x}$.

14. $x \tan^{-1} 2x$.

15. $x^2 \sin^{-1}\dfrac{x}{2}$.

16. $\sqrt{1 - 4x^2} \sin^{-1} 2x$.

17. $\dfrac{9 + 4x^2}{\tan^{-1}\dfrac{2x}{3}}$.

18. $\dfrac{2}{3}\tan^{-1}\sqrt{\dfrac{2x - 9}{9}}$.

19. $\sqrt{x^2 - 4} - 2\cos^{-1}\dfrac{2}{x}$.

20. $x\sqrt{(9 - x^2)^3} + \dfrac{27x}{2}\sqrt{9 - x^2} + \dfrac{243}{2}\sin^{-1}\dfrac{x}{3}$.

21. $x\sqrt{4 - x^2} + 4\sin^{-1}\dfrac{x}{2} - \dfrac{x}{2}\sqrt{(4 - x^2)^3}$.

22. $\dfrac{\sqrt{x^2 - 9}}{x^2} + \dfrac{1}{3}\cos^{-1}\dfrac{3}{x}$.

23. $8\sin^{-1}\dfrac{x}{4} - \dfrac{x}{2}\sqrt{16 - x^2}$.

24. $\dfrac{\sqrt{4 - x^2}}{x} + \sin^{-1}\dfrac{x}{2}$.

25. $\dfrac{x}{\sqrt{4 - x^2}} - \sin^{-1}\dfrac{x}{2}$.

26. $\dfrac{x - 3}{2}\sqrt{6x - x^2} + \dfrac{9}{2}\sin^{-1}\dfrac{x - 3}{3}$.

27. $\dfrac{2}{3}\tan^{-1}\left(\dfrac{5\tan\dfrac{x}{2} + 4}{3}\right)$.

28. $\dfrac{2}{3}\tan^{-1}\left(\dfrac{\tan\dfrac{x}{2}}{3}\right)$.

29. $2x\sin^{-1} 2x + \sqrt{1 - 4x^2}$.

30. $3x\cos^{-1} 3x - \sqrt{1 - 9x^2}$.

31. $x\left(\sin^{-1}\dfrac{x}{2}\right)^2 - 2x + 2\sqrt{4 - x^2}\sin^{-1}\dfrac{x}{2}$.

32. $(8x^2 - 1)\sin^{-1} 2x + 2x\sqrt{1 - 4x^2}$.

33. $2x^2 \sec^{-1} 2x - \tfrac{1}{2}\sqrt{4x^2 - 1}$.

34. $\tan^{-1}\dfrac{x}{2 + \sqrt{4 + x^2}}$.

35. A flagpole 45 ft. high stands at the top of a building 85 ft. high. If an observer's eye is 5 ft. above the ground, how far should he stand from the foot of the building in order that the angle between his lines of sight to the top and bottom of the flagpole should be a maximum?

49. Graphs of Trigonometric Functions.

The student is presumably familiar with the graphs of the trigonometric functions, but we shall discuss them here from the standpoint of calculus, making use of the first and second derivatives as a means of establishing their characteristic features. From these graphs we shall in the next article deduce those of the inverse trigonometric functions, which in turn will be of assistance in the evaluation of certain definite integrals.

In Fig. 49a, we give the graphs of $y = \sin x$, $y = \cos x$, and $y = \tan x$.

The values of the trigonometric functions, which are of course ratios, that is, pure numbers, are denoted by the ordinates, while the abscissas designate angles in radians. In order to give the curves a standard appearance, the same length which is laid off along the y-axis to repre-

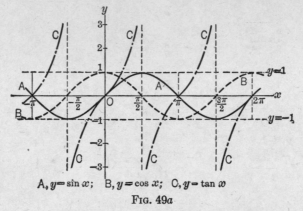

A, $y = \sin x$; B, $y = \cos x$; C, $y = \tan x$;

FIG. 49a

sent a ratio of one is laid off along the x-axis to represent an angle of one radian. Since, however, the angles of special importance are multiples and submultiples of π, and since $\dfrac{\pi}{3}$ (= 1.047) does not differ much from unity, it will be convenient in actual plotting to let unit abscissa stand for an angle of $\dfrac{\pi}{3}$ radians instead of one radian. The corresponding change in the appearance of the graphs will not be appreciable.

The Sine Curve. Evidently the abscissas of the points of the curve $y = \sin x$ for which $y = 0$ are roots of the equation $\sin x = 0$; these points, namely $(n\pi, 0)$, where n is any positive or negative integer or zero, are all points of intersection with the x-axis, because at each of them y undergoes a change of sign.

Since

$$\frac{dy}{dx} = \cos x,$$

the abscissas of the critical points are the roots of the equation

$$\cos x = 0,$$

that is,

$$x = \cdots, -\frac{3\pi}{2}, -\frac{\pi}{2}, \frac{\pi}{2}, \frac{3\pi}{2}, \cdots.$$

The corresponding ordinates are found from the equation of the curve. Thus the critical points are

$$\cdots, \left(-\frac{3\pi}{2}, 1\right), \left(-\frac{\pi}{2}, -1\right), \left(\frac{\pi}{2}, 1\right), \left(\frac{3\pi}{2}, -1\right), \cdots.$$

It is readily seen that the curve intersects the x-axis half way between any pair of consecutive critical points.

The second derivative

$$\frac{d^2y}{dx^2} = -\sin x = -y$$

is positive when y is negative, and negative when y is positive; therefore the critical points for which $y = -1$ are minimum points, and those for which $y = 1$ are maximum points.

Since $\frac{d^2y}{dx^2}$ changes sign when y passes through zero, we conclude that the curve has a point of inflection at every point at which it intersects the x-axis.

It is thus seen that the graph of $y = \sin x$ is a wave-like curve lying between the lines $y = 1$ and $y = -1$; the portion of the curve between $x = 0$ and $x = 2\pi$ is duplicated in each of the intervals of length 2π from $x = -2\pi$ to $x = 0$, from $x = 2\pi$ to $x = 4\pi$, from $x = 4\pi$ to $x = 6\pi$, etc. The number 2π representing the common length of these intervals is called the **period** of $\sin x$. The maximum value of $\sin x$, namely 1, is called the **amplitude**.

Let us now consider the graph of the equation $y = \sin (x + \alpha)$, where α is a positive number. If we put $x + \alpha = x'$, which amounts to taking as a new y-axis $O'y'$, α units to the left of the original y-axis, the given equation becomes $y = \sin x'$, and its graph is that obtained in the preceding discussion but referred to $O'y'$ as vertical axis (Fig. 49b).

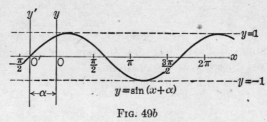

FIG. 49b

Hence the graph of $y = \sin (x + \alpha)$ may be found from that of $y = \sin x$ by displacing the latter to the left α units.

Similarly it may be shown that the graph of $y = \sin (x - \alpha)$ is that of $y = \sin x$ displaced α units to the right.

The Cosine Curve. Since $\cos x = \sin \left(x + \frac{\pi}{2}\right)$, we may immediately obtain the graph of $y = \cos x$ from that of $y = \sin x$ by displacing the latter $\frac{\pi}{2}$ units to the left (see Fig. 49a). Hence the period and amplitude of cos x are the same as those of sin x, namely, 2π and 1, respectively.

The Tangent Curve. Since $\tan x = \dfrac{\sin x}{\cos x}$ and cos x vanishes for other values of x than sin x, the curve $y = \tan x$ intersects the x-axis at the same points as the sine curve, namely, $(n\pi, 0)$, where n is any positive or negative integer, or zero. Moreover, the curve $y = \tan x$ is discontinuous for values of x satisfying the equation cos $x = 0$, i.e., for $x = \cdots$, $-\dfrac{\pi}{2}, \dfrac{\pi}{2}, \dfrac{3\pi}{2}, \cdots$. These discontinuities are all infinite; for instance, as x, while increasing, approaches $\dfrac{\pi}{2}$, tan x becomes positively infinite, and as x, while decreasing, approaches $\dfrac{\pi}{2}$, tan x becomes negatively infinite. From a graphical point of view, this means that the distance between the point (x, y) on the tangent curve and the point $\left(\dfrac{\pi}{2}, y\right)$ on the vertical line $x = \dfrac{\pi}{2}$ becomes and remains arbitrarily small as the numerical value of y increases indefinitely (see Fig. 49a). The line $x = \dfrac{\pi}{2}$ is called an **asymptote** of the tangent curve (cf. Art. 74); similarly, the lines $\cdots, x = -\dfrac{\pi}{2}, x = \dfrac{3\pi}{2}, x = \dfrac{5\pi}{2}, \cdots$ are also asymptotes.

The first derivative

$$\frac{d}{dx} \tan x = \sec^2 x$$

is positive for all values of x; hence the curve $y = \tan x$ has no critical points, but rises from left to right in every interval of length π between two consecutive discontinuities.

Since the second derivative

$$\frac{d^2}{dx^2} \tan x = 2 \sec^2 x \tan x = 2y(1 + y^2)$$

changes sign when y passes through zero, we conclude that the curve has a point of inflection at every point at which it intersects the x-axis.

From these considerations it is evident that the curve $y = \tan x$ consists of infinitely many branches similar to that between $x = -\dfrac{\pi}{2}$ and $x = \dfrac{\pi}{2}$; the period of tan x is therefore π.

The graphs of the other trigonometric functions will be left to the student (Problems 1–3).

Example 1.   Discuss the equation $y = 2 \cos 3x$, and plot its graph.

The points of intersection with the x-axis are evidently those for which $\cos 3x = 0$, or for which

$$3x = \cdots, -\frac{\pi}{2}, \frac{\pi}{2}, \frac{3\pi}{2}, \cdots .$$

The abscissas of these points are therefore

$$x = \cdots, -\frac{\pi}{6}, \frac{\pi}{6}, \frac{\pi}{2}, \cdots .$$

Setting the derivative

$$\frac{dy}{dx} = -6 \sin 3x$$

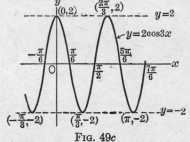

Fig. 49c

equal to zero, solving for x, and substituting in the given equation, we find the following critical points:

$$\cdots, \left(-\frac{\pi}{3}, -2\right), (0, 2), \left(\frac{\pi}{3}, -2\right), \left(\frac{2\pi}{3}, 2\right), \cdots .$$

Since the maximum value of $2 \cos 3x$ is 2, and the minimum value -2, these critical points are alternately minimum and maximum points.

The amplitude of the function $2 \cos 3x$ is therefore 2, and the period is the interval between consecutive maximum points, namely $\dfrac{2\pi}{3}$.

Thus $2 \cos 3x$ has an amplitude twice that of $\cos x$ and a period one-third as large. These two relations are associated respectively with the factor 2 multiplying the trigonometric function and the coefficient 3 in the angle.

The graph is shown in Fig. 49c.

Example 2.   Sketch the curve $y = 3 \sin \dfrac{x}{2}$.

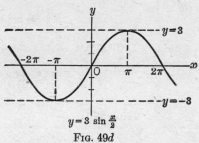

$y = 3 \sin \frac{x}{2}$

Fig. 49d

The amplitude of the function $3 \sin \dfrac{x}{2}$ is evidently 3, while the period is 4π, namely, twice that of $\sin x$. Noting that y is positive in the interval from 0 to 2π, we readily obtain the sketch (Fig. 49d).

Example 3.   Sketch the curve $y = 2 \cos \dfrac{2}{3}\left(x - \dfrac{\pi}{3}\right)$.

The graph (Fig. 49e) of the given equation is obtained from that of $y = 2 \cos \frac{2}{3}x$ by shifting the latter $\frac{\pi}{3}$ units to the right. It should be observed that the amplitude of the function $2 \cos \frac{2}{3}x$ is 2, while its period is 2π divided by $\frac{2}{3}$, that is, 3π.

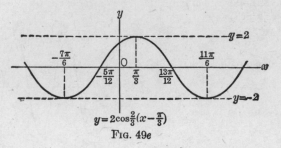

$$y = 2\cos\tfrac{2}{3}\left(x - \tfrac{\pi}{3}\right)$$

FIG. 49e

Example 4. Plot the curve $y = 2 \sin 2x + 2 \cos x$.

A simple way to proceed is by **composition of ordinates,** that is, by adding algebraically corresponding ordinates of the curves $y = 2 \sin 2x$ and $y = 2 \cos x$, as shown in Fig. 49f.

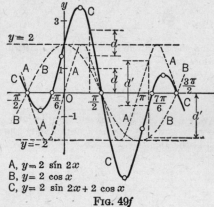

A, $y = 2 \sin 2x$
B, $y = 2 \cos x$
C, $y = 2 \sin 2x + 2 \cos x$

FIG. 49f

We can, however, establish the general appearance of the curve by finding the points of intersection with the axes, the critical points, and the points of inflection.

The curve intersects the y-axis at (0, 2). The abscissas of the points of intersection with the x-axis are obtained by setting y equal to zero and solving the resulting equation

$$2 \sin 2x + 2 \cos x = 0,$$

or

$$2 \cos x(2 \sin x + 1) = 0.$$

Thus either

$$\cos x = 0$$

and

$$x = \cdots, -\frac{\pi}{2}, \frac{\pi}{2}, \frac{3\pi}{2}, \cdots,$$

or

$$2 \sin x + 1 = 0$$

and

$$x = \cdots, -\frac{\pi}{6}, \frac{7\pi}{6}, \cdots.$$

The critical points have abscissas that are roots of the equation obtained by setting $\frac{dy}{dx}$ equal to zero, that is, of

$$4 \cos 2x - 2 \sin x = 0,$$

which is equivalent to

$$4 \sin^2 x + \sin x - 2 = 0;$$

whence

$$\sin x = \frac{-1 \pm \sqrt{1 + 32}}{8}$$

$$= 0.5931 \quad \text{or} \quad -0.8431.$$

Within the interval from $-\dfrac{\pi}{2}$ to $\dfrac{3\pi}{2}$ shown in the figure, we find from tables

$$\sin^{-1}(0.5931) = 0.635, \ 2.507$$

and

$$\sin^{-1}(-0.8431) = -1.003, \ 4.145,$$

these angles being expressed in radians. Computing the corresponding ordinates we obtain the following critical points:

$$(-1.003, -0.738), \ (0.635, 3.520), \ (2.507, -3.520), \ (4.145, 0.738).$$

It is evident that these are alternately minimum and maximum points.

Differentiating again, and setting $\dfrac{d^2y}{dx^2}$ equal to zero, we obtain, after reduction,

$$(8 \sin x + 1) \cos x = 0,$$

whence

$$x = \cos^{-1} 0, \quad \text{or} \quad \sin^{-1}(-\tfrac{1}{8}).$$

Since as x passes through any of these values, $\dfrac{d^2y}{dx^2}$ undergoes a change of sign, these solutions are the abscissas of points of inflection. Within the interval $-\dfrac{\pi}{2} \leq x \leq \dfrac{3\pi}{2}$, the points of inflection are found to be

$$\left(-\frac{\pi}{2}, 0\right), \ (-0.125, 1.488), \ \left(\frac{\pi}{2}, 0\right), \ (3.267, -1.488), \ \left(\frac{3\pi}{2}, 0\right).$$

The curve may now be easily sketched.

PROBLEMS

In Problems 1–13 discuss and plot the curves whose equations are given.

1. $y = \cot x.$
2. $y = \sec x.$
3. $y = \csc x.$
4. $y = 2 \sin 3x.$
5. $y = 3 \cos \dfrac{x}{2}.$
6. $y = \tan \left(x - \dfrac{\pi}{4}\right).$

7. $y = 2 \sin \left(x - \dfrac{\pi}{6}\right).$
8. $y = \tfrac{1}{2} \cos \left(x + \dfrac{\pi}{3}\right).$
9. $y = \sin x + \cos x.$
10. $y = \cos x - \tfrac{1}{2} \cos 2x.$
11. $y = \sin 2x - \cos x.$
12. $y = \tfrac{1}{2} \tan^2 2x.$

13. $y = \dfrac{\sin x}{x}.$ (See Arts. 7 and 46.)

In each of Problems 14–19 find the equation of the tangent and the normal to the given curve at the designated point.

14. $y = \sin x$; $\left(\dfrac{\pi}{6}, \dfrac{1}{2}\right).$

15. $y = \tan 2x$; $\left(\dfrac{\pi}{8}, 1\right).$

16. $y = 2 \sec^2 3x$; $\left(\dfrac{\pi}{12}, 4\right).$

17. $y = \dfrac{\cos 2x}{\sin x}$; $\left(\dfrac{\pi}{6}, 1\right).$

18. $y = x \cos x$; $\left(\dfrac{\pi}{3}, \dfrac{\pi}{6}\right).$

19. $y = x \sin \dfrac{1}{x}$; $\left(\dfrac{6}{\pi}, \dfrac{3}{\pi}\right).$

50. Graphs of Inverse Trigonometric Functions.

We shall consider in the text the graphs of the inverse sine and inverse tangent functions,

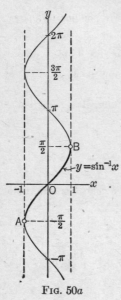

FIG. 50a

leaving to the student (Problems 1–4) the graphs of the other inverse trigonometric functions. The importance of the inverse sine and the inverse tangent has already been mentioned (Art. 48).

The Inverse Sine Curve. Since the equation $y = \sin^{-1}x$ is equivalent to $x = \sin y$, its graph (Fig. 50a) may be obtained from that of $y = \sin x$ by interchanging the rôles of x and y. Hence the graph is a wave-like curve lying between the lines $x = 1$ and $x = -1$, and crossing the y-axis at points whose ordinates are given by $n\pi$, where n is a positive or negative integer, or zero.

The graph exhibits the previously stated fact that the inverse sine function is multiple-valued, for it is seen that any value of x between -1 and 1 is the abscissa of infinitely many points on the curve.

Let us consider the arc AB extending from $\left(-1, -\dfrac{\pi}{2}\right)$ to $\left(1, \dfrac{\pi}{2}\right)$ and drawn heavy in Fig. 50a. We note that any value of x between -1 and 1 is the abscissa of one and only one point of this arc. If, therefore, we restrict the curve to the arc AB, only one value of y will correspond to an assigned value of x, so that y (i.e., $\sin^{-1} x$) is thereby rendered a single-valued function of x. Since it is advantageous to deal with single-valued functions, we shall usually regard the function $\sin^{-1} x$ as limited to the range from $-\dfrac{\pi}{2}$ to $\dfrac{\pi}{2}$. According to this convention, $\sin^{-1} \frac{1}{2}$ would mean only $\dfrac{\pi}{6}$, for no other angle having $\frac{1}{2}$ for its sine lies within the specified range. Similarly, $\sin^{-1}(-\frac{1}{2})$ would mean only $-\dfrac{\pi}{6}$.

The restriction we have just placed on the inverse sine function will change the differentiation formula

XVI
$$\frac{d}{dx}\sin^{-1} u = \pm\, \frac{1}{\sqrt{1-u^2}}\,\frac{du}{dx}, \quad |u| < 1,$$

into

XVIa
$$\frac{d}{dx}\sin^{-1} u = \frac{1}{\sqrt{1-u^2}}\,\frac{du}{dx}, \quad |u| < 1,$$

for, as was shown in Art. 48, the minus sign holds when $\sin^{-1} u$ is in the second or third quadrant, and we are now excluding such a possibility.

The Inverse Tangent Curve. The graph of $y = \tan^{-1} x$ may be obtained from that of $y = \tan x$ by interchanging x and y. Since the vertical lines $\cdots$, $x = -\dfrac{\pi}{2}, x = \dfrac{\pi}{2}, x = \dfrac{3\pi}{2}, \cdots$ are asymptotes of the tangent curve, it follows that the horizontal lines $\cdots$, $y = -\dfrac{\pi}{2}$, $y = \dfrac{\pi}{2}, y = \dfrac{3\pi}{2}, \cdots$ are asymptotes of the inverse tangent curve (Fig. 50b).

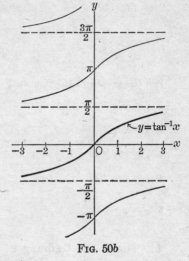

Fig. 50b

For any value of x, there are infinitely many values of y, each corresponding to a separate point on the graph. Thus for $x = 1$, we have the points $\cdots, \left(1, -\dfrac{3\pi}{4}\right), \left(1, \dfrac{\pi}{4}\right), \left(1, \dfrac{5\pi}{4}\right), \cdots$. As in the case of the inverse sine function, we shall usually restrict the graph to one of its representative portions. The most convenient portion to select is the branch passing through the origin, shown heavy in Fig. 50b. This selection, corresponding to that previously made for the inverse sine function, would limit $\tan^{-1} x$ to values between $-\dfrac{\pi}{2}$ and $\dfrac{\pi}{2}$. Thus, $\tan^{-1} 1$ would mean only the angle $\dfrac{\pi}{4}$, and $\tan^{-1}(-1)$ only $-\dfrac{\pi}{4}$.

Further discussion of the restrictions imposed on the inverse sine and inverse tangent functions will be given in Art. 94 in connection with definite integrals.

Example. Plot the graph of $y = \frac{1}{3} \sin^{-1} \frac{x}{2}$.

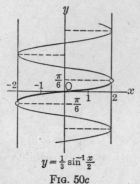

$$y = \tfrac{1}{3}\sin^{-1}\tfrac{x}{2}$$

Fig. 50c

The equation may be rewritten as

$$x = 2 \sin 3y.$$

Hence the period is $\frac{2\pi}{3}$ and the amplitude 2. Observing that x is positive when y is between 0 and $\frac{\pi}{3}$, we readily obtain the graph (Fig. 50c).

By imposing the restriction $-\frac{\pi}{6} \leq y \leq \frac{\pi}{6}$, we render y single-valued. The corresponding portion of the graph is shown heavy in the figure.

PROBLEMS

Plot the graphs of the following equations.

1. $y = \cos^{-1} x$.

2. $y = \cot^{-1} x$.

3. $y = \sec^{-1} x$.

4. $y = \csc^{-1} x$.

5. $y = 2 \tan^{-1} \frac{x}{3}$.

6. $y = \tan^{-1} \frac{3}{2x}$.

7. $y = \sin^{-1} (1 - x)$.

8. $y = \sin^{-1} (2x\sqrt{1 - x^2})$.

9. $y = \tan^{-1} \frac{2x}{1 - x^2}$.

10. $y = \frac{1}{2} \sin^{-1} \frac{x}{2} + \frac{\pi}{3}$.

51. The Limit Defining e. The differentiation of exponential and logarithmic functions depends on the existence of a certain limit, namely,

$$\lim_{n \to \pm \infty} \left(1 + \frac{1}{n}\right)^n.$$

Before establishing the existence of this limit, we shall show that $\left(1 + \frac{1}{n}\right)^n$ increases as n increases through positive integral values, or, equivalently, that

$$(1) \qquad \left(1 + \frac{1}{n}\right)^n < \left(1 + \frac{1}{n+1}\right)^{n+1},$$

where n is any positive integer.

For this purpose we write the difference

$$\left(1 + \frac{1}{n}\right)^n - \left(1 + \frac{1}{n+1}\right)^{n+1}$$

in the form

$$\left[\left(1 + \frac{1}{n}\right)^{n+1} - \left(1 + \frac{1}{n+1}\right)^{n+1}\right] - \frac{1}{n}\left(1 + \frac{1}{n}\right)^n,$$

and factor the expression in brackets. We thus obtain

$$\left(1 + \frac{1}{n}\right)^n - \left(1 + \frac{1}{n+1}\right)^{n+1} = \left(\frac{1}{n} - \frac{1}{n+1}\right)\left[\left(1 + \frac{1}{n}\right)^n\right.$$

$$+ \left(1 + \frac{1}{n}\right)^{n-1}\left(1 + \frac{1}{n+1}\right) + \cdots$$

$$\left. + \left(1 + \frac{1}{n+1}\right)^n\right] - \frac{1}{n}\left(1 + \frac{1}{n}\right)^n.$$

Since $\dfrac{1}{n} - \dfrac{1}{n+1}$, which reduces to $\dfrac{1}{n(n+1)}$, is positive, the right member is increased by replacing $1 + \dfrac{1}{n+1}$ by $1 + \dfrac{1}{n}$ within the brackets. Making this change and observing that each of the $n+1$ terms within the brackets is now $\left(1 + \dfrac{1}{n}\right)^n$, we have the inequality

$$\left(1 + \frac{1}{n}\right)^n - \left(1 + \frac{1}{n+1}\right)^{n+1} < \frac{1}{n(n+1)}(n+1)\left(1 + \frac{1}{n}\right)^n - \frac{1}{n}\left(1 + \frac{1}{n}\right)^n.$$

Since the right member vanishes, this inequality is equivalent to (1).

Having thus seen that $\left(1 + \dfrac{1}{n}\right)^n$ increases as n increases through positive integral values, we next proceed to show that a number can be found which exceeds $\left(1 + \dfrac{1}{n}\right)^n$ for any positive integral value of n, and hence (Theorem 5, Art. 5) that $\left(1 + \dfrac{1}{n}\right)^n$ approaches a limit as n becomes positively infinite through integral values.

For this purpose, we choose any positive integer a other than unity and write the difference

$$\left(1 + \frac{1}{an}\right)^{n+1} - 1$$

in the factored form

$$\left(1 + \frac{1}{an} - 1\right)\left[\left(1 + \frac{1}{an}\right)^n + \left(1 + \frac{1}{an}\right)^{n-1} + \cdots + 1\right].$$

Observing that the first of the $n + 1$ terms within the brackets is greater than any subsequent term, we readily obtain the inequality

$$\left(1 + \frac{1}{an}\right)^{n+1} - 1 < \frac{1}{an}(n + 1)\left(1 + \frac{1}{an}\right)^n.$$

Transposing and factoring, we have

$$\left(1 + \frac{1}{an}\right)^n\left[\left(1 + \frac{1}{an}\right) - \frac{n+1}{an}\right] < 1,$$

or

$$\left(1 + \frac{1}{an}\right)^n\left(1 - \frac{1}{a}\right) < 1.$$

Therefore

$$\left(1 + \frac{1}{an}\right)^n < \frac{a}{a-1},$$

and consequently

$$\left(1 + \frac{1}{an}\right)^{an} < \left(\frac{a}{a-1}\right)^a.$$

Since by an extension of (1)

$$\left(1 + \frac{1}{n}\right)^n < \left(1 + \frac{1}{an}\right)^{an},$$

it follows that

$$\left(1 + \frac{1}{n}\right)^n < \left(\frac{a}{a-1}\right)^a$$

regardless of the value of the positive integer n. Thus $\left(1 + \frac{1}{n}\right)^n$, which has previously been shown to increase with n, is always less than the constant $\left(\frac{a}{a-1}\right)^a$; then, by Theorem 5, Art. 5, $\lim\limits_{n \to \infty}\left(1 + \frac{1}{n}\right)^n$ exists and is not greater than $\left(\frac{a}{a-1}\right)^a$.

The value of this limit exceeds 2 but not 4, these being the respective values of $\left(1 + \frac{1}{n}\right)^n$ and $\left(\frac{a}{a-1}\right)^a$ for $n = 1$ and $a = 2$.

We have so far proved that, if n is restricted to positive integral values, then $\lim\limits_{n \to \infty} \left(1 + \dfrac{1}{n}\right)^n$ exists. We shall now show that, as the

continuous variable t becomes infinite, $\left(1 + \dfrac{1}{t}\right)^t$ approaches the same limit.

First, suppose that t has become and remains greater than unity. Then, for any value of t there exist positive integers, n and $n + 2$, such that

$$n < t < n + 2,*$$

whence

$$1 + \frac{1}{n + 2} < 1 + \frac{1}{t} < 1 + \frac{1}{n},$$

and

$$\left(1 + \frac{1}{n + 2}\right)^t < \left(1 + \frac{1}{t}\right)^t < \left(1 + \frac{1}{n}\right)^t.$$

Replacing t by n in the first member, and by $n + 2$ in the third member, thereby strengthening the inequality, we obtain

$$\left(1 + \frac{1}{n + 2}\right)^n < \left(1 + \frac{1}{t}\right)^t < \left(1 + \frac{1}{n}\right)^{n+2},$$

or

(2)
$$\frac{\left(1 + \dfrac{1}{n + 2}\right)^{n+2}}{\left(1 + \dfrac{1}{n + 2}\right)^2} < \left(1 + \frac{1}{t}\right)^t < \left(1 + \frac{1}{n}\right)^n \left(1 + \frac{1}{n}\right)^2.$$

Now let t, and therefore n, become infinite. Since

$$\lim_{n \to \infty} \left(1 + \frac{1}{n}\right)^2 = \left[\lim_{n \to \infty} \left(1 + \frac{1}{n}\right)\right]^2 = 1$$

and similarly

$$\lim_{n \to \infty} \left(1 + \frac{1}{n + 2}\right)^2 = 1,$$

and since obviously

$$\lim_{n \to \infty} \left(1 + \frac{1}{n + 2}\right)^{n+2} = \lim_{n \to \infty} \left(1 + \frac{1}{n}\right)^n,$$

a limit which has already been shown to exist, it follows that the limits of the first and third members of (2) are equal, whence

(3)
$$\lim_{t \to \infty} \left(1 + \frac{1}{t}\right)^t \text{ exists and equals } \lim_{n \to \infty} \left(1 + \frac{1}{n}\right)^n,$$

---

* The last member of this inequality is taken as $n + 2$ instead of $n + 1$ in order that t may be free to pass through integral values.

where n becomes infinite through positive integral values and t becomes positively infinite by varying continuously.

Finally, let t become and remain less than -1, so that $t = -u$, where u exceeds unity. Then

$$\left(1 + \frac{1}{t}\right)^t = \left(1 - \frac{1}{u}\right)^{-u} = \left(\frac{u}{u-1}\right)^u = \left(1 + \frac{1}{u-1}\right)^u$$

$$= \left(1 + \frac{1}{u-1}\right)^{u-1}\left(1 + \frac{1}{u-1}\right).$$

Now let t become negatively infinite, u becoming positively infinite; then since the limit of $1 + \dfrac{1}{u-1}$ is unity, we obtain, by (3),

$$\lim_{t \to -\infty}\left(1 + \frac{1}{t}\right)^t = \lim_{u \to \infty}\left(1 + \frac{1}{u-1}\right)^{u-1} = \lim_{n \to \infty}\left(1 + \frac{1}{n}\right)^n.$$

Thus it is no longer necessary to use different notations for a continuous variable and for one which is restricted to positive integral values, and we may summarize our results as follows:

The binomial power $\left(1 + \dfrac{1}{n}\right)^n$ *approaches a unique limit as n becomes positively or negatively infinite in any manner whatever.*

This limit, which, as we have seen, exceeds 2 but not 4, and which will be more accurately determined in the next article, is universally denoted by e. By definition, then, we have

(4) $$e = \lim_{n \to \pm\infty}\left(1 + \frac{1}{n}\right)^n.$$

Alternatively, as becomes evident by setting $n = \dfrac{1}{h}$, we may write

(4') $$e = \lim_{h \to 0}(1 + h)^{\frac{1}{h}}.$$

52. Evaluation of e. In the binomial power $(1 + h)^{\frac{1}{h}}$ occurring in the definition of e ((4') of the preceding article), let $\dfrac{1}{h}$ be a positive integer. Then, expanding by the binomial theorem (Formula 1, p. 507), we obtain

$$(1+h)^{\frac{1}{h}} = 1 + \frac{1}{h}h + \frac{\frac{1}{h}\left(\frac{1}{h}-1\right)}{2!}h^2 + \frac{\frac{1}{h}\left(\frac{1}{h}-1\right)\left(\frac{1}{h}-2\right)}{3!}h^3 + \cdots + h^{\frac{1}{h}},$$

or

(1) $(1 + h)^{\frac{1}{h}} = 1 + 1 + \dfrac{1 - h}{2!} + \dfrac{(1 - h)(1 - 2h)}{3!} + \cdots + h^{\frac{1}{h}}.$

This expansion continues to be valid as h is allowed to decrease in such a manner that $\dfrac{1}{h}$ remains integral, the number of terms increasing with $\dfrac{1}{h}$.

Now since the limit of the left side of (1) as h approaches zero is e, while the number of terms on the right side becomes infinite, it seems plausible that we may set h equal to zero in the right side of (1) and thus arrive at the following *infinite series* for e:

(2) $e = 1 + \dfrac{1}{1!} + \dfrac{1}{2!} + \dfrac{1}{3!} + \cdots + \dfrac{1}{(n - 1)!} + \cdots.$

That this series actually represents e will be shown in Arts. 139 and 142. We shall accordingly use (2) as a basis for computing the value of e as follows:

$$1 = 1.000000$$

$$1 = 1.000000$$

$$\frac{1}{2!} = 0.500000$$

$$\frac{1}{3!} = \frac{1}{3}\left(\frac{1}{2!}\right) = 0.166667$$

$$\frac{1}{4!} = \frac{1}{4}\left(\frac{1}{3!}\right) = 0.041667$$

$$\frac{1}{5!} = 0.008333$$

$$\frac{1}{6!} = 0.001389$$

$$\frac{1}{7!} = 0.000198$$

$$\frac{1}{8!} = 0.000025$$

$$\frac{1}{9!} = 0.000003$$

$$\cdot \qquad \cdot$$
$$\cdot \qquad \cdot$$
$$\cdot \qquad \cdot$$

$$e = 2.718282$$

Although only ten terms have been used, and the last seven of them are correct only to six decimal places, it happens that the result is also correct to six decimal places.

In calculus and its applications it is found advantageous (see Arts. 53 and 54) to use e as the base of logarithms. Logarithms to this base are called **natural logarithms,** or **Napierian logarithms,** after John Napier (1550–1617), the inventor of logarithms. We shall denote the logarithm of a number N to the base e by the symbol * $\ln N$; the logarithm of N to the base a where a is an arbitrary positive number other than unity will be denoted by $\log_a N$. In ordinary computation a is taken as 10; logarithms to this base are called **common logarithms.**

53. Differentiation of Exponential Functions. A function a^u where a is a positive constant other than unity and u is a variable is called an **exponential function;** a is the base.

In developing a formula for differentiating a^u, we shall first take as the base the number e.

Suppose that u is a differentiable function of x, and let

$$y = e^u.$$

Then

$$y + \Delta y = e^{u+\Delta u},$$

$$\Delta y = e^{u+\Delta u} - e^u = e^u(e^{\Delta u} - 1),$$

and

$$\frac{\Delta y}{\Delta u} = e^u \frac{e^{\Delta u} - 1}{\Delta u}.$$

Writing

$$e^{\Delta u} - 1 = v,$$

whence

$$e^{\Delta u} = 1 + v,$$

we have by the definition of a logarithm (cf. 3, p. 507),

$$\Delta u = \log_e (1 + v) = \ln (1 + v),$$

so that

$$\frac{e^{\Delta u} - 1}{\Delta u} = \frac{v}{\ln (1 + v)} = \frac{1}{\ln (1 + v)^{\frac{1}{v}}},$$

the last step being a consequence of Formula 4(c), p. 507. Therefore

$$\frac{\Delta y}{\Delta u} = \frac{e^u}{\ln (1 + v)^{\frac{1}{v}}}.$$

* Other symbols for the natural logarithm of N are $\log_e N$ and $\log N$.

As Δx approaches zero, Δu and v also approach zero, while $(1 + v)^{\frac{1}{v}}$ approaches e.   Hence

$$\frac{dy}{dx} = \lim_{\Delta x \to 0}\left(\frac{\Delta y}{\Delta u} \cdot \frac{\Delta u}{\Delta x}\right) = \frac{e^u}{\ln e}\frac{du}{dx} = e^u \frac{du}{dx},$$

since $\ln e = 1$.

We have thus established the formula

XXII $$\frac{d}{dx}e^u = e^u \frac{du}{dx}.$$

If, in particular, $u = x$, this becomes

XXIII $$\frac{d}{dx}e^x = e^x,$$

so that the function e^x has the property of being its own derivative.

Returning now to the general exponential function a^u, where u is a differentiable function of x and the base a is any positive constant other than unity, we let

$$y = a^u.$$

In order to find $\dfrac{dy}{dx}$, let us transform a^u into an equivalent exponential function with e as base.   Using the definition of a logarithm, we have

$$a = e^{\ln a},$$

whence

$$y = (e^{\ln a})^u = e^{u \ln a}.$$

Therefore, by XXII,

$$\frac{dy}{dx} = e^{u \ln a}\frac{d}{dx}(u \ln a)$$

$$= e^{u \ln a} \ln a \frac{du}{dx}$$

$$= a^u \ln a \frac{du}{dx}.$$

Thus the derivative of a^u is given by

XXIV $$\frac{d}{dx}a^u = a^u \ln a \frac{du}{dx},$$

or, alternatively, by Formula 4(i), p. 507,

XXIVa $$\frac{d}{dx}a^u = \frac{a^u}{\log_a e}\frac{du}{dx}.$$

Comparing XXIV or XXIVa with XXII, we note that the differentiation formula for an exponential function is simplest when e is the base. Moreover, if the base is not e, the derivative nevertheless involves e.

54. Differentiation of Logarithmic Functions. We now seek the derivative with respect to x of the **logarithmic function** ln u, where u is a differentiable function of x. Letting

$$y = \ln u,$$

so that

$$e^y = u,$$

and differentiating implicitly, we obtain, by XXII of the preceding article,

$$e^y \frac{dy}{dx} = \frac{du}{dx}.$$

Hence

$$\frac{dy}{dx} = \frac{1}{e^y}\frac{du}{dx} = \frac{1}{u}\frac{du}{dx}.$$

That is,

XXV
$$\frac{d}{dx}\ln u = \frac{1}{u}\frac{du}{dx}.$$

If in particular $u = x$, we get the very simple formula.

XXVI
$$\frac{d}{dx}\ln x = \frac{1}{x}.$$

Consider next a general logarithmic function $\log_a u$, where u is a differentiable function of x and the base a is any positive constant other than unity, and let

$$y = \log_a u,$$

or equivalently, by Formula 4(h), p. 507,

$$y = \log_a e \ln u.$$

Differentiating by XXV, we find

$$\frac{dy}{dx} = \log_a e \frac{1}{u}\frac{du}{dx}.$$

That is,

XXVII
$$\frac{d}{dx}\log_a u = \frac{\log_a e}{u}\frac{du}{dx} = \frac{1}{u \ln a}\frac{du}{dx}.$$

Comparison of XXV and XXVII shows that the use of e as a base results in the simplest formula for differentiating logarithmic functions.

In the preceding article a similar conclusion was reached with regard to exponential functions. We shall therefore most frequently employ e as the base for both logarithmic and exponential functions.

Example 1. Find $\dfrac{dy}{dx}$ if $y = e^{\sin 3x}$.

Differentiating by XXII, Art. 53, we obtain

$$\frac{dy}{dx} = e^{\sin 3x}\,\frac{d}{dx}\,\sin 3x$$

$$= 3e^{\sin 3x}\cos 3x.$$

Example 2. Find $\dfrac{dy}{dx}$ if $y = \ln \sqrt[5]{\dfrac{(1 - x^2)^3}{(1 + x^2)^4}}$.

We first simplify the given expression by the use of Formulas 4(*d*), (*b*), and (*c*) p. 507, obtaining

$$y = \tfrac{1}{5}[3 \ln (1 - x^2) - 4 \ln (1 + x^2)].$$

Next we differentiate by XXV, and find

$$\frac{dy}{dx} = \frac{1}{5}\left[\frac{3}{1 - x^2}\,\frac{d}{dx}\,(1 - x^2) - \frac{4}{1 + x^2}\,\frac{d}{dx}\,(1 + x^2)\right]$$

$$= \frac{1}{5}\left[\frac{-6x}{1 - x^2} - \frac{8x}{1 + x^2}\right]$$

$$= \frac{2x(x^2 - 7)}{5(1 - x^4)}.$$

PROBLEMS

Differentiate each of the functions in Problems 1–23.

1. $e^{\frac{1}{x}}$.
2. 10^{-x^2}.
3. $e^{\tan^{-1} x}$.
4. $a^{\sin x}$.
5. $x^2 e^{3x}$.
6. $\dfrac{a}{2}\left(e^{\frac{x}{a}} + e^{-\frac{x}{a}}\right)$.
7. $e^{-2x} \cos 3x$.
8. $\log_a (e^x + e^{-x})$.
9. $\ln (2x + 3)^2$.
10. $\ln \dfrac{x^2 - 9}{x^2 + 9}$.
11. $\ln \dfrac{e^{2x} + 1}{e^{2x} - 1}$.
12. $\ln (x \sin x + \cos x)$.
13. $\ln \dfrac{(e^x + 1)^2}{e^x - 1}$.

14. $\ln \sqrt{\dfrac{1 - \cos x}{1 + \cos x}}$.
15. $e^{\sin^2 2x}$.
16. $\ln \dfrac{(x + 2)^3}{(x^2 + 1)^4}$.
17. $\ln \dfrac{\sqrt{x + 4} + 2}{\sqrt{x + 4} - 2}$.
18. $\ln (x^3 \sqrt{1 + x^2})$.
19. $a^{\sqrt{4 - x^2}}$.
20. $\dfrac{\ln (2 - x)}{e^{2 - x}}$.
21. e^{e^x}.
22. $(e^e)^x$.
23. e^{x^e}.

24. If $y = ae^{bx}$, where a and b are constants, show that

$$\frac{dy}{dx} - by = 0.$$

NOTE: The equation to be verified involves a derivative and is known as a **differential equation.** The function y is said to be a **solution** of this differential equation.

25. Show that $y = e^x + e^{-x}$ is a solution of the differential equation $\dfrac{d^2y}{dx^2} - y = 0$.

26. Show that $y = 2e^{\sin^{-1} x}$ is a solution of the differential equation

$$(1 - x^2)\frac{d^2y}{dx^2} - x\frac{dy}{dx} - y = 0.$$

27. Show that $y = e^{x^2-x} - e^{x^2}$ is a solution of the differential equation

$$\frac{d^2y}{dx^2} - 4x\frac{dy}{dx} + (4x^2 - 3)y - e^{x^2} = 0.$$

28. Show that $y = x \sin (\ln x) + x \ln x$ is a solution of the differential equation

$$x^2\frac{d^2y}{dx^2} - x\frac{dy}{dx} + 2y - x \ln x = 0.$$

29. Show that $y = e^{-x} (\sin x + \cos x)$ is a solution of the differential equation

$$\frac{d^4y}{dx^4} + 4y = 0.$$

30. Find the maximum value of the function $\dfrac{\ln x}{x}$.

31. Find the maximum and minimum values of the function x^2e^{-4x}.

32. Investigate the function $x^3e^{-6x^2}$ for maximum and minimum values.

55. Graphs of Exponential and Logarithmic Functions.

The differentiation formulas developed in the last two articles facilitate the discussion of equations involving exponential and logarithmic functions and hence are of assistance in obtaining the graphs of such equations.

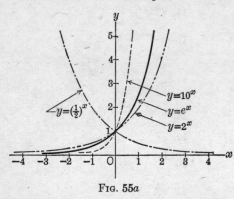

FIG. 55a

Exponential Curves. The graph of the equation $y = e^x$ lies wholly above the x-axis, since e^x is positive for all finite values of x. Moreover, since $\lim\limits_{x \to -\infty} e^x = 0$, the negative x-axis is an asymptote (see Art. 74) of the curve. Obviously $y = 1$ when $x = 0$, so that the curve crosses the y-axis at $(0, 1)$.

Observing that the derivative

$$\frac{dy}{dx} = e^x = y$$

is positive for all values of x, we conclude that the curve rises from left to right, the slope at any point being equal to the ordinate. There are thus no critical points, and since $\frac{d^2y}{dx^2}$ also equals e^x and is everywhere positive, the curve is concave upward.

The above discussion fixes the general appearance of the graph; it is desirable, however, to locate a few points, and for this purpose a table of powers of e may be consulted.

The graph of $y = e^x$ is shown in Fig. 55a; for purposes of comparison, the graphs of $y = 10^x$, $y = 2^x$, and $y = (\frac{1}{2})^x$, which are likewise special cases of $y = a^x$, are shown in the same figure. A detailed investigation of the last three curves is left to the student; it may be noted in passing, however, that the graph of $y = (\frac{1}{2})^x$ is the reflection of that of $y = 2^x$ in the y-axis, since $(\frac{1}{2})^x = 2^{-x}$ and thus to every point (x, y) on either of these curves there corresponds a point $(-x, y)$ on the other.

Logarithmic Curves. Since the equation $y = \ln x$ may be written in the form $x = e^y$, the graph of $y = \ln x$ may be obtained from that of $y = e^x$ by an interchange of x and y, and is thus a reflection of the latter curve in the line $y = x$. That this reflection results in a curve lying wholly to the right of the y-axis is consistent with the fact that only positive numbers have real logarithms.

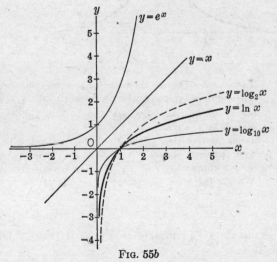

Alternatively, the graph of $y = \ln x$ may be plotted with the aid of a table of natural logarithms.

In Fig. 55b is shown the graph of $y = \ln x$,

Fig. 55b

together with the graphs of $y = \log_2 x$, $y = \log_{10} x$, $y = x$, and $y = e^x$.

Other exponential and logarithmic curves will now be considered.

Example 1. Discuss the equation $y = e^{-x^2}$ and sketch its graph.

The curve is symmetrical with respect to the y-axis (cf. Art. 74), and approaches the x-axis asymptotically for, as the absolute value of x increases indefinitely, y tends toward zero.

On differentiating, we find

$$\frac{dy}{dx} = -2xe^{-x^2}$$

and

$$\frac{d^2y}{dx^2} = -2e^{-x^2} + 4x^2e^{-x^2}$$

$$= 2e^{-x^2}(2x^2 - 1).$$

There is thus a critical point at $(0, 1)$; this is a maximum point, for $\frac{d^2y}{dx^2}$ is negative when $x = 0$. Since $\frac{d^2y}{dx^2}$ undergoes a change of sign as x passes through the values $\pm\sqrt{\frac{1}{2}} = \pm 0.707$ which satisfy the equation $2x^2 - 1 = 0$, these are the abscissas of points of inflection; the corresponding ordinate in each case is $e^{-\frac{1}{2}} = 0.607$.

From these considerations we at once obtain the graph (Fig. 55c).

A generalization of the function just discussed, namely, $\dfrac{k}{\sqrt{\pi}} e^{-k^2x^2}$, where k is constant, is called the **error function** and plays a prominent rôle in the theory of probability.

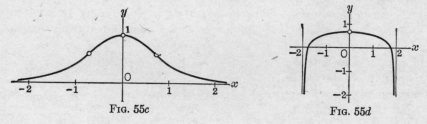

FIG. 55c   FIG. 55d

Example 2. Discuss the equation $y = \ln\sqrt{4 - x^2}$, and sketch its graph.

The curve is symmetrical with respect to the y-axis. It intersects the x-axis at points whose abscissas are $\pm\sqrt{3} = \pm 1.732$, and the y-axis at the point whose ordinate is $\ln 2 = 0.693$.

From the fact that y is real only for $-2 < x < 2$, it follows that the curve lies between the vertical lines $x = -2$ and $x = 2$; moreover, these lines are asymptotes, since, as x approaches 2 or -2, y becomes negatively infinite.

Writing the given equation as $y = \frac{1}{2}\ln(4 - x^2)$, we differentiate and find

$$\frac{dy}{dx} = -\frac{x}{4 - x^2},$$

so that there is a critical point at $(0, \ln 2)$; another differentiation yields

$$\frac{d^2y}{dx^2} = -\frac{4 + x^2}{(4 - x^2)^2}.$$

Since the second derivative is negative for all values of x, the curve is everywhere concave downward, and the critical point at $(0, \ln 2)$ is a maximum.

The sketch is shown in Fig. 55d.

Example 3.   Sketch the curve $y = e^{-x} \sin x$ for $x \geqq 0$.

The curve cuts the x-axis at points whose abscissas are roots of the equation $\sin x = 0$, that is, at $x = 0, \pi, 2\pi, \cdots$. Since $\sin x$ attains its maximum value 1 for $x = \dfrac{\pi}{2}, \dfrac{5\pi}{2}, \dfrac{9\pi}{2}, \cdots$, and attains its minimum value -1 for $x = \dfrac{3\pi}{2}, \dfrac{7\pi}{2}, \dfrac{11\pi}{2}, \cdots$, the curve $y = e^{-x} \sin x$ lies between the exponential curves $y = e^{-x}$ and $y = -e^{-x}$ touching one or the other of these curves at points whose abscissas are odd multiples of $\dfrac{\pi}{2}$.

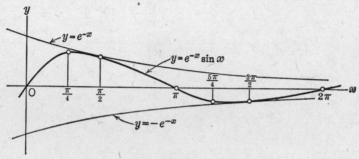

Fig. 55e

The maximum and minimum points of the curve $y = e^{-x} \sin x$ do not, however, coincide with the points of contact with the above-mentioned exponential curves. For equating the derivative

$$\frac{dy}{dx} = e^{-x}(\cos x - \sin x)$$

to zero, we find as the condition that y be a maximum or minimum

$$\tan x = 1,$$

whence

$$x = \frac{\pi}{4}, \frac{5\pi}{4}, \frac{9\pi}{4}, \cdots,$$

the corresponding values of y being

$$y = \frac{\sqrt{2}}{2} e^{-\frac{\pi}{4}}, \ -\frac{\sqrt{2}}{2} e^{-\frac{5\pi}{4}}, \ \frac{\sqrt{2}}{2} e^{-\frac{9\pi}{4}}, \cdots.$$

Thus every maximum point of the curve $y = e^{-x} \sin x$ is located $\dfrac{\pi}{4}$ units to the left of a point of contact of this curve with the curve $y = e^{-x}$; a similar situation holds with respect to the minimum points of $y = e^{-x} \sin x$ and the points of contact with $y = -e^{-x}$.

The graph is shown in Fig. 55e.

The equation of this curve in suitably generalized form occurs in mechanics in connection with damped vibration.

PROBLEMS

In each of the following problems, discuss the given equation and plot its curve:

1. $y = e^{-x}$.

2. $y = e^{x^2}$.

3. $y = xe^x$

4. $y = xe^{-x}$.

5. $y = \dfrac{e^x + e^{-x}}{2}$.

6. $y = \dfrac{e^x - e^{-x}}{2}$.

7. $y = \dfrac{e^x - e^{-x}}{e^x + e^{-x}}$.

8. $y = \dfrac{e^x + e^{-x}}{e^x - e^{-x}}$.

9. $y = e^{\frac{1}{x}}$.

10. $y = e^{-\frac{1}{x}}$.

11. $y = \ln 3x$.

12. $y = \ln x^2$.

13. $y = \ln \dfrac{1}{x^2}$.

14. $y = \ln \sqrt{x^2 - 4}$.

15. $y = x^2 e^{-x^2}$.

16. $y = x^3 e^{-8x^2}$.

17. $y = \ln \sin x$.

18. $y = \ln \cos x$.

19. $y = \dfrac{\ln x}{x}$.

20. $y = e^{-x} \cos x$ (for $x \geqq 0$).

21. $y = e^{-x^2} \sin \dfrac{\pi x}{2}$.

22. $y = \ln \dfrac{e^x + e^{-x}}{2}$.

56. Logarithmic Differentiation. In obtaining the derivatives of certain kinds of functions, such as complicated products and quotients, and functions of the type u^v, where u and v are both variable, it is best to take the logarithm before differentiating. This process is called **logarithmic differentiation.**

Example 1. Find $\dfrac{dy}{dx}$ for $y = \dfrac{(1 - x^2)^{\frac{2}{3}}(2 + x)^{\frac{3}{2}}}{(8 - x^3)^{\frac{5}{4}}}$.

Differentiating

$$\ln y = \tfrac{2}{3} \ln (1 - x^2) + \tfrac{3}{2} \ln (2 + x) - \tfrac{5}{4} \ln (8 - x^3),$$

we obtain

$$\frac{1}{y}\frac{dy}{dx} = -\frac{4x}{3(1 - x^2)} + \frac{3}{2(2 + x)} + \frac{15x^2}{4(8 - x^3)}$$

$$= \frac{144 - 256x - 182x^2 + 27x^3 - 58x^4 - 11x^5}{12(1 - x^2)(2 + x)(8 - x^3)},$$

whence

$$\frac{dy}{dx} = \frac{(2 + x)^{\frac{1}{2}}(144 - 256x - 182x^2 + 27x^3 - 58x^4 - 11x^5)}{12(1 - x^2)^{\frac{1}{3}}(8 - x^3)^{\frac{9}{4}}}.$$

Example 2. Find $\dfrac{dy}{dx}$ for $y = x^x$.

Differentiating

$$\ln y = x \ln x,$$

we obtain

$$\frac{1}{y}\frac{dy}{dx} = 1 + \ln x,$$

whence

$$\frac{dy}{dx} = (1 + \ln x)x^x.$$

Derivative of u^n for any n. By means of logarithmic differentiation we can readily show that, if u is a differentiable function of x, and n is any constant,

$$\frac{d}{dx} u^n = nu^{n-1} \frac{du}{dx}.$$

For, if
$$y = u^n,$$
then
$$\ln y = n \ln u$$
and
$$\frac{1}{y} \frac{dy}{dx} = \frac{n}{u} \frac{du}{dx}.$$

Hence
$$\frac{dy}{dx} = nu^{n-1} \frac{du}{dx}.$$

This result was proved in Art. 41 for rational n, a restriction which is here removed.

PROBLEMS

1. If $y = u^v$, where u and v are differentiable functions of x, prove by logarithmic differentiation that

$$\frac{dy}{dx} = vu^{v-1} \frac{du}{dx} + u^v \ln u \frac{dv}{dx}.$$

In each of Problems 2–10, find the derivative of the given function by logarithmic differentiation or by using the result of Problem 1.

2. x^{x^2}.

3. $x^{\frac{1}{x}}$.

4. $x^{\sqrt[3]{x}}$.

5. $x^{\cos x}$.

6. $x^{\tan^{-1} e^x}$.

7. $x^{e^{-x^2}}$.

8. $(\sin x)^{e^x}$.

9. $x^{\ln x}$.

10. $(\tan x)^{\ln x}$.

In each of Problems 11–16, differentiate the given function logarithmically.

11. $x\sqrt{1 - x} \sqrt{2 - x}$.

12. $\dfrac{\sqrt[3]{1 - x^3}}{\sqrt{1 + x^2}}$.

13. $\dfrac{(1 - x^7)^{\frac{3}{7}}}{(1 - 2x^5)^{\frac{4}{5}}}$.

14. $\dfrac{x^2 \sqrt{1 - x^2}}{\sqrt{1 - 2x^2}}$.

15. $\dfrac{\sqrt{1 - 2x}}{x^2(1 - 3x)^3}$.

16. $\dfrac{xe^{-3x}}{\sqrt{1 + x^2}}$.

57. Summary of Formulas. The following list comprises the more important formulas derived in this chapter:

X $\qquad \dfrac{d}{dx} \sin u = \cos u \dfrac{du}{dx}.$

XI $\qquad \dfrac{d}{dx} \cos u = - \sin u \dfrac{du}{dx}.$

XII $\qquad \dfrac{d}{dx} \tan u = \sec^2 u \dfrac{du}{dx}.$

XIII $\qquad \dfrac{d}{dx} \cot u = - \csc^2 u \dfrac{du}{dx}.$

XIV $\qquad \dfrac{d}{dx} \sec u = \sec u \tan u \dfrac{du}{dx}.$

XV $\qquad \dfrac{d}{dx} \csc u = - \csc u \cot u \dfrac{du}{dx}.$

XVIa $\qquad \dfrac{d}{dx} \sin^{-1} u = \dfrac{1}{\sqrt{1 - u^2}} \dfrac{du}{dx}, \quad -\dfrac{\pi}{2} < \sin^{-1} u < \dfrac{\pi}{2}.$

XVIII $\qquad \dfrac{d}{dx} \tan^{-1} u = \dfrac{1}{1 + u^2} \dfrac{du}{dx}.$

XXII $\qquad \dfrac{d}{dx} e^u = e^u \dfrac{du}{dx}.$

XXIV $\qquad \dfrac{d}{dx} a^u = a^u \ln a \dfrac{du}{dx}.$

XXV $\qquad \dfrac{d}{dx} \ln u = \dfrac{1}{u} \dfrac{du}{dx}.$

XXVII $\qquad \dfrac{d}{dx} \log_a u = \dfrac{\log_a e}{u} \dfrac{du}{dx}.$

In differential notation (cf. (6), Art. 24) these formulas are as follows:

X' $\qquad d \sin u = \cos u \, du.$

XI' $\qquad d \cos u = - \sin u \, du.$

XII' $\qquad d \tan u = \sec^2 u \, du.$

XIII' $\qquad d \cot u = - \csc^2 u \, du.$

XIV'　　　　$d \sec u = \sec u \tan u \, du.$

XV'　　　　$d \csc u = - \csc u \cot u \, du.$

XVIa'　　　$d \sin^{-1} u = \dfrac{du}{\sqrt{1 - u^2}}, \quad -\dfrac{\pi}{2} < \sin^{-1} u < \dfrac{\pi}{2}.$

XVIII'　　　$d \tan^{-1} u = \dfrac{du}{1 + u^2}.$

XXII'　　　$de^u = e^u du.$

XXIV'　　　$da^u = a^u \ln a \, du.$

XXV'　　　$d \ln u = \dfrac{du}{u}.$

XXVII'　　　$d \log_a u = \log_a e \, \dfrac{du}{u}.$

CHAPTER VI

FURTHER APPLICATIONS OF DERIVATIVES

58. Related Time-Rates. Suppose that two variables, v and w, both depending on the time t, are related by a given equation. Then if this equation is differentiated with respect to the time, another equation is obtained involving linearly the time-rates of change of v and w, namely, $\dfrac{dv}{dt}$ and $\dfrac{dw}{dt}$, and also, in general, involving v and w. Hence, if for a particular instant the values of v, w, and one of the rates, say $\dfrac{dv}{dt}$ are known, the corresponding value of the other rate $\dfrac{dw}{dt}$ is determined.

Since $\dfrac{dv}{dt}$ and $\dfrac{dw}{dt}$ are connected by an equation they are called **related time-rates,** or simply **related rates.**

The case of three or more related rates presents no additional difficulties. Thus if the values of the variables and the rates of change of all of them but one are known for a particular time, the unknown rate of change may be found by substituting these values in the equation resulting from the differentiation of the relation between the variables.

It should be remarked that an equation relating the variables is frequently not given, but must be obtained from the conditions of the problem.

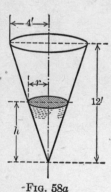

Example 1. Water escapes at the rate of 8 cu. ft./min. from an inverted conical container whose depth is 12 ft. and whose base is a circle of radius 4 ft. At what rate is the level of the water sinking when there are 6 ft. of water in the container?

If r is the base-radius of the conical mass of water in the container at any time, and h is its altitude, then the volume of the water is

$$V = \tfrac{1}{3}\pi r^2 h.$$

By similar triangles (Fig. 58a) we obtain

$$r = \tfrac{1}{3}h,$$

-Fig. 58a

whence

$$h^3 = \frac{27}{\pi} V.$$

This is the relation between the variables h and V.   On differentiating it implicitly with respect to the time, we find

$$3h^2 \frac{dh}{dt} = \frac{27}{\pi} \frac{dV}{dt},$$

so that

$$\frac{dh}{dt} = \frac{9}{\pi h^2} \frac{dV}{dt}.$$

Now $\dfrac{dV}{dt} = -8$ cu. ft./min.; hence when $h = 6$ ft.

$$\frac{dh}{dt} = -\frac{2}{\pi} \text{ ft./min.}$$

Therefore at the instant specified the surface of the water is sinking at the rate of $\dfrac{2}{\pi}$ ft./min.

Example 2.   One end of a ladder 26 ft. long slides down a vertical wall while the other end moves along a horizontal plane at the rate of 2 ft./sec.   What is the speed of the upper end of the ladder when the lower end is 24 ft. from the wall?

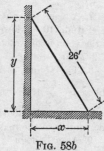

FIG. 58b

Denoting the variable distances from the bottom of the wall to the lower and upper ends of the ladder by x and y, respectively, we have (see Fig. 58b)

$$x^2 + y^2 = 26^2.$$

Differentiating with respect to the time, and dividing by 2, we obtain

$$x \frac{dx}{dt} + y \frac{dy}{dt} = 0.$$

Since $\dfrac{dx}{dt} = 2$, and $y = 10$ when $x = 24$, we find on substituting, that at the instant under consideration

$$\frac{dy}{dt} = -4.8.$$

Thus the upper end of the ladder is moving downward at the rate of 4.8 ft./sec.

PROBLEMS

1. A standard cell has an electromotive force (E) of 1.2 volts.   If the resistance (R) of the circuit is increasing at the rate of 0.03 ohm/sec., at what rate is the current (I, in amperes) changing at the instant when the resistance is 6 ohms?   Assume Ohm's Law $E = RI$.

2. The volume of a right circular cone is constant.   If the base-radius decreases at the rate of 2 in./sec., how fast is the altitude changing at the instant when the altitude is 12 in. and the base-radius 8 in.?

3. Sand is poured onto the ground at the rate of 3 cu. ft./min. and forms a pile whose shape is that of a right circular cone the altitude of which is half the base-radius.   How fast is the altitude increasing when the base-radius is 4 ft.?

4. If the quantity of wood in a tree varies as the cube of the diameter, and the latter increases uniformly, find the ratio of the rates of increase of the quantities of wood in two trees whose diameters are 6 in. and 2 ft., respectively.

5. The focal length (f) of a certain lens is 20 in. If the object whose image is formed by the lens is being moved toward the lens at the rate of 2 in./sec., at what rate is the image receding when the object is 60 in. from the lens? The distances (u and v, respectively) of the object and image from the lens are related to the focal length by the equation

$$\frac{1}{u} + \frac{1}{v} = \frac{1}{f}.$$

6. A conical funnel is 12 in. across the top and 8 in. deep. A liquid is flowing in at the rate of 8 cu. in./sec., and flowing out at the rate of 5 cu. in./sec. At what rate is the surface of the liquid rising when the liquid fills the funnel to a height of 6 in.?

7. A reservoir containing water has the shape of a frustum of a right circular cone of altitude 10 ft., lower base-radius 10 ft., and upper base-radius 15 ft. How fast is the volume of water increasing when the water is 6 ft. deep and rising at the rate of 2 ft./hr.?

8. The volume of the largest right circular cylinder which can be inscribed in a sphere is $\dfrac{1}{\sqrt{3}}$ times the volume of the sphere. If the radius of a sphere is 18 in., and is decreasing at the rate of $\frac{1}{9}$ in./sec., find the instantaneous rate of change of the volume of the maximum inscribed right circular cylinder.

9. As a balloon is inflated it maintains the shape of an ellipsoid of revolution whose longest axis is twice as long as each of the shorter axes. If the volume increases at the rate of 50 cu. ft./min., how fast is the length of the longest axis increasing when 20 ft. long? The volume of an ellipsoid is $\frac{4}{3}\pi abc$, where a, b, c are the lengths of the semi-axes.

10. Air expands isothermally in accordance with Boyle's Law

$$pv = \text{constant},$$

where p is the pressure and v the volume. If at a certain time the volume is 10 cu. in., while the pressure is 100 lb./sq. in. and decreasing at the rate of 2 lb./sq. in. per second, find the corresponding rate of change of the volume.

11. A certain mass of air is expanding adiabatically in accordance with the law

$$pv^{1.4} = \text{constant}.$$

At a particular instant the pressure is 40 lb./sq. in., while the volume is 32 cu. in. and increasing at the rate of 0.05 cu. in. per second. Find the rate at which the pressure is changing.

12. A man whose height is 6 ft. is moving directly away from a lamp-post at the rate of 5 ft./sec. At what rate is his shadow lengthening, if the lamp is 30 ft. above the ground?

13. Under the conditions of the preceding problem, find, for the instant when the shadow is 8 ft. long, the rate at which the end of the shadow is moving away from the lamp.

14. A man is walking at the rate of 5 mi./hr. toward the base of a tower 80 ft. high. At what rate is he approaching the top of the tower when he is 60 ft. from its base?

15. A kite is at a height of 144 ft., and there are 150 ft. of cord out. If the kite is moving horizontally at the rate of 5 ft./sec. away from the person who flies it, how fast is the cord being paid out?

16. A boat is pulled in by means of a rope which is wound at the rate of 12 ft./sec. about a windlass 30 ft. above the level at which the rope is attached to the boat. How fast is the boat moving at the instant when 78 ft. of rope are out?

17. A ship leaves a port at noon and sails west at the rate of 9 mi./hr. Another ship leaves the same port at 1 P.M., and sails north at the rate of 12 mi./hr. How fast are the ships separating at 2 P.M.?

18. A man is walking at the rate of 4 ft./sec. across a bridge 36 ft. above the water level. A man in a rowboat makes 12 ft./sec. downstream. If the boat was initially directly under the first man, how rapidly are the men separating at the end of 12 sec.?

19. A taut rope ABC, 42 ft. long, passes over a peg B 15 ft. above the horizontal line along which the ends A and C are constrained to move. If C moves at the rate of 17 ft./sec. away from E, the point on AC directly below B, find the speed of A when C is 8 ft. from E.

20. A weight is attached to one end of an 85-ft. rope passing over a small pulley 45 ft. above the ground. A man whose hand is 5 ft. above the ground grasps the other end of the rope and walks away at the rate of 4.1 ft./sec. How fast is the weight rising when the man is 9 ft. from the point directly below the pulley?

21. The speed v (feet per second) of a certain bullet which has penetrated a block of wood to a depth of x (feet) is given by

$$v = 400 \sqrt{1 - 3x}.$$

Find the rate at which the speed is decreasing.

22. Four rods, each 10 in. long, are fastened together with hinges so as to form a rhombus. If the length of one of the diagonals is increasing at the rate of 2 in./sec., at what rate is the area of the rhombus changing when this diagonal is 12 in. long?

23. In a certain engine, the distance x (feet) between the center lines of the driving-shaft and the cross-head is given by

$$x = \cos \theta + \sqrt{16.5 - \sin^2 \theta},$$

where θ is the angle between the crank and the path of the cross-head. If θ increases at the constant rate of 60 radians/sec., find the speed of the cross-head when $\theta = \dfrac{\pi}{4}$.

24. Each of two sides of a triangle increases at the rate of 3 in./sec., and the included angle decreases at the rate of $\frac{1}{10}$ radian/sec. At what rate is the area of the triangle changing when the two sides are each 15 in. long and the third side 18 in.?

25. The two arms of a double gate at a grade crossing rotate upward about a common axis at the rate of 6 radians/min. If the arm over the sidewalk is 8 ft. long and that over the roadway 15 ft. long, at what rate is the distance between their upper ends changing when each arm makes an angle of 45° with the horizontal?

26. A point P moves on the curve $y = x^3$ in such a way that its abscissa is increasing at the uniform rate of 2 units per second. At what rate is the inclination of the tangent to the curve at P changing as P passes through the point $(1, 1)$?

27. The relation between altitude above sea-level (h feet) and atmospheric pressure (p pounds per square foot) is, at a certain time and place, given by the formula

$$p = 2100e^{-0.000037h}.$$

To an observer in a balloon which rises at the rate of 20 ft./sec., at what rate is the pressure changing when the altitude of the balloon is 6000 ft.?

59. Differential of Arc in Rectangular Coördinates. Given the curve $y = f(x)$ and the points $P(x, y)$ and $Q(x + \Delta x, y + \Delta y)$ on the curve (Fig. 59). Then Δx (or dx), Δy, and dy are represented geo-

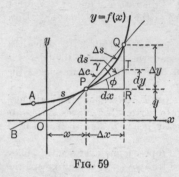

metrically by the segments PR, RQ, and RT, respectively, where PR and RQ are parallel to the coördinate axes and T is the intersection of RQ with the tangent line to the curve at P (cf. Art. 24).

FIG. 59

Choosing a point A on the curve to serve as an origin for the measurement of arcs, let us denote the arc AP by s. Evidently s is a function of the position of the point P, and therefore a function of x. When x is given the increment $\Delta x = PR$, the corresponding increment of s is the arc PQ, which we accordingly designate as Δs. It remains to obtain an expression for ds, the differential of s, in terms of dx and dy, and to interpret ds geometrically.

Evidently

$$(\text{chord } PQ)^2 = (\Delta x)^2 + (\Delta y)^2,$$

$$(\text{arc } PQ)^2 = (\Delta s)^2 = \frac{(\Delta s)^2}{(\text{chord } PQ)^2} [(\Delta x)^2 + (\Delta y)^2],$$

and

$$\left(\frac{\Delta s}{\Delta x}\right)^2 = \left(\frac{\Delta s}{\text{chord } PQ}\right)^2 \left[1 + \left(\frac{\Delta y}{\Delta x}\right)^2\right].$$

Passing to the limit as Δx approaches zero, using the definition of a derivative, and noting that $\lim\limits_{\Delta x \to 0} \left|\dfrac{\Delta s}{\text{chord } PQ}\right| = 1$,[*] we obtain

(1)
$$\left(\frac{ds}{dx}\right)^2 = 1 + \left(\frac{dy}{dx}\right)^2,$$

* This may be seen as follows: Denoting the length of the chord PQ by Δc, we have, when $|\Delta s|$ is sufficiently small, $\Delta c < |\Delta s| < PT + TQ$. Applying the sine law (Formula 20(a), p. 509) to the triangle PTQ, in which the angle at P is denoted by γ, we find that $PT = \dfrac{\cos (\phi + \gamma)}{\cos \phi} \Delta c$, where ϕ is the angle TPR. Moreover, by Art. 24, $TQ = \eta \Delta x$, where η tends to zero with Δx. Since $\Delta x = \cos (\phi + \gamma)\Delta c$, the above inequality, after division by Δc, becomes $1 < \dfrac{|\Delta s|}{\Delta c} < \dfrac{\cos (\phi + \gamma)}{\cos \phi} (1 + \eta \cos \phi)$, the last member of which approaches unity as Δx approaches zero because the limits of both γ and η are zero. Hence $\lim\limits_{\Delta x \to 0} \dfrac{|\Delta s|}{\Delta c} = 1$.

whence

(2) $$(ds)^2 = (dx)^2 + (dy)^2.$$

Another form of (1) is

(3) $$ds = \pm \sqrt{1 + \left(\frac{dy}{dx}\right)^2}\, dx,$$

where the plus or minus sign is used according as s increases with increasing x (as in Fig. 59), or decreases.

Since, in Fig. 59, $(PT)^2 = (dx)^2 + (dy)^2$, a relation which may be identified with (2), we conclude that the differential of arc ds is represented by the segment PT. As a matter of fact ds and Δs, which are both infinitesimal as Δx approaches zero, are related to each other as the differential and increment of any function of x, that is to say, they differ by an infinitesimal of higher order[*] than either of them. Thus, for a sufficiently small numerical value of Δx, PT (or ds) approximates in length the arc PQ (or Δs).

From Fig. 59, in which $dx = PR$, $dy = RT$, $ds = PT$, we immediately obtain

(4) $$\frac{dx}{ds} = \cos \phi,$$

(5) $$\frac{dy}{ds} = \sin \phi,$$

and

(6) $$\frac{dy}{dx} = \tan \phi,$$

where ϕ is the angle measured counterclockwise from PR to that direction along the tangent line which corresponds to increasing s. The angle ϕ is shown as the angle RPT in Fig. 59, because s has been so defined as to increase from P to Q; if s decreased, we should have to take as ϕ the counterclockwise angle RPR.

60. Vectors. A **vector quantity** is defined as a quantity having a magnitude, a direction, and a sense, and may therefore be represented by a directed line segment whose length, interpreted in terms of a scale, gives the numerical magnitude of the vector quantity and whose direction and sense agree with those of the vector quantity, the sense being indicated by an arrowhead placed at one end of the line segment. Such a

---

[*] For, by the preceding footnote, we have $\dfrac{ds}{\Delta s} = \dfrac{ds}{\Delta c} \cdot \dfrac{\Delta c}{\Delta s} = \left| \dfrac{\cos (\phi + \gamma)}{\cos \phi} \cdot \dfrac{\Delta c}{\Delta s} \right|$, whence $\lim\limits_{\Delta x \to 0} \dfrac{ds}{\Delta s} = 1$. Then by Theorem 1, Art. 25, the difference $\Delta s - ds$ is an infinitesimal of higher order than ds or Δs.

directed line segment is called a **vector**. The most familiar example of a vector quantity is a force.   Thus if a body is pulled up an inclined plane by a force of 2 lb. parallel to the plane, the force may be represented by the vector of Fig. 60a, whose length is twice that of an arbitrarily chosen unit.

In this book a vector quantity will be symbolized by a letter in heavy type surmounted by an arrow, as $\vec{u}$, $\vec{v}$, etc.

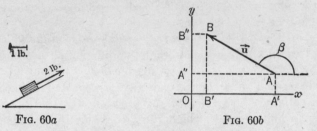

FIG. 60a FIG. 60b

Let the vector of Fig. 60b represent a vector quantity $\vec{u}$, whose magnitude, which is essentially positive, will be denoted by $|\vec{u}|$.   To simplify the language, let us overlook the distinction between vector and vector quantity and say that $\vec{u}$ is the vector extending from A to B and that $|\vec{u}|$ is the length of AB.   Let us project $\vec{u}$ on the axes shown, obtaining the segments $A'B'$ and $A''B''$.   The lengths of these segments, with appropriate signs, are called the **components** of $\vec{u}$ along the x-axis and the y-axis, or more simply the x-component and the y-component of $\vec{u}$, and denoted, respectively, by the symbols u_x and u_y; the former in this example is clearly negative.   If β is the angle, measured in a counterclockwise sense, from the positive x-axis to the direction of $\vec{u}$, we have

(1) $$u_x = |\vec{u}| \cos \beta$$

and

(2) $$u_y = |\vec{u}| \sin \beta.$$

Moreover,

(3) $$|\vec{u}|^2 = u_x{}^2 + u_y{}^2$$

and

(4) $$\tan \beta = \frac{u_y}{u_x}.$$

Suppose that the components of a vector $\vec{u}$ in the xy-plane change with the time t.   Then if $\vec{w}$ is another vector whose components are the time-derivatives of the respective components of $\vec{u}$, we call $\vec{w}$ the time-derivative of $\vec{u}$ and therefore designate it as $\dfrac{d\vec{u}}{dt}$. That is, if two vectors $\vec{u}$ and $\vec{w}$ are so related that

(5)
$$w_x = \frac{du_x}{dt},$$

and

(6)
$$w_y = \frac{du_y}{dt},$$

we write

(7)
$$\vec{w} = \frac{d\vec{u}}{dt}.$$

Here we have assumed that the vector $\vec{u}$ throughout its change remains in the xy-plane.

It should be remarked that (3), or its extension in three dimensions,

$$|\vec{u}|^2 = u_x{}^2 + u_y{}^2 + u_z{}^2,$$

is valid for any choice of coördinate axes, and that the derivative $\dfrac{d\vec{u}}{dt}$ of a variable vector $\vec{u}$ is independent of the orientation of the axes.

61. Components of Velocity and Acceleration. The **velocity** at any instant of a moving particle is the vector $\vec{v}$ whose direction is the instantaneous direction of motion and whose magnitude $|\vec{v}|$ is the absolute value of the instantaneous speed v. Thus $|\vec{v}| = |v|$; or $|\vec{v}| = \pm v$ according as v is positive or negative.

Suppose, for example, that a particle moves toward the left along the plane curve of Fig. 61, and that $P(x, y)$ is its instantaneous position; further, let us choose the point A on the curve as the origin of arcs, and agree that arcs measured from A be positive or negative according as they extend to the right of A (as does the arc $s = AP$) or to the left.

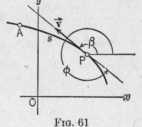

Then the speed, $v = \dfrac{ds}{dt}$, of the particle is negative. The velocity $\vec{v}$, having the instantaneous direction of the motion, is tangent to the curve, and since the absolute value of $\vec{v}$ is positive, we have, in this case,

Fig. 61

$$|\vec{v}| = -v.$$

The components, v_x and v_y, of the velocity of a particle moving on a curve in the xy-plane satisfy (3), (1), and (2) of the preceding article; that is

(1) $$|\vec{v}|^2 = v^2 = v_x{}^2 + v_y{}^2,$$

(2) $$v_x = |\vec{v}| \cos \beta,$$

and

(3) $$v_y = |\vec{v}| \sin \beta,$$

where β is the angle (measured counterclockwise) from the positive x-axis to the direction of $\vec{v}$.

We shall next find expressions for v_x and v_y in terms of the speed v and the counterclockwise angle ϕ defined as in Art. 59. For this purpose we shall again use Fig. 61, where $|\vec{v}| = -v$, and $\beta = \phi - \pi$ so that $\cos \beta = -\cos \phi$ and $\sin \beta = -\sin \phi$. With these substitutions (2) and (3) become

(4) $$v_x = v \cos \phi$$

and

(5) $$v_y = v \sin \phi,$$

whence

(6) $$\frac{v_y}{v_x} = \tan \phi,$$

or, by (6), Art. 59,

(7) $$\frac{v_y}{v_x} = \frac{dy}{dx}.$$

The student may verify the validity of (4) and (5) for rising as well as falling curves whether or not the direction of motion agrees with the chosen positive direction along the curve.

From (4) and (5), if we substitute $\dfrac{ds}{dt}$ for v and use (4) and (5), Art. 59, we readily find

(8) $$v_x = \frac{dx}{dt}$$

and

(9) $$v_y = \frac{dy}{dt}.$$

We defined (Art. 15) the **acceleration** of a particle moving along a straight line as the derivative of the speed with respect to the time. When a particle moves on a curve in the xy-plane, its acceleration is a vector $\vec{a}$ defined by the equation

$$\vec{a} = \frac{d\vec{v}}{dt}.$$

Hence by Art. 60, and by (8) and (9), the components of $\vec{a}$ are

$$(10) \qquad\qquad a_x = \frac{dv_x}{dt} = \frac{d^2x}{dt^2},$$

$$(11) \qquad\qquad a_y = \frac{dv_y}{dt} = \frac{d^2y}{dt^2}.$$

In accordance with (3) and (4), Art. 60,

$$(12) \qquad\qquad |\vec{a}|^2 = a_x{}^2 + a_y{}^2$$

and

$$(13) \qquad\qquad \tan \tau = \frac{a_y}{a_x},$$

where τ is the angle at which $\vec{a}$ is inclined to the x-axis.

Example. A particle moves toward the right on that part of the curve $y^2 = x^3$ (where x and y are in feet) which lies in the first quadrant. If the speed is constantly 5 ft./sec., find the components of the velocity and of the acceleration when the particle is at $(\frac{1}{4}, \frac{1}{8})$.

This is a problem on related rates (Art. 58).   From the equation $y = x^{\frac{3}{2}}$ we obtain

$$\frac{dy}{dt} = \frac{3}{2} x^{\frac{1}{2}} \frac{dx}{dt}.$$

Hence, when $x = \frac{1}{4}$, it follows from (8) and (9) that

$$v_y = \tfrac{3}{4} v_x.$$

Substituting this in (1), and recalling that by hypothesis $v^2 = 25$ and v_x is positive, we find

$$v_x = 4 \text{ ft./sec.},$$

whence

$$v_y = 3 \text{ ft./sec.}$$

A second differentiation gives

$$\frac{d^2y}{dt^2} = \frac{3}{4} x^{-\frac{1}{2}} \left(\frac{dx}{dt}\right)^2 + \frac{3}{2} x^{\frac{1}{2}} \frac{d^2x}{dt^2}.$$

Hence, when $x = \frac{1}{4}$ and $\dfrac{dx}{dt} = 4$, it follows from (10) and (11) that

$$(14) \qquad\qquad a_y = 24 + \tfrac{3}{4} a_x.$$

Differentiating both sides of the equation $v_x{}^2 + v_y{}^2 = 25$ implicitly with respect to the time, and dividing by 2 we obtain

$$v_x a_x + v_y a_y = 0,$$

whence, for $v_x = 4$ and $v_y = 3$,

$$(15) \qquad\qquad 4a_x + 3a_y = 0.$$

Solving (14) and (15) simultaneously, we arrive at the results

$$a_x = -11.52 \text{ ft./sec.}^2,$$

and

$$a_y = 15.36 \text{ ft./sec.}^2$$

62. Parametric Equations. If the coördinates, x and y, of a point on a curve are both expressed as functions of a third variable, say u, so that

(1)
$$x = f(u)$$
$$y = g(u),$$

then these equations are called **parametric equations** of the curve, the variable u being the **parameter.** If it is possible to eliminate u from (1), then this elimination yields the equation of the curve in the usual form in which x and y are the only variables, that is, the rectangular or **cartesian** equation of the curve.

To find $\dfrac{dy}{dx}$ and $\dfrac{d^2y}{dx^2}$ for the curve defined by (1), it is not necessary to use the cartesian equation, for by IX, Art. 42,

(2)
$$\frac{dy}{dx} = \frac{\dfrac{dy}{du}}{\dfrac{dx}{du}} = \frac{g'(u)}{f'(u)}.$$

Moreover, by VI and VIII, Art. 42, we have

$$\frac{d^2y}{dx^2} = \frac{d}{du}\left(\frac{dy}{dx}\right) \cdot \frac{du}{dx} = \frac{\dfrac{d}{du}\left(\dfrac{dy}{dx}\right)}{\dfrac{dx}{du}},$$

whence from (2)

(3)
$$\frac{d^2y}{dx^2} = \frac{f'(u)g''(u) - g'(u)f''(u)}{[f'(u)]^3}.$$

To obtain the expression for an element of arc of the curve defined by (1), we substitute the differentials

$$dx = f'(u)du$$

and

$$dy = g'(u)du$$

in (2), Art. 59, and find

(4)
$$ds = \pm \sqrt{[f'(u)]^2 + [g'(u)]^2}\,du,$$

where the sign is plus or minus according as the positive direction along the curve is chosen as that corresponding to increasing or to decreasing u.

In many problems relating to moving particles, the path is defined by its parametric equations, with the time t as parameter. This will at once be illustrated.

Example 1. As a particle moves on a curve, its position at any time t is given by $x = t^2 - 4t$, $y = t^2$, where x and y are in feet and t in seconds. Find the components of the velocity and the acceleration, the time at which the magnitude of the velocity is a minimum, and the cartesian equation of the curve.

We have, by (8), (9), (10), and (11) of the preceding article,

$$v_x = 2t - 4,$$
$$v_y = 2t,$$
$$a_x = 2,$$

and

$$a_y = 2.$$

Thus each component of the acceleration is constantly 2 ft./sec.²

The square of the magnitude of the velocity is, by (1) of the preceding article,

$$|\vec{v}|^2 = (2t - 4)^2 + 4t^2 = 8t^2 - 16t + 16.$$

This will attain its minimum value simultaneously with $|\vec{v}|$. Hence we set the derivative

$$\frac{d|\vec{v}|^2}{dt} = 16t - 16$$

equal to zero and solve for t, obtaining

$$t = 1.$$

It is easily shown that at this time $|\vec{v}|^2$, and therefore $|\vec{v}|$, is a minimum.

The equation of the path is found by eliminating t from the given equations. Thus, from the second equation,

$$t = \pm \sqrt{y},$$

whence, by the first equation,

$$x = y \mp 4\sqrt{y}.$$

This, or its rationalized form

$$(x - y)^2 - 16y = 0,$$

is the equation of the path. In the sketch (Fig. 62a), the portion OA of the curve corresponds to positive values of t, and OB to negative values.

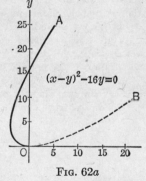

FIG. 62a

Example 2. A particle moves on a curve whose parametric equations are

$$x = 3 \cos t$$
$$y = 2 \sin 2t,$$

where x and y are in feet and the time t in seconds.   Find the magnitude of the velocity when $t = \dfrac{\pi}{6}$.

We have

$$v_x = \frac{dx}{dt} = -3 \sin t,$$

$$v_y = \frac{dy}{dt} = 4 \cos 2t.$$

When $t = \dfrac{\pi}{6}$,

$$v_x = -\tfrac{3}{2},$$

$$v_y = 2,$$

and

$$|\vec{v}| = \sqrt{v_x{}^2 + v_y{}^2} = \tfrac{5}{2} \text{ ft./sec.}$$

Or, alternatively, by (4),

$$ds = \pm \sqrt{9 \sin^2 t + 16 \cos^2 2t} \; dt,$$

whence, for $t = \dfrac{\pi}{6}$,

$$|\vec{v}| = |v| = \left| \frac{ds}{dt} \right| = \tfrac{5}{2} \text{ ft./sec.}$$

PROBLEMS

In the following problems, x and y are expressed in feet and t in seconds.

1. A particle moves on the parabola $y = x^2$ so that the y-component of its velocity is -12 ft./sec.   Find the x-component and the magnitude of the velocity when the abscissa of the particle is -1.2.

2. The magnitude of the velocity of a particle moving downward and toward the right on the curve $x^2 y = 8$ is constantly $5\sqrt{5}$ ft./sec.   Find the components of the velocity at the instant when the particle passes through the point $(2, 2)$.

3. Under the conditions of Problem 2, find the components of the acceleration.

4. If a particle moves along the curve $y = e^{-x}$ so that the x-component of the velocity is constantly 2 ft./sec., find the y-component of the velocity and of the acceleration as the particle passes through the point $(3, e^{-3})$.

5. A particle moves on a curve whose parametric equations are $x = e^{-3t} \cos 3t$, $y = e^{-3t} \sin 3t$.   Find the magnitudes of the velocity and acceleration at any time.

6. For a particle moving on the circle $x^2 + y^2 = r^2$ with constant speed v, show that

$$x a_x + y a_y = -v^2,$$

$$y a_x - x a_y = 0,$$

and thence obtain an expression for $|\vec{a}|$ in terms of v and r.

7. A particle moves on the curve $x = 3(\phi - \sin \phi)$, $y = 3(1 - \cos \phi)$ in such a way that the parameter ϕ increases at the rate of 2 radians/sec.   Find $|\vec{v}|$ and $|\vec{a}|$ when $\phi = \dfrac{\pi}{3}$.

8. The parametric equations of the path of a particle are $x = 8t^2$, $y = t^3 + 5$. Find the magnitudes of the velocity and acceleration when $t = 4$, and the cartesian equation of the path.

9. The parametric equations of the path of a particle are $x = 3t^2$, $y = 9t - t^3$. Find the maximum and minimum values of the magnitude of the velocity, and the corresponding positions of the particle.

10. For the motion defined by the equations of Problem 9, find when the magnitude of the acceleration is $6\sqrt{5}$ ft./sec.^{2}, and obtain the corresponding values of the components of the acceleration.

11. The parametric equations of the path of a particle are $x = \dfrac{t^2}{8}$, $y = \ln t$. Find the cartesian equation of the path, the time when the magnitude of the velocity is a minimum, and the magnitudes of the velocity and acceleration at this time.

12. The parametric equations of the path of a particle are $x = e^t$, $y = 2e^{-t}$. Show that the magnitudes of the velocity and acceleration are equal, and find when they attain their minimum value.

13. A particle moves in such a way that $v_x = \cos 3t$ and $v_y = \sin 3t$. Using (2) and (3), find $\dfrac{dy}{dx}$ and $\dfrac{d^2y}{dx^2}$ for that point of the path which corresponds to $t = \dfrac{\pi}{12}$.

14. A particle moves in such a way that $v_x = t \cos t$ and $v_y = t \sin t$. Find $\dfrac{dy}{dx}$ and $\dfrac{d^2y}{dx^2}$ for that point of the path which corresponds to $t = \dfrac{\pi}{3}$.

15. A particle traverses the curve $x^3 + y^3 - 2xy = 0$ with a constant speed of $2\sqrt{2}$ ft./sec. Find the components of the velocity and the acceleration as the particle moves toward the right through the point $(1, 1)$.

16. A ladder 34 ft. long is placed with its upper end against a vertical wall and its lower end on a horizontal floor. The lower end is then moved away from the wall at the constant rate of 8 ft./sec. Find the components of the velocity and of the acceleration of the middle point of the ladder when the bottom is 30 ft. from the wall.

17. When the resistance of the air is neglected, the path of a projectile is defined by the equations $x = v_0 t \cos \theta$, $y = v_0 t \sin \theta - \frac{1}{2}gt^2$, where θ (Fig. 62b) is the angle between the direction of projection and the horizontal, v_0 is the initial speed, and g is the acceleration of gravity (approximately 32 ft./sec.^{2}).

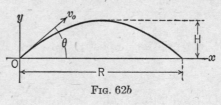

FIG. 62b

Find the components of the velocity and of the acceleration at any time.

18. Show that the cartesian equation of the path of a projectile is

$$y = x \tan \theta - \frac{gx^2}{2v_0^2 \cos^2 \theta}.$$

19. Show that a projectile attains its maximum height H (Fig. 62b) when $t = \dfrac{v_0 \sin \theta}{g}$, and that $H = \dfrac{v_0^2 \sin^2 \theta}{2g}$.

20. Show that the magnitude of the velocity of a projectile at any instant is $\sqrt{v_0^2 - 2gv_0 t \sin \theta + g^2 t^2}$, and that this attains its minimum value $v_0 \cos \theta$ when the projectile is at the highest point of its path.

21. Show that the range R (Fig. 62b) of a projectile is twice the abscissa of the highest point of its path.

22. Derive the parametric equations of the path of a projectile (Problem 17) by integration, using the conditions that $a_x = \dfrac{dv_x}{dt} = \dfrac{d^2x}{dt^2} = 0$, $a_y = \dfrac{dv_y}{dt} = \dfrac{d^2y}{dt^2} = -g$, and that for $t = 0$, $v_x = v_0 \cos\theta$, $v_y = v_0 \sin\theta$, $x = y = 0$.

63. Components of Acceleration in Circular Motion. Suppose that a particle moves with variable speed v on a circle of radius r, and that the positive direction for measuring displacements along the circumference is chosen as shown by the arrow (Fig. 63a). Let P be an arbitrary fixed

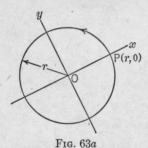

Fig. 63a

point on the circle, and, taking the center O of the circle as the origin of coördinates, let the x-axis be directed from O toward P, and the y-axis be obtained by rotating the x-axis about O through an angle of $90°$ in the sense corresponding to the positive direction along the circumference. The axes thus have the directions of the normal and the tangent to the circle at $P(r, 0)$, and, as the particle passes through P, the **normal component** and the **tangential component** of its acceleration are simply the instantaneous values of a_x and a_y, which we shall designate as $(a_P)_x$ and $(a_P)_y$ and for which we shall now derive expressions.

The coördinates x and y of the moving particle satisfy the equation of the circle

$$x^2 + y^2 = r^2.$$

Differentiating implicitly with respect to the time, we have

$$xv_x + yv_y = 0.$$

Differentiating again, we obtain

$$xa_x + v_x{}^2 + ya_y + v_y{}^2 = 0,$$

or

$$xa_x + ya_y = -v^2.$$

Hence, when the particle is at P, so that $x = r$, $y = 0$, and $a_x = (a_P)_x$, we have

$$r(a_P)_x = -v^2,$$

or

$$(1) \qquad\qquad (a_P)_x = -\frac{v^2}{r}.$$

The minus sign signifies that the projection on the x-axis of the instantaneous acceleration has the negative direction PO.

To obtain the tangential component of the acceleration, we differentiate

$$v_x^2 + v_y^2 = v^2$$

implicitly with respect to t; whence, for any position of the particle,

$$v_x a_x + v_y a_y = v \frac{dv}{dt}.$$

In particular, when the particle is at P, so that $v_x = 0$, $v_y = v$, and $a_y = (a_P)_y$, we have

(2) $$(a_P)_y = \frac{dv}{dt}.$$

Since in (1) and (2) the instantaneous position P of the particle is arbitrary, these results are readily generalized. Denoting the normal and tangential components of the acceleration of the particle at any position by a_n and a_t respectively, and omitting the minus sign from the former (which amounts to taking the positive direction along the normal as inward), we have

(1′) $$a_n = \frac{v^2}{r}$$

and

(2′) $$a_t = \frac{dv}{dt}.$$

Evidently the magnitude of the acceleration is

(3) $$|\vec{a}| = \sqrt{a_n^2 + a_t^2},$$

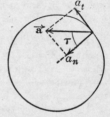

Fig. 63b

and the angle τ (Fig. 63b) which the acceleration makes with the radius to the instantaneous position of the particle is

(4) $$\tau = \tan^{-1} \frac{a_t}{a_n}.$$

For a particle moving in a circle it will be noticed that $\frac{dv}{dt}$, the rate of change of the speed, in general constitutes only a component of the acceleration, namely the tangential, the normal component $\frac{v^2}{r}$ always being present unless v is instantaneously zero. If $\frac{dv}{dt}$ vanishes, as it does identically when v is constant or instantaneously when v is a maximum or a minimum, then, by (3), $|\vec{a}| = a_n = \dfrac{v^2}{r}$ (cf. Problem 6, Art. 62).

Example 1. A particle moves in a circle of radius 4 ft. so that its speed v (feet per second) at any time t (seconds) is

$$v = t^2 - 3t + 4.$$

Find the normal component, the tangential component, the magnitude, and the direction of the acceleration when $t = 3$.

For $t = 3$, we have $v = 4$, and, by (1'),

$$a_n = 4 \text{ ft/sec.}^2$$

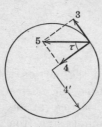

Moreover, by differentiation, we obtain

$$\frac{dv}{dt} = 2t - 3,$$

whence, for $t = 3$, we have, by (2'),

$$a_t = 3 \text{ ft./sec.}^2$$

Fig. 63c

Using (3), we find

$$|\vec{a}| = \sqrt{4^2 + 3^2} = 5 \text{ ft./sec.}^2,$$

when $t = 3$; and at this time the angle between $\vec{a}$ and the radius to the particle is $\tau = \tan^{-1} \frac{3}{4}$ (Fig. 63c).

Example 2. The coördinates of a moving particle at any time t are given by the equations $x = \cos (2t - t^2)$, $y = \sin (2t - t^2)$. Show that the path is a circle, find when $|\vec{a}|$ is a minimum, and determine the corresponding position of the particle.

Squaring and adding the given equations, we obtain $x^2 + y^2 = 1$; the path is therefore a circle of unit radius.

Differentiating the given equations, we find

$$v_x = - 2(1 - t) \sin (2t - t^2)$$

and

$$v_y = 2(1 - t) \cos (2t - t^2),$$

whence

$$v^2 = 4(1 - t)^2$$

and, by (1'), with $r = 1$,

$$a_n = 4(1 - t)^2.$$

The speed v is $\pm 2 (1 - t)$; to fix the sign, it would be necessary to specify a positive direction along the circle. In any case $\dfrac{dv}{dt}$ or a_t is constant, and hence $|\vec{a}|$ attains its minimum value when a_n does, namely, when $t = 1$. At this time the particle is situated at the point $(\cos 1, \sin 1)$, or, in decimals, at $(0.5403, 0.8415)$.

64. Angular Velocity and Angular Acceleration. If the line OL (Fig. 64a) revolves about the point O, so as always to remain in the same plane, the position of OL at any time can be described by stating the value of θ, the angle OL makes with some fixed line OA of the plane. The instantaneous rate at which θ is changing with respect to the time is called the **angular velocity** of the line, and is denoted by the symbol ω; we have therefore

$$(1) \qquad\qquad \omega = \frac{d\theta}{dt}.$$

FIG. 64a

The rate at which the angular velocity of OL changes with respect to the time is called the **angular acceleration** of the line and is denoted by α. Thus

$$(2) \qquad\qquad \alpha = \frac{d\omega}{dt} = \frac{d^2\theta}{dt^2}.$$

It will next be shown that the speed of any point on OL can be expressed in terms of ω and that the acceleration of such a point can be expressed in terms of ω and α.

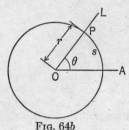

FIG. 64b

If P is a point on OL whose distance from O is r, so that P moves on a circle of radius r, and if s is the arc of the circle corresponding to the angular position θ of OL (Fig. 64b), then by Art. 45

$$(3) \qquad\qquad s = r\theta$$

where θ is measured in radians. If we differentiate (3) with respect to t, we obtain

$$(4) \qquad\qquad v = r\omega,$$

where v is the speed of P and ω is the angular velocity of the line OL in radians per unit time.

Differentiating (4) with respect to t, and observing that by (2′) of the preceding article $\frac{dv}{dt} = a_t$, we find

$$(5) \qquad\qquad a_t = r\alpha ,$$

where a_t is the tangential component of the acceleration of P, and α is the angular acceleration of the line OL in radians per (unit time)^2.

Finally, by (1′) of the preceding article and by (4) we obtain

$$(6) \qquad\qquad a_n = r\omega^2,$$

where a_n is the normal component of the acceleration of P and ω is the angular velocity of OL in radians per unit time.

Example. A wheel of radius 2 ft. revolves so that the angular position of a spoke is given in radians by the equation $\theta = 15t^2 - 24t$, where t is the time in seconds. Find, for $t = 1$, the speed and the magnitude of the acceleration of a point on the rim.

The angular velocity and angular acceleration of the spoke at any time are

$$\omega = \frac{d\theta}{dt} = 30t - 24$$

and

$$\alpha = \frac{d\omega}{dt} = 30 \text{ rad./sec.}^2, \text{ constantly.}$$

When $t = 1$, $\omega = 6$ rad./sec.

For a point on the rim we have, for $t = 1$,

$$v = 12 \text{ ft./sec. (by (4)),}$$

$$a_n = 72 \text{ ft./sec.}^2 \text{ (by (6)),}$$

$$a_t = 60 \text{ ft./sec.}^2 \text{ (by (5)),}$$

and

$$|\vec{a}| = \sqrt{72^2 + 60^2} = 12\sqrt{61} \text{ ft./sec.}^2$$

PROBLEMS

1. What is the angular velocity in radians per second of the minute hand of a clock? If the hand is 4 ft. long, find the magnitude of the acceleration of its end.

2. The angular position (in radians) of the radius to a particle traveling in a circle 4 ft. in diameter is given by the equation $\theta = 2t^3 - 9t^2 + 12t - 8$, where t is in seconds. Find the tangential component of the acceleration of the particle when the angular velocity of the radius vanishes, and the normal component of the acceleration when the angular acceleration vanishes.

3. The instantaneous magnitude of the acceleration of a particle traveling on a circle 4 ft. in diameter is 10 ft./sec.^{2}, and the angular velocity of the radius to the particle is 2 radians/sec. Find the instantaneous tangential component of the acceleration of the particle.

4. If α, the angular acceleration of a line, is constant, and if, for $t = 0$, $\omega = \omega_0$ and $\theta = 0$, derive by integration the following formulas:

$$\omega = \omega_0 + \alpha t,$$

$$\theta = \omega_0 t + \tfrac{1}{2}\alpha t^2.$$

Thence by algebraic procedure show that

$$\theta = \frac{\omega_0 + \omega}{2} t$$

and

$$\omega^2 = \omega_0^2 + 2\alpha\theta.$$

5. If the angular acceleration (in radians per second per second) of a wheel 2 ft. in radius is given by the equation $\alpha = 8 - 2t$, where t is in seconds, and if $\omega = 4$ radians/sec. when $t = 0$, find the magnitude of the acceleration of a point on the rim when $t = 1$.

6. A particle moves so that its position at any time t (seconds) is given by the equations $x = 5 \cos 4t$ and $y = 5 \sin 4t$, where x and y are expressed in feet. Show that the path is a circle, and find the normal and tangential components of the acceleration of the particle.

7. A particle moves so that its position at any time t (seconds) is given by the equations $x = 5 \cos (4t - t^2)$ and $y = 5 \sin (4t - t^2)$, where x and y are expressed in feet. Show that the path is a circle, and find the minimum value of the magntude of the acceleration.

8. The distance s (feet) which a particle moves in t seconds along the circumference of a circle of radius 3 ft. is given by the equation $s = \frac{1}{2}(1 + t)^2 + 9 \ln (1 + t)$. Find the magnitude of the acceleration when the speed is a minimum.

9. A particle travels in a circle 4 ft. in diameter. The angular position of the radius to the particle is given by the equation $\theta = t^2 e^{-t}$, where θ is expressed in radians and t in seconds. Find the tangential component of the acceleration of the particle at each instant for which the angular velocity of the radius vanishes.

10. A particle traverses the curve $y = \dfrac{1}{x}$ (where x and y are expressed in feet) in such a way that the x-component of the velocity is constantly $\frac{1}{2}$ ft./sec. What is the angular velocity of the line connecting the particle with the origin at the instant when the particle passes through the point $(\frac{1}{2}, 2)$?

HINT: $\theta = \tan^{-1} \dfrac{y}{x}$.

11. A particle traverses the curve $y = e^x$, where x and y are expressed in feet, in such a way that its abscissa increases at the constant rate of 3 ft./sec. Find the angular velocity of the line connecting the particle with the origin when the particle passes through the point $(1, e)$; through the point $(0, 1)$.

65. Simple Harmonic Motion.

Let Q (Fig. 65a) be a point which moves in the counterclockwise direction along the circumference of a circle of radius r with a constant speed, so that the radius OQ revolves about O with a constant angular velocity. Then the point P, the projection of Q on the x-axis, will oscillate between A and B, describing what is known as **simple harmonic motion** with O as **center** and r as **amplitude**.

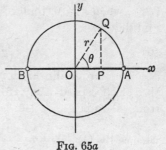

FIG. 65a

Suppose that initially the point Q (and hence also the point P) is situated at A. Then at the time t the radius OQ will have swept through an angle θ given by the equation

(1) $$\theta = \omega t,$$

where ω, the constant angular velocity of OQ, will be expressed in radians per unit time. Therefore the time T required for a complete oscillation of the point P, corresponding to a complete circuit of the point Q, may be obtained by setting $\theta = 2\pi$ in (1), and is thus

(2) $$T = \frac{2\pi}{\omega}.$$

The time T is called the **period** of the simple harmonic motion; its reciprocal, representing the number of periods per unit time, is called the **frequency,** and is denoted by ν, so that

(3) $$\nu = \frac{\omega}{2\pi}.$$

The instantaneous displacement OP of the point P will be designated by x; evidently

(4) $$x = r \cos \omega t.$$

The speed v of the point P, being the time-derivative of this displacement, is readily found to be

(5) $$v = - r\omega \sin \omega t.$$

Since $\sin \omega t = \dfrac{PQ}{r} = \pm \dfrac{\sqrt{r^2 - x^2}}{r}$, (5) may be rewritten as

(5') $$v = \mp \omega \sqrt{r^2 - x^2},$$

where the sign is minus or plus according as Q is above or below BA, that is, according as P is moving to the left or right.

From (5') it is evident that v attains its maximum numerical value $|v|_{max}$ when $x = 0$, that is, when the point P passes through the center, and that

(6) $$|v|_{max} = r\omega.$$

Since for rectilinear motion acceleration is defined as the time-derivative of the speed (Art. 15), the acceleration a of the point P is found from (5) to be

$$a = - r\omega^2 \cos \omega t,$$

whence by (4)

(7) $$a = - \omega^2 x.$$

Thus for a particle describing simple harmonic motion, the acceleration is proportional to the displacement of the particle from a fixed point of its path, and since the factor of proportionality $-\omega^2$ is negative, the acceleration and the displacement are oppositely directed.   Conversely any motion for which (7) holds may be shown to be of the type executed by the point P in the present discussion. Accordingly, (7) may be regarded as the characteristic equation of simple harmonic motion.

From (7) it follows that a attains its maximum numerical value $|a|_{\max}$ when $x = \pm r$, that is, when the point P is at A or B, and that

$$(8) \qquad |a|_{\max} = r\omega^2.$$

Example 1. A particle describing simple harmonic motion has a speed of 16 ft./sec. when it is three-fifths of the way from the center to an end of its path, and the maximum numerical value of its acceleration is 40 ft./sec.[2] Find the amplitude and the period.

By (5') and (8), we have

$$16 = \omega\sqrt{r^2 - \frac{9r^2}{25}} = \frac{4}{5}r\omega$$

and

$$40 = r\omega^2,$$

whence

$$r = 10 \text{ ft.}$$

and

$$\omega = 2 \text{ radians/sec.}$$

Substituting the latter in (2), we obtain for the period

$$T = \pi \text{ sec.}$$

It will now be shown that a material particle moving on a straight line will describe simple harmonic motion if the resultant force F acting on it is proportional, and oppositely directed, to the displacement x of the particle from a fixed point on the line, that is, if

$$(9) \qquad F = -kx,$$

where k is a positive constant. If m is the mass of the particle and a its acceleration, it follows from (9) by the fundamental law of dynamics,

$$(10) \qquad F = ma,$$

that

$$(11) \qquad a = -\frac{k}{m}x.$$

Since (11) is a relation of the same type as (7), with

$$(12) \qquad \omega = \sqrt{\frac{k}{m}},$$

we conclude that a particle subjected to a resultant force satisfying the condition (9) describes simple harmonic motion.

The connection between the mass m and the weight W of a body depends on the system of units adopted. Thus in the British gravitational system, in which the fundamental units are the foot, the pound, and the second, the mass of a body weighing W pounds is given by

$$(13) \qquad\qquad m = \frac{W}{g},$$

where the value of g, the acceleration of a freely falling body, is approximately 32 ft./sec.^{2} Using this value, we find, for example, that the mass of a 64-lb. body is 2 units.

Example 2. A helical spring of natural length l inches is stretched 2 in. when a body weighing 16 lb. is suspended from it (Fig. 65b). The body is pulled down and released. Assuming that the elastic force developed in the spring is proportional to the elongation, show that the body describes simple harmonic motion, and find its period.

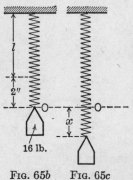

FIG. 65b   FIG. 65c

Since under the weight the spring stretches 2 in. (or $\frac{1}{6}$ ft.), the elastic force developed in the spring is 8 lb. per inch of elongation, or 96 lb. per foot. Hence if the weight is pulled below the position of equilibrium O and is allowed to oscillate, then the elastic force for any displacement x feet (Fig. 65c) will be $96\ (\frac{1}{6} + x)$ pounds. The resultant force F on the body is the algebraic sum of this elastic force and the weight of the body; that is,

$$F = 16 - 96(\tfrac{1}{6} + x) = -96x,$$

where downward forces and displacements are taken as positive. Comparing this with (9), we conclude that the motion of the body is simple harmonic, with O as center, and further that $k = 96$. Since, by (13), $m = \frac{1}{2}$, it follows from (12) that $\omega = \sqrt{192} = 8\sqrt{3}$. Then, by (2), the period is $\dfrac{2\pi}{8\sqrt{3}}$, or $\dfrac{\pi\sqrt{3}}{12}$ sec.

PROBLEMS

1. If at the time t the position of a particle moving on the x-axis is given by the equation $x = r \cos(\omega t + \epsilon)$, where r, ω, and ϵ are constants, show that the motion is simple harmonic.

2. Derive (5′) and (7) by projecting on the x-axis the velocity and the acceleration of the point Q (Fig. 65a).

3. A particle moves with a constant speed of 4 ft./sec. on the circle $x^2 + y^2 = 25$, where x and y are expressed in feet. Find the amplitude and the period of the simple harmonic motion described by the projection of the particle on the x-axis.

4. The speed of a particle describing simple harmonic motion is 36 ft./sec. when the particle is 5 ft. from the center, and the maximum acceleration is 117 ft./sec.^{2} Find the maximum speed of the particle and the amplitude of its motion.

5. When a particle describing simple harmonic motion is 3 ft. from the center, its speed is 3 ft./sec. If the maximum speed is 6 ft./sec., find the maximum acceleration.

6. A particle describing simple harmonic motion with an amplitude of 4 ft. has a speed of 6 ft./sec. as it passes a certain point of its path while receding from the center. Its next passage through the same point occurs one-third of the period later. Find the period and the maximum acceleration.

7. The position of a particle moving along the x-axis is given by the equation $x = 3 \cos 2t + 4 \sin 2t$, where x is expressed in feet and t in seconds. Show, by the use of (7), that the motion is simple harmonic, and find the period. Then find the amplitude by determining the maximum value of x. Also solve the problem by expressing x in the form $r \cos (\omega t + \epsilon)$.

8. The position of a particle moving along the x-axis is given by the equation $x + 2 \sin^2 3t = 0$, where x is expressed in feet and t in seconds. Show that the motion is simple harmonic with center at $x = -1$.

9. For the motion described in the preceding problem, find the period, the amplitude, and the maximum speed.

10. A particle describes simple harmonic motion along the x-axis, its position at the end of t seconds being given by the equation $x = 4 \cos \frac{\pi}{3} (t - 1)$. Find the earliest moment ($t > 0$) at which the numerical value of the speed is a maximum.

11. The position of a particle describing simple harmonic motion along the x-axis is given by the equation $x = 4 + 2 \cos^2 2t$, where x is expressed in feet and t in seconds. Find the center, the amplitude, and the maximum acceleration.

12. The position of a particle describing simple harmonic motion along the x-axis is given by the equation $x = 24 \cos 3t - 10 \sin 3t$, where x is expressed in feet and t in seconds. Find the period and the maximum acceleration.

13. A spring stretches $\frac{1}{16}$ in. when a weight of 1 lb. is hung from it. Find the frequency of oscillation of a 24-lb. weight suspended by the spring.

14. If in the preceding problem, the 24-lb. weight passes through its equilibrium position with a speed of 16 in./sec., find the amplitude of its motion and its maximum acceleration.

15. On the assumption that the earth is a homogeneous sphere, the force of gravity at an internal point varies as the distance of the point from the center of the earth. Show that a particle dropped into a hole extending diametrically through the earth will describe simple harmonic motion, and find the period. (Take 4000 mi. as the length of the earth's radius.)

16. Show that, in the absence of friction, a particle dropped into a hole extending through the earth but not passing through the center will describe simple harmonic motion with the same period as in Problem 15.

66. Curvature.

66. Curvature. In Chapter II we studied the geometrical significance of $\frac{dy}{dx}$ and $\frac{d^2y}{dx^2}$. In the present article we shall develop a formula (involving both derivatives) for the rate of change of the direction of a curve at any point. This rate of change, when computed with respect to the arc of a curve, is called **curvature.**

Let P and Q be two points on a curve, separated by an arc of length Δs; further let the tangent lines to the curve at these points make angles of ϕ and $\phi + \Delta\phi$ radians, respectively, with the horizontal (Fig. 66a). Then $\Delta\phi$ represents the change in the direction of the curve as the arc PQ is traversed. Hence $\dfrac{\Delta\phi}{\Delta s}$ is the average change in the direction

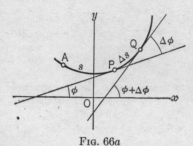

of the curve per unit length of the arc PQ, or the **average curvature** of this arc.

As the point Q approaches P, the average curvature may or may not approach a limit; if it does, this limit is called the *curvature at P* and will be denoted by κ. That is, by definition,

Fig. 66a

$$(1) \qquad \kappa = \lim_{\Delta s \to 0} \frac{\Delta\phi}{\Delta s} = \frac{d\phi}{ds}.$$

Since the cartesian equation of a curve involves x and y and not ϕ and s, we shall now proceed to convert (1) into a formula for finding directly the curvature of a curve whose equation is given in the form $y = f(x)$.

By IX, Art. 42, we have

$$\frac{d\phi}{ds} = \frac{\dfrac{d\phi}{dx}}{\dfrac{ds}{dx}}.$$

Now since $\phi = \tan^{-1}\left(\dfrac{dy}{dx}\right)$, we obtain on differentiation

$$\frac{d\phi}{dx} = \frac{\dfrac{d^2y}{dx^2}}{1 + \left(\dfrac{dy}{dx}\right)^2}.$$

Moreover, choosing as the positive direction along the curve that for which x increases, we have by (3), Art. 59,

$$\frac{ds}{dx} = +\sqrt{1 + \left(\frac{dy}{dx}\right)^2}.$$

Hence we find for the curvature at any point (x, y)

$$(2) \qquad \kappa = \frac{\dfrac{d^2y}{dx^2}}{\left[1 + \left(\dfrac{dy}{dx}\right)^2\right]^{\frac{3}{2}}}.$$

We note that at any point at which $\dfrac{d^2y}{dx^2}$ is zero, as for example at a point of inflection, the curvature vanishes.

Let us now obtain the curvature of a circle of radius r (Fig. 66b). Since in this case $\Delta\phi$ is the central angle POQ whose radian measure is $\dfrac{\Delta s}{r}$, the average curvature of the

arc PQ is given by

$$\frac{\Delta\phi}{\Delta s} = \frac{1}{r},$$

a constant which does not depend on the location of the point P or the length of the arc. Hence for the curvature at any point of the circle we have by (1)

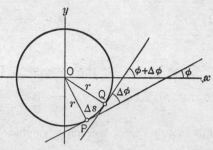

(3) $\qquad\qquad \kappa = \dfrac{1}{r}.$

Fig. 66b

Thus the curvature of a circle is constant and equal to the reciprocal of the radius.

If (2) had been used to calculate the curvature of the circle $x^2 + y^2 = r^2$, the result would have been $\kappa = -\dfrac{1}{r}$ for $y > 0$ and $\kappa = \dfrac{1}{r}$ for $y < 0$. Since, however, the definition (1) led unambiguously to the expression (3), we shall regard the curvature of a circle as essentially positive, in accordance with (3).

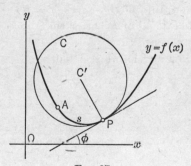

Fig. 67a

67. Radius of Curvature. Suppose that the curve $y = f(x)$ and the circle C of Fig. 67a are tangent at the point P, that the curve and the circle lie on the same side of their common tangent line, and that the curvature of the curve at P is numerically equal to the curvature of the circle C. Then this circle is called the **circle of curvature** of the curve $y = f(x)$ at the point P; denoting the length of its radius by r, we have by (2) and (3) of the preceding article

$$\left| \frac{\left[1 + \left(\dfrac{dy}{dx}\right)^2\right]^{\frac{3}{2}}}{\dfrac{d^2y}{dx^2}} \right| = r.$$

Since the expression whose absolute value appears on the left side of the last equation is numerically equal to the radius of the circle of curvature at the point P, we shall call it the **radius of curvature** of the curve $y = f(x)$ at this point; designating it by ρ, we have by definition

(1)
$$\rho = \frac{\left[1 + \left(\dfrac{dy}{dx}\right)^2\right]^{\frac{3}{2}}}{\dfrac{d^2y}{dx^2}}.$$

Since by Art. 21 the concavity of the curve $y = f(x)$ is upward or downward according as $\dfrac{d^2y}{dx^2}$ is positive or negative, and ρ has the same sign as $\dfrac{d^2y}{dx^2}$, we may conclude that ρ is in general positive for points at which the curve is concave upward and negative for points at which the curve is concave downward. At a point of the curve for which $\dfrac{d^2y}{dx^2}$ is zero, such as for example a point of inflection, the radius of curvature is infinite.

The center C' of the circle of curvature is called the **center of curvature** of the curve $y = f(x)$ at the point P; it may evidently be located by laying off from P a distance equal to $|\rho|$ along the inward normal to the curve.

It can be shown that the circle of curvature of the curve $y = f(x)$ at the point P fits the curve in the neighborhood of P better than does any other circle with the same common tangent.

Comparing (1) with (2) of the preceding article, we see that

$$\rho = \frac{1}{\kappa},$$

or, by (1) of the preceding article,

(1')
$$\rho = \frac{ds}{d\phi}.$$

In Art. 63 we saw that the normal component of the acceleration of a particle moving on a circle of radius r with instantaneous speed v is

$$a_n = \frac{v^2}{r}.$$

It can be shown that for motion on an arbitrary curve

(2)
$$a_n = \frac{v^2}{|\rho|},$$

where v is the instantaneous speed and ρ is the radius of curvature of the curve at the position of the particle.

Example 1. Find the radius of curvature of the curve $y = \ln \cos x$ at the point where $x = \dfrac{\pi}{4}$.

Since

$$\frac{dy}{dx} = -\tan x, \quad \text{and} \quad \frac{d^2y}{dx^2} = -\sec^2 x,$$

we obtain by (1)

$$\rho = \frac{[1 + \tan^2 x]^{\frac{3}{2}}}{-\sec^2 x} = -\sec x.$$

For $x = \dfrac{\pi}{4}$, $\rho = -\sqrt{2}$, the minus sign denoting downward concavity.

When a curve is defined by its parametric equations, its radius of curvature may be computed either by (1) (as illustrated in Example 2) or, more directly, by a formula given in Problem 21 below.

Example 2. If a cord, originally stretched along the circumference of a circle, is kept taut and unwound in such a way as always to remain in the plane of the circle, any point of the cord traces a curve known as an **involute of the circle**. If the tracing point is initially at A (Fig. 67b), the curve has the appearance shown, and its parametric equations are

$$x = a(\cos \phi + \phi \sin \phi)$$

and

$$y = a(\sin \phi - \phi \cos \phi),$$

where ϕ (expressed in radians) is the angle AOT through which the cord has turned and a is the radius of the circle. Find the radius of curvature at any point $P(x, y)$ of this curve.

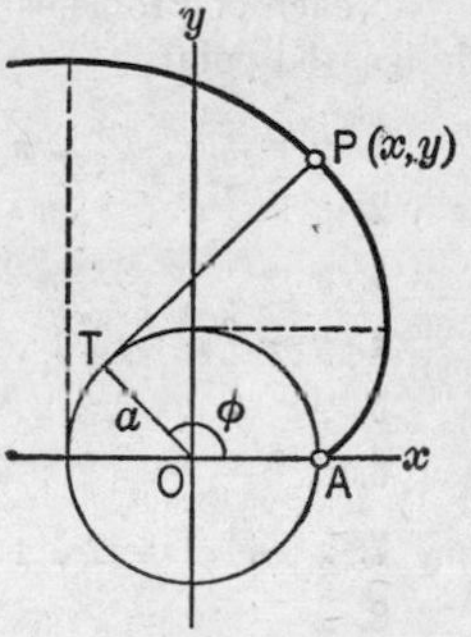

From the given equations we find

$$dx = a\phi \cos \phi \, d\phi$$

and

$$dy = a\phi \sin \phi \, d\phi,$$

whence

$$\frac{dy}{dx} = \tan \phi$$

and

$$\sqrt{1 + \left(\frac{dy}{dx}\right)^2} = \pm \sec \phi,$$

Fig. 67b

where the sign is plus or minus according as $\sec \phi$ is positive or negative. Moreover,

$$\frac{d^2y}{dx^2} = \frac{d}{dx}\left(\frac{dy}{dx}\right) = \frac{d}{d\phi}\left(\frac{dy}{dx}\right) \cdot \frac{d\phi}{dx}$$

$$= \sec^2 \phi \cdot \frac{1}{a\phi \cos \phi}$$

$$= \frac{\sec^3 \phi}{a\phi}.$$

Hence by (1) we obtain

$$\rho = \pm \, a\phi.$$

It thus develops that the numerical value of the radius of curvature of the involute at the point P is equal to the length of the arc AT; moreover, since, from the manner in which the involute is generated, the segment TP has the same length as this arc and since it is readily shown that TP is normal to the involute at P, we may conclude that T is the center of curvature of the involute at P.

Consider an arc, such as that assumed by a loaded beam, at every point of which the slope $\dfrac{dy}{dx}$ is numerically small. Then if $\left(\dfrac{dy}{dx}\right)^2$ is sufficiently small to be neglected in comparison with unity, we may write in place of (1)

(3) $\rho = \dfrac{1}{\dfrac{d^2y}{dx^2}}$, approximately.

This approximation for the radius of curvature is regularly used in the theory of beams.

PROBLEMS

In each of Problems 1–20, find the radius of curvature of the given curve at the designated point.

1. $y = \frac{1}{2}x^2$; $(2, 2)$.

2. $y = \frac{1}{3}x^3$; $(1, \frac{1}{3})$.

3. $y = x^2 - 3x + 2$; $(2, 0)$.

4. $y = \frac{2}{3}x^{\frac{3}{2}}$; $(3, 2\sqrt{3})$.

5. $9x^2 + 16y^2 = 288$; $(4, 3)$.

6. $4x^2 - y^2 = 20$; $(3, 4)$.

7. $x^{\frac{2}{3}} + y^{\frac{2}{3}} = 2\sqrt[3]{4}$; $(2, 2)$.

8. $x^{\frac{1}{2}} + y^{\frac{1}{2}} = 7$; $(9, 16)$.

9. $xy = a^2$; (x, y).

10. $y^2 = 2 - x$; $(-2, 2)$.

11. $y = \ln x$; (x, y).

12. $y = \cos x$; $\left(\dfrac{\pi}{3}, \dfrac{1}{2}\right)$.

13. $y = \ln \sin x$; (x, y).

14. $y = \tan^3 x$; $\left(\dfrac{\pi}{4}, 1\right)$.

15. $y = \tan^{-1} \sqrt{x}$; $\left(1, \dfrac{\pi}{4}\right)$.

16. $y = e^{-x^2}$; $(0, 1)$.

17. $y = xe^{-\frac{x^2}{2}}$; $\left(1, \dfrac{1}{\sqrt{e}}\right)$.

18. $y = \dfrac{a}{2}(e^{\frac{x}{a}} + e^{-\frac{x}{a}})$; $(0, a)$.

19. $y = \sin^{-1}(\ln x)$; $(1, 0)$.

20. $y = \ln \sec x$; (x, y).

21. Show that, for the curve whose parametric equations are $x = f(t)$ and $y = g(t)$, the radius of curvature is given by the formula

$$\rho = \frac{\{[f'(t)]^2 + [g'(t)]^2\}^{\frac{3}{2}}}{f'(t)g''(t) - g'(t)f''(t)} .$$

(Cf. (3), Art. 62.)

22. Find the radius of curvature of the curve $x = 2 \sin t$, $y = \sin 2t$, at the point for which $t = \dfrac{\pi}{6}$.

23. Find the radius of curvature of the curve $x = 2 \cos^3 t$, $y = 2 \sin^3 t$, at any point.

24. Find the radius of curvature of the path

$$x = v_0 t \cos \theta,$$

$$y = v_0 t \sin \theta - \tfrac{1}{2} g t^2,$$

of a projectile at the highest point.

25. Find the point on the parabola $y = x^2 - 6x + 5$ at which the radius of curvature is a minimum.

26. Show that the coördinates X and Y of the center of curvature of the curve $y = f(x)$ at the point (x, y) are given by the equations

$$X = x - \frac{f'(x)\{1 + [f'(x)]^2\}}{f''(x)} ,$$

$$Y = y + \frac{1 + [f'(x)]^2}{f''(x)} .$$

27. Find the center of curvature of the curve $y = \cos x$ at the point $(0, 1)$.

28. Find the center of curvature of the curve $y = \dfrac{x^2 + 9}{x}$ at the point $(3, 6)$.

29. A particle moves on the curve $x = f(t)$, $y = g(t)$, where t is the time.   Assuming that, for arbitrary curvilinear motion, $a_t = \dfrac{dv}{dt}$ (cf. (2'), Art. 63), find a_t^2; then, from the relations $|\mathbf{a}|^2 = a_x^2 + a_y^2 = a_n^2 + a_t^2$, obtain an expression for a_n^2, and show by the result of Problem 21 that it agrees with (2).

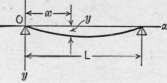

30. The deflection y (Fig. 67c) at any point of a uniformly loaded simple beam

FIG. 67c

is given in terms of the distance x of the point from an end of the beam by the formula

$$y = \frac{W}{24LEI} (2Lx^3 - x^4 - L^3x),$$

where W is the total load, L is the length between supports, and E and I are constants depending, respectively, on the material and on the cross-section.   Find approximately the radius of curvature at a point for which $x = \dfrac{L}{4}$.

68. Polar Coördinates. Various systems of coördinates have been devised for the location of a point in a plane or in space. Hitherto we have used only rectangular coördinates; we now introduce the *polar coördinates* of a point in a plane. Polar coördinates are commonly studied in analytic geometry. We are concerned with them here because many calculus problems are conveniently formulated and solved in terms of polar coördinates.

The following relations between the polar coördinates (radius vector r and polar angle θ) and the rectangular coördinates (x and y) of a point P are evident from Fig. 68a:

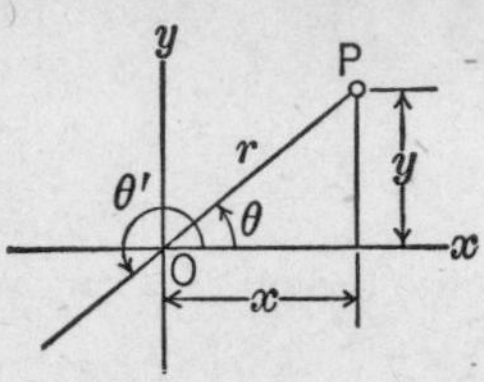

Fig. 68a

$$x = r \cos \theta,$$

$$y = r \sin \theta,$$

$$r = \sqrt{x^2 + y^2},$$

$$\theta = \tan^{-1} \frac{y}{x},$$

where θ is any positive or negative angle measured from the positive x-axis to the radius vector OP.

Alternatively, we may take r' and θ' as the polar coördinates of the point P, where r' is the negative of r and θ' is any positive or negative angle measured from the positive x-axis to the extension of OP through the origin. We then obtain

$$x = r' \cos \theta',$$

$$y = r' \sin \theta',$$

$$r' = -r = - \sqrt{x^2 + y^2},$$

$$\theta' = \tan^{-1} \frac{y}{x}.$$

The two sets of equations relating the rectangular and the polar coördinates of a point may be combined into

(1) $$x = r \cos \theta,$$

(2) $$y = r \sin \theta,$$

(3) $$r = \pm \sqrt{x^2 + y^2},$$

(4) $$\theta = \tan^{-1} \frac{y}{x},$$

where it is understood that the lower sign in (3) is to be associated with a value of θ which corresponds to the prolongation of OP across the origin.

The student will note that, whereas the rectangular coördinates of a point are unique, there are innumerably many ways of stating its polar coördinates. Thus in Fig. 68b, the point P may be designated in polar coördinates as $(2, 30°)$; but it can also be called $(2, 390°)$, $(2, -330°)$, $(-2, 210°)$, $(-2, -150°)$, etc.

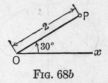

Fig. 68b

A few authors prefer to restrict r to positive values. In favor of this point of view, the following advantages may be cited: First, the number of ways the location of a point can be given in polar coördinates is reduced by half; secondly, the exclusion of negative values of r conforms to usage in trigonometry, where, in the definitions of the trigonometric functions of the general angle, r is taken as positive. We shall return to this question in Example 3 below.

Example 1. Transform to polar coördinates: $x^4 + x^2y^2 - a^2y^2 = 0$.
The given equation may be written
$$x^2 + y^2 = a^2 \frac{y^2}{x^2}.$$
By (3) and (4) we obtain
$$r^2 = a^2 \tan^2 \theta,$$
or
$$r = \pm\, a \tan \theta.$$

Example 2. Transform to rectangular coördinates: $r = 2a \cos \theta$.
By (1) we have
$$r = 2a \frac{x}{r},$$
or
$$r^2 = 2\, ax,$$
which by (3) becomes
$$x^2 + y^2 = 2\, ax.$$

Example 3. Plot the curve $r = a \sin 2\theta$, where $a > 0$.
We assign values to θ, calculate the corresponding values of r, and obtain points whose coördinates are pairs of related values of r and θ, as given in the following table:

θ	$0°$	$15°$	$22\frac{1}{2}°$	$30°$	$45°$	$60°$	$67\frac{1}{2}°$	$75°$	$90°$
r	0	$0.500a$	$0.707a$	$0.866a$	a	$0.866a$	$0.707a$	$0.500a$	0

When we plot the corresponding points we obtain the first-quadrant loop of Fig. 68c.
For $90° < \theta < 180°$, $\sin 2\theta < 0$ and hence $r < 0$. The corresponding portion of the graph is the fourth-quadrant loop of Fig. 68c.

For $180° < \theta < 270°$, $r > 0$. The corresponding portion of the graph is the third-quadrant loop of Fig. 68c.

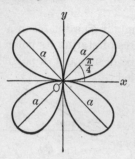

For $270° < \theta < 360°$, $r < 0$. The corresponding portion of the graph is the second-quadrant loop of Fig. 68c.

If we had limited r to positive values, we would have obtained only the loops in the first and third quadrants. It is thus a matter of definition whether the graph of the given equation consists of four or of two loops. By using (1), (2), and (3), the student may show that the equation, in rectangular coördinates, of the loops in the first and third quadrants is $(x^2 + y^2)^{\frac{3}{2}} = 2\,axy$, while the equation of the other loops is $-(x^2 + y^2)^{\frac{3}{2}} = 2\,axy$; the equation of all four loops is $\pm (x^2 + y^2)^{\frac{3}{2}} = 2axy$, or $(x^2 + y^2)^3 = 4a^2x^2y^2$.

FIG. 68c

PROBLEMS

In each of Problems 1–10, transform the given equation to polar coördinates.

1. $x^2 + y^2 = a^2$.

2. $x^2 + y^2 - 2ax = 0$.

3. $x^2 - y^2 = a^2$.

4. $xy = 6$.

5. $x^2 + y^2 = e^2(x + a)^2$.

6. $(x^2 + y^2)^2 = a^2(x^2 - y^2)$.

7. $y^2 = 4a(a - x)$.

8. $y^2 = \dfrac{x^3}{a - x}$.

9. $x^2(y^2 - a^2) - y^4 = 0$.

10. $x^2 - xy - y^2 = 0$.

In each of Problems 11–20, transform the given equation to rectangular coördinates.

11. $r = 2a \sin \theta$.

12. $r = a \cot \theta$.

13. $r = a(1 - \sin 2\theta)$.

14. $r = \dfrac{a}{1 - \cos \theta}$.

15. $r \sin\left(\theta + \dfrac{\pi}{4}\right) + r \sin\left(\theta - \dfrac{\pi}{4}\right) = 4$.

16. $r = \tan \dfrac{\theta}{2} + \cot \dfrac{\theta}{2}$.

17. $r = \cot \dfrac{\theta}{2} - \tan \dfrac{\theta}{2}$.

18. $r^2 - 2r \sin \theta - \cos \theta = 0$.

19. $r^2 - 2 \tan \theta - 1 = 0$.

20. $r^2 - 2r - \sec^2 \theta = 0$.

In each of Problems 21–32, plot the curve whose equation is given.

21. $r = a(1 - \cos \theta)$: *Cardioid.*

22. $r = a\theta$: *Spiral of Archimedes.*

23. $r = e^{a\theta}$: *Logarithmic Spiral.*

24. $r = a \sin 3\theta$: *Three-Leaved Rose.*

25. $r = a \cos 2\theta$: *Four-Leaved Rose.*

26. $r^2 = a^2 \cos 2\theta$: *Lemniscate.*

27. $r = 2 + 3 \sin \theta$.

28. $r = 1 - 2 \sin 2\theta$.

29. $r = a(1 + 2 \cos 2\theta)$.

30. $r = a \tan 2\theta$.

31. $r = a \sin \dfrac{\theta}{2}$.

32. $r = a \cos \dfrac{\theta}{3}$.

69. Differential of Arc in Polar Coördinates. Consider a curve whose equation in polar coördinates is $r = f(\theta)$, and let the fixed point A on the curve serve as an origin of arcs. Then, denoting the arc from A to the arbitrary point $P(r, \theta)$ on the curve by s (Fig. 69), let us obtain ds in terms of the polar coördinates of P and their differentials.

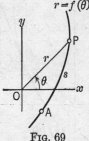

Instead of solving this problem directly in polar coördinates, let us start with (2), Art. 59, namely

$$(ds)^2 = (dx)^2 + (dy)^2,$$

and make the substitutions

$$dx = \cos \theta \, dr - r \sin \theta \, d\theta,$$

$$dy = \sin \theta \, dr + r \cos \theta \, d\theta,$$

FIG. 69

which expressions arise by differentiation from (1) and (2), Art. 68. The result is

(1) $$(ds)^2 = (dr)^2 + r^2(d\theta)^2,$$

or

(2) $$ds = \pm \sqrt{\left(\frac{dr}{d\theta}\right)^2 + r^2} \, d\theta,$$

where it is understood that θ is expressed in radians and the sign is plus or minus according as the positive direction along the curve corresponds to increasing or to decreasing θ.

Example. Find the differential of arc for the *logarithmic spiral* $r = e^{k\theta}$, where θ is expressed in radians.
Since

$$\frac{dr}{d\theta} = ke^{k\theta},$$

we obtain by (2)

$$ds = \pm e^{k\theta} \sqrt{k^2 + 1} \, d\theta.$$

70. Radial and Transverse Components of Velocity. Let a particle P move according to a given law on the curve $r = f(\theta)$ shown in Fig. 70. Then designating the component of the instantaneous velocity of P along the radius vector OP (that is, the *radial component*) by v_r, and the component of the velocity at right angles to OP (that is, the *transverse component*) by v_θ, let us obtain expressions for v_r and v_θ.

From the geometry of the figure it appears that

$$v_r = v_x \cos \theta + v_y \sin \theta.$$

Consequently by (8) and (9), Art. 61, and by (1) and (2), Art. 68, we obtain

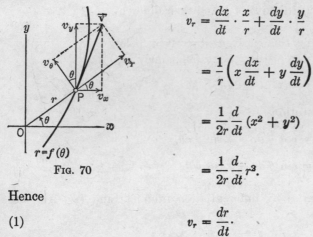

$$v_r = \frac{dx}{dt} \cdot \frac{x}{r} + \frac{dy}{dt} \cdot \frac{y}{r}$$

$$= \frac{1}{r}\left(x\frac{dx}{dt} + y\frac{dy}{dt}\right)$$

$$= \frac{1}{2r}\frac{d}{dt}(x^2 + y^2)$$

$$= \frac{1}{2r}\frac{d}{dt}r^2.$$

$r = f(\theta)$

Fig. 70

Hence

(1) $$v_r = \frac{dr}{dt}.$$

Thus the radial component of the velocity of a particle is simply the rate at which its radius vector r changes. Returning to the figure, we see that

$$v_\theta = v_y \cos\theta - v_x \sin\theta$$

$$= \frac{dy}{dt}\cdot\frac{x}{r} - \frac{dx}{dt}\cdot\frac{y}{r}$$

$$= \frac{x^2}{r}\cdot\frac{x\dfrac{dy}{dt} - y\dfrac{dx}{dt}}{x^2}$$

$$= \frac{x^2}{r}\frac{d}{dt}\left(\frac{y}{x}\right)$$

$$= \frac{x^2}{r}\frac{d}{dt}(\tan\theta)$$

$$= \frac{x^2}{r}\sec^2\theta\,\frac{d\theta}{dt}.$$

Therefore, since $x\sec\theta = r$,

(2) $$v_\theta = r\frac{d\theta}{dt},$$

where θ is expressed in radians.

Recalling (Art. 64) that $\dfrac{d\theta}{dt}$ is the angular velocity of the line OP, we see that the transverse component of the velocity of the particle P is equal to its radius vector times the angular velocity thereof.

Since v_r and v_θ are components of the velocity of a particle along two mutually perpendicular lines, we obtain for the speed of the particle

$$(3) \qquad v = \pm \sqrt{\left(\frac{dr}{dt}\right)^2 + \left(r\frac{d\theta}{dt}\right)^2},$$

the sign being positive or negative according as the particle moves in the positive direction along the curve or in the opposite direction.

We observe that (3) may be deduced from (1) of the preceding article by dividing both members by $(dt)^2$, extracting the square root, and writing v for $\dfrac{ds}{dt}$.

Example. A particle starts from the origin and, moving with a constant speed of $2\sqrt{5}$ ft./sec., describes the first-quadrant portion of the curve $r^2 = 4 \tan 2\theta$, where r is expressed in feet and θ in radians. Find v_r and v_θ when the particle is at $\left(2, \dfrac{\pi}{8}\right)$.

On differentiating the equation of the curve with respect to t, we obtain

$$2r\frac{dr}{dt} = 8(\sec^2 2\theta)\frac{d\theta}{dt},$$

or

$$r^2\frac{dr}{dt} = 4(\sec^2 2\theta)r\frac{d\theta}{dt}.$$

Hence by (1) and (2)

$$r^2 v_r = 4v_\theta \sec^2 2\theta,$$

and at $\left(2, \dfrac{\pi}{8}\right)$ we have

$$v_r = 2v_\theta,$$

where by hypothesis both v_r and v_θ are positive. Moreover, since the speed is constantly $2\sqrt{5}$ ft./sec.,

$$v_r{}^2 + v_\theta{}^2 = 20.$$

Solving the last two equations simultaneously, we find for the required components of the instantaneous velocity

$$v_r = 4 \text{ ft./sec.}$$

and

$$v_\theta = 2 \text{ ft./sec.}$$

PROBLEMS

In each of Problems 1–10, find the differential of arc for the curve whose equation is given.

1. $r = a \cos \theta$.

2. $r = a \sin^2 \dfrac{\theta}{2}$.

3. $r = a \cos^3 \dfrac{\theta}{3}$.

4. $r = a(1 - \cos \theta)$.

5. $r = \dfrac{a}{1 + \cos \theta}$.

6. $r = 3 \sin \theta + 4 \cos \theta$.

7. $r = a \sec \theta$.

8. $r = a \sec^2 \dfrac{\theta}{2}$.

9. $r = a \csc^3 \dfrac{\theta}{3}$.

10. $r = a(\tan \theta + \sec \theta)$.

11. A particle moving with a constant speed of $\sqrt{13}$ ft./sec. describes in a counterclockwise sense the first-quadrant loop of the curve $r = a \sin 2\theta$. If r is expressed in feet, find the radial and transverse components of the velocity of the particle when $\theta = \dfrac{\pi}{12}$.

12. A particle moves along the curve $r = a(1 - \cos \theta)$ in such a way that the angular velocity of the radius vector is 2 radians/sec. If r is expressed in feet, find the radial and transverse components of the velocity of the particle when $\theta = \dfrac{\pi}{2}$.

13. A particle moves along the curve $r = \dfrac{a}{1 - \cos \theta}$ in such a way that $r^2 \dfrac{d\theta}{dt} = k$, where k is a constant. Find v^2 in terms of θ.

Note: The path is parabolic, with focus at the origin, and the condition $r^2 \dfrac{d\theta}{dt} = k$ is such as would result from the action of an attractive force depending only on the radius vector and radially directed. The same condition holds for the elliptic motion of a planet if the origin is taken at the sun.

14. For the motion described in Problem 13, show that $r \dfrac{d^2\theta}{dt^2} + 2 \dfrac{dr}{dt} \dfrac{d\theta}{dt} = 0$.

Note: The left member of this equation is the transverse component of the acceleration of the particle; the vanishing of this component signifies that the acceleration is radially directed, as may be inferred from the preceding note.

15. The radial component a_r of the acceleration of a particle moving along a curve $r = f(\theta)$ is given by the formula $a_r = \dfrac{d^2r}{dt^2} - r \left(\dfrac{d\theta}{dt} \right)^2$. Find a_r in terms of r for the case $r = \dfrac{a}{1 + 2 \cos \theta}$, $r^2 \dfrac{d\theta}{dt} = k$.

16. A particle moves along the curve $r = \cos^2 \dfrac{\theta}{2}$, where r is expressed in feet, in such a way that the transverse component of its velocity is constantly 3 ft./sec. Find the radial component of the velocity of the particle when $\theta = \dfrac{\pi}{3}$.

71. Angle between Radius Vector and Tangent. Let a particle move along the curve $r = f(\theta)$, where θ is expressed in radians, and let $\vec{v}$ be its instantaneous velocity at the point P (Fig. 71a). Then, by the preceding article, the radial component of the velocity is

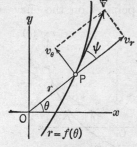

$$v_r = \frac{dr}{dt}$$

and the transverse component

$$v_\theta = r\,\frac{d\theta}{dt}.$$

FIG. 71a

If ψ denotes the angle between the radius vector OP and the vector $\vec{v}$ which is tangent to the curve at P, then

$$\tan \psi = \frac{v_\theta}{v_r} = \frac{r\,\dfrac{d\theta}{dt}}{\dfrac{dr}{dt}},$$

or

(1)
$$\tan \psi = r\,\frac{d\theta}{dr}.$$

Alternatively,

(1′)
$$\tan \psi = \frac{r}{\dfrac{dr}{d\theta}};$$

this form is more convenient when r is expressed as a function of θ.

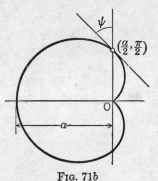

FIG. 71b

Example. Find the tangent of the angle between the radius vector and the tangent to the curve $r = a \sin^2 \dfrac{\theta}{2}$ at $\left(\dfrac{a}{2}, \dfrac{\pi}{2}\right)$.

On differentiation we obtain

$$\frac{dr}{d\theta} = a \sin \frac{\theta}{2} \cos \frac{\theta}{2},$$

whence by (1′)

$$\tan \psi = \frac{a \sin^2 \dfrac{\theta}{2}}{a \sin \dfrac{\theta}{2} \cos \dfrac{\theta}{2}} = \tan \frac{\theta}{2}.$$

For $\theta = \dfrac{\pi}{2}$, $\tan \psi = 1$. (See Fig. 71b.)

72. Radius of Curvature in Polar Coördinates. Let $r = f(\theta)$ be the equation of a curve (Fig. 72) whose radius of curvature ρ at the point P (r, θ) is required. Denoting the length of the arc from some fixed point A on the curve to the point P by s, and the angle (in radians) between the positive x-axis and the tangent to the curve at P by ϕ, we have by (1′), Art. 67,

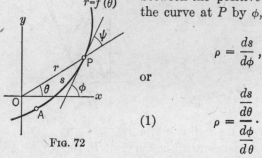

Fig. 72

$$\rho = \frac{ds}{d\phi},$$

or

$$(1) \qquad \rho = \frac{\dfrac{ds}{d\theta}}{\dfrac{d\phi}{d\theta}}.$$

Now by (2), Art. 69, if θ is expressed in radians,

$$(2) \qquad \frac{ds}{d\theta} = \sqrt{r^2 + \left(\frac{dr}{d\theta}\right)^2},$$

provided that we choose as the positive direction along the curve that for which θ is increasing. Moreover, if, as in the preceding article, ψ is the angle between the radius vector OP and the tangent to the curve at P, it follows from the figure that

$$\phi = \theta + \psi^*,$$

whence

$$(3) \qquad \frac{d\phi}{d\theta} = 1 + \frac{d\psi}{d\theta}.$$

Since by (1′) of the preceding article

$$\psi = \tan^{-1}\left(\frac{r}{\dfrac{dr}{d\theta}}\right),$$

so that

$$\frac{d\psi}{d\theta} = \frac{\left(\dfrac{dr}{d\theta}\right)^2 - r\dfrac{d^2r}{d\theta^2}}{r^2 + \left(\dfrac{dr}{d\theta}\right)^2},$$

---

* In many cases the two sides of this equation will be found to differ by an integral multiple of π; such a discrepancy, however, would not invalidate (3).

we may write in place of (3)

(4)
$$\frac{d\phi}{d\theta} = \frac{r^2 + 2\left(\dfrac{dr}{d\theta}\right)^2 - r\dfrac{d^2r}{d\theta^2}}{r^2 + \left(\dfrac{dr}{d\theta}\right)^2}.$$

Substituting (2) and (4) into (1), we obtain

(5)
$$\rho = \frac{\left[r^2 + \left(\dfrac{dr}{d\theta}\right)^2\right]^{\frac{3}{2}}}{r^2 + 2\left(\dfrac{dr}{d\theta}\right)^2 - r\dfrac{d^2r}{d\theta^2}}.$$

Since $\dfrac{ds}{d\theta}$ has been taken as positive, it is evident from (1) that ρ will be positive or negative according as ϕ increases or decreases as θ increases.

There is no reason to expect that the result found by applying (5) to the equation of a curve in polar coördinates will agree in sign with that found by applying (1), Art. 67, to the cartesian equation of the curve, for in the derivation of these formulas entirely different criteria have been adopted regarding the choice of a positive direction along the curve.

Example.   Find the radius of curvature of $r = a \sin 2\theta$ at $\left(a, \dfrac{\pi}{4}\right)$.   (See Fig. 68c.)

Evidently
$$\frac{dr}{d\theta} = 2a \cos 2\theta, \qquad \frac{d^2r}{d\theta^2} = -4a \sin 2\theta,$$

and, for $\theta = \dfrac{\pi}{4}$,
$$\frac{dr}{d\theta} = 0, \qquad \frac{d^2r}{d\theta^2} = -4a,$$

whence by (5)
$$\rho = \frac{[a^2 + 0]^{\frac{3}{2}}}{a^2 + 0 + 4a^2} = \frac{a}{5}.$$

PROBLEMS

1. Find the angle between the radius vector and the tangent to the logarithmic spiral $r = e^{a\theta}$ at any point.

2. Find the tangent of the angle between the radius vector and the tangent to the cardioid $r = a(1 - \cos\theta)$ at the point in the first quadrant for which $\tan\theta = \frac{3}{4}$.

3. Find the angle between the radius vector and the tangent to the curve $r = \dfrac{a}{1 + \cos\theta}$ at the point for which $\theta = \dfrac{\pi}{2}$.

4. Find the angle between the radius vector and the tangent to the curve $r = a \cos 2\theta$ at a point for which $\theta = \tan^{-1} \frac{3}{4}$.

5. Find the angle between the radius vector and the tangent to the curve $r = a \cos^2 \frac{\theta}{2}$ at the point for which $\theta = \frac{\pi}{2}$.

6. Find the angle between the radius vector and the tangent to the curve $r = a \csc^2 \frac{\theta}{2}$ at the point for which $\theta = \frac{\pi}{3}$.

7. Find the angle between the radius vector and the tangent to the curve $r = a \tan 2\theta$ at the point for which $\theta = \frac{\pi}{8}$.

8. Using the relation $\tan \phi = \tan (\theta + \psi)$, find the slope of the lemniscate $r^2 = a^2 \cos 2\theta$ at the point for which $\theta = \frac{\pi}{6}$.

9. Find the slope of the cardioid $r = a(1 + \cos \theta)$ at the point in the first quadrant for which $\theta = \sin^{-1} \frac{3}{5}$.

10. Find, in rectangular coördinates, the equation of the line tangent to the curve $r^2 = 9 \sec 2\theta$ at the point in the first quadrant for which $\tan \theta = \frac{4}{5}$.

11. *Pedal Curve.* The locus of the foot of the perpendicular from the origin to a tangent line to a curve is called the **pedal** of the curve with respect to the origin.

Show that a perpendicular from the origin to the tangent to the circle $r = a \cos \theta$ at the point (r, θ) meets the tangent at the point $(a \cos^2 \theta, 2\theta)$. Then designating the latter point as (r_1, θ_1), show that the pedal of the circle with respect to the origin is the cardioid $r_1 = \frac{a}{2} (1 + \cos \theta_1)$.

12. By the method outlined in the preceding problem, show that the pedal of any one of the family of curves $r^m = a^m \cos m\theta$ with respect to the origin is given by the equation $r^{\frac{m}{m+1}} = a^{\frac{m}{m+1}} \cos \frac{m\theta}{m + 1}$, and hence infer that the pedal belongs to the same family of curves and that its equation is obtainable from that of the original curve by changing m to $\frac{m}{m + 1}$.

13. Find the acute angle at which the curves $r = 4 \cos 2\theta$ and $r = 4 \sin 2\theta$ intersect at a point other than the origin.

14. Find the angle at which the curves $r = a(1 - \sin 2\theta)$ and $r^2 = \frac{1}{2}a^2 \sin 2\theta$ intersect at a point other than the origin.

15. Find the angle at which the curves $r = a \tan \left(\theta - \frac{\pi}{12} \right)$ and $r = 2a \cos \theta$ intersect at the point $\left(a, \frac{\pi}{3} \right)$.

16. Find the angle at which the curves $r = a(1 + \sin \theta)$ and $r = a(1 - \sin \theta)$ intersect at the point $(a, 0)$.

17. Find the radius of curvature of the curve $r = 4 \cos 2\theta$ at the point for which $\theta = \frac{\pi}{4}$.

18. Find the radius of curvature of the curve $r = 2 \cos 3\theta$ at the point for which $\theta = \frac{2\pi}{3}$.

19. Find the radius of curvature of the curve $r^2 = a^2 \csc 2\theta$ at any point.

20. Find the radius of curvature of the curve $r = \dfrac{a}{1 - \cos \theta}$ at the point for which $\theta = \dfrac{\pi}{3}$.

21. Find the radius of curvature of the lemniscate $r^2 = 2a^2 \cos 2\theta$ at the point for which $\theta = \dfrac{\pi}{6}$.

73. Newton's Method. The student will recall from algebra that the irrational real roots of an equation containing only positive integral powers of the unknown with numerical coefficients may be determined to as close an approximation as desired by Horner's Method. We shall now consider another process, known as **Newton's Method,** which involves differentiation and has the advantage of being applicable to a greater variety of equations than Horner's Method.

Suppose that from tables, or a graph, or otherwise, we have found that the equation

(1) $$f(x) = 0$$

has a root in the neighborhood of x_1, and suppose that we wish to evaluate this root.   Writing $y = f(x)$, we may expect that

$$y_1 = f(x_1)$$

has a small numerical value; and if we could apply to x_1 a suitable correction Δx such that

(2) $$f(x_1 + \Delta x) = y_1 + \Delta y = 0,$$

then $x_1 + \Delta x$ would be the required root of (1).

Our problem is thus to find, or at least to approximate, that value of Δx which renders

$$\Delta y = - y_1,$$

in accordance with (2).   Now if, when $x = x_1$, we assign to x an increment $\Delta_1 x$ of such a value that the corresponding *differential* of y is given by

(3) $$dy = - y_1,$$

it follows that the increment $\Delta_1 x$, while differing from Δx, will be an approximation to it.   But, by Art. 24, $dy = f'(x_1)\Delta_1 x$, where $f'(x_1)$ denotes the value of $f'(x)$ for $x = x_1$.   Therefore (3) may be written

$$f'(x_1)\Delta_1 x = - y_1 = - f(x_1),$$

whence as an approximation to Δx we have

$$\Delta_1 x = - \frac{f(x_1)}{f'(x_1)} \, .$$

Hence, if x_1 is taken as the first approximation to the required root of (1), a second approximation is given by

$$x_2 = x_1 + \Delta_1 x,$$

or

$$(4) \qquad\qquad x_2 = x_1 - \frac{f(x_1)}{f'(x_1)}.$$

Now regarding x_2 as the initial value of x, and repeating the above procedure, we obtain as the third approximation to the required root

$$(5) \qquad\qquad x_3 = x_2 - \frac{f(x_2)}{f'(x_2)}.$$

Higher approximations are given by similar formulas. In a particular problem we stop when the difference between two successive approximations is sufficiently small.

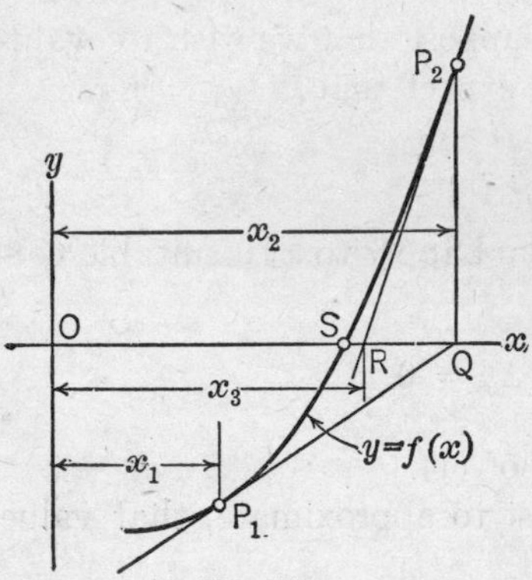

Fig. 73a

A geometrical interpretation of Newton's Method will now be given. Let the curve (Fig. 73a) be the graph of the equation $y = f(x)$ in the neighborhood of a root of $f(x) = 0$, and let $P_1(x_1, y_1)$ be the point on the curve whose abscissa is the assumed first approximation to the root. Then the second approximation, x_2, is the abscissa of the point Q where the tangent line to the curve at P_1 cuts the x-axis. For, from the equation

$$y - y_1 = f'(x_1)(x - x_1)$$

of this line, it is evident that the abscissa of Q is $x_1 - \dfrac{f(x_1)}{f'(x_1)}$, which by (4) is the value of the second approximation x_2.

Let P_2 be that point on the curve whose abscissa is x_2, and let the tangent to the curve at P_2 cut the x-axis at R. Then, reasoning as above, we may show that the abscissa of R is equal to the third approximation, x_3.

Continuing with the tangent-line construction, we obtain the higher approximations. It is evident from the figure that the points of intersection of the successive tangents with the x-axis approach as a limit the point S where the curve cuts the x-axis and whose abscissa is therefore the root of $f(x) = 0$.

One may readily sketch curves for which Newton's Method fails. The conditions under which this method yields a required root of $f(x) = 0$ will not be discussed here.

Example 1.   Find to three places of decimals that root of the equation

$$x^4 + x^3 - 11x^2 + 12x - 10 = 0$$

which lies between 2 and 3.

Calling the polynomial $f(x)$, we find

$$f(2) = -6 \text{ and } f(3) = 35.$$

Hence it appears probable that the root is nearer to 2 than to 3, and we take at the first approximation $x_1 = 2$.

Since

$$f'(x) = 4x^3 + 3x^2 - 22x + 12$$

and $f'(2) = 12$, the second approximation is by (4)

$$x_2 = 2 + \tfrac{6}{12} = 2.5.$$

Next, substituting in (5), we find for the third approximation

$$x_3 = 2.5 - \frac{f(2.5)}{f'(2.5)} = 2.5 - \frac{5.9375}{38.250} = 2.3$$

to the nearest tenth.

Continuing in the same manner, we obtain for the fourth approximation

$$x_4 = 2.3 - \frac{f(2.3)}{f'(2.3)} = 2.3 + \frac{0.4389}{25.938} = 2.317$$

to the nearest thousandth.

The fifth approximation is

$$x_5 = 2.317 - \frac{f(2.317)}{f'(2.317)} = 2.317 - \frac{0.010}{26.887}.$$

Since the difference between x_4 and x_5 is too small to affect the third decimal place, we are justified in taking the root, determined with the accuracy required, as 2.317.

Example 2.   Determine to four decimals that root of the equation $x - \tan x = 0$ which lies between π and $\dfrac{3\pi}{2}$.

This equation, which arises in connection with the diffraction of light, may be solved graphically, for writing it in the form $x = \tan x$, we note that it has as roots the abscissas of the points of intersection of the line $y = x$ with the curve $y = \tan x$. The abscissa of the point P (Fig. 73b) is the root we are seeking.

In applying Newton's Method, we obtain a start by consulting a table giving values of $\tan x$ with x expressed in radians.   But since in tables x is not carried as far as π radians, we set $x = \pi + z$, and, using the identity tan $(\pi + z) =$ tan z, we rewrite the given equation as

(6) $$\pi + z = \tan z,$$

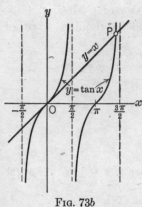

FIG. 73b

of which the root to be investigated lies between zero and $\dfrac{\pi}{2}$.

From tables we find:

z	$\pi + z$	tan z
1.3500	4.4916	4.4552
1.3600	4.5016	4.6734

It is thus evident that $\pi + z$ will be equal to tan z for some value of z between 1.3500 and 1.3600; accordingly, we take as the first approximation

$$z_1 = 1.35.$$

Putting $f(z) = \pi + z - \tan z$, whence $f'(z) = -\tan^2 z$, we obtain as the second approximation (cf. (4))

$$z_2 = 1.35 + \frac{4.4916 - 4.4552}{(4.4552)^2} = 1.3518,$$

to the nearest ten-thousandth.

To four decimal places, the third approximation is the same as z_2. Hence the required root of (6) is, to four decimals, 1.3518 radians, and the third-quadrant angle satisfying the given equation $x - \tan x = 0$ is therefore $\pi + 1.3518$, or 4.4934 radians.

PROBLEMS

1. Find by Newton's Method the real root of the equation $x^3 + x - 3 = 0$ to three decimals.

2. Find by Newton's Method to three decimals that root of the equation $x^3 + 2x^2 - 7 = 0$ which lies between 1 and 2.

3. Find by Newton's Method to three decimals that root of the equation $x^3 + 3x^2 - 5x - 2 = 0$ which lies between zero and -1.

4. Find by Newton's Method to two decimals that root of the equation $x^4 - 4x^3 + 5x^2 - 10x + 12 = 0$ which lies between 1 and 2.

5. Van der Waals' equation for carbon dioxide is, approximately,

$$pv^3 - (1.16p + 1.87T)v^2 + 2240v - 2600 = 0,$$

where p is the pressure in atmospheres, v the specific volume in cubic centimeters per gram, and T the absolute temperature in degrees Centigrade. Find to two decimals the value of v for $p = 80$ and $T = 320$.

6. The volume of a spherical segment is given by $V = \dfrac{\pi h^2}{3}(3r - h)$, where r is the radius of the sphere and h the height of the segment. If $r = 4$ ft. and $V = 12$ cu. ft., find the value of h to two decimals.

7. A sphere of radius a has a volume which is 30π cu. ft. less than half the volume of an ellipsoid whose semi-axes are a, $a + 2$, and $a + 4$. Find to two decimals the smaller of the possible values of a. (The volume of an ellipsoid is $\frac{4}{3}\pi$ times the product of the lengths of the semi-axes.)

8. Find to three decimals the coördinates of the first-quadrant point where the line $y = x - 2$ intersects the curve $y = \ln x$.

HINT: From a table of natural logarithms obtain a first approximation to the larger root of the equation $\ln x = x - 2$.

9. Find to three decimals the abscissa of the point where the line $2x + y - 26 = 0$ intersects the curve $y = e^x$.

10. Find to three decimals the value of x between zero and $\frac{\pi}{2}$ for which the function $x \cos x$ is a maximum.

11. For angles which are not too large, $\sin x$ is given to a close approximation by the equation $\sin x = x - \dfrac{x^3}{6}$. Find to four decimals the value of x for which $\sin x = 0.3000$.

12. A particle P (Fig. 73c) describes an ellipse under the gravitational attraction of a massive particle O situated at a focus of the ellipse. If the eccentricity e of the ellipse is small enough, the polar angle θ is given approximately by the equation $\theta = nt + 2e \sin nt$, where t is the time measured from the moment when the particle P passes the end A of the major axis, and n is 2π divided by the period. If $e = 0.03$ and $n = \frac{1}{5}$, find to two decimals the value of t for which $\theta = 0.60$ radian.

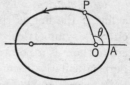

FIG. 73c

13. The equation $e^{-x} + \dfrac{x}{5} - 1 = 0$ arises in the quantum theory of radiation. Find the positive root to three decimals.

14. When the ends of a cable, whose load per unit length is w, are attached to two supports at the same height and separated by a distance b, the sag h and the tension P at the middle point of the cable are related to each other and to w and b by the equation

$$h = \frac{P}{2w}(e^{\frac{wb}{2P}} + e^{-\frac{wb}{2P}} - 2).$$

If $w = 2$ lb./ft., $h = 3$ ft., and $b = 6$ ft., find the value of P to three decimals.

HINT: After making the substitutions, write the equation in the form

$$\frac{12}{P} + 2 = e^{\frac{6}{P}} + e^{-\frac{6}{P}}$$

and use tables for e^x and e^{-x} to obtain a first approximation to the value of $\dfrac{6}{P}$.

15. For a certain particle moving with *damped harmonic motion* along a straight line, the displacement x (feet) from a fixed point on the line is given in terms of the time t (seconds) by the equation $x = 10te^{-0.2t}$. Find to three decimals the value of t between zero and unity for which $x = 1$.

16. Find to three decimals the abscissa of the point of inflection of the curve $y = \dfrac{x^2}{4}(2 \ln x - 3) + \cos x$.

CHAPTER VII

PLANE CURVES—RECTANGULAR COÖRDINATES

74. Curve Tracing in Rectangular Coördinates. In analytic geometry the student has become acquainted with an algebraic procedure whereby certain properties of a curve can be determined from the equation, so that the labor of plotting the curve is materially reduced. By way of review and in preparation for the further study of curves with the aid of calculus, we list these properties together with the tests bearing on them.

1. Symmetry. Two points P and Q, are **symmetrical** with respect to a line if the line is the perpendicular bisector of the segment PQ. A curve is symmetrical with respect to a line if for every point P on the curve there is a point Q also on the curve such that the segment PQ is perpendicularly bisected by the line. A curve is therefore symmetrical with respect to the x-axis if for every point $P(x, y)$ on the curve there is a point $Q(x, -y)$ also on the curve. Hence if the equation of a curve is not altered when y is changed to $-y$, the curve is symmetrical with respect to the x-axis. Thus a curve whose equation contains y in even powers only, as for example the curve $2x^3y^2 + xy^4 - 5 = 0$, is symmetrical with respect to the x-axis.

Similarly, if the equation of a curve is not altered when x is changed to $-x$, the curve is symmetrical with respect to the y-axis. Examples of curves having this type of symmetry are $y = \cos x$ (Fig. 49a) and $y = x^2(1 - x^2)$.

A curve is symmetrical with respect to the origin as a center if for every point $P(x, y)$ on the curve there is a point $Q(-x, -y)$ also on the curve, so that the segment PQ is bisected at the origin. Hence, if the equation of a curve is not altered when the signs of both x and y are changed, then the curve is symmetrical with respect to the origin. Thus the curve $y = x^3$ (Fig. 74a) is symmetrical with respect to the origin because, when the signs of x and y are changed, the equation becomes $-y = (-x)^3$ and this reduces to $y = x^3$. Likewise the ellipse $9x^2 + 16y^2 = 144$ (Fig. 74b) is symmetrical with respect to the origin. The latter curve, but not the former, is also symmetrical with respect to the x-axis and the y-axis. As these examples indicate, symmetry with

196

respect to both coördinate axes implies symmetry with respect to the origin, but not conversely.

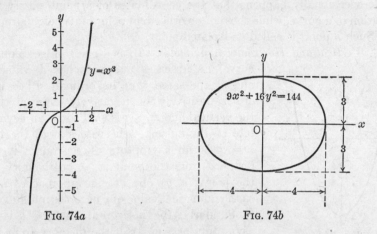

FIG. 74a   FIG. 74b

2. Intercepts. The **intercepts** of a curve are the distances, with appropriate signs, from the origin to the points at which the curve touches or intersects the coördinate axes. The x-intercepts of a curve may thus be obtained from the equation of the curve by setting y equal to zero and solving for x. For instance, in the case of the ellipse $9x^2 + 16y^2 = 144$ we find that the x-intercepts are 4 and -4. Similarly the y-intercepts of a curve are found by setting $x = 0$ in the equation of the curve, and solving for y.

3. Extent. The **horizontal extent** of a curve is given by the range, or ranges, of values of x that serve as abscissas of points on the curve. Similarly, the **vertical extent** of a curve is given by the range, or ranges, of values of y that serve as ordinates of points on the curve.

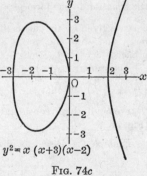

$y^2 = x\,(x+3)(x-2)$

FIG. 74c

Thus in the case of the curve $y^2 = x(x + 3)(x - 2)$, the horizontal extent is described by the inequalities $-3 \leq x \leq 0$ and. $x \geq 2$, for only when the value of x lies within one or the other of these ranges is y^2 positive and y real. The curve is shown in Fig. 74c.

The horizontal extent of the parabola $y = x^2 - 4$ (Fig. 74d) is unlimited, for any real value of x renders y real. The vertical extent of the same parabola, however, is given by the inequality $y \geq -4$, for the equation of the curve may be written $x^2 = y + 4$, and in order for x to be real y must be at least -4.

It occasionally happens that the coördinates of a point satisfy the equation of a curve, while those of no other real point of its neighborhood do. Such a point is called an **isolated point**.

4. Vertical and Horizontal Asymptotes. If, as a point moves along a

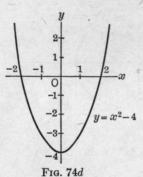

FIG. 74d

curve, its abscissa x approaches a value a and at the same time its ordinate y becomes either positively or negatively infinite, then the vertical line $x = a$ is said to be an **asymptote** of the curve. Otherwise stated, the line $x = a$ is an asymptote of the curve if the distance from the point (x, y) on the curve to the point (a, y) on the line approaches zero as the numerical value of y becomes infinite.

Similarly, the horizontal line $y = b$ is an asymptote of a curve if the distance from the point (x, y) on the curve to the point (x, b) on the line approaches zero as the numerical value of x becomes infinite.

If a curve has a horizontal or a vertical asymptote, this asymptote may be found from the equation of the curve, as is illustrated in the ensuing examples.

In the next article we shall formulate methods for finding oblique asymptotes.

Example 1. Discuss and sketch the curve $xy^2 = 2 - x$.

The curve is symmetrical with respect to the x-axis because its equation contains y in an even power only. It has an x-intercept of 2 and no y-intercept. If we write the equation in the form $y^2 = \dfrac{2 - x}{x}$, we note that the horizontal extent of the curve is given by the inequality $0 < x \leq 2$ (for only for this range of values of x is y real), and that the y-axis is an asymptote (for, as x approaches zero, y becomes infinite).

The student may show that there are points of inflection at $\left(\dfrac{3}{2}, \pm \dfrac{\sqrt{3}}{3}\right)$ and that the slope of the curve is infinite at $(2, 0)$.

From all these considerations the curve is easily sketched (Fig. 74e).

Example 2. Discuss and sketch the curve
$$(x - 2)^2 = \frac{4}{(y + 2)^3}.$$

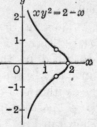

FIG. 74e

The curve is symmetrical with respect to the line $x = 2$. For setting $x' = x - 2$, we see that the transformed equation contains x' only in an even power, and conclude that the curve has as an axis of symmetry the line $x' = 0$, or $x = 2$. Or else, on solving the given equation for x, we find $x = 2 \pm \dfrac{2}{(y+2)^{\frac{3}{2}}}$, which shows that for any permissible value of y there are two points symmetrically situated with respect to the line $x = 2$.

The curve has x-intercepts of $2 \pm \dfrac{\sqrt{2}}{2}$, as we find on setting $y = 0$. The y-intercept is -1.

The vertical extent of the curve is given by the inequality $y > -2$. The horizontal extent is unlimited.

The curve has the horizontal asymptote $y = -2$ and the vertical asymptote $x = 2$. The latter fact appears immediately when the equation is written in the form

$$(y + 2)^3 = \frac{4}{(x - 2)^2},$$

whence y becomes infinite as x approaches 2.

It will be left to the student to show that there are no maximum or minimum points, or points of inflection.

The curve is shown in Fig. 74f.

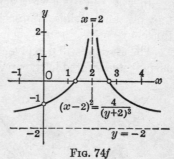

Fig. 74f

PROBLEMS

In each of the following problems, discuss and sketch the curve whose equation is given.

1. $y = \dfrac{8a^3}{x^2 + 4a^2}$.

2. $y = \dfrac{4}{4 - x^2}$.

3. $y = \dfrac{x}{x^2 + 4}$.

4. $y = \dfrac{x}{x^2 - 4}$.

5. $y = \dfrac{x^2}{3 - x}$.

6. $y = \dfrac{x^2}{3 + x}$.

7. $x^2 = \dfrac{3 + y}{y}$.

8. $(y + 2)^2 = x^2(x - 1)$.

9. $(y + 2)^2 = x(x^2 - 1)$.

10. $x^2 = y^4(4 - y^2)$.

11. $y^7 = \dfrac{4 - x}{x^2}$

12. $(y + 2)^2 = \dfrac{x}{x^2 - 1}$.

13. $y^2 = \dfrac{x^3}{2a - x}$.

14. $y^2 = \dfrac{x^2}{4 - x}$.

15. $y^2 = \dfrac{x^2}{x + 4}$.

16. $y^2 = \dfrac{x^2}{(x + 1)(x - 2)}$.

17. $2x - xy + 4y - 9 = 0$.
18. $y^2(x^2 - 4) + 16 = 0$.
19. $y^2(x^2 - 4) - 16 = 0$.
20. $y^2(1 - x^2) = x^2(1 + 3y^2)$.

75. Asymptotes. We have seen that a horizontal or a vertical asymptote of a curve can in many problems be determined by inspection. Oblique asymptotes, however, are usually more difficult to find. Their determination will be made to depend on one or the other of two equivalent general definitions of an asymptote.

Definition 1. An asymptote of a curve of infinite extent is a line whose position is approached as a limit by a tangent to the curve as the point of tangency recedes indefinitely along the curve. There is no necessity, of course, that such a limiting position exists; when it fails to exist, the curve has no asymptote.

In Fig. 75a is shown a curve having an asymptote MN. Here the moving tangent line approaches coincidence with MN as the point of tangency passes through the positions $P, P', P'', \cdots$.

The student will perceive that Definition 1 covers the special cases of asymptotes treated in the preceding article.

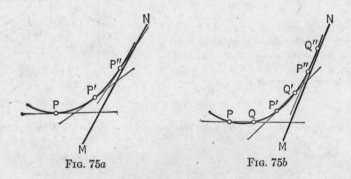

FIG. 75a   FIG. 75b

Definition 2. An asymptote of a curve of infinite extent is a line whose position is approached as a limit by a secant to the curve as two of the points in which the secant intersects the curve recede indefinitely along the curve.

The limiting position, if it exists, of the secant line is independent of the separation of the moving points of intersection. If these points are allowed to coincide, the secant becomes a tangent; hence Definition 2 is equivalent to Definition 1.

Fig. 75b shows a curve having an asymptote MN and illustrates how a secant line, moving through the positions $PQ, P'Q', P''Q'', \cdots$, approaches coincidence with the asymptote.

We shall now develop two methods for determining asymptotes: the method of limiting intercepts and the method of substitution.

The Method of Limiting Intercepts. Let $y = f(x)$ be a curve of infinite extent, and let (x_1, y_1) be a point on the curve. Then the equation of the tangent to the curve at (x_1, y_1) is

$$y - y_1 = f'(x_1)(x - x_1).$$

The intercepts of the tangent on the axes are

(1) $$x\text{-intercept} = x_1 - \frac{y_1}{f'(x_1)},$$

(2) $$y\text{-intercept} = y_1 - x_1 f'(x_1).$$

To determine whether an asymptote exists, and if it does, to find its position, we investigate in accordance with Definition 1 the limiting values of the intercepts given by (1) and (2) as the point of tangency (x_1, y_1) recedes indefinitely along the curve.   Four cases arise.

Case 1.   If both intercepts of the tangent become infinite, the tangent has no limiting position and hence there is no asymptote.

Case 2.   If the intercept of the tangent on one of the coördinate axes becomes infinite, while the intercept on the other axis has a limit, there is an asymptote parallel to the former axis and its equation will be evident.

Case 3.   If both intercepts of the tangent have limits other than zero, these limits are the intercepts of an asymptote whose equation can be found by Formula 23(d), p. 509.

Case 4.   If both intercepts of the tangent approach zero as a limit, there is an asymptote passing through the origin with a slope given by the limiting value of $f'(x_1)$.

Example 1.   Show that the parabola $y = x^2$ has no asymptote.
Since $f'(x_1) = 2x_1$ and $y_1 = x_1{}^2$ we have, by (1) and (2), for the intercepts of the tangent line at (x_1, y_1)

$$x\text{-intercept} = \frac{x_1}{2} = \pm \frac{\sqrt{y_1}}{2},$$

$$y\text{-intercept} = -x_1{}^2 = -y_1;$$

and since both of these become infinite with x_1 and y_1, it follows that the parabola has no asymptote.

Example 2.   Find the asymptotes of the hyperbola $b^2x^2 - a^2y^2 = a^2b^2$ (Fig. 75c).
Using implicit differentiation, we obtain by (1) and (2)

$$x\text{-intercept} = \frac{a^2}{x_1},$$

$$y\text{-intercept} = -\frac{b^2}{y_1}.$$

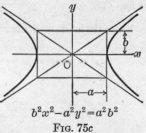

$$b^2x^2 - a^2y^2 = a^2b^2$$
Fig. 75c

The limit of each of these expressions is zero as the point (x_1, y_1) recedes indefinitely along the curve.   Hence by Case 4 any asymptote of the hyperbola passes through the origin, and therefore has an equation of the form $y = mx$, where the slope m is the limiting value of $\dfrac{dy}{dx}$ at the point of tangency.   Now from the given equation we

find $\dfrac{dy}{dx} = \pm \dfrac{b}{a\left(1 - \dfrac{a^2}{x^2}\right)^{\frac{1}{2}}}$; whence, denoting y by $f(x)$, we have $\lim\limits_{x_1 \to \pm\infty} f'(x_1) = \pm \dfrac{b}{a}$.

Thus there are two asymptotes whose respective equations are $y = \dfrac{b}{a}x$ and $y = -\dfrac{b}{a}x$.

NOTE: We applied to this problem a general method for determining asymptotes, but an elementary special method can here be used to advantage. For, writing the equation of the hyperbola in the form

$$y = \pm \frac{b}{a}\sqrt{x^2 - a^2},$$

whence

$$y \mp \frac{bx}{a} = \pm \frac{b}{a}\left(\sqrt{x^2 - a^2} - x\right)$$

$$= \mp \frac{ab}{\sqrt{x^2 - a^2} + x},$$

we obtain

$$\lim_{x \to \pm\infty}\left(y \mp \frac{bx}{a}\right) = 0.$$

Since y denotes the ordinate of a point on the hyperbola and $\pm \dfrac{bx}{a}$ can be regarded as the ordinate of a point on one or the other of lines $y = \pm \dfrac{bx}{a}$, we conclude that the vertical distance between the hyperbola and either of the lines $y = \pm \dfrac{bx}{a}$ approaches zero as a limit, and hence that these lines are asymptotes of the hyperbola.

Example 3. Determine the asymptotes of the curve $y = x\sqrt{\dfrac{x+1}{x-1}}$.

It is evident that, as x approaches unity, y becomes infinite. Hence, by the preceding article, the curve has a vertical asymptote $x = 1$.

We proceed to investigate the possible existence of other asymptotes by the method of limiting intercepts. Denoting the right side of the given equation by $f(x)$, we find $f'(x) = \dfrac{x^2 - x - 1}{(x+1)^{\frac{1}{2}}(x-1)^{\frac{3}{2}}}$.

Hence the intercepts of the tangent line to the curve at (x_1, y_1) are, by (1) and (2),

$$x\text{-intercept} = x_1 - x_1\sqrt{\frac{x_1+1}{x_1-1}} \cdot \frac{(x_1+1)^{\frac{1}{2}}(x_1-1)^{\frac{3}{2}}}{x_1^2 - x_1 - 1}$$

$$= -\frac{x_1^2}{x_1^2 - x_1 - 1} = -\frac{1}{1 - \dfrac{1}{x_1} - \dfrac{1}{x_1^2}},$$

$$y\text{-intercept} = x_1\sqrt{\frac{x_1+1}{x_1-1}} - x_1 \cdot \frac{x_1^2 - x_1 - 1}{(x_1+1)^{\frac{1}{2}}(x_1-1)^{\frac{3}{2}}}$$

$$= \frac{x_1^2}{(x_1+1)^{\frac{1}{2}}(x_1-1)^{\frac{3}{2}}} = \frac{1}{\left(1 + \dfrac{1}{x_1}\right)^{\frac{1}{2}}\left(1 - \dfrac{1}{x_1}\right)^{\frac{3}{2}}}.$$

The limits of these expressions as x_1 becomes positively or negatively infinite are, respectively, -1 and 1, and these are the intercepts of a second asymptote. Hence by Formula 23(d), p. 509, the equation of this asymptote is

$$y = x + 1.$$

The curve $y = x\sqrt{\dfrac{x+1}{x-1}}$ is sketched in Fig. 75d. Together with its reflection

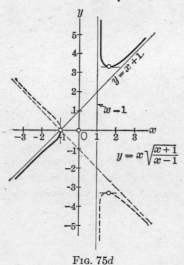

in the x-axis (shown dotted), it constitutes the graph of the equation $y^2 = x^2\left(\dfrac{x+1}{x-1}\right)$.

A discussion leading to the graph would show that there is an isolated point at the origin.

NOTE: It might appear to the student that $y = x$ is an asymptote of the curve $y = x\sqrt{\dfrac{x+1}{x-1}}$, since with numerically increasing x the radical approaches unity. However, it can be shown algebraically in a manner analogous to that used in the note to the preceding example that $\lim\limits_{x \to \pm\infty} (y - x)$, instead of being zero, is unity, so that the oblique asymptote is $y = x + 1$, in agreement with the result given by the method of limiting intercepts.

FIG. 75d

The Method of Substitution. Let the equation of a curve of infinite extent be

$$(3) \qquad\qquad f(x, y) = 0,$$

where $f(x, y)$, the general symbol for a function of the variables x and y, is here restricted to represent a polynomial of the nth degree in x and y.* Then (3) is said to be an **algebraic equation** defining x and y as **algebraic functions** of each other, while the graph of (3) is said to be an **algebraic curve.**

If this curve is cut by a variable line

$$(4) \qquad\qquad y = mx + b,$$

and two of the points of intersection recede indefinitely along the curve, then by Definition 2 the line (4) approaches coincidence with an asymptote of the curve, if an asymptote exists.

---

* The **degree** of a term composed (aside from a numerical coefficient) of the product of positive integral powers of x and y is the sum of the exponents of x and y. The degree of a polynomial in x and y is that of the term of highest degree. Thus, for example, the polynomial $x^3 - x^2y^2 + 4xy^3 - y^3$ is of the fourth degree.

We shall now formulate analytically the problem of determining the asymptotes of the curve (3).

The abscissas of the points of intersection, real and imaginary, of the curve (3) a.d the line (4) are the roots of the equation which results from substituting (4) into (3), namely

$$f(x, mx + b) = 0,$$

which is reducible to the form

(5) $\qquad a_0x^n + a_1x^{n-1} + a_2x^{n-2} + \cdots + a_{n-1}x + a_n = 0,$

where a_0 is a function of m alone, a_n is a function of b alone, and a_1, a_2, $\cdots$, a_{n-1} are, in general, functions of m and b.

As two of the points of intersection of (3) and (4) recede indefinitely along the curve, their abscissas become infinite unless the secant line (4) is approaching a vertical asymptote of the curve (3). We may therefore investigate the horizontal and oblique asymptotes of (3) by applying the condition that (5) have a pair of infinite roots. Now this condition is that the coefficients of x^n and x^{n-1} vanish.* Thus we obtain the simultaneous equations

(6) $\qquad\qquad\qquad\qquad a_0 = 0$

and

(7) $\qquad\qquad\qquad\qquad a_1 = 0.$

Any pair of real values of m and b which satisfy these equations are, respectively, the slope and the y-intercept of an asymptote of (3). More specifically, since a_0 depends only on m, the roots of (6) are the slopes of all oblique and horizontal asymptotes. Except in special cases soon to be mentioned, we need only substitute into (7) the value of m for any asymptote in order to find the corresponding value of b. Then substituting consecutively into (4) all the pairs of values of m and b thus obtained, we arrive at the equations of all the asymptotes of (3) which are not parallel to the y-axis.

A special case may arise in which some or all of the values of m satisfying (6) likewise render the left side of (7) zero irrespective of what b is. We then find the values of b corresponding to such values of m by means of the equation $a_2 = 0$, where a_2 is the coefficient of x^{n-2} in

---

* To prove this, set $z = \dfrac{1}{x}$, whereupon (5) takes the form $a_nz^n + a_{n-1}z^{n-1} + \cdots$ $+ a_1z + a_0 = 0$. Now let a_1 and a_0 approach zero. Then the left side of the equation in z becomes divisible by z^2, and consequently $z = 0$ becomes a double root. But when z approaches zero, x becomes infinite. Therefore the equation (5) has a pair of infinite roots if the coefficients of x^n and x^{n-1} vanish.

(5). If the term in x^{n-1} does not appear in (5), we likewise use the equation $a_2 = 0$ to determine b. We shall not attempt to justify these remarks or consider the case in which a_2 vanishes either identically or for values of m arising from (6).

Vertical asymptotes may be found by a modification of the method of substitution, as will be illustrated in Example 4.

Example 4. By the method of substitution find the asymptotes of the curve $(x - 2)^2(y^2 - 1) - x^3y = 0$.

Substituting $y = mx + b$, we obtain

$$(m^2 - m)x^4 + (2mb - 4m^2 - b)x^3 + \cdots + 4b^2 - 4 = 0.$$

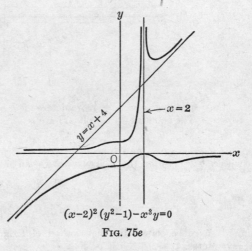

FIG. 75e

The values of m and b associated with oblique and horizontal asymptotes satisfy the equations

$$m^2 - m = 0$$

and

$$2mb - 4m^2 - b = 0,$$

whose solutions are

$$m = 1, 0$$

and

$$b = 4, 0.$$

Therefore the lines

$$y = x + 4$$

and

$$y = 0$$

are asymptotes of the curve.

We proceed to investigate vertical asymptotes as follows. Substitute $x = c$ into the equation of the curve, and arrange the result in descending powers of y, obtaining as the equation satisfied by the ordinate of any point of intersection of the curve with the vertical line $x = c$

$$(8) \qquad\qquad (c - 2)^2y^2 - c^3y - (c - 2)^2 = 0.$$

Regarding (8) as of the same degree (i.e., the fourth) as the given equation, we observe that the coefficients of y^4 and y^0 vanish identically. Moreover, the coefficient of y^2 vanishes for $c = 2$. Hence we conclude that the line $x = 2$ is a vertical asymptote of the curve.

The curve is sketched in Fig. 75e.

Example 5. By the method of substitution find the asymptotes of the curve $3y^3 + xy^2 - 3xy + y^2 + 2x - 2y = 0$.

Substituting $y = mx + b$, we obtain

$(3m^3 + m^2)x^3 + (9m^2b + 2mb - 3m + m^2)x^2 + (9mb^2 + b^2 - 3b + 2mb + 2 - 2m)x + 3b^3 + b^2 - 2b = 0.$

Equating to zero the coefficient of x^3, we have

$$3m^3 + m^2 = 0,$$

whence the slopes of any horizontal and oblique asymptotes are given by

$$m = 0 \quad \text{and} \quad m = -\tfrac{1}{3}.$$

For $m = 0$, the coefficient of x^2 vanishes irrespective of the value of b. We therefore equate to zero the coefficient of x, which, with $m = 0$, reduces to $b^2 - 3b + 2$. The roots of the equation $b^2 - 3b + 2 = 0$ are $b = 1$ and $b = 2$; hence the curve has as horizontal asymptotes the lines

$$y = 1 \quad \text{and} \quad y = 2.$$

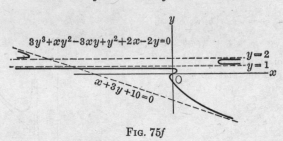

$$3y^3 + xy^2 - 3xy + y^2 + 2x - 2y = 0$$

Fig. 75f

Corresponding to $m = -\tfrac{1}{3}$, we determine b by setting the coefficient of x^2 equal to zero. The equation to be solved for b is

$$b - \tfrac{2}{3}b + 1 + \tfrac{1}{9} = 0,$$

whence $b = -\tfrac{10}{3}$, so that the curve has as an oblique asymptote the line

$$y = -\tfrac{1}{3}x - \tfrac{10}{3},$$

or

$$x + 3y + 10 = 0.$$

It may be shown by the method of Example 4 that there are no vertical asymptotes.

The curve is sketched in Fig. 75f.

PROBLEMS

In each of the following problems find the asymptotes of the given curve.

1. The hyperbola $4x^2 - 9y^2 - 36 = 0$.
2. The hyperbola $12x^2 + 24x - 7xy - 7y - 12y^2 - 25 = 0$.
3. $x^3 + x^2y - 4 = 0$.
4. $x^2y - 4x^2 - xy^2 - 7 = 0$.
5. $x^3 - 2x^2y - 3xy^2 - 4 = 0$.
6. $x^3 - 2x^2y - 3xy^2 - 4y^2 = 0$.
7. $x^3 + y^3 - 3axy = 0$.
8. $x^3 + y^3 - 2x^2y = 0$.
9. $x^3 + y^3 - 2xy^2 = 0$.
10. $x^2y - (x + 2)(y^2 - 4) = 0$.
11. $x^3 - 3x^2y + 2xy^2 - xy - 5 = 0$.
12. $x^2y - y^3 + y^2 + 1 = 0$.
13. $2x^3 - 3x^2y + xy^2 - xy + 5 = 0$.
14. $x^3 + x^2 - xy^2 + y^2 = 0$.

15. $x^4 + x^3y - 5x^2 - y^3 - 6 = 0$.
16. $x^4 + 6x^3 - 5x^2y^2 + 4y^4 + 6 = 0$.
17. $x^4 + 2x^2y^2 - 3xy^3 - 4 = 0$.
18. $x^4 + 20x^3 - y^4 = 0$.
19. $x^4 - x^3y + x^2y^2 - xy^8 - 8 = 0$.
20. $2x^3y - x^2y^2 + xy^2 - y^3 - 4 = 0$.
21. $x^3y - x^2y^2 + 4x^2 + 6xy^2 - 24x - 9y^2 + 36 = 0$.

76. Singular Points. Let the equation of a curve, written in the implicit form, be

(1) $$f(x, y) = 0.$$

Then by implicit differentiation we obtain for the slope of the curve at any point

(2) $$\frac{dy}{dx} = \frac{g(x, y)}{h(x, y)},$$

where $g(x, y)$ and $h(x, y)$ are, in general, functions of both x and y. If there is a point on the curve whose coördinates satisfy, in addition to (1), the equations

(3) $$g(x, y) = 0$$

and

(4) $$h(x, y) = 0,$$

the point is called a **singular point.** Clearly the coördinates of all the singular points of the curve may be found as the common solutions of (1), (3), and (4), if such solutions exist. It will be noted that, by (2), (3), and (4), the slope of the curve at a singular point has the indeterminate form* $\frac{0}{0}$.

If it is found that the curve (1) has a singular point at (x_1, y_1), then we may transform (1) into an equation in x' and y' by making the substitutions

(5) $$x = x' + x_1$$

and

(6) $$y = y' + y_1,$$

thereby locating the singular point at the new origin of coördinates. Accordingly, we may without loss of generality develop the theory of singular points on the supposition that the singular points in question are at the origin.

* Indeterminate forms will be studied in Chapter XII.

We shall now specialize the function $f(x, y)$ to a polynomial of the nth degree $(n \geq 2)$ and suppose that the origin is a point on the curve $f(x, y) = 0$, whose equation may therefore be written

$$(1') \qquad a_1x + b_1y + a_2x^2 + b_2xy + c_2y^2 + \cdots + k_ny^n = 0.$$

We shall investigate the conditions under which the curve $(1')$ has a singular point at the origin.

Differentiating implicitly, we find

$$(2') \qquad \frac{dy}{dx} = -\frac{a_1 + 2a_2x + b_2y + \cdots}{b_1 + b_2x + 2c_2y + \cdots + nk_ny^{n-1}}.$$

In order that the curve $(1')$ have a singular point at the origin, it is necessary that the numerator and denominator of the right member of $(2')$ vanish for $x = y = 0$, and hence that

$$(7) \qquad\qquad a_1 = b_1 = 0.$$

Conversely, if (7) holds, $(1')$ must have a singular point at the origin. In other words, *a curve $f(x, y) = 0$ has a singular point at the origin if $f(x, y)$ is a polynomial in x and y containing no terms of lower degree than the second.*

Having thus found that the curve

$$(1'') \qquad\qquad a_2x^2 + b_2xy + c_2y^2 + \cdots + k_ny^n = 0$$

has a singular point at the origin, we shall consider what bearing the coefficients of $(1'')$ have on the type to which the singular point in question may belong.

Suppose that in $(1'')$ not all the coefficients of the second-degree terms vanish; more specifically, suppose that at least c_2 is different from zero. Now let the curve be cut by a line $y = mx$, where the slope m may be freely varied. The abscissas of the points of intersection are the roots of the equation

$$(8) \qquad (a_2 + b_2m + c_2m^2)x^2 + \cdots + k_nm^nx^n = 0.$$

By hypothesis, the coefficient of x^2 is not zero for all values of m; hence, in general, the highest power of x by which the left side of (8) is divisible is x^2, so that $x = 0$ is a double root of (8). Therefore the line $y = mx$ has, in general, two coincident points of intersection with the curve $(1'')$ at the origin (as in Fig. 76a), and the origin is said to be a **singular point of the second order,** or a **double point** of the curve. Most of the singular points with which we shall deal will be double points, and of these, as will soon develop, there are several kinds.

As m is allowed to vary, it will pass through values that are roots of the quadratic equation

$$(9) \qquad\qquad a_2 + b_2 m + c_2 m^2 = 0 \quad (c_2 \neq 0)$$

obtained by setting the coefficient of x^2 in (8) equal to zero.   For a value of m that satisfies (9) the line $y = mx$ has at least three points of intersection with the curve (1″) at the origin, for then the left side of (8) will be divisible by x^3, or even by a higher power of x if the coefficient of x^3 also vanishes.   Since at least one additional point of intersection (such as P, Fig. 76a) moves to the origin as m assumes a value satisfying (9), it is clear that a line $y = mx$ whose slope is a real root of (9) is tangent to the curve at the origin.   The existence and number of such tangent lines depend on the nature of the roots of (9);   accordingly a

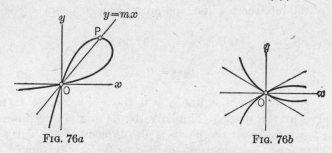

FIG. 76a   FIG. 76b

discussion of (9) will provide a basis for classifying double points as follows:

Node.   If the roots of (9) are real and distinct, the curve has two tangents at the origin, each associated with a branch of the curve; moreover, it can be shown that in this case the branches must cross each other.   The double point at the origin is then said to be a **node**, illustrated in Fig. 76b.

Isolated Point.   If the roots of (9) are imaginary, there is no real tangent line to the curve at the origin.   Therefore the double point at the origin is the only real point of its neighborhood which lies on the curve; in other words, it is an **isolated point.**   Isolated points have been mentioned previously (Arts. 6 and 74).

Cusp; Tacnode.   If the roots of (9) are equal, generally two real branches of the curve meet at the origin and have a common tangent there, the double point at the origin being either a **cusp** (Figs. 76c, 76d) or a **tacnode** (Fig. 76e) according as the branches stop at the origin or pass through it.   In exceptional instances, however, when the repeated root is zero, the curve may have an isolated point at the origin.   (See Example 1, Art. 77.)

The foregoing discussion of double points was based on the condition $c_2 \neq 0$.

If in (1″) $c_2 = 0$ but $a_2 \neq 0$, there will likewise be a double point at the origin; its nature may be determined by taking $x = ny$ as the

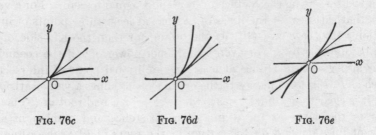

FIG. 76c   FIG. 76d   FIG. 76e

equation of the intersecting line, and proceeding as above.   (See Example 4.)

If in (1″) $a_2 = c_2 = 0$ but $b_2 \neq 0$, (9) becomes

$$b_2 m = 0,$$

whence $m = 0$. Hence the line $y = 0$ (i.e., the x-axis) is tangent to the curve at the origin. Similarly, by taking as the intersecting line $x = ny$, we find that the y-axis is also tangent to the curve at the origin. Therefore the conditions $a_2 = c_2 = 0$, $b_2 \neq 0$, signify a node at the origin, the coördinate axes being there tangent to the curve.

If in (1″) $a_2 = b_2 = c_2 = 0$, but at least one term of the third degree is present, a line $y = mx$ or $x = ny$ will intersect the curve at the origin generally in three coincident points. The origin will then be a **singular point of the third order**, i.e., a **triple point.** An illustration of a triple point at the origin, with three distinct tangent lines, will be given in Example 5.

Although we shall not consider singular points of higher order than the third, the following statement holds for singular points of all orders:

Any curve $f(x, y) = 0$, where $f(x, y)$ is a polynomial without a constant term and without first-degree terms, must have a singular point at the origin, whose order is the same as the degree of the terms of lowest degree.

Example 1. Show by the method of this article that the curve $y^2 = \dfrac{x^2(x + 1)}{x - 1}$ has an isolated point at the origin (cf. Example 3, Art. 75).

Observing that the given equation when written in the form

$$x^2 + y^2 + x^3 - xy^2 = 0$$

contains only terms of the second and third degree, we conclude that the curve has a double point at the origin.

To determine the nature of this double point, we substitute mx for y and equate the coefficient of x^2 to zero, obtaining the quadratic equation

$$1 + m^2 = 0,$$

whence

$$m = \pm \sqrt{-1} = \pm i.$$

Since these roots are imaginary, the double point at the origin is an isolated point.

Example 2. Classify the singular point of the curve $y^2 = x^3$.

Since the term of lowest degree is y^2, the curve has a double point at the origin, where the two branches $y = x^{\frac{3}{2}}$ and $y = -x^{\frac{3}{2}}$ meet. Substituting $y = mx$, and equating the coefficient of x^2 to zero, we obtain

$$m^2 = 0,$$

whence $m = 0$ only, and the x-axis is tangent to both branches of the curve at the origin.

That the double point is a cusp and not a tacnode follows from the fact that the curve extends only to the right of the origin.

The curve is shown in Fig. 76f.

We may also determine the slope of the curve at the double point directly. By implicit differentiation we find

$$\frac{dy}{dx} = \frac{3x^2}{2y},$$

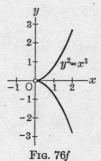

FIG. 76f

and while this assumes, as it should, the indeterminate form $\dfrac{0}{0}$ at the origin, we may replace y from the equation of the curve by $\pm x^{\frac{3}{2}}$, whereupon the derivative becomes

$$\frac{dy}{dx} = \pm \frac{3}{2} x^{\frac{1}{2}}$$

and is clearly zero at the origin.

Example 3. Discuss the singular point of the curve $y^2 = (x - 2)^2(x^2 + 1)$.

Differentiating implicitly, we find

$$\frac{dy}{dx} = \frac{(x - 2)(2x^2 - 2x + 1)}{y}.$$

By inspection we see that $(2, 0)$ is the only singular point on the curve, for the coördinates of no other point satisfying the given equation will render both the numerator and denominator of the derivative zero. Next we apply the transformation (cf. (5) and (6))

$$x = x' + 2$$

$$y = y'$$

in order to place the singular point at the new origin of coördinates; the equation of the curve then becomes

$$y'^2 = x'^2(x'^2 + 4x' + 5).$$

Since the terms of lowest degree are of the second degree, there is a double point at $x' = 0$, $y' = 0$.

To determine the nature of the double point we put $y' = mx'$ and equate the coefficient of x'^2 to zero, obtaining

$$m^2 - 5 = 0,$$

whence $m = \pm \sqrt{5}$. Thus at the double point there are two distinct tangent lines whose equations are $y' = \pm \sqrt{5}x'$, or $y = \pm \sqrt{5}(x - 2)$. Hence the double point is a node.

The curve is sketched in Fig. 76g.

In this problem also it is possible to evaluate the derivative at the singular point in order to obtain directly the slopes of the tangent lines at this point. Thus

$$\frac{dy}{dx} = \pm \frac{2x^2 - 2x + 1}{\sqrt{x^2 + 1}}$$

and, for $x = 2$, $\dfrac{dy}{dx} = \pm \sqrt{5}$.

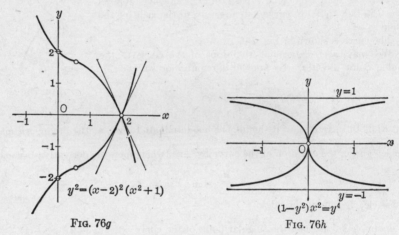

$$y^2 = (x-2)^2 (x^2 + 1)$$

Fig. 76g

$$(1-y^2)x^2 = y^4$$

Fig. 76h

Example 4. Discuss the singular point of the curve $(1 - y^2)x^2 - y^4 = 0$.

Since the term of lowest degree is of the second degree, there is a double point at the origin. Comparing the given equation with (1''), we see that $c_2 = 0$, $a_2 = 1$; therefore to determine the nature of the double point we set $x = ny$, obtaining

$$n^2 y^2 - (n^2 + 1)y^4 = 0.$$

Next we equate the coefficient of y^2 to zero. From the result,

$$n^2 = 0,$$

it follows that the line $x = 0$, or the y-axis, is tangent to the curve at the origin where the two branches $x = \dfrac{y^2}{\sqrt{1 - y^2}}$ and $x = -\dfrac{y^2}{\sqrt{1 - y^2}}$ meet. There is a tacnode, and not a cusp, at the origin because the curve extends on both sides of the x-axis.

The curve is sketched in Fig. 76h.

Example 5. Discuss the singular point which the curve $x^4 + 2x^3 - x^2y - 2xy^2 + y^3 = 0$ has at the origin.

Since the terms of lowest degree are of the third degree, the curve has a triple point at the origin. On setting $y = mx$, we obtain

$$(10) \qquad\qquad (2 - m - 2m^2 + m^3)x^3 + x^4 = 0.$$

The condition that the line $y = mx$ be tangent to the curve at the origin is, by an obvious extension of (9),

$$2 - m - 2m^2 + m^3 = 0,$$

the roots of which are $m = \pm 1, 2$. Hence there are three distinct tangent lines to the curve at the origin, namely, the lines $y = -x$, $y = x$, and $y = 2x$.

The curve will be plotted in Example 2, Art. 77.

PROBLEMS

Locate and classify the singular points of each of the following curves, and except in the case of isolated points determine the corresponding slopes.

1. $y^2 = x^3 - 4x^2$.
2. $x^3 + y^3 + 9x^2 - 18xy + 9y^2 = 0$.
3. $(x + y)^3 - (x - y)^2 = 0$.
4. $(x + 1)^2(x + 2)(x + 3)^2 - y^2 = 0$.
5. $y^2 = x^4(9 - x^2)$.
6. $x^3 + x^2 + y^3 = 0$.
7. $x^2 + 6x + 9 + y^2 + y^3 = 0$.
8. $x^7 - (x^2 - y)^2 = 0$.

9. $x^{\frac{2}{3}} + y^{\frac{2}{3}} = a^{\frac{2}{3}}$.
10. $(x^2 + y^2)^2 - a^2(x^2 - y^2) = 0$.
11. $x^2y^2 - (y - 2)^2(5 - y^2) = 0$.
12. $(x^2 + y^2 - 2x)^2 - 4(x^2 + y^2) = 0$.
13. $y^2 - 2x^2y - x^6 = 0$.
14. $(x^2 + y^2)^2 - y(3x^2 - y^2) = 0$.
15. $x^4 + y^4 + y^3 - xy^2 = 0$.
16. $x^4 + y^4 - 2x^2y + xy^2 + y^3 = 0$.

77. Curve Tracing; Résumé.

For the purpose of tracing a curve whose equation may be written in the form $f(x, y) = 0$, where $f(x, y)$ is a polynomial in x and y, it is advisable first to discuss the curve with reference to symmetry, intercepts, extent, and vertical and horizontal asymptotes, as in Art. 74. Then oblique asymptotes and singular points should be investigated by the methods of Arts. 75 and 76. Frequently it is helpful to examine the curve for maximum and minimum points, sense of concavity, and points of inflection (Chapter II).

Supplemented, if necessary, by the location of additional points from the equation of the curve, this procedure, or even part of it, will suffice as a basis for sketching the curve.

Example 1. Discuss and trace the curve $y^2 = \dfrac{x^4}{x^2 - 1}$.

The curve is symmetrical with respect to both coördinate axes, and therefore with respect to the origin. It contains the origin, but no other point on either axis. Since y is real if $x = 0$ or if $|x| > 1$, the curve has an isolated point at the origin and extends indefinitely to the right of the line $x = 1$ and to the left of the line $x = -1$. The vertical extent may be determined by solving the equation of the curve for x^2; the result

$$x^2 = \frac{y^2 \pm y \sqrt{y^2 - 4}}{2}$$

shows that x is real if $y = 0$ or if $|y| \geq 2$. Thus, aside from the origin, no other point on the curve lies within the rectangle bounded by the lines $y = \pm 2$ and $x = \pm 1$. The lines $x = \pm 1$ are vertical asymptotes; there are no horizontal asymptotes.

We shall examine the curve for oblique asymptotes by the method of substitution. Putting $y = mx + b$ in the equation of the curve, we obtain

$$(1 - m^2)x^4 - 2mbx^3 + \cdots = 0,$$

whence

$$m = \pm 1$$

and

$$b = 0.$$

Hence the lines $y = \pm x$ are oblique asymptotes.

We have already proved that the curve has an isolated point at the origin. If we try to confirm this by applying the theory of singular points, we encounter the exceptional situation mentioned on p. 209, for, putting $y = mx$ in the equation of the curve and setting the coefficient of x^2 equal to zero, we find

$$m^2 = 0$$

whence

$$m = 0.$$

At any point on the upper half of the curve, the first and second derivatives are

$$\frac{dy}{dx} = \frac{x(x^2 - 2)}{(x^2 - 1)^{\frac{3}{2}}}$$

and

$$\frac{d^2y}{dx^2} = \frac{x^2 + 2}{(x^2 - 1)^{\frac{5}{2}}}.$$

Hence there are critical points at $x = \pm \sqrt{2}$, but no points of inflection, the portion of the curve under consideration being concave upward throughout. Therefore the critical points $(\sqrt{2},\ 2)$ and $(-\sqrt{2},\ 2)$ are minimum points. By symmetry, the points $(\pm \sqrt{2},\ -2)$ are maximum points.

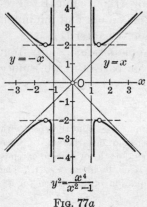

$$y^2 = \frac{x^4}{x^2 - 1}$$

FIG. 77a

From the above discussion, the curve is readily sketched (Fig. 77a). If a few additional points are determined by means of the equation of the curve, the graph can be plotted quite accurately.

If a curve has a singular point at the origin, the work of plotting the curve is often facilitated by the method of the following example.

Example 2. Plot the curve $x^4 + 2x^3 - x^2y - 2xy^2 + y^3 = 0$.

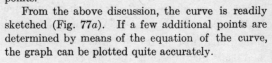

In Example 5, Art. 76, this curve was found to have a triple point at the origin. From (10) of that article it is evident that the line $y = mx$, besides cutting the curve at three points coincident with the origin, cuts it at a fourth point generally distinct from the origin, and whose coördinates are given by

(1) $$x = -m^3 + 2m^2 + m - 2,$$

(2) $$y = mx = -m^4 + 2m^3 + m^2 - 2m.$$

(If $m = \pm 1$, or $m = 2$, the line $y = mx$ is tangent to the curve, and the fourth point of intersection is likewise at the origin.)

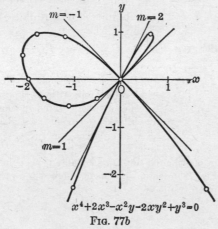

$$x^4 + 2x^3 - x^2y - 2xy^2 + y^3 = 0$$

FIG. 77b

Evidently (1) and (2) may be regarded as parametric equations of the curve, with m as the parameter. The coördinates of various points on the curve may be found by assigning values to m, and computing x from (1) and y from either the second or the third member of (2).

We give a table of corresponding values of m, x, and y, and a sketch of the curve (Fig. 77b).

m	$-\frac{5}{4}$	-1	$-\frac{3}{4}$	$-\frac{1}{2}$	$-\frac{1}{4}$	0	$\frac{1}{4}$	$\frac{1}{2}$	$\frac{3}{4}$	1	$\frac{3}{2}$	2	$\frac{9}{4}$
x	$\frac{117}{64}$	0	$-\frac{77}{64}$	$-\frac{15}{8}$	$-\frac{135}{64}$	-2	$-\frac{105}{64}$	$-\frac{9}{8}$	$-\frac{35}{64}$	0	$\frac{5}{8}$	0	$-\frac{65}{64}$
y	$-\frac{585}{256}$	0	$\frac{231}{256}$	$\frac{15}{16}$	$\frac{135}{256}$	0	$-\frac{105}{256}$	$-\frac{9}{16}$	$-\frac{105}{256}$	0	$\frac{15}{16}$	0	$-\frac{585}{256}$

PROBLEMS

Discuss and sketch each of the following curves:

1. $y^2 = x^2 \dfrac{a + x}{a - x}$: *Strophoid.*

2. $x^3 + y^3 - 3axy = 0$: *Folium of Descartes.*

3. $(4y - 5x^2)^2 = 16x^5$.

4. $4x^2 - x^2y - y^3 = 0$.

5. $2y^3 = 3x^2 - 2x^3$.

6. $y^2 = \dfrac{x^4}{1 - x^2}$.

7. $y^2 = \dfrac{x^3 - 1}{x - 2}$.

8. $xy(x + y) - 4 = 0$.

9. $y = \dfrac{x^3}{x^2 - 3x + 2}$.

10. $y^3 = (x - 2)(x - 1)^2$.

11. $x^2y^2 - (y + 1)^2(4 - y^2) = 0$.

12. $x^3 + 3x^2 - xy^2 - y^2 = 0$.

78. Roulettes. If a plane curve C_1 rolls without slipping on a fixed coplanar curve C_2, then the curve C traced by a point P of C_1 is called a **roulette** (Fig. 78a).

If Q is the instantaneous point of contact of the curves C_1 and C_2,

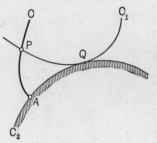

and A is the point of C_2 with which the tracing point P initially coincides, it follows from the definition of a roulette that

(1)   arc PQ = arc AQ.

Example. The roulette traced by any point of a circle which rolls without slipping on a straight line is called a **cycloid**. Find the equation of the cycloid described by a point $P(x, y)$ of a circle of radius a which rolls on the x-axis, if P is initially at the origin.

Fig. 78a

Let G be the center of the circle and Q its instantaneous point of contact with the x-axis. Then, if ϕ (Fig. 78b) denotes the angle, expressed in radians, through which the radius GP has turned, we have by (1)

$$OQ = \text{arc } PQ = a\phi.$$

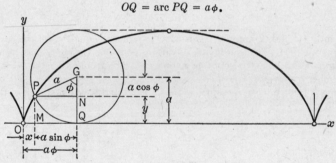

Fig. 78b

Through P draw a vertical line meeting the x-axis at M and a horizontal line meeting the ordinate QG of the center G at N. The coördinates of the tracing point P are

$$x = OM = OQ - MQ = a\phi - a \sin \phi$$

and

$$y = MP = a - NG = a - a \cos \phi.$$

Therefore the parametric equations of the cycloid, with ϕ as parameter, are

(2) $x = a(\phi - \sin \phi),$

(3) $y = a(1 - \cos \phi).$

Eliminating ϕ from (2) and (3), we obtain the cartesian equation of the cycloid

$$x = a \cos^{-1} \frac{a - y}{a} \mp \sqrt{2ay - y^2},$$

where the sign is minus when $\cos^{-1} \dfrac{a-y}{a}$ is an angle in the first or second quadrant, and plus when in the third or fourth quadrant.

PROBLEMS

1. If the angular velocity $\omega = \dfrac{d\phi}{dt}$ of the circle of Fig. 78b is constant, show that the vertical velocity-component of the moving point P is a maximum when the ordinate of the point is equal to the length a of the radius.

2. Under the conditions of Problem 1, find the maximum magnitude of the velocity of P and the corresponding positions of this point.

3. Under the conditions of Problem 1, find the positions of P when the magnitude of its velocity is half the maximum value.

4. Show that the parametric equations of the curve traced by any point of the radius GP (Fig. 78b), or of the radius extended, are

$$x = a\phi - b \sin \phi,$$

$$y = a - b \cos \phi,$$

where b is the distance of the tracing point from the center of the circle. If $b \neq a$, the curve is called a **trochoid**.

5. Find the y-intercepts of the trochoid for which $a = 2$ and $b = 4$.

HINT: Newton's Method (Art. 73) may be used in finding one of these intercepts.

6. If a circle of radius b rolls without slipping on the outside of a circle of radius a any point of the first circle traces a roulette known as an **epicycloid**. If (Fig. 78c), the tracing point $P(x, y)$ is initially at $A(a, 0)$, the center of the fixed circle being taken as the origin, and the angle described by the radius vector to the center of the rolling circle is denoted by ϕ, show that the parametric equations of the epicycloid are

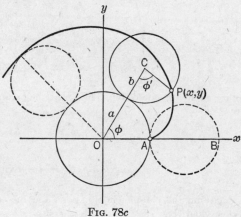

Fig. 78c

(4)
$$x = (a + b) \cos \phi - b \cos \frac{a+b}{b} \phi,$$

$$y = (a + b) \sin \phi - b \sin \frac{a+b}{b} \phi.$$

HINT: Designate by ϕ' (Fig. 78c) the angle OCP, where C is the center of the rolling circle, and observe that $b\phi' = a\phi$.

7. Show that the epicycloid of one cusp (obtained from (4) by putting $b = a$) is the cardioid whose equation in polar coördinates is

$$r = 2a(1 - \cos \theta),$$

where $r = AP$ and $\theta =$ angle BAP (Fig. 78c).

HINT: When the origin is transferred from O to A, the abscissa of P becomes $x - a$; moreover, since $b = a$ and $\phi = \phi'$, it follows that $\phi = \theta$.

8. How many revolutions does a circle make in rolling once around a circle of equal radius?

9. If a circle of radius b rolls without slipping on the inside of a circle of radius a, any point of the first circle traces a roulette known as a **hypocycloid**. If (Fig. 78d) the tracing point $P(x, y)$ is initially at $A(a, 0)$, the center of the fixed circle being taken as the origin, and the angle described by the radius vector to the center of the

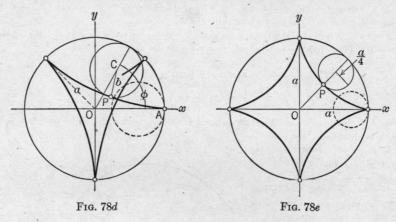

FIG. 78d   FIG. 78e

rolling circle is denoted by ϕ, show that the parametric equations of the hypocycloid are

$$x = (a - b) \cos \phi + b \cos \frac{a - b}{b} \phi,$$

$$y = (a - b) \sin \phi - b \sin \frac{a - b}{b} \phi.$$

10. Find the parametric equations and the cartesian equation of a four-cusped hypocycloid (Fig. 78e), for which $a = 4b$.

11. If, in Problem 9, $a = 2b$ and $\dfrac{d\phi}{dt}$ is constant, show that the point P describes simple harmonic motion.

12. The equation of a parabola, which rolls on the parabola $x^2 = 4ay$, is initially $x^2 = -4ay$. Find the equation of the curve traced by the vertex of the rolling parabola.

79. Involutes. A roulette C (Fig. 79a) traced by a point P of a line L which rolls without slipping on a fixed plane curve C' is called an **involute** of the curve C'.

For convenience, we shall say that L is the **generating line** of the involute C.

Several theorems on involutes will now be proved.

THEOREM 1. *The generating line of an involute of a curve is in every position normal to the involute.*

With reference to the axes shown in Fig. 79a, let X and Y be the coördinates of the point B at which the line L is instantaneously tangent to the curve C', and let x and y be the coördinates of the point P which traces the involute C. Let the initial position of P be the point A of the curve C', and write

$$S = \text{arc } AB, \quad s = \text{arc } AP.$$

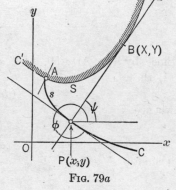

FIG. 79a

Finally, let the directions of the line L and of the tangent to C at P be represented by the angles ψ and ϕ as shown in the figure. Then, since the length of the line-segment PB is equal to S, we have

$$(1) \qquad x = X - S \cos \psi,$$

$$(2) \qquad y = Y - S \sin \psi.$$

Taking differentials of (1) and (2), and observing that by (4) and (5), Art. 59, $dX = \cos \psi\, dS$ and $dY = \sin \psi\, dS$, we obtain

$$(3) \qquad dx = dX + S \sin \psi\, d\psi - \cos \psi\, dS = S \sin \psi\, d\psi,$$

$$(4) \qquad dy = dY - S \cos \psi\, d\psi - \sin \psi\, dS = -S \cos \psi\, d\psi.$$

Hence

$$(5) \qquad -\frac{dx}{dy} = \tan \psi.$$

But $\tan \psi$ is the slope of the generating line L, and $-\dfrac{dx}{dy}$ is the slope of the normal to the involute C at P. Therefore in every position the generating line of an involute is normal to the involute, and the theorem is proved.

Designating P and B as a pair of corresponding points, we may restate Theorem 1 as follows: *The line normal to an involute of a curve at any point of the involute is tangent to the curve at the corresponding point.*

THEOREM 2. *The locus of the centers of curvature of an involute of a curve is the curve itself.*

This theorem will be proved by showing that B (Fig. 79a) is the center of curvature of the involute C at the point P.

By Theorem 1 the line L, of which PB is a segment, is normal to the involute at P; therefore (cf. Art. 67) L contains the center of curvature in question. Moreover, the latter lies on the concave side of the curve C, as does the point B. Hence, denoting the radius of curvature of C at P by ρ, we must show that $|\rho| = PB$.*

Using (1'), Art. 67, and the data of Fig. 79a, we have

$$\rho = \frac{ds}{d\phi} = \frac{ds}{d\left(\psi + \dfrac{3\pi}{2}\right)} = \frac{ds}{d\psi}.$$

Since by (2), Art. 59, $(ds)^2 = (dx)^2 + (dy)^2$, it follows from (3) and (4) that

$$(ds)^2 = S^2(d\psi)^2,$$

whence

$$\left|\frac{ds}{d\psi}\right| = S.$$

Therefore

$$|\rho| = S,$$

and since $S = PB$ the theorem is proved.

For use in the next article, we shall derive expressions for the coördinates X and Y of a point on a curve in terms of the coördinates x and y of the corresponding point on an involute of the curve and also in terms of the derivatives $\dfrac{dy}{dx}$ and $\dfrac{d^2y}{dx^2}$. Although the following derivation is based on Fig. 79a, for which $\psi = \phi - \dfrac{3\pi}{2}$ and $\rho = +S$, the results are valid in general.

From (1) and (2), from (4) and (5), Art. 59, and from (1'), Art. 67, we obtain

$$X = x + S \cos \psi = x - \rho \sin \phi = x - \frac{ds}{d\phi} \cdot \frac{dy}{ds} = x - \frac{dx}{d\phi} \cdot \frac{dy}{dx}$$

and

$$Y = y + S \sin \psi = y + \rho \cos \phi = y + \frac{ds}{d\phi} \cdot \frac{dx}{ds} = y + \frac{dx}{d\phi}.$$

Now

$$\phi = \tan^{-1}\left(\frac{dy}{dx}\right),$$

---

* In Fig. 79a, ρ happens to be positive, since ϕ increases with s.

whence

$$\frac{d\phi}{dx} = \frac{\dfrac{d^2y}{dx^2}}{1 + \left(\dfrac{dy}{dx}\right)^2},$$

and $\dfrac{dx}{d\phi}$ is the reciprocal of this. Hence

(6) $$X = x - \frac{\left[1 + \left(\dfrac{dy}{dx}\right)^2\right]\dfrac{dy}{dx}}{\dfrac{d^2y}{dx^2}},$$

and

(7) $$Y = y + \frac{1 + \left(\dfrac{dy}{dx}\right)^2}{\dfrac{d^2y}{dx^2}}.$$

Since, by Theorem 2, the point (X, Y) is the center of curvature of the involute C at the point (x, y), and this involute was obtained from an arbitrary curve C', we may interpret (6) and (7) as formulas for the co-ordinates of the center of curvature of any curve $y = f(x)$ (cf. Problem 26, p. 179).

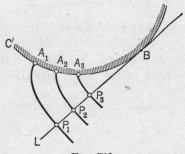

FIG. 79b

A curve has, in general, an infinite number of involutes. Thus, in Fig. 79b, the points $P_1, P_2, P_3, \cdots$ of the rolling line L trace the involutes A_1P_1, A_2P_2, A_3P_3, $\cdots$ of the curve C'. Since the line L is, by Theorem 1, always normal to each of these involutes and since the equalities

$$P_1P_2 = \text{arc } A_1A_2, \qquad P_2P_3 = \text{arc } A_2A_3, \cdots$$

hold for all positions of L, we have

THEOREM 3. *The involutes of a curve have the same normals on all of which any two involutes intercept equal distances; i.e., all the involutes of a curve are parallel.*

A mechanical method of constructing an involute of a curve is based on the definition of an involute. Suppose that a cord extends along the arc AQ of a curve (Fig. 79c) and is fastened at Q. If now the cord is kept taut and unwound, its end-point, originally at A, will describe an arc of an involute of the curve until the point of tangency reaches Q.

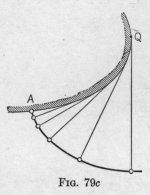

FIG. 79c

80. Evolutes. If C is an involute of C', then C' is said to be the **evolute** of C. Alternatively, by Theorem 2 of the preceding article, the evolute of a curve may be defined as the locus of the centers of curvature of the curve. While a curve has infinitely many involutes, it has only one evolute.

The equation of the evolute of a curve may be found from (6) and (7) of the preceding article where x and y denote the coördinates of a point on the given curve and X and Y the coördinates of the corresponding point on the evolute. For if y, $\dfrac{dy}{dx}$, and $\dfrac{d^2y}{dx^2}$ can be expressed in terms of x, then (6) and (7) can be regarded as parametric equations of the evolute, and if the parameter x can then be eliminated from these equations, the result will be the cartesian equation of the evolute. A similar situation holds if x, $\dfrac{dy}{dx}$, and $\dfrac{d^2y}{dx^2}$ can be expressed in terms of y.

If the given curve is represented parametrically, that is, if x and y are expressed in terms of a third variable, say t, then (6) and (7) of the preceding article may be used to obtain the parametric equations of the evolute of the curve, with the same parameter t.

Example 1. Find the equation of the evolute of the curve $y^2 = \dfrac{x^3}{2 - x}$.

Substituting the derivatives

$$\frac{dy}{dx} = \pm \frac{x^{\frac{1}{2}}(3 - x)}{(2 - x)^{\frac{3}{2}}} \quad \text{and} \quad \frac{d^2y}{dx^2} = \pm \frac{3}{x^{\frac{1}{2}}(2 - x)^{\frac{5}{2}}}$$

in (6) and (7) of the preceding article, and simplifying, we find

(1)
$$X = \frac{5x^2 - 12x}{3(2 - x)^2},$$

(2)
$$Y = \pm \frac{8x^{\frac{1}{2}}}{3(2 - x)^{\frac{1}{2}}}.$$

Squaring both sides of (2), solving for x, substituting in (1), and simplifying, we obtain as the equation of the evolute

$$27Y^4 + 1152Y^2 + 4096X = 0.$$

Since the coördinates X and Y are referred to the same axes as x and y, the equation of the evolute may be written

$$27y^4 + 1152y^2 + 4096x = 0.$$

Fig. 80a shows the given curve as COC' and its evolute as EOE'.

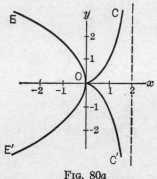

FIG. 80a   FIG. 80b

Example 2. Find the equation of the evolute of the curve

$$x = a(\cos t + t \sin t),$$

$$y = a(\sin t - t \cos t).$$

Taking differentials we obtain

$$dx = at \cos t \, dt,$$

$$dy = at \sin t \, dt,$$

so that

$$\frac{dy}{dx} = \tan t$$

and

$$\frac{d^2y}{dx^2} = \frac{d}{dt} \tan t \cdot \frac{dt}{dx} = \sec^2 t \cdot \frac{\sec t}{at} = \frac{\sec^3 t}{at}.$$

Hence by (6) and (7) of the preceding article,

$$X = a(\cos t + t \sin t) - \frac{at \sec^2 t \tan t}{\sec^3 t}$$

and

$$Y = a(\sin t - t \cos t) + \frac{at \sec^2 t}{\sec^3 t}.$$

On reduction we find as the parametric equations of the evolute

$$X = a \cos t,$$

$$Y = a \sin t.$$

Eliminating t by squaring and adding, we obtain as the cartesian equation of the evolute

$$X^2 + Y^2 = a^2,$$

or equivalently

$$x^2 + y^2 = a^2.$$

Therefore the evolute is a circle, and the given curve is one of its involutes (Fig. 80b).

PROBLEMS

In Problems 1–6, find the cartesian equations of the evolutes of the given curves.

1. $y^2 = 4x$.

2. $xy = 4$.

3. $4x^2 + 9y^2 = 36$.

4. $4x^2 - 9y^2 = 36$.

5. $x^{\frac{2}{3}} + y^{\frac{2}{3}} = a^{\frac{2}{3}}$.

6. $y = \frac{1}{2}(e^x + e^{-x})$.

In Problems 7–10, find parametric equations of the evolutes of the given curves.

7. The cubical parabola $x = t$, $y = t^3$.

8. The semicubical parabola $x = t^2$, $y = t^3$.

9. The cycloid $x = a(\phi - \sin \phi)$, $y = a(1 - \cos \phi)$.

10. The cosine curve $x = t$, $y = \cos t$.

CHAPTER VIII

INTEGRATION

81. Introductory Remarks. In Chapter III integration was defined as the inverse process of differentiation. We saw there that the equation

$$\int f(x)dx = F(x) + C$$

is equivalent to the statement that $F(x)$ is a function whose differential is $f(x)dx$. The symbol $\int$ was there called the integral sign, $f(x)$ the integrand, and C the constant of integration.

Thus far integration has been limited to polynomial functions. Now, however, we shall extend the process of integration to those other elementary types of functions which appear in Chapters IV and V.

We have found that any combination of the elementary functions can be differentiated by the application of suitable formulas. But the same does not hold in the case of integration. Thus no formulas exist in terms of elementary functions for the integrals of many comparatively simple functions, as for example,

$$\int \frac{e^x}{x}\,dx \quad \text{and} \quad \int \frac{dx}{\sqrt{4 - 5x^2 + x^4}}.$$

In this chapter we shall consider only those integrals which can be found in terms of the elementary functions.

82. Compilation of Formulas. Below are listed for convenience the standard formulas of integration which are to be studied in the articles cited. The student should have no difficulty in memorizing those of the Primary Group, since most of them arise from corresponding formulas of differentiation given in Chapters IV and V. It is not so important that the formulas of the Secondary Group be memorized, for, as we shall see, the integrals occurring in them can, after certain transformations have been made, be found by the formulas of the Primary Group.

PRIMARY GROUP

I $\displaystyle\int du = u + C$ Art. 83

II $\displaystyle\int a\,du = a\int du = au + C$ Art. 83

III $\displaystyle\int [f_1(u) + f_2(u) + \cdots + f_n(u)]du$

             $\displaystyle= \int f_1(u)du + \int f_2(u)du + \cdots + \int f_n(u)du$ Art. 83

IV $\displaystyle\int u^n du = \frac{u^{n+1}}{n+1} + C, \quad n \neq -1$ Art. 83

V $\displaystyle\int \frac{du}{u} = \ln u + C$ Art. 83

VI $\displaystyle\int a^u du = \frac{a^u}{\ln a} + C$ Art. 84

VII $\displaystyle\int e^u du = e^u + C$ Art. 84

VIII $\displaystyle\int \sin u\,du = -\cos u + C$ Art. 85

IX $\displaystyle\int \cos u\,du = \sin u + C$ Art. 85

X $\displaystyle\int \sec^2 u\,du = \tan u + C$ Art. 85

XI $\displaystyle\int \csc^2 u\,du = -\cot u + C$ Art. 85

XII $\displaystyle\int \sec u \tan u\,du = \sec u + C$ Art. 85

XIII $\displaystyle\int \csc u \cot u\,du = -\csc u + C$ Art. 85

XIV $\displaystyle\int \tan u\,du = -\ln \cos u + C = \ln \sec u + C$ Art. 85

XV $\displaystyle\int \cot u\,du = \ln \sin u + C = -\ln \csc u + C$ Art. 85

XVI $\displaystyle\int \sec u\,du = \ln (\sec u + \tan u) + C$ Art. 85

XVII $\displaystyle\int \csc u\,du = -\ln (\csc u + \cot u) + C$ Art. 85

XVIII $\qquad \displaystyle\int \frac{du}{\sqrt{a^2 - u^2}} = \sin^{-1}\frac{u}{a} + C$ $\qquad$ Art. 87

XIX $\qquad \displaystyle\int \frac{du}{a^2 + u^2} = \frac{1}{a}\tan^{-1}\frac{u}{a} + C$ $\qquad$ Art. 87

XX $\qquad \displaystyle\int u\,dv = uv - \int v\,du$ $\qquad$ Art. 88

SECONDARY GROUP

XXI $\qquad \displaystyle\int \frac{du}{\sqrt{u^2 + a^2}} = \ln(u + \sqrt{u^2 + a^2}) + C$ $\qquad$ Art. 90

XXII $\qquad \displaystyle\int \frac{du}{\sqrt{u^2 - a^2}} = \ln(u + \sqrt{u^2 - a^2}) + C$ $\qquad$ Art. 90

XXIII $\qquad \displaystyle\int \frac{du}{a^2 - u^2} = \frac{1}{2a}\ln\frac{a + u}{a - u} + C$ $\qquad$ Art. 90

XXIV $\qquad \displaystyle\int \frac{du}{u^2 - a^2} = \frac{1}{2a}\ln\frac{u - a}{u + a} + C$ $\qquad$ Art. 90

XXV $\qquad \displaystyle\int \frac{du}{u\sqrt{u^2 - a^2}} = \frac{1}{a}\sec^{-1}\frac{u}{a} + C$ $\qquad$ Art. 90

83. Integration of Sums, Powers, etc. Let us now derive and illustrate the use of the first five formulas of the Primary Group.

Since $d(u + C) = du$ and $d(au + C) = a\,du$, where a is a constant and u is variable, we have at once

I $\qquad\qquad \displaystyle\int du = u + C$

and

II $\qquad\qquad \displaystyle\int a\,du = a\int du = au + C.$

In Formula II we see that the integral of the product of a constant and a variable is equal to the product of the constant by the integral of the variable. Therefore, *a constant factor may be transposed from one side of the sign of integration to the other without changing the value of the integral.*

The student is warned not to take a variable factor outside the sign of integration.

To derive III we observe that if

$$\int f_1(u)du = F_1(u) + C_1, \quad \int f_2(u)du = F_2(u) + C_2, \quad \cdots,$$

$$\int f_n(u)du = F_n(u) + C_n,$$

and we write $C = C_1 + C_2 + \cdots + C_n$, then we have

$$d\left[F_1(u) + F_2(u) + \cdots + F_n(u) + C\right]$$

$$= f_1(u)du + f_2(u)du + \cdots + f_n(u)du$$

$$= \left[f_1(u) + f_2(u) + \cdots + f_n(u)\right] du,$$

and hence

$$\int \left[f_1(u) + f_2(u) + \cdots + f_n(u)\right]du$$

$$= F_1(u) + F_2(u) + \cdots + F_n(u) + C,$$

whence

III $$\int \left[f_1(u) + f_2(u) + \cdots + f_n(u)\right]du$$

$$= \int f_1(u)du + \int f_2(u)du + \cdots + \int f_n(u)du.$$

This formula may be stated in words: *The integral of the algebraic sum of a finite number of functions is equal to the sum of the integrals of the functions.*

From VII', Art. 42, it follows that

$$d\left(\frac{u^m}{m} + C\right) = u^{m-1}du$$

for any constant value of m other than zero. Hence, if we replace m by $n + 1$ and integrate, we obtain

IV $$\int u^n du = \frac{u^{n+1}}{n+1} + C, \quad n \neq -1.$$

If $n = -1$, $u^n du$ becomes $\dfrac{du}{u}$, which by XXV', Art. 57, may be regarded as the differential of $\ln u + C$. Therefore

V $$\int \frac{du}{u} = \ln u + C.$$

The formula for integrating a polynomial (2), Art. 28, may evidently be derived from II, III, and IV.

Example 1. $\int \sqrt{5x}\, dx = \sqrt{5} \int x^{\frac{1}{2}}\, dx = \sqrt{5} \cdot \dfrac{x^{\frac{3}{2}}}{\frac{3}{2}} + C = \dfrac{2\sqrt{5}}{3}\, x^{\frac{3}{2}} + C$ (by II and IV).

Example 2. $\int (4x^5 - 5x^2 + \sqrt{7x} - 3)dx$

$$= \int 4x^5 dx - 5 \int x^2 dx + \sqrt{7} \int x\, dx - 3 \int dx \qquad \text{(by II and III)}$$

$$= \frac{2}{3}\, x^6 - \frac{5}{3}\, x^3 + \frac{\sqrt{7}}{2}\, x^2 - 3x + C \qquad \text{(by I and IV)}.$$

Example 3. $\int (x+2)dx.$

First Solution.

$$\int (x+2)dx = \frac{x^2}{2} + 2x + C \qquad \text{(cf. Example 2, Art. 28)}.$$

Second Solution. Since $dx = d(x+2)$, the integral has the form $\int u^n du$, where $n = 1$ and $u = x + 2$. Hence by IV

$$\int (x+2)dx = \int (x+2)d(x+2)$$

$$= \frac{(x+2)^2}{2} + C_1.$$

That these two results agree can be shown by expanding the second form of the integral, for

$$\frac{(x+2)^2}{2} + C_1 = \frac{x^2}{2} + 2x + 2 + C_1,$$

and if we now let $2 + C_1 = C$ the two results are identical.

Example 4. Evaluate $\int (3x^2 + 2)^3 dx.$

Expanding by the binomial theorem and using I, II, III, and IV, we obtain

$$\int (3x^2 + 2)^3 dx = \int (27x^6 + 54x^4 + 36x^2 + 8)dx$$

$$= \tfrac{27}{7}\, x^7 + \tfrac{54}{5}\, x^5 + 12x^3 + 8x + C.$$

Example 5. Evaluate $\int (3x^2 + 2)^3 x\, dx.$

First Solution.

$$\int (3x^2 + 2)^3 x\, dx = \int (27x^7 + 54x^5 + 36x^3 + 8x)dx$$

$$= \tfrac{27}{8}\, x^8 + 9x^6 + 9x^4 + 4x^2 + C.$$

Note that this result is not the result of Example 4 multiplied by x.

Second Solution. The fact that $x\, dx$ is a constant times the differential of $3x^2 + 2$ suggests the following solution:

$$\int (3x^2 + 2)^3 x\, dx = \int (3x^2 + 2)^3\, \frac{6x\, dx}{6}$$

$$= \tfrac{1}{6} \int (3x^2 + 2)^3 d(3x^2 + 2) \qquad \text{(by II)}$$

$$= \frac{1}{6} \frac{(3x^2 + 2)^4}{4} + C_1 \qquad \text{(by IV)}$$

$$= \tfrac{1}{24} (3x^2 + 2)^4 + C_1.$$

The student may readily show that the results of the two solutions are in agreement.

Example 6.   Evaluate $\displaystyle\int \sqrt{5 - 4x^2} \, x \, dx$.

By the method used in the second solution of Example 5, we have

$$\int \sqrt{5 - 4x^2} \, x \, dx = \int (5 - 4x^2)^{\frac{1}{2}} \left(\frac{-8 \, x \, dx}{-8} \right)$$

$$= - \tfrac{1}{8} \int (5 - 4x^2)^{\frac{1}{2}} d(5 - 4x^2) \qquad \text{(by II)}$$

$$= - \frac{1}{8} \frac{(5 - 4x^2)^{\frac{3}{2}}}{\frac{3}{2}} + C \qquad \text{(by IV)}$$

$$= - \tfrac{1}{12} (5 - 4x^2)^{\frac{3}{2}} + C.$$

If the factor x appearing after the radical were missing, or if it were replaced by any power of x other than the first, the integral could not be evaluated by any method thus far studied.

Example 7. $\displaystyle\int \sin^3 2x \cos 2x \, dx = \int \sin^3 2x \frac{2 \cos 2x \, dx}{2}$

$$= \tfrac{1}{2} \int \sin^3 2x \, d(\sin 2x) \qquad \text{(by II)}$$

$$= \frac{1}{2} \frac{\sin^4 2x}{4} + C \qquad \text{(by IV)}$$

$$= \tfrac{1}{8} \sin^4 2x + C.$$

Example 8. $\displaystyle\int \frac{dx}{x^3} = \int x^{-3} dx = \frac{x^{-2}}{-2} + C = - \frac{1}{2x^2} + C_1 \qquad \text{(by IV)}$

Example 9. $\displaystyle\int \frac{dx}{(2x + 1)^3} = \int (2x + 1)^{-3} \frac{2 \, dx}{2}$

$$= \tfrac{1}{2} \int (2x + 1)^{-3} d(2x + 1) \qquad \text{(by II)}$$

$$= \frac{1}{2} \frac{(2x + 1)^{-2}}{-2} + C \qquad \text{(by IV)}$$

$$= - \frac{1}{4(2x + 1)^2} + C_1.$$

Example 10.   Evaluate $\displaystyle\int \frac{dx}{2x + 1}$.

If we compare the given integral with the integral $\int u^n du$ we see that $n = -1$ and hence that V and not IV must be used. Accordingly we obtain

$$\int \frac{dx}{2x + 1} = \frac{1}{2} \int \frac{d(2x + 1)}{2x + 1} \qquad \text{(by II)}$$

$$= \tfrac{1}{2} \ln (2x + 1) + C. \qquad \text{(by V)}$$

Example 11.   Evaluate $\int \dfrac{4x^2 - 8x - 8}{2x + 1}\, dx.$

We observe that the integrand is a rational algebraic fraction whose numerator is of higher degree than the denominator. In any such case we resort to the following general rule:

To integrate a rational algebraic fraction whose numerator is not of lower degree than the denominator, convert the integrand, by division, into a polynomial plus a fraction whose numerator is of lower degree than the denominator, and apply III.

Thus in the present example we find that

$$\frac{4x^2 - 8x - 8}{2x + 1} = 2x - 5 - \frac{3}{2x + 1}.$$

Hence

$$\int \frac{4x^2 - 8x - 8}{2x + 1}\, dx = \int \left(2x - 5 - \frac{3}{2x + 1} \right) dx$$

$$= x^2 - 5x - \tfrac{3}{2} \ln (2x + 1) + C.$$

$$\text{(by II, III, IV, and V)}$$

Example 12. $\displaystyle\int \frac{(3 - 4x)dx}{4x^2 - 6x + 17} = -\frac{1}{2} \int \frac{(8x - 6)dx}{4x^2 - 6x + 17}$ \qquad (by II)

$$= -\frac{1}{2} \int \frac{d(4x^2 - 6x + 17)}{4x^2 - 6x + 17}$$

$$= -\tfrac{1}{2} \ln (4x^2 - 6x + 17) + C \qquad \text{(by V)}$$

$$= \ln \frac{1}{\sqrt{4x^2 - 6x + 17}} + C.$$

PROBLEMS

Evaluate the following integrals:

1. $\displaystyle\int x^4 dx.$

2. $\displaystyle\int 2x^{-2} dx.$

3. $\displaystyle\int 2x^{-\frac{1}{2}} dx.$

4. $\displaystyle\int \frac{3\, dx}{x^5}.$

5. $\displaystyle\int \frac{dx}{2x^4}.$

6. $\displaystyle\int (x^4 - 5x^3 - 2x + 8) dx.$

7. $\displaystyle\int 7t\, dt.$

8. $\displaystyle\int \sqrt{6s}\, ds.$

9. $\int (6\theta^2 - 5\theta + 2)d\theta.$

10. $\int 2x\sqrt{x}\, dx.$

11. $\int (t^3 - t^{-2})dt.$

12. $\int (t^2 - 2)^2 t^{-3}dt.$

13. $\int (t^2 - 2)^2 t\, dt.$

14. $\int (x + 1)(3x - 2)dx.$

15. $\int x^4(2 - x^2)dx.$

16. $\int \frac{4x^2 - 3\sqrt{x}}{x}\, dx.$

17. $\int \frac{x^4 - 10x - 5}{x^2}\, dx.$

18. $\int \frac{ds}{\sqrt{15s}}.$

19. $\int (x^{-\frac{1}{2}} + x^{-\frac{3}{2}})dx.$

20. $\int \frac{(x^2 - 2)dx}{x^3 - 6x}.$

21. $\int \frac{dx}{x + 1}.$

22. $\int \frac{x\, dx}{x + 1}.$

23. $\int \frac{x\, dx}{x^2 + 1}.$

24. $\int \sqrt{1 + 3x}\, dx.$

25. $\int \sqrt{1 - 3x^2}\, x\, dx.$

26. $\int \frac{dx}{\sqrt{3 - 5x}}.$

27. $\int \frac{x\, dx}{(x^2 + 1)^2}.$

28. $\int \frac{dx}{(x + 1)^3}.$

29. $\int \frac{x\, dx}{\sqrt{x^2 - 9}}.$

30. $\int \frac{x^2 dx}{x^3 + 1}.$

31. $\int \frac{x^2\, dx}{\sqrt{x^3 + 1}}.$

32. $\int \frac{x^2 dx}{(x^3 + 1)^3}.$

33. $\int \frac{(2ax + b)dx}{ax^2 + bx + c}.$

34. $\int \frac{\ln x\, dx}{x}.$

35. $\int \frac{e^x - e^{-x}}{e^x + e^{-x}}\, dx.$

36. $\int \frac{e^{2x}dx}{e^{2x} + 9}.$

37. $\int \sin^2 2x \cos 2x\, dx.$

38. $\int \frac{1 - x + 2x^3}{x^3}\, dx.$

39. $\int \frac{x^3 dx}{x - 1}.$

40. $\int \frac{1 - \cos 3x}{3x - \sin 3x}\, dx.$

41. $\int \frac{1 - \cos 3x}{(3x - \sin 3x)^2}\, dx.$

42. $\int \sin 3x \cos^3 3x\, dx.$

43. $\int \frac{dx}{2 + 3x}.$

44. $\int \frac{dx}{1 - x}.$

45. $\int \frac{dx}{(1 - x)^2}.$

46. $\int \frac{x\, dx}{1 - x^2}.$

47. $\int \tan^5 2x \sec^2 2x\, dx.$

48. $\int \frac{1 + 2x}{x^2 + x}\, dx.$

49. $\int \frac{2x + 5}{x^2 + 5x}\, dx.$

50. $\int \frac{(2x + 5)dx}{x^2 + 5x - 8}.$

51. $\int \frac{e^{3x} + \sec^2 3x}{e^{3x} + \tan 3x}\, dx.$

52. $\int \frac{\sec^2 2x}{1 + \tan 2x}\, dx.$

53. $\int (3 + e^{2x})^2 e^{2x} \, dx.$

57. $\int \dfrac{x^2 + 4}{x - 2} \, dx.$

54. $\int \dfrac{x + 2}{x - 1} \, dx.$

58. $\int \dfrac{x \, dx}{5x^2 + 9}.$

55. $\int \dfrac{2(x - 1)^2}{x} \, dx.$

59. $\int \dfrac{x \, dx}{\sqrt{5x^2 + 9}}.$

56. $\int \sin^2 \dfrac{x}{3} \cos \dfrac{x}{3} \, dx.$

60. $\int (5x^2 + 9)^2 \, x \, dx.$

84. Integration of Exponential Functions. It follows from XXIV and XXII′, Art. 57, that

$$d(a^u + C_1) = a^u \ln a \, du, \qquad d(e^u + C) = e^u du.$$

Hence by integration we find that

VI
$$\int a^u du = \frac{a^u}{\ln a} + C$$

and

VII
$$\int e^u du = e^u + C,$$

where, in VI, $C = \dfrac{C_1}{\ln a}$.

Formula VII, though only a special case of VI, is of greater importance than the latter in pure and applied mathematics.

Example 1. $\int 10^{2x} \, dx = \frac{1}{2} \int 10^{2x} \, (2 \, dx)$ (by II)

$$= \frac{10^{2x}}{2 \ln 10} + C.$$ (by VI)

Example 2. $\int \dfrac{e^{\tan^{-1} x} \, dx}{1 + x^2} = \int e^{\tan^{-1} x} \, d(\tan^{-1} x)$

$$= e^{\tan^{-1} x} + C.$$ (by VII)

PROBLEMS

Evaluate the following integrals:

1. $\int 5 e^{3x} dx.$

4. $\int a^{3y} dy.$

2. $\int 2 e^{\frac{x}{2}} dx.$

5. $\int e^{x^2} x \, dx.$

3. $\int 10^x e^x dx.$

6. $\int \dfrac{dx}{e^x}.$

7. $\int e^{\sin 2x} \cos 2x\, dx.$

8. $\int e^{3-x} dx.$

9. $\int 4 e^{\frac{x}{5}} dx.$

10. $\int (e^x + e^{-x})^2\, dx.$

11. $\int (e^{2x} + x^{2e} + x^2 + e^2) dx.$

12. $\int \dfrac{e^{2x} - e^{-2x}}{e^x - e^{-x}}\, dx.$

13. $\int a^{2x} e^{2x} dx.$

14. $\int \dfrac{e^{2x} - 3}{e^{2x}}\, dx.$

15. $\int t e^{-t^2}\, dt.$

16. $\int e^{\tan \theta} \sec^2 \theta\, d\theta.$

17. $\int 8^x\, dx.$

18. $\int e^{2x-1} dx.$

19. $\int \dfrac{x^2 dx}{e^{x^3}}.$

20. $\int (e^{\frac{x}{2}} + e^{-\frac{x}{2}}) dx.$

21. $\int \sqrt{e^{2s}}\, ds.$

22. $\int \sqrt{e^s}\, ds.$

23. $\int (e^{2x})^4 dx.$

24. $\int \dfrac{e^{2x} + 1}{e^{2x} - 1}\, dx.$

25. $\int \dfrac{e^x dx}{e^x + 1}.$

26. $\int e^{\ln x}\, dx.$

85. Integration of Trigonometric Functions.

The student may readily verify the following six formulas:

VIII $\qquad \int \sin u\, du = -\cos u + C.$

IX $\qquad \int \cos u\, du = \sin u + C.$

X $\qquad \int \sec^2 u\, du = \tan u + C.$

XI $\qquad \int \csc^2 u\, du = -\cot u + C.$

XII $\qquad \int \sec u \tan u\, du = \sec u + C.$

XIII $\qquad \int \csc u \cot u\, du = -\csc u + C.$

To evaluate $\int \tan u\, du$, we may express $\tan u$ as either $\dfrac{\sin u}{\cos u}$ or as $\dfrac{\sec u \tan u}{\sec u}$. Thus

$$\int \tan u\, du = \int \frac{\sin u}{\cos u}\, du = -\int \frac{d(\cos u)}{\cos u},$$

or alternatively

$$\int \tan u \, du = \int \frac{\sec u \tan u \, du}{\sec u} = \int \frac{d \,(\sec u)}{\sec u}.$$

We then obtain by V

XIV $\qquad \int \tan u \, du = - \ln \cos u + C = \ln \sec u + C.$

The alternative derivation of XIV illustrates the device occasionally used of multiplying and dividing an integrand by the same variable factor in order to convert the integral to a standard form.   This device may be employed to evaluate $\int \sec u \, du$.   Thus

$$\int \sec u \, du = \int \sec u \, \frac{\sec u + \tan u}{\sec u + \tan u} \, du$$

$$= \int \frac{\sec u \tan u + \sec^2 u}{\sec u + \tan u} \, du$$

$$= \int \frac{d \,(\sec u + \tan u)}{\sec u + \tan u},$$

whence

XVI $\qquad \int \sec u \, du = \ln (\sec u + \tan u) + C.$

By methods analogous to those used in deriving Formulas XIV and XVI, the student may show that

XV $\qquad \int \cot u \, du = \ln \sin u + C = - \ln \csc u + C,$

XVII $\qquad \int \csc u \, du = - \ln (\csc u + \cot u) + C.$

In memorizing Formulas VIII to XVII the student may find it helpful to observe that a minus sign follows the equality sign in each of those formulas in which the right member involves one or more cofunctions.

86. Powers of Trigonometric Functions.   Odd integral powers of sin u or cos u, even integral powers of sec u or csc u, and any integral powers of tan u or cot u may be integrated by methods that have general similarity, as will be illustrated in Examples 1 to 5.

Example 1:

$$\int \cos^3 2x \, dx = \int \cos^2 2x \cos 2x \, dx$$

$$= \int (1 - \sin^2 2x) \cos 2x \, dx$$

$$= \int \cos 2x \, dx - \int \sin^2 2x \cos 2x \, dx$$

$$= \tfrac{1}{2} \int \cos 2x \, d(2x) - \tfrac{1}{2} \int \sin^2 2x \, d(\sin 2x)$$

$$= \tfrac{1}{2} \sin 2x - \tfrac{1}{6} \sin^3 2x + C. \qquad \text{(by IX and IV)}$$

Note that $\int \cos^3 2x \, dx$ is not equal to $\left(\int \cos 2x \, dx \right)^3$:

Example 2.

$$\int \sin^5 3x \, dx = \int \sin^4 3x \sin 3x \, dx$$

$$= \int (1 - \cos^2 3x)^2 \sin 3x \, dx$$

$$= \int (1 - 2\cos^2 3x + \cos^4 3x) \sin 3x \, dx$$

$$= \int \sin 3x \, dx - 2 \int \cos^2 3x \sin 3x \, dx + \int \cos^4 3x \sin 3x \, dx$$

$$= -\tfrac{1}{3} \cos 3x + \tfrac{2}{9} \cos^3 3x - \tfrac{1}{15} \cos^5 3x + C. \quad \text{(by VIII and IV)}$$

Example 3.

$$\int \sec^6 4x \, dx = \int \sec^4 4x \sec^2 4x \, dx$$

$$= \int (1 + \tan^2 4x)^2 \sec^2 4x \, dx$$

$$= \int (1 + 2\tan^2 4x + \tan^4 4x) \sec^2 4x \, dx$$

$$= \tfrac{1}{4} \int \sec^2 4x \, d(4x) + \tfrac{2}{4} \int \tan^2 4x \, d(\tan 4x) + \tfrac{1}{4} \int \tan^4 4x \, d(\tan 4x)$$

$$= \tfrac{1}{4} \tan 4x + \tfrac{1}{6} \tan^3 4x + \tfrac{1}{20} \tan^5 4x + C. \qquad \text{(by X and IV)}$$

A method of integrating odd integral powers of sec u or csc u will be given in Example 3, Art. 88.

Example 4.

$$\int \tan^5 2x \, dx = \int \tan^3 2x \tan^2 2x \, dx$$

$$= \int \tan^3 2x \, (\sec^2 2x - 1) dx$$

$$= \tfrac{1}{2} \int \tan^3 2x \, d(\tan 2x) - \int \tan^3 2x \, dx$$

$$= \frac{1}{2} \frac{\tan^4 2x}{4} - \int \tan 2x \, (\sec^2 2x - 1) dx \qquad \text{(by IV)}$$

$$= \tfrac{1}{8} \tan^4 2x - \tfrac{1}{2} \int \tan 2x \, d(\tan 2x) + \int \tan 2x \, dx$$

$$= \tfrac{1}{8} \tan^4 2x - \tfrac{1}{4} \tan^2 2x + \tfrac{1}{2} \ln \sec 2x + C. \quad \text{(by IV and XIV)}$$

Example 5. $\displaystyle\int \cot^4 3x\,dx = \int \cot^2 3x\,(\csc^2 3x - 1)dx$

$\displaystyle\qquad\qquad = -\tfrac{1}{3}\int \cot^2 3x\,d(\cot 3x) - \int \cot^2 3x\,dx$

$\displaystyle\qquad\qquad = -\tfrac{1}{9}\cot^3 3x - \int (\csc^2 3x - 1)dx \qquad\qquad\text{(by IV)}$

$\displaystyle\qquad\qquad = -\tfrac{1}{9}\cot^3 3x + \tfrac{1}{3}\cot 3x + x + C. \qquad\qquad\text{(by XI)}$

Guided by the solutions of Examples 4 and 5, the student should be able to evaluate any integral of the form $\displaystyle\int \tan^n u\,du$ or $\displaystyle\int \cot^n u\,du$, where n is an integer.

In the integration of positive even powers of $\sin u$ and $\cos u$, we make use of the identities

$$\sin^2 u = \tfrac{1}{2}(1 - \cos 2u)$$

and

$$\cos^2 u = \tfrac{1}{2}(1 + \cos 2u),$$

as illustrated in Examples 6 and 7.

Example 6. $\displaystyle\int \sin^2 \theta\,d\theta = \tfrac{1}{2}\int (1 - \cos 2\theta)d\theta$

$\displaystyle\qquad\qquad = \tfrac{1}{2}\int d\theta - \tfrac{1}{2}\int \cos 2\theta\,d\theta$

$\displaystyle\qquad\qquad = \tfrac{1}{2}\theta - \tfrac{1}{4}\sin 2\theta + C.$

Example 7. $\displaystyle\int \cos^4 x\,dx = \int \left(\frac{1 + \cos 2x}{2}\right)^2 dx$

$\displaystyle\qquad\qquad = \tfrac{1}{4}\int [1 + 2\cos 2x + \cos^2 2x]\,dx$

$\displaystyle\qquad\qquad = \tfrac{1}{4}\int [1 + 2\cos 2x + \tfrac{1}{2}(1 + \cos 4x)]\,dx$

$\displaystyle\qquad\qquad = \tfrac{1}{4}\int [\tfrac{3}{2} + 2\cos 2x + \tfrac{1}{2}\cos 4x]\,dx$

$\displaystyle\qquad\qquad = \tfrac{3}{8}x + \tfrac{1}{4}\sin 2x + \tfrac{1}{32}\sin 4x + C.$

Examples 8, 9, and 10 illustrate certain methods of integrating the product of powers of $\sin u$ and $\cos u$. If one of these powers is odd and integral, then, regardless of the exponent of the other power, the product may be integrated as in Examples 8 and 9. If the exponents of both powers are positive and even the method of Example 10 may be used.

Example 8. $\displaystyle\int \sin^2 3x \cos^3 3x\,dx = \int \sin^2 3x \cos^2 3x \cos 3x\,dx$

$\displaystyle\qquad\qquad = \int \sin^2 3x\,(1 - \sin^2 3x)\cos 3x\,dx$

$\displaystyle\qquad\qquad = \int \sin^2 3x \cos 3x\,dx - \int \sin^4 3x \cos 3x\,dx$

$\displaystyle\qquad\qquad = \tfrac{1}{9}\sin^3 3x - \tfrac{1}{15}\sin^5 3x + C.$

Example 9. $\displaystyle\int \sin^3 5x \cos^5 5x\, dx = \int \sin^2 5x \sin 5x \cos^5 5x\, dx$

$$= \int (1 - \cos^2 5x) \cos^5 5x \sin 5x\, dx$$

$$= \int \cos^5 5x \sin 5x\, dx - \int \cos^7 5x \sin 5x\, dx$$

$$= -\tfrac{1}{30} \cos^6 5x + \tfrac{1}{40} \cos^8 5x + C.$$

Example 10. $\displaystyle\int \sin^2 3x \cos^4 3x\, dx = \tfrac{1}{4} \int \sin^2 6x \cos^2 3x\, dx$

$$= \tfrac{1}{4} \int \sin^2 6x \cdot \frac{1 + \cos 6x}{2}\, dx$$

$$= \tfrac{1}{8} \int \sin^2 6x\, dx + \tfrac{1}{8} \int \sin^2 6x \cos 6x\, dx$$

$$= \tfrac{1}{576} (36x - 3 \sin 12x + 4 \sin^3 6x) + C.$$

A study of the above examples should enable the student to integrate many other combinations of trigonometric functions.

PROBLEMS

Evaluate the integrals in Problems 1 to 52.

1. $\displaystyle\int \sin 3x\, dx.$

2. $\displaystyle\int \sin \frac{x}{3}\, dx.$

3. $\displaystyle\int \cos 2x\, dx.$

4. $\displaystyle\int \sin (3x + 2)dx.$

5. $\displaystyle\int \cos (2 - 3x)dx.$

6. $\displaystyle\int \sin \left(\frac{\pi}{2} - x\right)dx.$

7. $\displaystyle\int \sin (3 - 2x)dx.$

8. $\displaystyle\int (\sin 2x - \cos 3x)dx.$

9. $\displaystyle\int \sec 3x \tan 3x\, dx.$

10. $\displaystyle\int \sec^2 2x\, dx.$

11. $\displaystyle\int \tan^2 2x\, dx.$

12. $\displaystyle\int \sin 2x \cos 2x\, dx.$

13. $\displaystyle\int \sin 2x \cos^2 2x\, dx.$

14. $\displaystyle\int \sin^3 \frac{x}{3}\, dx.$

15. $\displaystyle\int \csc^2 5x\, dx.$

16. $\displaystyle\int \tan \frac{x}{2}\, dx.$

17. $\displaystyle\int \cot 3x\, dx.$

18. $\displaystyle\int \csc 2x\, dx.$

19. $\displaystyle\int \sec \frac{x}{3}\, dx.$

20. $\displaystyle\int \sec \frac{x}{2} \tan \frac{x}{2}\, dx.$

21. $\displaystyle\int \csc 5x \cot 5x\, dx.$

22. $\displaystyle\int \sin^3 x\, dx.$

23. $\displaystyle\int \cos^3 \frac{3x}{2}\, dx.$

24. $\displaystyle\int \frac{\cos 2x}{\sin x}\, dx.$

25. $\displaystyle\int \sec^2 2x \tan 2x\, dx.$

26. $\displaystyle\int \sec^3 2x \tan 2x\, dx.$

27. $\int \csc^4 3x \cot 3x \, dx.$

28. $\int \dfrac{\sin 3x}{\cos^3 3x} \, dx.$

29. $\int \cos^5 \dfrac{x}{2} \, dx.$

30. $\int \sin^3 x \cos^2 x \, dx.$

31. $\int \dfrac{\cos 2x \, dx}{\sin 2x}.$

32. $\int \sin^5 2x \cos^2 2x \, dx.$

33. $\int \sin^4 2x \cos^3 2x \, dx.$

34. $\int \sin^3\theta \cos^7\theta \, d\theta.$

35. $\int \sqrt{\sin x} \cos^3 x \, dx.$

36. $\int \sin^2 3x \sec^6 3x \, dx.$

37. $\int \tan^3 2x \, dx.$

38. $\int \sec^4 2x \, dx.$

39. $\int \sec^4 2x \tan^3 2x \, dx.$

40. $\int \cot^5 \dfrac{x}{2} \, dx.$

41. $\int \csc^3 2x \cot 2x \, dx.$

42. $\int \left(\sin \dfrac{x}{3} + \cos \dfrac{x}{3} \right)^2 dx.$

43. $\int \sqrt{1 + \cos \dfrac{3x}{2}} \, dx.$

44. $\int \dfrac{\tan \theta}{\sec \theta} \, d\theta.$

45. $\int \dfrac{\sin x + \cos x}{\sin x - \cos x} \, dx.$

46. $\int (\tan 2x + \cot 2x)^2 \, dx.$

47. $\int \dfrac{1 + \cos x}{x + \sin x} \, dx.$

48. $\int \dfrac{(1 + \cos x)dx}{(x + \sin x)^3}.$

49. $\int \dfrac{\sin 6x}{\cos 3x} \, dx.$

50. $\int \dfrac{1 - \cos 2x}{1 + \cos 2x} \, dx.$

51. $\int \tan^4 4x \, dx.$

52. $\int \cot^6 2x \, dx.$

53. Show that

$$\int \tan^n u \, du = \frac{\tan^{n-1} u}{n - 1} - \int \tan^{n-2} u \, du,$$

where n is an integer greater than unity.

54. Show that

$$\int \cot^n u \, du = - \frac{\cot^{n-1} u}{n - 1} - \int \cot^{n-2} u \, du,$$

where n is an integer greater than unity.

87. Integrals Leading to Inverse Trigonometric Functions. From Art. 48, it follows that

$$d \left(\sin^{-1} \frac{u}{a} + C \right) = \pm \frac{du}{\sqrt{a^2 - u^2}}$$

and hence that

(1)
$$\int \frac{du}{\sqrt{a^2 - u^2}} = \pm \sin^{-1} \frac{u}{a} + C,$$

where the sign is plus if $\sin^{-1}\dfrac{u}{a}$ is an angle in the first or fourth quadrant, and minus if in the second or third quadrant.

By referring to Art. 48, we see that the right member of (1) may be replaced by $\pm\cos^{-1}\dfrac{u}{a} + C$, with a different correlation between the sign and the quadrant of the angle. Since, however, in the evaluation of definite integrals, (1) is less likely to cause confusion than the alternative formula, we discard the latter.

In formal work on the evaluation of indefinite integrals, we shall choose the plus sign in (1), which then becomes

XVIII $$\int \frac{du}{\sqrt{a^2 - u^2}} = \sin^{-1}\frac{u}{a} + C.$$

Since by Art. 48,

$$d\left(\frac{1}{a}\tan^{-1}\frac{u}{a} + C\right) = \frac{du}{a^2 + u^2},$$

we obtain at once the formula

XIX $$\int \frac{du}{a^2 + u^2} = \frac{1}{a}\tan^{-1}\frac{u}{a} + C.$$

The student should note that in XIX $\dfrac{1}{a}\tan^{-1}\dfrac{u}{a}$ may be replaced by $-\dfrac{1}{a}\cot^{-1}\dfrac{u}{a}$ (cf. Art. 48); the given form of XIX, however, is preferable to the alternative.

Example 1. $$\int \frac{dx}{\sqrt{9 - 4x^2}} = \frac{1}{2}\int \frac{d(2x)}{\sqrt{3^2 - (2x)^2}}$$

$$= \frac{1}{2}\sin^{-1}\frac{2x}{3} + C. \qquad\qquad \text{(by XVIII)}$$

Example 2. $$\int \frac{dx}{9 + 4x^2} = \frac{1}{2}\int \frac{d(2x)}{3^2 + (2x)^2}$$

$$= \frac{1}{6}\tan^{-1}\frac{2x}{3} + C. \qquad\qquad \text{(by XIX)}$$

Example 3. Evaluate $\displaystyle\int \frac{dx}{\sqrt{7 + 6x - x^2}}.$

This integral may be converted to the form of $\displaystyle\int \frac{du}{\sqrt{a^2 - u^2}}$ by completing the square in the terms in x, for

$$7 + 6x - x^2 = 16 - 9 + 6x - x^2 = 4^2 - (x - 3)^2,$$

and hence

$$\int \frac{dx}{\sqrt{7 + 6x - x^2}} = \int \frac{d(x - 3)}{\sqrt{4^2 - (x - 3)^2}}$$

$$= \sin^{-1} \frac{x - 3}{4} + C. \qquad \text{(by XVIII)}$$

Example 4. Evaluate $\int \frac{(6x + 1)dx}{3x^2 + 8x + 7}$.

Noting that $d(3x^2 + 8x + 7) = (6x + 8)dx$, and that $6x + 1 = (6x + 8) - 7$, we replace the given integral by the difference

$$\int \frac{(6x + 8)dx}{3x^2 + 8x + 7} - \int \frac{7\,dx}{3x^2 + 8x + 7},$$

of which the first integral has the form $\int \frac{du}{u}$, so that, by V,

$$\int \frac{(6x + 8)\,dx}{3x^2 + 8x + 7} = \ln\,(3x^2 + 8x + 7) + C_1.$$

Moreover, taking a factor 3 out of the denominator of the second integral, completing the square in the terms in x, and applying XIX, we obtain

$$\int \frac{7\,dx}{3x^2 + 8x + 7} = \frac{7}{3} \int \frac{d(x + \frac{4}{3})}{(x + \frac{4}{3})^2 + \frac{5}{9}}$$

$$= \frac{7}{\sqrt{5}} \tan^{-1} \frac{x + \frac{4}{3}}{\frac{\sqrt{5}}{3}} + C_2$$

$$= \frac{7}{\sqrt{5}} \tan^{-1} \frac{3x + 4}{\sqrt{5}} + C_2.$$

Therefore

$$\int \frac{(6x + 1)dx}{3x^2 + 8x + 7} = \ln\,(3x^2 + 8x + 7) - \frac{7}{\sqrt{5}} \tan^{-1} \frac{3x + 4}{\sqrt{5}} + C,$$

where $C = C_1 + C_2$.

Example 5. $\qquad \int \frac{e^x dx}{4 + e^{2x}} = \int \frac{d(e^x)}{2^2 + (e^x)^2}$

$$= \frac{1}{2} \tan^{-1} \frac{e^x}{2} + C. \qquad \text{(by XIX)}$$

It is important that the student be able to distinguish instantly between the formulas for evaluating such apparently similar integrals as

$$\int \frac{dx}{9 + 4x^2}, \quad \int \frac{x\,dx}{9 + 4x^2}, \quad \int \frac{dx}{\sqrt{9 - 4x^2}}, \quad \text{and} \quad \int \frac{x\,dx}{\sqrt{9 - 4x^2}}.$$

Unless he can recognize at a glance that the integrals suggest the use of Formulas XIX, V, XVIII, and IV, respectively, he has not adequately mastered the rudiments of integration. With a view to developing the skill of the student, we have included in the following set of problems not only integrals leading to inverse trigonometric functions, but also integrals of the forms $\int u^n \, du$ and $\int \dfrac{du}{u}$.

PROBLEMS

Evaluate the following integrals:

1. $\int \dfrac{dx}{(3 + 2x)^3}$.

2. $\int \dfrac{dx}{\sqrt{3 + 2x}}$.

3. $\int \dfrac{dx}{3 + 2x}$.

4. $\int \dfrac{dx}{9 + x^2}$.

5. $\int \dfrac{dx}{\sqrt{9 - x^2}}$.

6. $\int \dfrac{dx}{25 + 9x^2}$.

7. $\int \dfrac{x \, dx}{25 + 9x^2}$.

8. $\int \dfrac{x \, dx}{(25 + 9x^2)^2}$.

9. $\int \dfrac{x \, dx}{\sqrt{25 + 9x^2}}$.

10. $\int \dfrac{x \, dx}{\sqrt{25 - 9x^2}}$.

11. $\int \dfrac{dx}{\sqrt{25 - 9x^2}}$.

12. $\int \dfrac{dx}{4x^2 + 3}$.

13. $\int \dfrac{dx}{\sqrt{16 - 4x^2}}$.

14. $\int \dfrac{dx}{\sqrt{7 + 12x - 4x^2}}$.

15. $\int \dfrac{dx}{x^2 + 6x + 13}$.

16. $\int \dfrac{x \, dx}{1 + x^4}$.

17. $\int \dfrac{x^3 dx}{1 + x^4}$.

18. $\int \dfrac{x \, dx}{\sqrt{1 - x^4}}$.

19. $\int \dfrac{x^3 dx}{\sqrt{1 - x^4}}$.

20. $\int \dfrac{(x - 5)dx}{4x^2 + 9}$.

21. $\int \dfrac{dx}{x^2 - 8x + 25}$.

22. $\int \dfrac{dx}{x^2 + 2x + 17}$.

23. $\int \dfrac{e^{2x} \, dx}{1 + e^{4x}}$.

24. $\int \dfrac{(4x - 3)dx}{\sqrt{9 - 16x^2}}$.

25. $\int \dfrac{dx}{(1 + x)\sqrt{x}}$.

26. $\int \dfrac{(3x - 1)dx}{3x^2 - 2x + 5}$.

27. $\int \dfrac{dx}{x^2 - 2x + 5}$.

28. $\int \dfrac{dx}{\sqrt{3 + 2x - x^2}}$.

29. $\int \dfrac{(1 - x)dx}{\sqrt{3 + 2x - x^2}}$.

30. $\int \dfrac{x \, dx}{x^2 - 2x + 5}$.

31. $\int \dfrac{x + 2}{9x^2 + 16} \, dx$.

32. $\int \dfrac{dx}{e^x + e^{-x}}$.

33. $\int \dfrac{\cos x \, dx}{25 + \sin^2 x}$.

34. $\int \dfrac{(3x + 1)dx}{x^2 - 2x + 5}$.

88. Integration by Parts. The formula for the differential of a product (IV′, Art. 42)

$$d(uv) = u\,dv + v\,du$$

may be written

$$u\,dv = d(uv) - v\,du.$$

Integrating both sides, we obtain

XX
$$\int u\,dv = uv - \int v\,du.$$

This is known as the formula for **integration by parts,** a designation arising from the fact that, when XX is applied to a given integral, the expression to be integrated must be separated into two parts, or factors, which are to be identified with the parts u and dv appearing on the left side of the formula. The factor corresponding to dv must obviously contain the differential of the variable of integration.

Evidently XX will be effective only if the factor identified with dv can be integrated, and if $\int v\,du$ is simpler than the given integral.

Integration by parts constitutes a powerful method of evaluating many integrals to which the standard formulas previously studied do not directly apply.

Example 1. Evaluate $\int \ln x\,dx$.

Letting
$$u = \ln x \quad \text{and} \quad dv = dx,$$

whence
$$du = \frac{dx}{x} \quad \text{and} \quad v = x,$$

we have by XX
$$\int \ln x\,dx = x \ln x - \int \frac{x\,dx}{x} = x \ln x - x + C.$$

It should be observed that it is not necessary to add a constant of integration in obtaining v from dv, for by taking $x + C_1$ as the expression for v we obtain

$$\int \ln x\,dx = (x + C_1) \ln x - \int (x + C_1)\frac{dx}{x}$$
$$= x \ln x - x + C,$$

in agreement with the previous result.

Example 2. Evaluate $\int x^2 e^{2x}dx$.

Letting
$$u = x^2 \quad \text{and} \quad dv = e^{2x}dx,$$

whence
$$du = 2x\,dx \quad \text{and} \quad v = \tfrac{1}{2}e^{2x},$$

we have by XX

(1) $$\int x^2 e^{2x} dx = \tfrac{1}{2} x^2 e^{2x} - \int x e^{2x} dx.$$

To evaluate the second integral we repeat the process, letting

$$u = x \quad \text{and} \quad dv = e^{2x} dx,$$

whence

$$du = dx \quad \text{and} \quad v = \tfrac{1}{2} e^{2x}.$$

Thus we find

$$\int x e^{2x} dx = \tfrac{1}{2} x e^{2x} - \tfrac{1}{2} \int e^{2x} dx$$

$$= \tfrac{1}{2} x e^{2x} - \tfrac{1}{4} e^{2x}.$$

Substituting this result in (1) we obtain

$$\int x^2 e^{2x} dx = \tfrac{1}{2} x^2 e^{2x} - \tfrac{1}{2} x e^{2x} + \tfrac{1}{4} e^{2x} + C$$

$$= \frac{e^{2x}}{4} (2x^2 - 2x + 1) + C.$$

Of the various ways of choosing u and dv, only the choice made in the above solution results in a simpler expression to integrate than was originally given. Thus if we choose

$$u = e^{2x} \quad \text{and} \quad dv = x^2 dx$$

then we find

$$\int x^2 e^{2x} dx = \tfrac{1}{3} x^3 e^{2x} - \tfrac{2}{3} \int x^3 e^{2x} dx,$$

where the integral on the right side is of the same type as the given integral but with a higher power of x, so that this attempt fails.

No general rule can be given regarding the choice of parts. However, it is noteworthy that integrals of the forms

$$\int x^n e^{kx} dx, \qquad \int x^n \sin kx \, dx, \qquad \int x^n \cos kx \, dx$$

can be evaluated by n successive integrations by parts, in the first of which u is taken as x^n, while the integrals

$$\int x^m \ln x \, dx \quad \text{and} \quad \int x^m \tan^{-1} kx \, dx$$

can be evaluated by a single application of XX by choosing $dv = x^m dx$.

Example 3. Evaluate $\int \sec^3 x \, dx$.

Letting

$$u = \sec x \quad \text{and} \quad dv = \sec^2 x \, dx,$$

whence

$$du = \sec x \tan x \, dx \quad \text{and} \quad v = \tan x,$$

we find by **XX**

$$\int \sec^3 x\, dx = \sec x \tan x - \int \sec x \tan^2 x\, dx,$$

or, using the identity $\tan^2 x = \sec^2 x - 1$,

$$\int \sec^3 x\, dx = \sec x \tan x - \int \sec^3 x\, dx + \int \sec x\, dx.$$

Solving this equation for $\int \sec^3 x\, dx$ and applying **XVI** we obtain

$$\int \sec^3 x\, dx = \tfrac{1}{2} \left[\sec x \tan x + \ln\,(\sec x + \tan x) \right] + C.$$

Thus $\int \sec^3 x\, dx$ leads to $\int \sec x\, dx$ which we have previously evaluated.

In the same manner $\int \sec^5 x\, dx$ depends on $\int \sec^3 x\, dx$, so that by applying **XX** a sufficient number of times we can integrate any higher odd power of $\sec x$. To integrate odd powers of $\csc x$ we proceed similarly.

Example 4. Evaluate $\int e^{ax} \sin bx\, dx$ and $\int e^{ax} \cos bx\, dx$.

Letting $u = e^{ax}$ and $dv = \sin bx\, dx$ and applying **XX** to the first of these integrals, we obtain

$$\int e^{ax} \sin bx\, dx = -\frac{1}{b} e^{ax} \cos bx + \frac{a}{b} \int e^{ax} \cos bx\, dx.$$

Now letting $u = \sin bx$ and $dv = e^{ax} dx$, and again applying **XX** to $\int e^{ax} \sin bx\, dx$, we have

$$\int e^{ax} \sin bx\, dx = \frac{1}{a} e^{ax} \sin bx - \frac{b}{a} \int e^{ax} \cos bx\, dx.$$

Solving these two equations simultaneously for $\int e^{ax} \sin bx\, dx$ and $\int e^{ax} \cos bx\, dx$ we find

$$\int e^{ax} \sin bx\, dx = \frac{e^{ax}\,(a \sin bx - b \cos bx)}{a^2 + b^2} + C,$$

$$\int e^{ax} \cos bx\, dx = \frac{e^{ax}\,(a \cos bx + b \sin bx)}{a^2 + b^2} + C.$$

The student may show that the same results are obtainable by applying the above process to the second of the given integrals.

PROBLEMS

Evaluate the following integrals by parts:

1. $\int x\, e^x\, dx.$

2. $\int x\, e^{2x}\, dx.$

3. $\int x^2\, e^x\, dx.$

4. $\int x \sin 2x\, dx.$

5. $\int x^2 \cos x\, dx.$

6. $\int \sin^{-1} x\, dx.$

7. $\int \tan^{-1} 2x \, dx.$

8. $\int e^{2x} \cos 2x \, dx.$

9. $\int x \sec^2 2x \, dx.$

10. $\int \tan^{-1} \dfrac{x}{3} \, dx.$

11. $\int x \sin^2 x \, dx.$

12. $\int x^3 \ln x \, dx.$

13. $\int e^{-x} \cos x \, dx.$

14. $\int e^x \sin 2x \, dx.$

15. $\int x^2 \tan^{-1} x \, dx.$

16. $\int \cos^2 x \, dx.$

17. $\int \csc^3 5x \, dx.$

18. $\int \sec^5 2x \, dx.$

19. $\int (\ln \cos x) \sin x \, dx.$

89. Methods of Integration. It was remarked in Art. 82 that the integrals occurring in the formulas of the Secondary Group can, after certain transformations have been made, be found by the formulas of the Primary Group. Such transformations are effected either by the method of *substitution* or the method of *partial fractions*. These methods of integration are applicable to many types of integrals other than those appearing in the formulas of the Secondary Group, and will be developed in the following two articles. In the problems of these articles the student will be called upon to derive the formulas of the Secondary Group.

90. Integration by Substitution. In integration it is frequently convenient, and often necessary, to replace the given variable by some function of a new variable, so chosen as to render the transformed integral simpler than the original one. Especially is this true if the integrand is irrational. Integration by this method is known as **integration by substitution.** The substitutions which we shall consider here are (*a*) **algebraic** and (*b*) **trigonometric.**

(*a*) *Algebraic Substitution.* THEOREM. *If in*

$$\int x^m (a + bx^n)^{\frac{p}{q}} \, dx \qquad (q > 0)$$

m, n, p, and q are integers, the substitution

(1) $$v = \sqrt[q]{a + bx^n}$$

will rationalize $x^m (a + bx^n)^{\frac{p}{q}} \, dx$ *provided that* $\dfrac{m+1}{n}$ *is a positive or negative integer or zero.*

We readily find from (1) that

$$x^m = \left(\frac{v^q - a}{b}\right)^{\frac{m}{n}},$$

$$(a + bx^n)^{\frac{p}{q}} = v^p,$$

$$dx = \frac{q}{bn}\, v^{q-1} \left(\frac{v^q - a}{b}\right)^{\frac{1}{n}-1} dv,$$

so that

$$x^m(a + bx^n)^{\frac{p}{q}}\, dx = \frac{q}{bn}\, v^{p+q-1} \left(\frac{v^q - a}{b}\right)^{\frac{m+1}{n}-1} dv.$$

Hence when the integrand is expressed in terms of v it becomes **rational** provided

$$\frac{m + 1}{n}$$

is any integer or zero.   Thus the theorem is proved.

Example 1.   Evaluate $\int x(3 - 2x)^{\frac{1}{4}} dx$.

Using the notation of the theorem we see that $\dfrac{m + 1}{n} = 2$ and hence that the substitution

(2) $$v = \sqrt[4]{3 - 2x}$$

will rationalize $x(3 - 2x)^{\frac{1}{4}} dx$.

Writing (2) in the form

$$v^4 = 3 - 2x,$$

we obtain

$$x = \tfrac{1}{2}(3 - v^4) \quad \text{and} \quad dx = - 2v^3 dv.$$

Therefore

$$\int x(3 - 2x)^{\frac{1}{4}} dx = \int \tfrac{1}{2}(3 - v^4)(v)(-2v^3 dv)$$

$$= \int (v^8 - 3v^4) dv$$

$$= \frac{v^5}{45}(5v^4 - 27) + C.$$

Restoring the original variable x we have

$$\int x(3 - 2x)^{\frac{1}{4}} dx = - \tfrac{2}{45}(3 - 2x)^{\frac{5}{4}}(5x + 6) + C.$$

Example 2.   Evaluate $\int (4 + 3x^2)^{\frac{2}{3}} x^5\, dx$.

Here $\dfrac{m + 1}{n} = 3$ and we make the substitution

$$v = \sqrt[3]{4 + 3x^2}.$$

Writing $(4 + 3x^2)^{\frac{2}{3}} x^5 \, dx = (4 + 3x^2)^{\frac{2}{3}}(x^4)(x \, dx)$ and observing that

$$(4 + 3x^2)^{\frac{2}{3}} = v^2, \quad x^4 = \tfrac{1}{9}(v^3 - 4)^2, \quad \text{and} \quad x \, dx = \tfrac{1}{2} v^2 dv,$$

we have

$$\int (4 + 3x^2)^{\frac{2}{3}} x^5 dx = \int (v^2) \, [\tfrac{1}{9} \, (v^3 - 4)^2] \, (\tfrac{1}{2} \, v^2 \, dv)$$

$$= \tfrac{1}{18} \int (v^{10} - 8v^7 + 16v^4) dv$$

$$= \frac{1}{18} \left(\frac{v^{11}}{11} - v^8 + \frac{16}{5} v^5 \right) + C$$

$$= \frac{v^5}{990} \, (5v^6 - 55v^3 + 176) + C$$

$$= \frac{(4 + 3x^2)^{\frac{5}{3}}}{110} \, (5x^4 - 5x^2 + 4) + C.$$

Many integrals which in their given forms do not satisfy the conditions of the theorem may readily be converted to forms which do, as is illustrated in the following example.

Example 3. Evaluate $\displaystyle\int \frac{dx}{x^3(1 + x^3)^{\frac{4}{3}}}.$

Here $\dfrac{m + 1}{n} = -\tfrac{2}{3}$ which is not an integer; hence the conditions of the theorem are not satisfied. Since, however,

$$(1 + x^3)^{\frac{4}{3}} = x^4(x^{-3} + 1)^{\frac{4}{3}},$$

the integral may be written in the form

$$\int x^{-7}(x^{-3} + 1)^{-\frac{4}{3}} dx,$$

where now $\dfrac{m + 1}{n} = 2$, an integer. Accordingly by (1) we make the substitution

$$v = (x^{-3} + 1)^{\frac{1}{3}}.$$

Writing

$$x^{-7}(x^{-3} + 1)^{-\frac{4}{3}} dx = x^{-3}(x^{-3} + 1)^{-\frac{4}{3}}(x^{-4} \, dx)$$

and observing that

$$x^{-3} = v^3 - 1, \quad (x^{-3} + 1)^{-\frac{4}{3}} = v^{-4}, \quad \text{and} \quad x^{-4} dx = - v^2 dv,$$

we have

$$\int x^{-7}(x^{-3} + 1)^{-\frac{4}{3}} dx = \int (v^3 - 1)(v^{-4})(-v^2 dv)$$

$$= - \int (v - v^{-2}) dv$$

$$= - \left(\frac{v^2}{2} + \frac{1}{v} \right) + C$$

$$= -\frac{1}{2v}(v^3 + 2) + C$$

$$= -\frac{1 + 3x^3}{2x^2(1 + x^3)^{\frac{1}{3}}} + C.$$

(b) *Trigonometric Substitution.* Trigonometric substitution is frequently employed to integrate expressions involving functions of $\sqrt{a^2 - u^2}$, $\sqrt{a^2 + u^2}$, or $\sqrt{u^2 - a^2}$. Its purpose is primarily to render the integrand rational in terms of trigonometric functions of a new variable, though in certain special instances it may be effective when the resulting integrand is irrational. Various cases in which irrational integrands may always be expressed rationally in terms of trigonometric functions will now be considered.

If the integrand is algebraic and involves no irrational function of u aside from integral powers of

(3) $\qquad\qquad \sqrt{a^2 - u^2},$ substitute $u = a \sin \theta,$

(4) $\qquad\qquad \sqrt{a^2 + u^2},$ substitute $u = a \tan \theta,$

(5) $\qquad\qquad \sqrt{u^2 - a^2},$ substitute $u = a \sec \theta,$

where for simplicity in indefinite integration θ may be regarded, without loss of generality, as an acute angle.

It is easily seen that these substitutions convert the respective radicals to rational expressions in terms of trigonometric functions; for

$$\sqrt{a^2 - u^2} = \sqrt{a^2 - a^2 \sin^2 \theta} = a \cos \theta, \text{ when } u = a \sin \theta,$$

$$\sqrt{a^2 + u^2} = \sqrt{a^2 + a^2 \tan^2 \theta} = a \sec \theta, \text{ when } u = a \tan \theta,$$

$$\sqrt{u^2 - a^2} = \sqrt{a^2 \sec^2 \theta - a^2} = a \tan \theta, \text{ when } u = a \sec \theta.$$

Appropriate triangle constructions, such as those illustrated in the following examples, obviate the use of trigonometric identities in transforming integrands.

Example 4. Evaluate $\int \dfrac{x^2 dx}{(9 - x^2)^{\frac{3}{2}}}.$

In accordance with (3) we substitute

(6) $\qquad\qquad\qquad x = 3 \sin \theta.$

This substitution may be presented geometrically by constructing a right triangle (Fig. 90a) whose side opposite the base angle θ is x and whose hypotenuse is 3. From the figure

$$\sqrt{9 - x^2} = 3 \cos \theta,$$

and hence

$$(9 - x^2)^{\frac{3}{2}} = 27 \cos^3 \theta,$$

while by (6)

$$dx = 3 \cos \theta \, d\theta.$$

Therefore

$$\int \frac{x^2 dx}{(9 - x^2)^{\frac{3}{2}}} = \int \frac{9 \sin^2 \theta \cdot 3 \cos \theta \, d\theta}{27 \cos^3 \theta}$$

$$= \int \tan^2 \theta \, d\theta = \int (\sec^2 \theta - 1) d\theta$$

$$= \tan \theta - \theta + C.$$

Restoring the original variable x by the help of the figure we obtain

$$\int \frac{x^2 dx}{(9 - x^2)^{\frac{3}{2}}} = \frac{x}{\sqrt{9 - x^2}} - \sin^{-1} \frac{x}{3} + C.$$

The integrand could have been rationalized by the substitution $x = 3 \cos \phi$ (Fig. 90a).

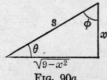

FIG. 90a   FIG. 90b

Example 5. Evaluate $\displaystyle \int \frac{dx}{\sqrt{25 + 4x^2}}.$

Here, in accordance with (4), we let

$$2x = 5 \tan \theta,$$

whence

$$\sqrt{25 + 4x^2} = 5 \sec \theta \quad \text{(cf. Fig. 90b)}$$

and

$$dx = \tfrac{5}{2} \sec^2 \theta \, d\theta.$$

Therefore

$$\int \frac{dx}{\sqrt{25 + 4x^2}} = \int \frac{\tfrac{5}{2} \sec^2 \theta \, d\theta}{5 \sec \theta}$$

$$= \tfrac{1}{2} \int \sec \theta \, d\theta$$

$$= \tfrac{1}{2} \ln (\tan \theta + \sec \theta) + C_1$$

$$= \tfrac{1}{2} \ln \left(\frac{2x}{5} + \frac{\sqrt{25 + 4x^2}}{5} \right) + C_1$$

$$= \tfrac{1}{2} \ln (2x + \sqrt{25 + 4x^2}) - \tfrac{1}{2} \ln 5 + C_1$$

$$= \tfrac{1}{2} \ln (2x + \sqrt{25 + 4x^2}) + C.$$

This result follows immediately from Formula XXI, Art. 82.

Example 6.   Evaluate $\int \dfrac{\sqrt{x^2 - 4}}{x}\, dx$.

Here, in accordance with (5), we let

$$x = 2 \sec \theta,$$

whence

$$\sqrt{x^2 - 4} = 2 \tan \theta \quad \text{(cf. Fig. 90c)}$$

and

$$dx = 2 \sec \theta \tan \theta\, d\theta.$$

Therefore

$$\int \frac{\sqrt{x^2 - 4}}{x}\, dx = \int \frac{(2 \tan \theta)(2 \sec \theta \tan \theta\, d\theta)}{2 \sec \theta}$$

$$= 2 \int \tan^2 \theta\, d\theta$$

$$= 2(\tan \theta - \theta) + C$$

$$= \sqrt{x^2 - 4} - 2 \sec^{-1} \frac{x}{2} + C.$$

This could have been integrated by the algebraic substitution $v = \sqrt{x^2 - 4}$.

In Art. 92, we shall give some additional consideration to a few forms involving $\sqrt{a^2 \pm u^2}$ and $\sqrt{u^2 - a^2}$.

PROBLEMS

Evaluate the integrals in Problems 1 to 56 but do not apply substitution if the integration can be accomplished by the formulas of the Primary Group.

1. $\int x \sqrt{2 - x}\, dx.$

2. $\int \dfrac{x^2\, dx}{\sqrt{x - 4}}.$

3. $\int \sqrt{5x}\, dx.$

4. $\int x^2 \sqrt{x + 2}\, dx.$

5. $\int \sqrt[3]{8 - x}\, dx.$

6. $\int \dfrac{x^2\, dx}{\sqrt{4 - x}}.$

7. $\int \dfrac{x^2\, dx}{\sqrt{4 - x^3}}.$

8. $\int \dfrac{x^2\, dx}{4 - x^3}.$

9. $\int \dfrac{x\, dx}{4 + x^4}.$

10. $\int s \sqrt[3]{1 - s}\, ds.$

11. $\int \dfrac{dx}{(4 - 3x)^4}.$

12. $\int x \sqrt{16 + x}\, dx.$

13. $\int x \sqrt{16 + x^2}\, dx.$

14. $\int \dfrac{x\, dx}{\sqrt{1 + x}}.$

15. $\int (2 - x) \sqrt[3]{x}\, dx.$

16. $\int \dfrac{dx}{9 + 4x^2}.$

17. $\int \dfrac{x\,dx}{9 + 4x^2}$.

18. $\int \dfrac{x\,dx}{(x^2 + 2)^2}$.

19. $\int \dfrac{x^2\,dx}{\sqrt{x - 9}}$.

20. $\int \dfrac{x^5\,dx}{\sqrt{x^3 + 1}}$.

21. $\int x^5 \sqrt{4 + x^3}\,dx$.

22. $\int x^3 \sqrt[4]{4 + x^2}\,dx$.

23. $\int x \sqrt[3]{(4 + x^2)^2}\,dx$.

24. $\int \dfrac{x^5\,dx}{\sqrt[3]{1 + x^3}}$.

25. $\int \dfrac{x^2\,dx}{2x + 1}$.

26. $\int \dfrac{x^2\,dx}{\sqrt{2x + 1}}$.

27. $\int \dfrac{x\,dx}{\sqrt{9 - 4x^2}}$.

28. $\int \dfrac{dx}{\sqrt{9 - 4x^2}}$.

29. $\int \dfrac{x^3\,dx}{\sqrt{9 - 4x^2}}$.

30. $\int \dfrac{x^5\,dx}{\sqrt[5]{3x^2 + 1}}$.

31. $\int \dfrac{\sqrt{x^2 - 1}}{x}\,dx$.

32. $\int x^3 (8 + x^2)^{\frac{3}{2}}\,dx$.

33. $\int \sqrt{x^2 + 25}\,dx$.

34. $\int \sqrt{x^2 - 9}\,dx$.

35. $\int \sqrt{4 - x^2}\,dx$.

36. $\int \dfrac{x^2\,dx}{\sqrt{x^2 + 9}}$.

37. $\int \dfrac{x\,dx}{\sqrt{x^2 + 9}}$.

38. $\int \dfrac{x^2\,dx}{\sqrt{4 - x^2}}$.

39. $\int \dfrac{x^3\,dx}{\sqrt{x^2 + 9}}$.

40. $\int \dfrac{x^3\,dx}{\sqrt{4 - x^2}}$.

41. $\int \dfrac{x^3\,dx}{(x^2 + 4)^{\frac{3}{2}}}$.

42. $\int \dfrac{dx}{x^2 \sqrt{1 + 9x^2}}$.

43. $\int x \sqrt{3x - 5}\,dx$.

44. $\int x^2 \sqrt{4 - x^2}\,dx$.

45. $\int x \sqrt{4 - x^2}\,dx$.

46. $\int \dfrac{dx}{(x^2 + 4)^{\frac{3}{2}}}$.

47. $\int \dfrac{dx}{x^2 + 8x + 17}$.

48. $\int \dfrac{dx}{\sqrt{8x - x^2}}$.

49. $\int \dfrac{2x + 3}{\sqrt{36 - x^2}}\,dx$.

50. $\int \dfrac{3x + 13}{\sqrt{x^2 + 9}}\,dx$.

51. $\int \dfrac{3x + 13}{x^2 + 9}\,dx$.

52. $\int \dfrac{dx}{x \sqrt{9x^2 - 4}}$.

53. $\int \dfrac{x^2\,dx}{\sqrt{9x^2 - 4}}$.

54. $\int \dfrac{dx}{4x^2 - 25}$.

55. $\int \dfrac{dx}{\sqrt{x^2 + 1}}$.

56. $\int \dfrac{dx}{9 - x^2}$.

57. Derive the formulas of the Secondary Group, Art. 82, by trigonometric substitutions.

58. Derive Formula XXV, Art. 82, by an algebraic substitution.

91. Integration by Partial Fractions. We shall now consider the integration of a general rational algebraic fraction whose numerator and denominator are polynomials with real coefficients and have no factor in common. It is sufficient to limit the discussion to the case in which the numerator is of lower degree than the denominator, for, if this condition is not satisfied, then by division the fraction may be expanded in the form

$$\frac{N(x)}{D(x)} = Q(x) + \frac{R(x)}{D(x)},$$

where $N(x)$, $D(x)$, $Q(x)$, and $R(x)$ are all polynomials with real coefficients, and $R(x)$ is of lower degree than $D(x)$—that is, $\frac{R(x)}{D(x)}$ is a proper fraction. Since

$$\int \frac{N(x)}{D(x)} \, dx = \int Q(x) \, dx + \int \frac{R(x)}{D(x)} \, dx$$

and $Q(x)$ is readily integrated, it follows that the integration of any rational fraction depends essentially on the integration of a proper fraction.

Suppose then that $\frac{N(x)}{D(x)}$ is a proper fraction in its lowest terms. We know from the fundamental theorem of algebra that $D(x)$ is equal to the product of factors of one or both of the types $x - a$ and $x^2 + px + q$, where a, p, and q are real, and the factors of $x^2 + px + q$ are imaginary (that is, $p^2 < 4q$). Moreover, it is proved in advanced algebra that, when such factors of $D(x)$ can be found, $\frac{N(x)}{D(x)}$ can be expressed in one and only one way as the sum of certain proper fractions, called the **partial fractions** of $\frac{N(x)}{D(x)}$, which are found as illustrated in the examples below, and are related to the factors of $D(x)$ as follows:

(*a*) For each unrepeated factor $x - a$ there is a partial fraction of the form $\frac{A}{x - a}$, where $A \neq 0$.

(*b*) For each factor of the type $(x - b)^r$ there is a sum of the form

$$\frac{B_1}{x - b} + \frac{B_2}{(x - b)^2} + \cdots + \frac{B_r}{(x - b)^r},$$

where any of the numerators may be zero except B_r.

(c) For each unrepeated factor $x^2 + px + q$ there is a partial fraction of the form $\dfrac{Cx + D}{x^2 + px + q}$, where C and D cannot both be zero.

(d) For each factor of the type $(x^2 + px + q)^s$ there is a sum of the form

$$\frac{E_1 x + F_1}{x^2 + px + q} + \frac{E_2 x + F_2}{(x^2 + px + q)^2} + \cdots + \frac{E_s x + F_s}{(x^2 + px + q)^s},$$

where $E_1, F_1, \cdots, E_s, F_s$ are constants of which E_s and F_s cannot both be zero.

In these partial fractions the numbers A, B_r, C, D, etc., are real constants, whose values must be found in each problem. There are exactly as many such constants to be determined as there are roots (real or imaginary) of the equation $D(x) = 0$.

The integral of the proper fraction $\dfrac{N(x)}{D(x)}$ is evidently equal to the sum of the integrals of its partial fractions.

Example 1. Evaluate $\displaystyle\int \frac{x^2 - 5x - 3}{x^3 - 4x}\,dx.$

In accordance with (a) we write

$$\frac{x^2 - 5x - 3}{x^3 - 4x} = \frac{A}{x} + \frac{B}{x - 2} + \frac{C}{x + 2}$$

$$= \frac{A(x - 2)(x + 2) + Bx(x + 2) + Cx(x - 2)}{x^3 - 4x},$$

whence

(1) $x^2 - 5x - 3 = A(x - 2)(x + 2) + Bx(x + 2) + Cx(x - 2).$

Here we must determine A, B, and C so as to render (1) an identity. There are two simple methods of doing this.

First Method. In general an equation involving the three unknowns A, B, and C results from assigning an arbitrary value to x in (1); and if three arbitrary values are assigned to x in turn the resulting equations may be solved for A, B, and C. The work is simplified, however, by restricting the choice each time to such a value of x as will cause the coefficients of two of the unknowns to vanish, thereby leaving an equation from which the third unknown may be determined. Accordingly making in (1) the successive substitutions $x = 0$, $x = 2$, and $x = -2$, we obtain

$$-3 = -4A, \text{ whence } A = \tfrac{3}{4},$$

$$-9 = 8B, \text{ whence } B = -\tfrac{9}{8},$$

$$11 = 8C, \text{ whence } C = \tfrac{11}{8}.$$

Second Method. We write (1) in the form

(2) $x^2 - 5x - 3 = (A + B + C)x^2 + (2B - 2C)x - 4A.$

In order for this to be an identity it is necessary that the *undetermined coefficients* of the powers of x in the right member of (2) be equal to the corresponding coefficients in the left member.   Hence

$$A + B + C = 1$$
$$2B - 2C = -5$$
$$-4A = -3.$$

Solving these equations simultaneously, we find, as before,

$$A = \tfrac{3}{4}, \quad B = -\tfrac{9}{8}, \quad \text{and} \quad C = \tfrac{11}{8}.$$

Using these values of A, B, and C, we have

$$\int \frac{x^2 - 5x - 3}{x^3 - 4x}\, dx = \int \left[\frac{3}{4x} - \frac{9}{8(x-2)} + \frac{11}{8(x+2)} \right] dx$$

$$= \tfrac{3}{4} \int \frac{dx}{x} - \tfrac{9}{8} \int \frac{dx}{x-2} + \tfrac{11}{8} \int \frac{dx}{x+2}$$

$$= \tfrac{3}{4} \ln x - \tfrac{9}{8} \ln (x-2) + \tfrac{11}{8} \ln (x+2) + C$$

$$= \ln \sqrt[8]{\frac{x^6(x+2)^{11}}{(x-2)^9}} + C.$$

Example 2.   Evaluate $\int \dfrac{x^5 + 2x^4 - 8x^2 - 4}{x^4 - x^3 - x + 1}\, dx.$

The integrand being an improper fraction we divide the numerator by the denominator, obtaining

$$\frac{x^5 + 2x^4 - 8x^2 - 4}{x^4 - x^3 - x + 1} = x + 3 + \frac{3x^3 - 7x^2 + 2x - 7}{x^4 - x^3 - x + 1}$$

$$= x + 3 + \frac{3x^3 - 7x^2 + 2x - 7}{(x-1)^2(x^2 + x + 1)}.$$

In accordance with (b) and (c) we write

$$\frac{3x^3 - 7x^2 + 2x - 7}{(x-1)^2(x^2+x+1)} = \frac{A}{x-1} + \frac{B}{(x-1)^2} + \frac{Cx+D}{x^2+x+1}$$

$$= \frac{A(x-1)(x^2+x+1) + B(x^2+x+1) + (Cx+D)(x-1)^2}{(x-1)^2(x^2+x+1)},$$

whence

$$3x^3 - 7x^2 + 2x - 7 = A(x-1)(x^2+x+1) + B(x^2+x+1) + (Cx+D)(x-1)^2$$
$$= (A+C)x^3 + (B - 2C + D)x^2 + (B + C - 2D)x$$
$$+ (-A + B + D).$$

Equating coefficients we find

$$A \quad + C \quad\quad = 3$$
$$B - 2C + D = -7$$
$$B + C - 2D = 2$$
$$-A + B \quad + D = -7.$$

Solving simultaneously, we obtain

$$A = 2, \quad B = -3, \quad C = 1, \quad \text{and} \quad D = -2.$$

The given integral may now be written

$$\int \frac{x^5 + 2x^4 - 8x^2 - 4}{x^4 - x^3 - x + 1} \, dx = \int \left[x + 3 + \frac{3x^3 - 7x^2 + 2x - 7}{x^4 - x^3 - x + 1} \right] dx$$

$$= \int \left[x + 3 + \frac{2}{x - 1} - \frac{3}{(x - 1)^2} + \frac{x - 2}{x^2 + x + 1} \right] dx$$

$$= \frac{x^2}{2} + 3x + 2 \ln (x - 1) + \frac{3}{x - 1}$$

$$+ \tfrac{1}{2} \ln (x^2 + x + 1) - \frac{5\sqrt{3}}{3} \tan^{-1} \frac{2x + 1}{\sqrt{3}} + C,$$

where the method of Example 4, Art. 87, was used to evaluate $\int \frac{x - 2}{x^2 + x + 1} \, dx$.

Example 3. Evaluate $\int \frac{4x^2 - 8x}{(x - 1)^2 (x^2 + 1)^2} \, dx$.

In accordance with (b) and (d) we write

$$\frac{4x^2 - 8x}{(x - 1)^2 (x^2 + 1)^2} = \frac{A}{x - 1} + \frac{B}{(x - 1)^2} + \frac{Cx + D}{x^2 + 1} + \frac{Ex + F}{(x^2 + 1)^2}.$$

By the method used in the preceding example we find that

$$A = 2, \quad B = -1, \quad C = -2, \quad D = -1, \quad E = -2, \quad \text{and} \quad F = 4,$$

and hence that

$$\int \frac{4x^2 - 8x}{(x-1)^2(x^2+1)^2} \, dx = 2 \int \frac{dx}{x-1} - \int \frac{dx}{(x-1)^2} + \int \frac{-2x-1}{x^2+1} \, dx + \int \frac{-2x+4}{(x^2+1)^2} \, dx.$$

Noting that $\int \frac{4 \, dx}{(x^2 + 1)^2}$ may be evaluated by the substitution $x = \tan \theta$, carrying out all integrations, and simplifying, we finally obtain

$$\int \frac{4x^2 - 8x}{(x - 1)^2 (x^2 + 1)^2} \, dx = \frac{3x^2 - x}{(x - 1)(x^2 + 1)} + \ln \frac{(x - 1)^2}{x^2 + 1} + \tan^{-1} x + C.$$

Example 4. Evaluate $\int \frac{dx}{x^4 + 16}$.

It is convenient to modify the forms of the numerators occurring under (c), and write

$$(3) \qquad \frac{1}{x^4 + 16} = \frac{A(2x + 2\sqrt{2}) + B}{x^2 + 2\sqrt{2}x + 4} + \frac{C(2x - 2\sqrt{2}) + D}{x^2 - 2\sqrt{2}x + 4}.$$

This modification constitutes no essential departure from the text; for the numerators of the partial fractions are linear expressions as required by (c). The purpose is simply to provide A and C with coefficients which are the derivatives of the respective denominators. This method would have been effective in Example 2.

Multiplying both sides of equation (3) by $x^4 + 16$ and collecting terms, we obtain the identity

$$1 = (2A + 2C)x^3 + (-2\sqrt{2}A + B + 2\sqrt{2}C + D)x^2 + (-2\sqrt{2}B + 2\sqrt{2}D)x$$
$$+ (8\sqrt{2}A + 4B - 8\sqrt{2}C + 4D).$$

Equating coefficients and solving the resulting equations for A, B, C, and D, we find

$$A = \frac{1}{32\sqrt{2}}, \quad B = \frac{1}{16}, \quad C = -\frac{1}{32\sqrt{2}}, \quad \text{and} \quad D = \frac{1}{16}.$$

Hence

$$\int \frac{dx}{x^4 + 16} = \int \frac{\frac{1}{32\sqrt{2}}(2x + 2\sqrt{2}) + \frac{1}{16}}{x^2 + 2\sqrt{2}x + 4} \, dx + \int \frac{-\frac{1}{32\sqrt{2}}(2x - 2\sqrt{2}) + \frac{1}{16}}{x^2 - 2\sqrt{2}x + 4} \, dx$$

$$= \frac{1}{32\sqrt{2}} \int \frac{(2x + 2\sqrt{2}) \, dx}{x^2 + 2\sqrt{2}x + 4} + \frac{1}{16} \int \frac{dx}{(x + \sqrt{2})^2 + (\sqrt{2})^2}$$

$$- \frac{1}{32\sqrt{2}} \int \frac{(2x - 2\sqrt{2}) \, dx}{x^2 - 2\sqrt{2}x + 4} + \frac{1}{16} \int \frac{dx}{(x - \sqrt{2})^2 + (\sqrt{2})^2}$$

$$= \frac{1}{32\sqrt{2}} \ln \frac{x^2 + 2\sqrt{2}x + 4}{x^2 - 2\sqrt{2}x + 4} + \frac{1}{16\sqrt{2}} \tan^{-1} \frac{x + \sqrt{2}}{\sqrt{2}}$$

$$+ \frac{1}{16\sqrt{2}} \tan^{-1} \frac{x - \sqrt{2}}{\sqrt{2}} + C.$$

PROBLEMS

In Problems 1–44 apply the method of partial fractions except where the formulas of the Primary Group are directly applicable.

1. $\displaystyle\int \frac{x^2 + 6x - 8}{x^3 - 4x} \, dx.$

2. $\displaystyle\int \frac{(x - 1)dx}{(x - 3)(x + 2)}.$

3. $\displaystyle\int \frac{x^2 + x - 3}{x^2 + x - 6} \, dx.$

4. $\displaystyle\int \frac{(x + 2)dx}{x^2 - 2x - 3}.$

5. $\displaystyle\int \frac{(x + 5)dx}{x^2 + 2x - 3}.$

6. $\displaystyle\int \frac{x^2 + x + 2}{x^3 + 2x^2 - 3x} \, dx.$

7. $\displaystyle\int \frac{(x - 5)dx}{x^3 + x^2 - 6x}.$

8. $\displaystyle\int \frac{1 + x^2}{x - x^3} \, dx.$

9. $\displaystyle\int \frac{x^4 dx}{x^3 + 2x^2 - x - 2}.$

10. $\displaystyle\int \frac{(x^3 + 1)dx}{x(x - 1)^3}.$

11. $\displaystyle\int \frac{(x - 8)dx}{x^3 - 4x^2 + 4x}.$

12. $\displaystyle\int \frac{(6 - 4x)dx}{x^3 - 6x^2 + 11x - 6}.$

13. $\displaystyle\int \frac{x^2 + 1}{(x + 2)^2} \, dx.$

14. $\displaystyle\int \frac{6x^3 - 8x^2 - 4x + 1}{x^4 - 2x^3 + x^2} \, dx.$

15. $\int \dfrac{3x^2 - 2}{(x+2)^3} \, dx.$

16. $\int \dfrac{x \, dx}{(x+1)(x^2+1)}.$

17. $\int \dfrac{dx}{1+x^3}.$

18. $\int \dfrac{dx}{x^4 - 16}.$

19. $\int \dfrac{(4x+2)dx}{(x+2)(x^2-1)}.$

20. $\int \dfrac{2x^2 - 4x - 1}{2x^3 - x^2 - x} \, dx.$

21. $\int \dfrac{x \, dx}{4x^2 + 4x - 3}.$

22. $\int \dfrac{x^2 + 6x - 18}{x^3 - 9x} \, dx.$

23. $\int \dfrac{x^2 - 45}{2x^3 - 18x} \, dx.$

24. $\int \dfrac{(x+8)dx}{x^2 + 6x + 8}.$

25. $\int \dfrac{x \, dx}{2x^2 - x - 3}.$

26. $\int \dfrac{(x-3)dx}{3x^2 + 2x - 5}.$

27. $\int \dfrac{(3x+2)dx}{3x^2 + 4x + 1}.$

28. $\int \dfrac{(x-3)dx}{x^3 + 6x^2 + 8x}.$

29. $\int \dfrac{x^4 dx}{x^2 - 4}.$

30. $\int \dfrac{2x^2 - 4x - 5}{x^2 - 9} \, dx.$

31. $\int \dfrac{2x^3 - x^2 + 8x - 3}{x^2 + 4} \, dx.$

32. $\int \dfrac{(x^3 + 2)dx}{x^3 + x^2 + x + 1}.$

33. $\int \dfrac{x^2 \, dx}{(2x+3)(x^2+9)}.$

34. $\int \dfrac{3x^2 - 3x + 5}{(x+3)(x-3)^2} \, dx.$

35. $\int \dfrac{(5x+12)dx}{x(x^2+4)}.$

36. $\int \dfrac{x^3 - 1}{x^3 + 3x} \, dx.$

37. $\int \dfrac{dx}{(x^2+1)(x^2+x)}.$

38. $\int \dfrac{x^3 + x - 1}{(x^2+2)^2} \, dx.$

39. $\int \dfrac{x^3 \, dx}{(x+1)^4}.$

40. $\int \dfrac{(3x^2 + 3x + 14)dx}{2x^3 + 3x^2 + 2x + 3}.$

41. $\int \dfrac{dx}{(x-1)^5}.$

42. $\int \dfrac{dx}{x^4 + 1}.$

43. $\int \dfrac{dx}{x^6 - 64}.$

44. $\int \dfrac{x^2 dx}{x^6 + 64}.$

45. Derive Formula XXIII, Art. 82.
46. Derive Formula XXIV, Art. 82.

92. Certain Related Integrals. The nine integrals

$$\int \frac{dx}{\sqrt{a^2 - x^2}}, \quad \int \sqrt{a^2 - x^2} \, dx, \quad \int \frac{x^2 \, dx}{\sqrt{a^2 - x^2}};$$

$$\int \frac{dx}{\sqrt{a^2 + x^2}}, \quad \int \sqrt{a^2 + x^2} \, dx, \quad \int \frac{x^2 \, dx}{\sqrt{a^2 + x^2}};$$

$$\int \frac{dx}{\sqrt{x^2 - a^2}}, \quad \int \sqrt{x^2 - a^2} \, dx, \quad \int \frac{x^2 \, dx}{\sqrt{x^2 - a^2}}$$

arise so often that we shall consider them as a special group.

While all these integrals can be found by trigonometric substitution, and those of the first column by standard formulas, it is our purpose here to call attention to the close relationship of the three integrals in any row.

Let us consider, for example, the integrals in the second row. The first of these we shall integrate by an interesting special device.

Let $y = \sqrt{a^2 + x^2}$, so that $y^2 = a^2 + x^2$, and $y\,dy = x\,dx$. Then

$$\frac{dx}{y} = \frac{dy}{x} = \frac{dx + dy}{y + x} = \frac{d(x + y)}{x + y},$$

and

$$\int \frac{dx}{\sqrt{a^2 + x^2}} = \int \frac{dx}{y} = \int \frac{d(x + y)}{x + y} = \ln (x + y) + C$$

$$= \ln (x + \sqrt{a^2 + x^2}) + C$$

as given by XXI, Art. 82.

Next consider the second integral of the second row, namely, $\int \sqrt{a^2 + x^2}\,dx$. To integrate this by parts, we let

$$u = \sqrt{a^2 + x^2} \quad \text{and} \quad dv = dx,$$

whence

$$du = \frac{x\,dx}{\sqrt{a^2 + x^2}} \quad \text{and} \quad v = x.$$

Then applying XX, Art. 82, we have

$$(1) \quad \int \sqrt{a^2 + x^2}\,dx = x\sqrt{a^2 + x^2} - \int \frac{x^2\,dx}{\sqrt{a^2 + x^2}}$$

$$= x\sqrt{a^2 + x^2} - \int \frac{x^2 + a^2 - a^2}{\sqrt{a^2 + x^2}}\,dx$$

$$= x\sqrt{a^2 + x^2} - \int \sqrt{a^2 + x^2}\,dx + a^2 \int \frac{dx}{\sqrt{a^2 + x^2}}.$$

Now transposing the term $-\int \sqrt{a^2 + x^2}\,dx$ and dividing by 2, we find that

$$\int \sqrt{a^2 + x^2}\,dx = \tfrac{1}{2} x\sqrt{a^2 + x^2} + \tfrac{1}{2} a^2 \int \frac{dx}{\sqrt{a^2 + x^2}}.$$

Finally substituting the expression found above for the last integral we obtain

$$(2) \quad \int \sqrt{a^2 + x^2}\,dx = \tfrac{1}{2} x\sqrt{a^2 + x^2} + \tfrac{1}{2} a^2 \ln (x + \sqrt{a^2 + x^2}) + C$$

To evaluate the third integral of the second row we find by rearranging the terms in the first line of (1) that

$$\int \frac{x^2 \, dx}{\sqrt{a^2 + x^2}} = x\sqrt{a^2 + x^2} - \int \sqrt{a^2 + x^2} \, dx$$

and hence by (2) that

$$\int \frac{x^2 \, dx}{\sqrt{a^2 + x^2}} = x\sqrt{a^2 + x^2} - [\tfrac{1}{2} x\sqrt{a^2 + x^2}$$
$$+ \tfrac{1}{2} a^2 \ln (x + \sqrt{a^2 + x^2})] + C$$
$$= \tfrac{1}{2} x\sqrt{a^2 + x^2} - \tfrac{1}{2} a^2 \ln (x + \sqrt{a^2 + x^2}) + C.$$

From this discussion it appears that, if any integral of the second row is known, the other two may be readily found. It will be left for the student to show that this statement holds for the integrals of the first and third rows.

93. General Observations. The formulas and methods of this chapter should enable the student to perform the majority of integrations that are likely to arise in elementary applications. Not infrequently, however, problems are encountered which require other formulas besides those hitherto considered. Accordingly a table of integrals more complete than that comprising the Primary and Secondary Groups is given in Chapter XVIII, together with an explanation of its use. This table is incorporated principally for future reference, and is not intended for indiscriminate use on the part of the beginning student.

It should be remarked that not every elementary function can be integrated in finite form in terms of elementary functions. This is true, for example, of the integrals

$$\int \frac{e^x}{x} \, dx, \quad \int \sqrt{x} \cos x \, dx, \quad \text{and} \quad \int \sqrt{\frac{16 - 3x^2}{4 - x^2}} \, dx.$$

Many functions, however, that are non-integrable in terms of elementary functions can be expanded into infinite series (Chapter XIV) and then integrated.

GENERAL PROBLEMS

Evaluate the following integrals:

1. $\int (1 + x)(1 + x^2)dx.$

2. $\int \sqrt{1 - x}\, dx.$

3. $\int \dfrac{1 + 2x + 2x^2}{x^2}\, dx.$

4. $\int \dfrac{dx}{\sqrt{1 - 3x}}.$

5. $\int \dfrac{y^2\, dy}{\sqrt{1 - y^3}}.$

6. $\int \sqrt{(1 + kt)^3}\, dt.$

7. $\int (x^2 - 4)x\, dx.$

8. $\int \sqrt{x^2 - 4}\, x\, dx.$

9. $\int \dfrac{x\, dx}{9 - 4x^2}.$

10. $\int \dfrac{dx}{9 - 4x^2}.$

11. $\int \dfrac{dx}{9 + 4x^2}.$

12. $\int \dfrac{x\, dx}{9 + 4x^2}.$

13. $\int \dfrac{dx}{\sqrt{9 - 4x^2}}.$

14. $\int \dfrac{x\, dx}{\sqrt{9 - 4x^2}}.$

15. $\int \dfrac{x^3\, dx}{x^2 + 1}.$

16. $\int \dfrac{(2 + x^2)dx}{\sqrt[3]{1 + 6x + x^3}}.$

17. $\int \dfrac{(1 + x^2)dx}{(3x + x^3)^{\frac{3}{2}}}.$

18. $\int (a^{\frac{2}{3}} - x^{\frac{2}{3}})^2\, dx.$

19. $\int (a^{\frac{2}{3}} - x^{\frac{2}{3}})^2 \dfrac{dx}{x^{\frac{1}{3}}}.$

20. $\int \dfrac{(\ln x)^2\, dx}{x}.$

21. $\int \dfrac{(\sin^{-1} x)^3\, dx}{\sqrt{1 - x^2}}.$

22. $\int e^{\sin^2 x} \sin 2x\, dx.$

23. $\int \dfrac{\tan^{-1} x\, dx}{1 + x^2}.$

24. $\int \sec^6 3x\, dx.$

25. $\int \sec^5 2x \tan 2x\, dx.$

26. $\int \sin x \cos^7 x\, dx.$

27. $\int \sin^2 2\theta\, d\theta.$

28. $\int \cos^3 5x\, dx.$

29. $\int \csc^4 2x \cot^2 2x\, dx.$

30. $\int \sin^5 3x\, dx.$

31. $\int \sin^2 2x \cos^2 2x\, dx.$

32. $\int \cos x \sqrt{\sin x}\, dx.$

33. $\int \sec^2 2x \sqrt{1 + 3 \tan 2x}\, dx.$

34. $\int \sin 3\theta \tan 3\theta\, d\theta.$

35. $\int \tan^2 4\theta\, d\theta.$

36. $\int \sec^3 5\theta\, d\theta.$

37. $\int \dfrac{(3x + 2)dx}{3x^2 + 4x + 1}.$

38. $\int \dfrac{dx}{x \ln x}.$

39. $\int \dfrac{dx}{(\tan^{-1} x)(1 + x^2)}.$

40. $\int \dfrac{e^{2x} - e^{-2x}}{e^{2x} + e^{-2x}}\, dx.$

41. $\int \dfrac{e^{2x} - 1}{e^{2x} + 1}\, dx.$

42. $\int (\sin^2 3x + \cos^2 3x)^3\, dx.$

43. $\int \frac{\sin 4\theta}{\cos 2\theta} \, d\theta.$

44. $\int \left(\frac{\sin 3x}{\sin x} - \frac{\cos 3x}{\cos x} \right) dx.$

45. $\int \frac{\sin^3 \theta}{\cos^5 \theta} \, d\theta.$

46. $\int \frac{x \, dx}{\sqrt{x-3}}.$

47. $\int \frac{dx}{x\sqrt{x+9}}.$

48. $\int \frac{dx}{x\sqrt{x^2+9}}.$

49. $\int \frac{x \, dx}{9+x^4}.$

50. $\int \frac{\cot^{-1} x \, dx}{1+x^2}.$

51. $\int \frac{(\tan^{-1} x)^2 \, dx}{1+x^2}.$

52. $\int \frac{dx}{x^2+4x+5}.$

53. $\int \frac{3x+7}{x^2+9} \, dx.$

54. $\int \frac{(x+4)dx}{x^2+6x+18}.$

55. $\int \frac{dx}{\sqrt{6x-x^2}}.$

56. $\int \frac{dx}{x^2-4x-5}.$

57. $\int \frac{\sqrt{1+x^3}}{x} \, dx.$

58. $\int \frac{dx}{x\sqrt{4x^2-9}}.$

59. $\int \sqrt{x^2-4} \, dx.$

60. $\int \sqrt{4-x^2} \, dx.$

61. $\int \frac{dx}{\sqrt{x^2-4}}.$

62. $\int \frac{x^2 \, dx}{\sqrt{x^2-4}}.$

63. $\int \frac{x \, dx}{\sqrt{x^2-4}}.$

64. $\int x^3\sqrt{4-x^2} \, dx.$

65. $\int x^3 \sin x \, dx.$

66. $\int x^2 e^{3x} dx.$

67. $\int \tan^{-1} 2x \, dx.$

68. $\int x^2 \ln x \, dx.$

69. $\int x^2 \sin^{-1} x \, dx.$

70. $\int x^3 (\ln x)^2 \, dx.$

71. $\int x \sin^{-1} x \, dx.$

72. $\int \frac{dx}{(x^2+4)(x-1)^2}.$

73. $\int \frac{x^2 \, dx}{x^4+12x^3+52x^2+96x+64}.$

74. $\int \frac{(4x^2-3)dx}{(x-2)(x^2+2x+5)}.$

CHAPTER IX

DEFINITE INTEGRALS

94. Definite Integrals. In Art. 33 the definite integral $\int_a^b f(x)dx$ was defined by the equation

$$(1) \qquad \int_a^b f(x)dx = [F(x)]_a^b = F(b) - F(a),$$

where $F(x)$ is a function whose derivative is $f(x)$; that is

$$(2) \qquad \int f(x)dx = F(x) + C.$$

Now, in view of the work of the preceding chapter, we are in a position to consider a greater variety of definite integrals than were studied in Chapter III, where only polynomial functions were integrated. For, if $F(x)$ can be found in any manner whatever, the evaluation of the last member of (1) is, for the most part, merely a routine process. Certain cases, however, require elaboration. Some of these will now be discussed.

(a) *Integrals Leading to Inverse Trigonometric Functions.* When Formulas XVIII and XIX, Art. 82, are used in evaluating definite integrals, care must be exercised in substituting the limits of integration in the multiple-valued functions appearing in the right members. The necessary precautions are discussed in what follows.

Example 1. Evaluate $\int_{-\frac{1}{2}}^{\frac{1}{2}} \dfrac{dx}{\sqrt{1-x^2}}.$

By XVIII, Art. 82, and (1) we have

$$(3) \qquad \int_{-\frac{1}{2}}^{\frac{1}{2}} \frac{dx}{\sqrt{1-x^2}} = [\sin^{-1} x]_{-\frac{1}{2}}^{\frac{1}{2}} = \sin^{-1}(\tfrac{1}{2}) - \sin^{-1}(-\tfrac{1}{2}).$$

Evidently there is ambiguity here; for $\sin^{-1}(\tfrac{1}{2})$ and $\sin^{-1}(-\tfrac{1}{2})$ have infinitely many values. However, the ambiguity may be removed by choosing those values of $\sin^{-1}(\tfrac{1}{2})$ and $\sin^{-1}(-\tfrac{1}{2})$ which correspond to points on the branch AB of the curve $y = \sin^{-1} x$ (Fig. 94) or to points on any other branch, such as CD, which slopes upward to the right.[*]

Thus if we use values of $\sin^{-1}\left(\frac{1}{2}\right)$ and $\sin^{-1}\left(-\frac{1}{2}\right)$ which correspond to points on AB we find that

$$\int_{-\frac{1}{2}}^{\frac{1}{2}} \frac{dx}{\sqrt{1 - x^2}} = \frac{\pi}{6} - \left(-\frac{\pi}{6}\right) = \frac{\pi}{3}.$$

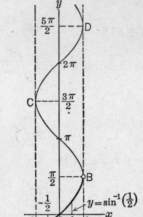

FIG. 94

The same result is obtained by using the branch CD; for then

$$\int_{-\frac{1}{2}}^{\frac{1}{2}} \frac{dx}{\sqrt{1 - x^2}} = \frac{13\pi}{6} - \frac{11\pi}{6} = \frac{\pi}{3}.$$

Example 2. Evaluate $\displaystyle\int_{-2\sqrt{3}}^{2} \frac{dx}{4 + x^2}$.

We have by XIX, Art. 82, and (1)

$$(4) \quad \int_{-2\sqrt{3}}^{2} \frac{dx}{4 + x^2} = \left[\frac{1}{2}\tan^{-1}\frac{x}{2}\right]_{-2\sqrt{3}}^{2}$$
$$= \tfrac{1}{2}[\tan^{-1}(1) - \tan^{-1}(-\sqrt{3})].$$

Using arguments similar to those given in Example 1 we remove the ambiguity occurring in the last member of (4) by restricting the function $\tan^{-1}\dfrac{x}{2}$ to values between $-\dfrac{\pi}{2}$ and $\dfrac{\pi}{2}$, so that $\tan^{-1}(1) = \dfrac{\pi}{4}$ and $\tan^{-1}(-\sqrt{3}) = -\dfrac{\pi}{3}$.

Thus

$$\int_{-2\sqrt{3}}^{2} \frac{dx}{4 + x^2} = \frac{1}{2}\left[\frac{\pi}{4} - \left(-\frac{\pi}{3}\right)\right] = \frac{7\pi}{24}.$$

Generalizing from these examples we adopt the following convenient rule:

In using the formulas

$$\int_{c}^{d} \frac{dx}{\sqrt{a^2 - x^2}} = \left[\sin^{-1}\frac{x}{a}\right]_{c}^{d} = \sin^{-1}\frac{d}{a} - \sin^{-1}\frac{c}{a}$$

[*] In the equation

$$\int_{c}^{d} \frac{dx}{\sqrt{1 - x^2}} = \sin^{-1} d - \sin^{-1} c$$

which is a generalization of (3), $\sin^{-1} d$ and $\sin^{-1} c$ must be values of $\sin^{-1} x$ occurring on the same branch of the curve $y = \sin^{-1} x$, for only then will the definite integral approach zero, as it obviously should, when c and d approach equality.

Moreover, we must not choose a branch like CB which slopes downward toward the right, for the points on such a branch correspond to values of $\sin^{-1} x$ belonging to the second and third quadrants, and for these values XVIII is not valid (Art. 87).

and

$$\int_c^a \frac{dx}{a^2 + x^2} = \left[\frac{1}{a}\tan^{-1}\frac{x}{a}\right]_c^a = \frac{1}{a}\left(\tan^{-1}\frac{d}{a} - \tan^{-1}\frac{c}{a}\right),$$

we impose the respective conditions that

$$-\frac{\pi}{2} < \sin^{-1}\frac{x}{a} < \frac{\pi}{2}$$

and

$$-\frac{\pi}{2} < \tan^{-1}\frac{x}{a} < \frac{\pi}{2}.$$

(b) *Integration by Parts.* When applied to a definite integral, the formula (XX, Art. 82) for integrating by parts becomes

(5)
$$\int_{x=a}^{x=b} u\,dv = [uv]_{x=a}^{x=b} - \int_{x=a}^{x=b} v\,du$$

or

(6)
$$\int_{x=a}^{x=b} u\,dv = \left[uv - \int v\,du\right]_{x=a}^{x=b},$$

where x is the variable of integration.

Example 3.   Evaluate $\int_0^1 xe^x dx$.

Letting $u = x$ and $dv = e^x dx$ we obtain by (6)

$$\int_0^1 xe^x dx = \left[xe^x - \int e^x dx\right]_0^1$$
$$= [e^x(x - 1)]_0^1$$
$$= 1.$$

(c) *Integration by Substitution.* When the evaluation of a definite integral involves the method of substitution (Art. 90), it is convenient to change the limits of integration so as to correspond with the change of variable. This device makes it unnecessary to restore the original variable after the integration is performed.

Example 4.   Evaluate $\int_7^{14} \frac{x\,dx}{\sqrt{2 + x}}$.

Letting $v = \sqrt{2 + x}$ whence $x = v^2 - 2$ and $dx = 2\,v\,dv$, and observing that

$$v = 3 \text{ when } x = 7$$

and

$$v = 4 \text{ when } x = 14,$$

we obtain

$$\int_7^{14} \frac{x\,dx}{\sqrt{2+x}} = 2\int_3^4 (v^2 - 2)dv$$

$$= 2\left[\frac{v^3}{3} - 2v\right]_3^4$$

$$= \frac{62}{3}.$$

Example 5. Evaluate $\int_1^2 \frac{\sqrt{4-x^2}}{x^4}\,dx.$

Letting $x = 2\sin\theta$, whence $\sqrt{4-x^2} = 2\cos\theta$ and $dx = 2\cos\theta\,d\theta$, and observing that

$$\theta = \frac{\pi}{6} \text{ when } x = 1$$

and

$$\theta = \frac{\pi}{2} \text{ when } x = 2,$$

we obtain

$$\int_1^2 \frac{\sqrt{4-x^2}}{x^4}\,dx = \frac{1}{4}\int_{\frac{\pi}{6}}^{\frac{\pi}{2}} \cot^2\theta \csc^2\theta\,d\theta$$

$$= \left[-\frac{1}{12}\cot^3\theta\right]_{\frac{\pi}{6}}^{\frac{\pi}{2}}$$

$$= \frac{\sqrt{3}}{4}.$$

PROBLEMS

Evaluate the following definite integrals:

1. $\int_{-3}^3 \frac{dx}{9+x^2}.$

2. $\int_{-1}^1 \frac{dx}{\sqrt{4-x^2}}.$

3. $\int_{-5}^1 \frac{dx}{x^2+4x+13}.$

4. $\int_2^3 \frac{dx}{\sqrt{4x-x^2}}.$

5. $\int_1^{\sqrt{3}} \frac{2+x}{\sqrt{4-x^2}}\,dx.$

6. $\int_{-2}^2 \frac{4-x^2}{4+x^2}\,dx.$

7. $\int_{\frac{1}{2}}^1 \ln 2x\,dx.$

8. $\int_2^4 x^3 \ln x\,dx.$

9. $\int_0^1 x\,e^{-x}\,dx.$

10. $\int_{\frac{\pi}{6}}^{\frac{\pi}{2}} (\ln\sin x)\cos x\,dx.$

11. $\int_0^{\frac{\pi}{6}} e^{-x}\cos 2x\,dx.$

12. $\int_0^{\frac{\pi}{4}} x\sin^2 2x\,dx.$

13. $\int_0^1 \tan^{-1} x\,dx.$

14. $\int_0^{\frac{1}{4}} \sin^{-1} 2x\,dx.$

15. $\int_{-\frac{1}{2}}^{\frac{1}{2}} x \sin^{-1} x \, dx.$

20. $\int_{1}^{\frac{5}{8}} \frac{\sqrt{25 - 9x^2}}{x} \, dx.$

16. $\int_{5}^{12} \frac{\sqrt{4 + x}}{x} \, dx.$

21. $\int_{0}^{1} \frac{dx}{(25 - 9x^2)^{\frac{3}{2}}}.$

17. $\int_{0}^{5} x\sqrt{1 + 3x} \, dx.$

22. $\int_{0}^{1} \sqrt{25 - 16x^2} \, dx.$

18. $\int_{4}^{7} \frac{x \, dx}{\sqrt{x - 3}}.$

23. $\int_{-\frac{3}{2}}^{\frac{3}{2}} \frac{x^2 \, dx}{\sqrt{9 - x^2}}.$

19. $\int_{4}^{11} \frac{x^2 \, dx}{\sqrt[3]{x - 3}}.$

24. $\int_{0}^{3} \sqrt{x^2 + 16} \, dx.$

95. Improper Integrals. Hitherto in the consideration of

$$(1) \qquad \int_{a}^{b} f(x)dx$$

we have taken a and b as finite and assumed that $f(x)$ is continuous for all values of x in the interval from $x = a$ to $x = b$, including the end-points. If, however, a or b is infinite, or if $f(x)$ is discontinuous within or at an end of the interval, (1) is said to be an **improper integral,** and its meaning must be defined. The two cases will be discussed separately.

Case 1. Infinite Limits of Integration. If $f(x)$ is continuous within and at the ends of the interval from $x = a$ to $x = t$, and $\int_{a}^{t} f(x)dx$ approaches a limit as $t \to \infty$, we designate this limit as $\int_{a}^{\infty} f(x)dx$. Thus by definition

$$(2) \qquad \int_{a}^{\infty} f(x)dx = \lim_{t \to \infty} \int_{a}^{t} f(x)dx.$$

Similarly, if $f(x)$ is continuous within and at the ends of the interval from $x = t'$ to $x = b$ we adopt the definition

$$(3) \qquad \int_{-\infty}^{b} f(x)dx = \lim_{t' \to -\infty} \int_{t'}^{b} f(x)dx,$$

provided the limit exists.

Moreover, if a and b have any common finite value, and if the limits in (2) and (3) exist, we designate the sum of these limits as $\int_{-\infty}^{\infty} f(x)dx$. Accordingly, by definition, we write

$$(4) \qquad \int_{-\infty}^{\infty} f(x)dx = \int_{-\infty}^{a} f(x)dx + \int_{a}^{\infty} f(x)dx.$$

It is of course evident that the left members of (2) and (3) are without meaning when the limits in the right members fail to exist.

Example 1.   Evaluate $\int_1^\infty \dfrac{dx}{x^3}$.

In accordance with (2) we write

$$\int_1^\infty \frac{dx}{x^3} = \lim_{t \to \infty} \int_1^t \frac{dx}{x^3} = \lim_{t \to \infty} \left(-\frac{1}{2t^2} + \frac{1}{2} \right) = \frac{1}{2}.$$

It follows from Art. 34 that $\int_1^t \dfrac{dx}{x^3}$ represents the area $BCDE$ (Fig. 95a). Since $\int_1^\infty \dfrac{dx}{x^3} = \dfrac{1}{2}$, we conclude that this area approaches $\frac{1}{2}$ as its right boundary CD recedes indefinitely.

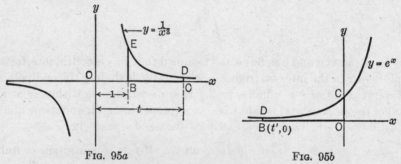

FIG. 95a   FIG. 95b

Example 2.   Evaluate $\int_{-\infty}^0 e^x dx$.

In accordance with (3)

$$\int_{-\infty}^0 e^x dx = \lim_{t' \to -\infty} \int_{t'}^0 e^x dx = \lim_{t' \to -\infty} (1 - e^{t'}) = 1.$$

This result shows that the area $BOCD$ (Fig. 95b) approaches unity as the left boundary recedes indefinitely.

Case 2.   Discontinuous Integrand.   If $f(x)$ is continuous for the range $a \leq x < b$, but is discontinuous for $x = b$, we shall define $\int_a^b f(x)dx$ by the equation

(5) $$\int_a^b f(x)dx = \lim_{x \to b^-} \int_a^x f(x)dx,$$

provided the limit exists. Here the notation $x \to b^-$ means that x approaches b through values less than b (Art. 6).

Similarly, if $f(x)$ is continuous for the range $a < x \leq b$, but is discontinuous for $x = a$, we adopt the definition

(6) $$\int_a^b f(x)dx = \lim_{x \to a^+} \int_x^b f(x)dx,$$

provided the limit exists.   The notation $x \to a^+$ means that x approaches a through values greater than a.

Finally, if $f(x)$ is discontinuous for some value of x, say $x = c$ (where $a < c < b$), but is continuous for all other values of x from $x = a$ to $x = b$ inclusive, we shall define $\int_a^b f(x)dx$ by the equation

(7)
$$\int_a^b f(x)dx = \int_a^c f(x)dx + \int_c^b f(x)dx,$$

where the integrals in the right member are evaluated in accordance with (5) and (6), respectively.

Example 3.   Evaluate $\int_0^1 \dfrac{dx}{\sqrt{1-x^2}}.$

Since the integrand becomes infinite as x approaches the upper limit of integration, we write, in accordance with (5)

$$\int_0^1 \frac{dx}{\sqrt{1-x^2}} = \lim_{x \to 1^-} \int_0^x \frac{dx}{\sqrt{1-x^2}} = \lim_{x \to 1^-} [\sin^{-1} x]_0^x = \frac{\pi}{2}.$$

This result shows that the area $OBCD$ (Fig. 95c) approaches $\dfrac{\pi}{2}$ as the right boundary approaches coincidence with the line $x = 1$.

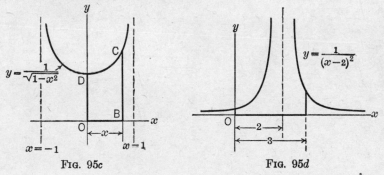

FIG. 95c   FIG. 95d

Example 4.   Show that $\int_0^3 \dfrac{dx}{(x-2)^2}$ has no meaning.

Since the integrand is discontinuous for $x = 2$, a value lying between the limits of integration, we write, in accordance with (7),

$$\int_0^3 \frac{dx}{(x-2)^2} = \int_0^2 \frac{dx}{(x-2)^2} + \int_2^3 \frac{dx}{(x-2)^2},$$

where the integrals are to be evaluated by means of (5) and (6), respectively. However, it is readily shown that each of these integrals is without meaning; for example,

$$\int_0^2 \frac{dx}{(x-2)^2} = \lim_{x \to 2^-} \int_0^x \frac{dx}{(x-2)^2} = \lim_{x \to 2^-} \left(\frac{1}{2-x} - \frac{1}{2} \right),$$

and this limit fails to exist. Accordingly the area under the curve $y = \dfrac{1}{(x-2)^2}$ (Fig. 95d) from $x = 0$ to $x = 3$ is unlimited.

It should be observed that if the discontinuity of the integrand for $x = 2$ is ignored and the limits 0 and 3 are substituted in the indefinite integral $\dfrac{1}{2-x}$, the erroneous result $-\frac{3}{2}$ would be obtained.

PROBLEMS

In each of the following problems evaluate the definite integral or show that it has no meaning.

1. $\displaystyle\int_5^\infty \frac{dx}{x^2}$.

2. $\displaystyle\int_3^\infty \frac{dx}{(x-1)^4}$.

3. $\displaystyle\int_1^\infty e^{-x}\, dx$.

4. $\displaystyle\int_1^\infty \frac{dx}{\sqrt{x}}$.

5. $\displaystyle\int_1^\infty \frac{dx}{x}$.

6. $\displaystyle\int_1^\infty \frac{\ln x^2}{x}\, dx$.

7. $\displaystyle\int_{-\infty}^0 \frac{dx}{x^2+4}$.

8. $\displaystyle\int_{-\infty}^\infty \frac{8a^3\, dx}{x^2+4a^2}$.

9. $\displaystyle\int_0^3 \frac{dx}{\sqrt{9-x^2}}$.

10. $\displaystyle\int_2^3 \frac{dx}{\sqrt{x-2}}$.

11. $\displaystyle\int_0^3 \frac{x\, dx}{(9-x^2)^{\frac{3}{2}}}$.

12. $\displaystyle\int_0^3 \frac{x\, dx}{\sqrt{9-x^2}}$.

13. $\displaystyle\int_0^1 \frac{dx}{1-x^2}$.

14. $\displaystyle\int_0^{\frac{\pi}{4}} \tan 2x\, dx$.

15. $\displaystyle\int_0^1 \frac{dx}{x^2}$.

16. $\displaystyle\int_{-1}^1 \frac{dx}{x^2}$.

17. $\displaystyle\int_0^3 \frac{x\, dx}{(x^2-8)^{\frac{2}{3}}}$.

18. $\displaystyle\int_1^{34} \frac{dx}{\sqrt[5]{x-2}}$.

CHAPTER X

APPLICATIONS OF INTEGRATION

96. Introductory Remarks. The formulas and methods of integration developed in Chapter VIII and the technique of evaluating definite integrals studied in Chapter IX provide the means of solving a greater variety of problems in area, volume, pressure, and work than were considered earlier (Chapter III). Accordingly we shall return to these topics; moreover, we shall apply the definite integral to many other types of problems.

In this chapter it will be assumed that the student is able to set up definite integrals involving the familiar elements of integration previously used. Detailed explanations will be given, however, of any new types of elements that are introduced.

97. Area (Rectangular Coördinates). Before proceeding with the following examples the student should review Art. 34.

Example 1. Find the area under the curve $y = \dfrac{9}{\sqrt{9 - x^2}}$ from $x = -\dfrac{3}{2}$ to $x = \dfrac{3\sqrt{3}}{2}$.

Using vertical elements we have for the required area (Fig. 97a)

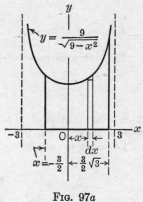

$$A = \int_{-\frac{3}{2}}^{\frac{3\sqrt{3}}{2}} \frac{9\,dx}{\sqrt{9 - x^2}} = 9\left[\sin^{-1}\frac{x}{3}\right]_{-\frac{3}{2}}^{\frac{3}{2}\sqrt{3}}$$

$$= 9\left[\sin^{-1}\frac{\sqrt{3}}{2} - \sin^{-1}\left(-\frac{1}{2}\right)\right]$$

$$= 9\left[\frac{\pi}{3} - \left(-\frac{\pi}{6}\right)\right]$$

$$= \frac{9\pi}{2}.$$

FIG. 97a

Example 2. Find the closed area bounded by the curves $y = \dfrac{1}{x+1}$ and $y = \dfrac{6}{x^2+5}$.

271

We find by solving the given equations simultaneously that their graphs (Fig. 97*b*) intersect at points whose abscissas are, to three decimals, -0.162 and 6.162. Hence, using vertical elements, we have for the required area

$$A = \int_{-0.162}^{6.162} \left(\frac{6}{x^2 + 5} - \frac{1}{x + 1} \right) dx$$

$$= \left[\frac{6}{\sqrt{5}} \tan^{-1} \frac{x}{\sqrt{5}} - \ln (x + 1) \right]_{-0.162}^{6.162}$$

$$= \left[\frac{6}{\sqrt{5}} \tan^{-1} \frac{6.162}{2.236} - \ln (7.162) \right] - \left[\frac{6}{\sqrt{5}} \tan^{-1} \left(-\frac{0.162}{2.236} \right) - \ln (0.838) \right]$$

$$= \frac{6}{\sqrt{5}} \tan^{-1} 2.756 - \ln (7.162) - \frac{6}{\sqrt{5}} \tan^{-1} (-0.0725) + \ln (0.838)$$

$$= \frac{6}{\sqrt{5}} (1.2227) - 1.9698 - \frac{6}{\sqrt{5}} (-0.0724) - 0.177$$

$$= 1.33, \text{ to two decimals.}$$

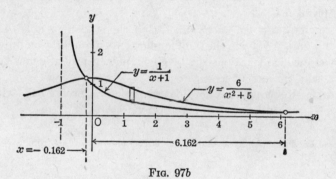

FIG. 97*b*

Example 3. Show that the curve whose parametric equations (Art. 62) are $x = a \cos\phi$, $y = b \sin\phi$ is an ellipse, and find the area enclosed by it.

Eliminating ϕ from the two equations we find

$$\frac{x^2}{a^2} + \frac{y^2}{b^2} = 1.$$

This is the equation of an ellipse; the significance of ϕ, which is called the *eccentric angle*, is shown in Fig. 97*c*.

Evidently the required area is given by

$$A = 4 \int_{0}^{a} y \, dx.$$

Using ϕ as the variable of integration and observing that

$$\phi = \frac{\pi}{2} \text{ when } x = 0$$

and

$$\phi = 0 \text{ when } x = a,$$

we have

$$A = 4 \int_{\frac{\pi}{2}}^{0} (b \sin \phi)(-a \sin \phi \, d\phi)$$

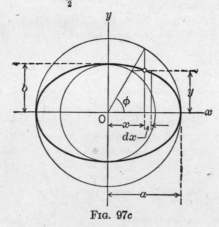

FIG. 97c

$$= 4 \, ab \int_{0}^{\frac{\pi}{2}} \sin^2 \phi \, d\phi$$

$$= 4 \, ab \left[\frac{\phi}{2} - \frac{\sin 2\phi}{4} \right]_{0}^{\frac{\pi}{2}}$$

$$= \pi ab.$$

PROBLEMS

In the following problems the elements of integration should be formulated so as to yield positive areas. Sketch the graphs of all equations.

1. Find the area enclosed by the circle $x^2 + y^2 = 16$.

2. Find the area enclosed by the ellipse $9x^2 + 16y^2 = 144$.

3. Find the area bounded by the hyperbola $4x^2 - 9y^2 = 36$ and the line $x = 5$.

4. Find the area enclosed by the circle $x^2 + y^2 - 2ax = 0$.

5. Find the smaller area bounded by the circle $x^2 + y^2 - 10x = 0$ and the line $x + 7y - 30 = 0$.

6. Find the first-quadrant area bounded by the circle $x^2 + y^2 = 25$ and the hyperbola $xy = 12$.

7. Find the larger area bounded by the curve $y = \dfrac{5}{4 + x^2}$ and the circle $x^2 + y^2 - 2y = 0$.

8. Find the area between the curve $y = \dfrac{15}{4 + x^2}$ and the hyperbola $y = \dfrac{3}{x + 2}$.

9. Find the area bounded by the curve $y = \dfrac{12}{\sqrt{25 - x^2}}$ and the chord through the points for which $x = -3$ and $x = 4$, respectively.

10. Find the area under the curve $y = \ln x$ from $x = 2$ to $x = 4$.

11. Find the area under the curve $y = e^x$ from $x = -1$ to $x = 2$.

12. Find the area under the curve $y = xe^x$ from $x = 0$ to $x = 1$.

13. Find the area under the catenary $y = \dfrac{a}{2}(e^{\frac{x}{a}} + e^{-\frac{x}{a}})$ from $x = -a$ to $x = a$.

14. Find the area under one arch of the curve $y = \sin x$.

15. Find the area bounded by the y-axis and the curves $y = \sin x$ and $y = \cos x$ from the y-axis to the first point of intersection of the curves that lies to the right of the y-axis.

16. Find the area under the curve $y = \sec x$ from $x = -\dfrac{\pi}{4}$ to $x = \dfrac{\pi}{4}$.

17. Find the area under one arch of the cycloid (see Example, Art. 78) $x = a\ (\phi - \sin \phi)$, $y = a\ (1 - \cos \phi)$.

18. Find the total area enclosed by the four-cusped hypocycloid $x^{\frac{2}{3}} + y^{\frac{2}{3}} = a^{\frac{2}{3}}$. HINT: In the integral representing the area make the substitution $x = a \sin^3\phi$.

19. Find the area bounded by the coördinate axes and the curve $x^{\frac{1}{2}} + y^{\frac{1}{2}} = a^{\frac{1}{2}}$.

20. Find the area enclosed by the loop of the curve $y^2 = (x - 1)(x - 3)^2$.

21. Find the area enclosed by the loop of the curve $y^2 = x^4(3 + x)$.

22. Find the area included between the parabola $x^2 = 4y$ and the curve $y(x^2 + 4) = 8$.

23. Find the entire area between the curve $y(x^2 + 4) = 8$ and its asymptote.

24. Find the entire area included between the cissoid $(2a - x)y^2 = x^3$ and its asymptote.

HINT: In the integral representing the area make the substitution $x = 2a \sin^2\phi$.

25. Find the area under the curve $y^3 = \dfrac{1}{(x - 1)^2}$ from $x = 0$ to $x = 9$.

26. Find the area bounded by $y = xe^{-x}$, the x-axis, and the maximum ordinate.

27. Find the area between the curve $x^2y^2 = 25 - x^2$ and the line $x = 4$.

28. Find the area bounded by the curve $x^2(y^2 + 16) = 25$ and the lines $y = 3$ and $y = -3$.

29. Find the area bounded by the curve $y = \ln \dfrac{y}{x}$, the y-axis, and the maximum abscissa.

HINT: Convert the given equation to exponential form and use horizontal strips.

30. Find the area bounded by the curve $\ln y^n = xy$, the y-axis, and the maximum abscissa.

98. Area (Polar Coördinates).

Hitherto we have confined our attention to areas bounded by lines or curves defined by cartesian equations. Suppose now that the equation of a curve in polar coördinates, $r = f(\theta)$, is given, and consider the problem of evaluating the area A bounded by this curve and the two lines $\theta = \alpha$ and $\theta = \beta$ (Fig. 98a).

Let $f(\theta)$ be a single-valued and continuous function from $\theta = \alpha$ to $\theta = \beta$, and assume further that $f(\theta)$ increases throughout the same interval. The last restriction is imposed merely for simplicity of exposition and may be removed without affecting the final result.

Now divide the angle $\beta - \alpha$ into n equal increments $\Delta\theta = \dfrac{\beta - \alpha}{n}$

by means of radial lines through the origin O, thereby dividing the area A into n increments, such as the ith increment ΔA_i bounded by the curve and the lines OP_i and OP_{i+1}. Next draw a circular arc $P_i Q$ with center at O from P_i to the line OP_{i+1}. Then by (2), Art. 45, we have

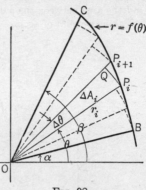

FIG. 98a

(1)   area $OP_i Q = \frac{1}{2} r_i^2 \Delta\theta,$

where $r_i = OP_i$, and $\Delta\theta$ is expressed in radians. Moreover, since

$$A = \sum_{i=1}^{i=n} \Delta A_i,$$

whatever be the value of n, we may write

(2) $A = \lim\limits_{n \to \infty} \sum_{i=1}^{i=n} \Delta A_i.$

Now the infinitesimal ΔA_i appearing in (2) differs from the area of the corresponding circular sector $OP_i Q$ by an infinitesimal of higher order than $\Delta\theta$. Therefore, in view of (1), we conclude from Duhamel's Theorem (Art. 35) that (2) may be replaced by

$$A = \lim_{n \to \infty} \sum_{i=1}^{i=n} \frac{1}{2} r_i^2 \Delta\theta.$$

Hence, by the Fundamental Theorem (Art. 35), we obtain for the required area OBC

(3) $A = \dfrac{1}{2} \displaystyle\int_\alpha^\beta r^2 d\theta,$

where θ, α, and β are expressed in radians.

Example 1. Using polar coördinates find the area of the triangle OBC (Fig. 98b).

Introducing polar coördinates as shown in the figure, we see that the polar angle θ of points on the line BC ranges from $\tan^{-1}\left(-\frac{1}{4}\right)$ to $\tan^{-1}(1)$ and that the equation of this line is $r = 4 \sec\theta$. Hence by (3) we obtain for the required area

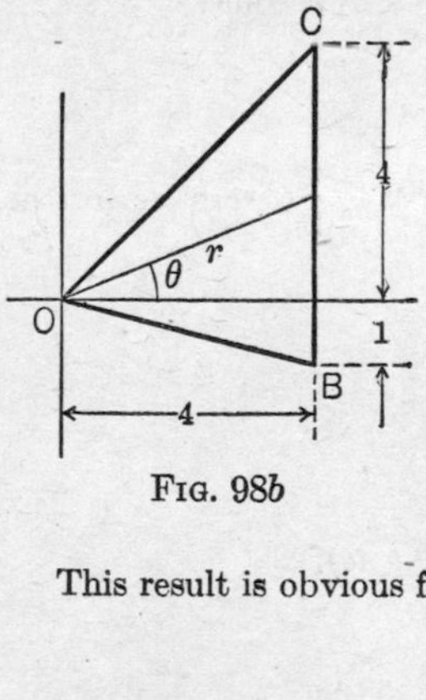

$$A = \frac{16}{2} \int_{\tan^{-1}\left(-\frac{1}{4}\right)}^{\tan^{-1}(1)} \sec^2\theta \, d\theta$$

$$= 8[\tan\theta]_{\tan^{-1}(-\frac{1}{4})}^{\tan^{-1}(1)}$$

$$= 10.$$

FIG. 98b

This result is obvious from geometry.

Example 2. The equation

$$r = \frac{2a}{1 + \cos \theta}$$

represents a parabola whose focus is at the origin and whose axis is the line $\theta = 0$. Find the area between the parabola and its latus rectum (BC, Fig. 98c).

Taking account of symmetry and using (3) we have for the required area

$$A = 2 \cdot \frac{1}{2} \int_0^{\frac{\pi}{2}} \frac{4a^2 d\theta}{(1 + \cos \theta)^2} = 4a^2 \int_0^{\frac{\pi}{2}} \frac{d\theta}{4 \cos^4 \frac{\theta}{2}}$$

$$= a^2 \int_0^{\frac{\pi}{2}} \sec^4 \frac{\theta}{2} d\theta = 2a^2 \left[\tan \frac{\theta}{2} + \frac{1}{3} \tan^3 \frac{\theta}{2} \right]_0^{\frac{\pi}{2}}$$

$$= \tfrac{8}{3} a^2.$$

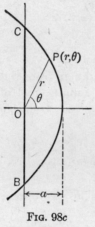

FIG. 98c

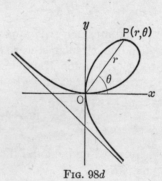

FIG. 98d

Example 3. Find the area (Fig. 98d) enclosed by the loop of the folium of Descartes

$$x^3 + y^3 = 3axy.$$

The equation of this curve transformed to polar coördinates becomes

$$r = \frac{3a \sin \theta \cos \theta}{\cos^3 \theta + \sin^3 \theta}.$$

Observing that the loop is generated as θ ranges from 0 to $\frac{\pi}{2}$, we have for the required area

$$A = \tfrac{1}{2} \int_0^{\frac{\pi}{2}} r^2 \, d\theta$$

$$= \frac{1}{2} 9a^2 \int_0^{\frac{\pi}{2}} \frac{\sin^2 \theta \cos^2 \theta}{(\cos^3 \theta + \sin^3 \theta)^2} \, d\theta$$

$$= \frac{9a^2}{2} \int_0^{\frac{\pi}{2}} (1 + \tan^3 \theta)^{-2} (\tan^2 \theta \sec^2 \theta \, d\theta).$$

Since for the upper limit $\dfrac{\pi}{2}$ the integrand is discontinuous the integral is an improper one to which we apply the method of Art. 95, Case 2. Thus we write

$$A = \lim_{\theta \to \frac{\pi}{2}^-} \frac{9a^2}{2} \int_0^\theta (1 + \tan^3 \theta)^{-2} \tan^2 \theta \sec^2 \theta \, d\theta$$

$$= \lim_{\theta \to \frac{\pi}{2}^-} \frac{3a^2}{2} \left[\frac{(1 + \tan^3 \theta)^{-1}}{-1} \right]_0^\theta$$

$$= \frac{3a^2}{2}.$$

PROBLEMS

In the following problems the graphs of all equations should be sketched.

1. Find the area enclosed by the circle $r = 2 \sin \theta$.
2. Find the area enclosed by one loop of the curve $r = 3 \sin 2\theta$.
3. Find the area enclosed by one loop of the curve $r = 2 \cos 2\theta$.
4. Find the whole area enclosed by the cardioid $r = a(1 - \cos \theta)$.
5. Find the entire area enclosed by the lemniscate $r^2 = a^2 \cos 2\theta$.
6. Find the area bounded by the curve $r = 3 + \cos 3\theta$.
7. Find the area lying inside the circle $r = 6 \cos \theta$ and outside the circle $r = 3$.
8. Find the larger area bounded by the circle $r = 8 \cos \theta$ and the line $r = 2 \sec \theta$.
9. Find the smaller area bounded by the circle $r = 4 \sin \theta$ and the line $\theta = \dfrac{\pi}{3}$.
10. Find the common area enclosed by the circles $r = 4 \cos \theta$ and $r = 4 \sin \theta$.
11. Find the area bounded by the curve $r^3 = \csc \theta \sec^2 \theta$, its asymptote $\theta = 0$, and the line $\theta = \dfrac{\pi}{4}$.

HINT: Express the integral representing the area in the form $\displaystyle\int_a^b u^n du$, where $u = \tan \theta$.

99. Volume.

The most convenient element of volume for many solids is one lying between a pair of parallel neighboring planes. Such elements were used with the solids of Art. 36 and require no further explanation here. In the case of a solid of revolution these elements are right circular cylindrical discs or else have the shape of washers.

The volume of a solid of revolution may also be found by use of hollow cylindrical elements. To see this, consider the volume V formed by revolving about the y-axis the area under the curve $y = f(x)$ from $x = a$ to $x = b$.

Let this area be divided into n vertical strips of equal width $\Delta x = \dfrac{b - a}{n}$; then, as the area is revolved about the y-axis, each of these strips, such as $BCP_{i+1}P_i$ (Fig. 99a), will generate an increment of volume

ΔV_i whose inner and outer radii are respectively x_i and $x_{i+1}(i = 1, \cdots, n)$. Since the total volume is the sum of these increments we have

$$V = \sum_{i=1}^{i=n} \Delta V_i.$$

Moreover, as this holds for any value of n, we may write

(1)
$$V = \lim_{n \to \infty} \sum_{i=1}^{i=n} \Delta V_i.$$

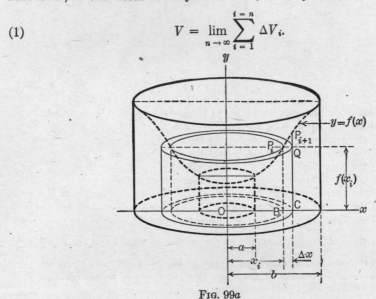

FIG. 99a

Now the infinitesimal ΔV_i appearing in (1) differs by an infinitesimal of higher order than Δx from the volume $\pi[(x_i + \Delta x)^2 - x_i^2]f(x_i)$ of the hollow cylindrical element generated by a rectangular strip such as $BCQP_i$. Therefore, in accordance with Duhamel's Theorem (Art. 35), we may replace ΔV_i by the volume of this element, obtaining

(2)
$$V = \lim_{n \to \infty} \sum_{i=1}^{i=n} \pi[(x_i + \Delta x)^2 - x_i^2]f(x_i)$$

$$= \lim_{n \to \infty} \sum_{i=1}^{i=n} \pi[2x_i\Delta x + (\Delta x)^2]f(x_i),$$

where now the term $(\Delta x)^2$, being an infinitesimal of higher order than $2x_i\Delta x$, may, by Duhamel's Theorem, be neglected. Thus we have

$$V = \lim_{n \to \infty} \sum_{i=1}^{i=n} 2\pi x_i f(x_i)\Delta x,$$

whence, by the Fundamental Theorem,

(3) $$V = 2\pi \int_a^b xy\ dx,$$

where $y = f(x)$.

Thus by this method *we may find the exact volume of a solid of revolution by multiplying a circumference of a hollow cylindrical element by its altitude and thickness, and then integrating.*

Example 1. The area bounded by the curve $y = \dfrac{8}{4 + x^2}$, the coördinate axes, and the line $x = 2$ is revolved about the x-axis. Find the volume of the solid generated.

Using cylindrical discs as elements of volume (Fig. 99b) we have for the required volume

$$V = \pi \int_0^2 y^2\ dx$$

$$= 64\pi \int_0^2 \frac{dx}{(4 + x^2)^2}.$$

Substituting $x = 2 \tan \theta$ and observing that the new limits are 0 and $\dfrac{\pi}{4}$, we obtain

$$V = 8\pi \int_0^{\frac{\pi}{4}} \cos^2 \theta\ d\theta$$

$$= 4\pi \int_0^{\frac{\pi}{4}} (1 + \cos 2\theta)d\theta$$

$$= \pi(\pi + 2).$$

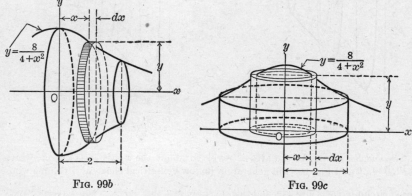

FIG. 99b FIG. 99c

Example 2. Find the volume generated by revolving the area of Example 1 about the y-axis.

Using hollow cylindrical elements, a typical one of which is shown in Fig. 99c we have by (3)

$$V = 2\pi \int_0^2 xy\ dx$$

$$= 2\pi \int_0^2 \frac{8x\,dx}{4 + x^2}$$

$$= 8\pi \ln 2.$$

Example 3.   Find the volume of the solid generated by revolving about the x-axis the area bounded by the hyperbola $xy = 5$ and the line $x + y = 6$.

First Solution.   As the area is revolved about the x-axis, the element of area $ABCD$ shown in Fig. 99d will generate a washer-shaped element whose volume is

$$dV = \pi \left[(6 - x)^2 - \left(\frac{5}{x} \right)^2 \right] dx,$$

so that the total volume is

$$V = \pi \int_1^5 \left[(6 - x)^2 - \frac{25}{x^2} \right] dx$$

$$= \frac{64\pi}{3}.$$

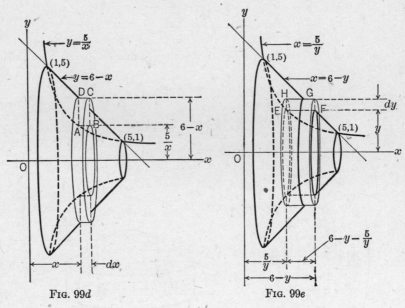

FIG. 99d FIG. 99e

Second Solution.   As the area is revolved about the x-axis the element of area $EFGH$ shown in Fig. 99e will generate a hollow cylindrical element of volume whose inner circumference, altitude, and thickness are $2\pi y$, $(6 - y) - \dfrac{5}{y}$, and dy, respectively. Hence

$$V = 2\pi \int_1^5 \left[(6 - y) - \frac{5}{y} \right] y\,dy$$

$$= \frac{64\pi}{3}.$$

PROBLEMS

1. The first-quadrant area bounded by the curve $x^2y^2 + 9y^2 - 12 = 0$, the axes, and the line $x = 3$, is revolved about the x-axis. Find the volume of the solid generated.

2. Revolve the area of Problem 1 about the y-axis and find the volume of the solid generated.

3. Revolve the area of Problem 1 about the line $x = 3$ and find the volume of the solid generated.

4. Find the volume of the torus generated by revolving the area of the circle $x^2 + y^2 - 10x + 21 = 0$ about the y-axis, (a) using washer-shaped elements, and (b) using hollow cylinders. Note that the result is equal to the product of the area of the generating circle by the circumference described by its center.

5. Find the volume of the solid generated by revolving about the x-axis the area bounded on the left by the curve $y^2 = \dfrac{x - 2}{16 + x^2}$ and on the right by the line $x = 4$.

6. Find the volume of the solid generated by revolving about the x-axis the area bounded by the curve $(9 + x^2)y^2 = 9 - x^2$.

7. Find the volume of the solid generated by revolving about the x-axis the first-quadrant area bounded by the curve $y^4 = x^2(4 - x)$ and the x-axis.

8. Find the volume of the solid generated by revolving about the x-axis the area bounded by the curve $y = e^x$, the coördinate axes, and the line $x = 2$.

9. Revolve the area of Problem 8 about the y-axis and find the volume of the solid generated.

10. Revolve the area of Problem 8 about the line $x = 2$ and find the volume of the solid generated.

11. Find the volume of the solid generated by revolving about the x-axis the area in the first quadrant under the curve $y = e^{-x}$.

12. Revolve about the x-axis the area bounded by the curve $y = \ln x$, the x-axis, and the line $x = 3$, and find the volume of the solid generated.

13. Revolve the area of Problem 12 about the y-axis and find the volume of the solid generated.

14. Revolve the area of Problem 12 about the line $x = 3$ and find the volume of the solid generated.

15. Find the volume of the solid generated by revolving about the x-axis the area under the curve $y = \sin x$ from $x = 0$ to $x = \pi$.

16. Revolve about the line $x = \pi$ the area under the curve $y = \sin x$ from $x = 0$ to $x = \pi$, and find the volume of the solid generated.

17. Find the volume of the solid generated by revolving about the x-axis the area bounded by the curve $y = \sec x$, the coördinate axes, and the line $x = \dfrac{\pi}{4}$.

18. Find the volume of the solid generated by revolving about the y-axis the area bounded by the curve $y = \tan^{-1} x$, the x-axis, and the line $x = 1$.

19. A hole of radius a is drilled through a circular cylindrical rod of radius a, the axes of the drill and rod intersecting at right angles. Find the volume of material removed.

20. The diameter of a right circular cylindrical tank is 6 ft. and its length is 18 ft. If the tank is placed with its axis horizontal and is filled with oil to a depth of $1\frac{1}{2}$ ft. find the volume of the oil.

21. A tank is 4 ft. long and its axis horizontal. Its cross-section in a plane perpendicular to the axis is an ellipse whose axes are 6 in. and 8 in., respectively, the major axis being vertical. Find the volume of gasoline required to fill the tank to a depth of 6 in.

22. If the tank in Problem 21 is turned so that the major axis of the elliptical section is horizontal, find the volume of gasoline required to fill the tank to a depth of 4 in.

23. A tank with horizontal axis has the form of a right circular cylinder with protruding hemispherical ends. The common diameter of the cylinder and hemispheres is 10 in. and the cylinder is 40 in. long. Find the volume of liquid required to fill the tank to a depth of 8 in.

100. Pressure; Work. The principles and methods employed in the determination of liquid pressure and work were sufficiently explained in Arts. 37 and 39. Now, however, in view of the developments of Chapters VIII and IX, we are in a position to solve a greater variety of problems on pressure and work than was possible earlier.

PROBLEMS

1. Find the total pressure on either end of the tank of Problem 20, Art. 99, if the oil weighs 50 lb./cu. ft., and its depth is 3 ft.

2. Find the total pressure on either end of the tank of Problem 21, Art. 99, if the gasoline weighs 43 lb./cu. ft., and the tank is half full.

3. Find the total pressure on either end of the tank of Problem 22, Art. 99, if the gasoline weighs 43 lb./cu. ft., and the tank is half full.

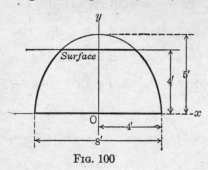

FIG. 100

4. Find the total pressure on the semi-elliptical area shown in Fig. 100. The area is submerged in water with the major axis of the ellipse vertical, and the minor axis horizontal and 4 ft. below the surface.

5. The face of a dam is in a plane whose dihedral angle with the surface of the water is $\tan^{-1}\dfrac{24}{7}$. Find the total pressure on a circular area, of diameter 8 ft., lying in this plane with its center at a depth of 12 ft. vertically below the surface of the water.

6. A particle moves along a straight line from an origin O under the action of a resultant force in pounds numerically equal to $\dfrac{ka^2}{x^2 + a^2}$, where k and a are constants and x is the variable distance of the particle from O, expressed in feet. Find the work done by this force in moving the particle from O to a distance a from O.

7. A particle moves along a straight line under the action of a resultant force in pounds numerically equal to $\dfrac{x}{\sqrt{25 - x^2}}$, where x is expressed in feet. Find the work done by this force in moving the particle from $x = 0$ to $x = 3$.

8. The mutual attraction between a charge q of electricity and a unit charge is

$\frac{q}{r^2}$, where r is their distance apart. If a unit charge is initially at a distance r_0 from a fixed charge q, find the work done in displacing the former indefinitely along the straight line through the charges.

9. When a gas expands isothermally in a cylinder, the relation between the volume v of the gas and the pressure p (the force per unit area exerted on the piston) is $pv = k$, where k is constant. Find the work done by the gas on the piston as the gas expands from a volume v_1 to a volume v_2.

10. Solve the preceding problem under the assumption that the gas expands adiabatically according to the law $pv^{1.41} = k$.

11. The diameter of the cylinder of an engine is 18 in., and the length of the stroke is 24 in. Find the work done on the piston during one stroke if steam is admitted for one-fourth of the stroke at 150 lb./sq. in. and then the valves are closed and the steam in the cylinder expands under the law $pv = k$.

101. Length of a Plane Curve (Rectangular Coördinates). Let $y = f(x)$ be the equation of the curve shown in Fig. 101a and let it be required to find the length of arc from $A(x_1, y_1)$ to $B(x_2, y_2)$.

Designating by s the length of the arc AP, where P is any point (x, y) on the curve, we have by Art. 59 that the differential of s is

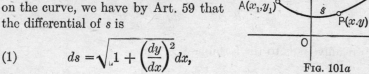

FIG. 101a

$$(1) \qquad ds = \sqrt{1 + \left(\frac{dy}{dx}\right)^2}\, dx,$$

and hence that

$$s = F(x) + C,$$

where $F(x)$ is a function such that $\dfrac{d}{dx} F(x) = \sqrt{1 + \left(\dfrac{dy}{dx}\right)^2}$, and C is a constant to be determined.

Observing that $s = 0$ when $x = x_1$, we see that

$$C = -F(x_1),$$

whence

$$s = F(x) - F(x_1).$$

Setting $x = x_2$, we obtain

$$\text{arc } AB = F(x_2) - F(x_1).$$

But by Art. 33

$$F(x_2) - F(x_1) = \int_{x_1}^{x_2} \sqrt{1 + \left(\frac{dy}{dx}\right)^2}\, dx.$$

Denoting now for convenience the length of the required arc AB by s, we thus have

(2)
$$s = \int_{x_1}^{x_2} \sqrt{1 + \left(\frac{dy}{dx}\right)^2} \, dx,$$

where it is understood that $\dfrac{dy}{dx}$ is expressed in terms of x.

Similarly, since (1) may be written

(1')
$$ds = \sqrt{1 + \left(\frac{dx}{dy}\right)^2} \, dy,$$

we obtain

(2')
$$s = \int_{y_1}^{y_2} \sqrt{1 + \left(\frac{dx}{dy}\right)^2} \, dy$$

where $\dfrac{dx}{dy}$ is expressed in terms of y.   In some problems this formula is more advantageous than (2).

If x and y are given in terms of a parameter t, so that

$$dx = \frac{dx}{dt} \, dt, \qquad dy = \frac{dy}{dt} \, dt,$$

(2) or (2') readily leads to the formula

(2'')
$$s = \int_{t_1}^{t_2} \sqrt{\left(\frac{dx}{dt}\right)^2 + \left(\frac{dy}{dt}\right)^2} \, dt,$$

where t_1 and t_2 are the values of t corresponding to the end-points of the arc, and the derivatives are expressed in terms of t.

Example 1.   Find the length of the curve

$$y = \frac{x^2}{2} - \frac{1}{4} \ln x$$

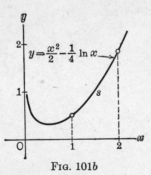

FIG. 101b

between the points for which $x = 1$ and $x = 2$ (Fig. 101b).

Since $1 + \left(\dfrac{dy}{dx}\right)^2 = 1 + \left(x - \dfrac{1}{4x}\right)^2 = \left(\dfrac{4x^2 + 1}{4x}\right)^2$,

we have by (2)

$$s = \int_1^2 \frac{4x^2 + 1}{4x} \, dx$$

$$= \left[\frac{x^2}{2} + \frac{1}{4} \ln x \right]_1^2$$

$$= \tfrac{3}{2} + \tfrac{1}{4} \ln 2.$$

Example 2. Find the length of one arch of the cycloid (Fig. 78b, p. 216) $x = a(\phi - \sin \phi)$, $y = a(1 - \cos \phi)$.

For the arch from $x = 0$ to $x = 2\pi a$, that is from $\phi = 0$ to $\phi = 2\pi$, we have by (2″)

$$s = \int_0^{2\pi} \sqrt{a^2(1 - \cos \phi)^2 + a^2 \sin^2 \phi}\, d\phi$$

$$= a \int_0^{2\pi} \sqrt{2(1 - \cos \phi)}\, d\phi$$

$$= 2a \int_0^{2\pi} \sin \frac{\phi}{2}\, d\phi$$

$$= 8a.$$

102. Length of a Plane Curve (Polar Coördinates).

Suppose that the equation $r = f(\theta)$ represents the curve shown in Fig. 102a, and let us find the length of the arc from $A(r_1, \theta_1)$ to $B(r_2, \theta_2)$.

Since by Art. 69

$$ds = \sqrt{(dr)^2 + r^2(d\theta)^2} = \sqrt{\left(\frac{dr}{d\theta}\right)^2 + r^2}\, d\theta = \sqrt{1 + r^2\left(\frac{d\theta}{dr}\right)^2}\, dr,$$

we readily obtain, by an argument similar to that given in the preceding article,

(1) $$s = \int_{\theta_1}^{\theta_2} \sqrt{r^2 + \left(\frac{dr}{d\theta}\right)^2}\, d\theta,$$

or

(1′) $$s = \int_{r_1}^{r_2} \sqrt{1 + r^2\left(\frac{d\theta}{dr}\right)^2}\, dr.$$

Example. Find the total length of the curve $r = a \sin^3 \dfrac{\theta}{3}$ (Fig. 102b).

Fig. 102a

Since $\dfrac{dr}{d\theta} = a \sin^2 \dfrac{\theta}{3} \cdot \cos \dfrac{\theta}{3}$, and

since as the curve is traced θ increases continuously from 0 to 3π, we have by (1)

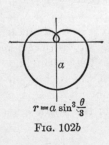

$r = a \sin^3 \dfrac{\theta}{3}$

Fig. 102b

$$s = \int_0^{3\pi} \sqrt{a^2 \sin^6 \frac{\theta}{3} + a^2 \sin^4 \frac{\theta}{3} \cos^2 \frac{\theta}{3}}\, d\theta$$

$$= a \int_0^{3\pi} \sin^2 \frac{\theta}{3}\, d\theta$$

$$= \frac{a}{2}\left[\theta - \frac{3}{2} \sin \frac{2\theta}{3}\right]_0^{3\pi}$$

$$= \tfrac{3}{2}\pi a.$$

PROBLEMS

1. Find the length of the curve $9y^2 = 4x^3$ from the point $(0, 0)$ to the point $(3, 2\sqrt{3})$.

2. Find the length of the curve $(y - 1)^2 = 4x^3$ from the point $(0, 1)$ to the point $(1, 3)$.

3. Find the length of the curve $3y^2 = (2x + 8)^3$ from the point $\left(0, \dfrac{16\sqrt{6}}{3}\right)$ to the point $\left(4, \dfrac{64\sqrt{3}}{3}\right)$.

4. Find the length of the curve $y = \frac{2}{3}(1 + x^2)^{\frac{3}{2}}$ from $x = 0$ to $x = 3$.

5. Find the length of the curve $3x^2 = y^3$ from the origin to the point in the first quadrant for which $y = 15$.

6. Find the circumference of the circle $x^2 + y^2 = a^2$.

7. Find the total length of the four-cusped hypocycloid $x^{\frac{2}{3}} + y^{\frac{2}{3}} = a^{\frac{2}{3}}$.

8. Solve the preceding problem using the parametric equations

$$x = a \cos^3 \phi, \qquad y = a \sin^3 \phi$$

of the hypocycloid.

9. Find the length of the curve in Problem 1, using its parametric equations $x = \frac{9}{4} t^2$, $y = \frac{9}{4} t^3$.

10. Find the circumference of the circle whose parametric equations are

$$x = 2 \sin \phi, \qquad y = 2 \cos \phi.$$

11. Find by integration the length of the line whose parametric equations are $x = \sqrt{2} \sin^2 \phi$, $y = \sqrt{2} \cos^2 \phi$, from $\phi = 0$ to $\phi = \dfrac{\pi}{4}$.

12. Find the length of the catenary $y = \dfrac{a}{2} (e^{\frac{x}{a}} + e^{-\frac{x}{a}})$ from $x = 0$ to $x = a$.

13. Find the length of the curve $y = 12 \ln x$ from $x = 5$ to $x = 9$.

14. Find the length of the curve $y = \ln \cos x$ from $x = 0$ to $x = \dfrac{\pi}{3}$.

15. Find the length of the curve $y = e^x$ from $x = 0$ to $x = 1$ using equation (2′), Art. 101.

16. Find the length of the cardioid $r = a(1 + \cos \theta)$.

17. Find the length of the spiral of Archimedes $r = a\theta$, from $\theta = 0$ to $\theta = 2\pi$.

18. Find the circumference of the circle $r = a \sin \theta$.

19. Find in two ways the length of the curve $r = e^{a\theta}$ from (r_1, θ_1) to (r_2, θ_2).

20. Find the length of the curve $8y = x^4 + 6x^2$ from $(0, 0)$ to $(2, 5)$.

103. Surface of Revolution. If a plane curve is revolved about a line in its plane, it generates a surface of revolution whose axis is the line.

Let the equation $y = f(x)$ represent the curve in Fig. 103a and consider the problem of finding the area S of the surface of revolution generated by revolving through a complete turn about the x-axis a portion AB of the curve which lies wholly on one side of the x-axis and extends from (a, c) to (b, d).

For this purpose divide the interval along the x-axis into n equal increments $\Delta x = \dfrac{b-a}{n}$, and at the points of division thus found draw

the vertical lines $x = x_i$ (where $i = 1, \cdots, n$), thereby dividing the arc AB (at points P_i) into n increments Δs_i. Then when the curve is revolved about the x-axis each of these increments of arc generates a surface increment of area ΔS_i.

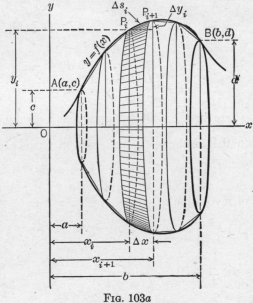

Fig. 103a

It is now apparent that the required total area S is the limit as n becomes infinite of the sum of the lateral areas of the n conical frustums generated by the chords $P_i P_{i+1}$. Therefore, since the lateral area of such a frustum is the product of its slant height and average circumference, we have

$$S = \lim_{n \to \infty} \sum_{i=1}^{i=n} 2\pi \left(y_i + \frac{\Delta y_i}{2}\right) \sqrt{(\Delta x)^2 + (\Delta y_i)^2},$$

where $y_i = f(x_i)$ and $\Delta y_i = f(x_{i+1}) - f(x_i)$.

Now since the length $\sqrt{(\Delta x)^2 + (\Delta y_i)^2}$ of the chord $P_i P_{i+1}$ differs from Δs_i by an infinitesimal of higher order than Δs_i (Art. 59), we obtain by Duhamel's Theorem (Art. 35),

$$S = \lim_{n \to \infty} \sum_{i=1}^{i=n} 2\pi(y_i \Delta s_i + \tfrac{1}{2}\Delta y_i \Delta s_i).$$

Furthermore by a second application of Duhamel's Theorem we may neglect the infinitesimal $\Delta y_i \Delta s_i$ and write

$$S = \lim_{n \to \infty} \sum_{i=1}^{i=n} 2\pi y_i \Delta s_i.$$

Now applying the Fundamental Theorem (Art. 35), we have

$$(1) \qquad S = 2\pi \int_{x=a}^{x=b} y \, ds,$$

which by (1) and (1'), Art. 101, may be written

$$(2) \qquad S = 2\pi \int_a^b y \sqrt{1 + \left(\frac{dy}{dx}\right)^2} \, dx = 2\pi \int_c^d y \sqrt{1 + \left(\frac{dx}{dy}\right)^2} \, dy,$$

where in the first integral y and $\dfrac{dy}{dx}$ are expressed in terms of x, and in the second $\dfrac{dx}{dy}$ is expressed in terms of y.

Similarly, if an arc of the curve $x = g(y)$, extending from (a, c) to (b, d), is revolved about the y-axis, we obtain for the area S of the surface of revolution generated

$$(1') \qquad S = 2\pi \int_{y=c}^{y=d} x \, ds$$

or

$$(2') \qquad S = 2\pi \int_c^d x \sqrt{1 + \left(\frac{dx}{dy}\right)^2} \, dy = 2\pi \int_a^b x \sqrt{1 + \left(\frac{dy}{dx}\right)^2} \, dx,$$

where in the first integral x and $\dfrac{dx}{dy}$ are expressed in terms of y, and in the second $\dfrac{dy}{dx}$ is expressed in terms of x.

From (1) or (1') it is evident that *the area of the surface generated by revolving an arc about an axis is obtained by integrating the product of the length of an arc element by the circumference of the circle described by a point of the element.* This remark will be helpful in problems in which the axis of revolution is parallel to, instead of coincident with, a coordinate axis.

Example 1. Find the area of the surface of a sphere of radius a.

Considering this surface as generated by revolving the upper half of the circle $x^2 + y^2 = a^2$ about the x-axis and observing that $\dfrac{dy}{dx} = -\dfrac{x}{y}$ we have by (2)

$$S = 2\pi \int_{-a}^a \sqrt{1 + \frac{x^2}{y^2}} \, y \, dx = 2\pi \int_{-a}^a \sqrt{x^2 + y^2} \, dx = 2\pi \int_{-a}^a a \, dx = 4\pi a^2.$$

Example 2. Find the area of the surface of the torus generated by the revolution of a circle of radius a about an axis in the plane of the circle and situated at a distance c from the center.

Choosing axes as shown in the sketch (Fig. 103b), so that for any point on the circle $x = c + a \cos \theta$, we have, by analogy with (1'), for the required area

$$S = 2\pi \int_{\theta=0}^{\theta=2\pi} x \, ds$$

$$= 2\pi \int_0^{2\pi} xa \, d\theta = 2\pi a \int_0^{2\pi} (c + a \cos \theta) d\theta = 2\pi a [c\theta + a \sin \theta]_0^{2\pi}$$

$$= 4\pi^2 ac.$$

Note that the result is equal to the product of the circumference of the given circle by that of the circle described by its center. (See Problem 51, p. 306.)

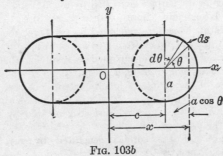

FIG. 103b

PROBLEMS

1. Find by integration the area of the surface of the cone generated by revolving about the x-axis the segment of the line $y = \frac{3}{4}x$ extending from $x = 0$ to $x = 4$.

2. Find by integration the area of the surface generated by revolving about the x-axis the segment of the line $y = \frac{1}{2}x + 4$ extending from $x = 0$ to $x = 6$.

3. Find by integration the area of the surface generated by revolving about the line $y = 2$ the segment of the line $y = \frac{1}{4}x + 3$ extending from $x = 0$ to $x = 4$.

4. Find by integration the area of the surface generated by revolving about the line $x + 1 = 0$ the line-segment extending from the point $(2, 2)$ to the point $(4, 8)$.

5. Find the area of the surface generated by revolving about the x-axis the arc of the curve $y = x^3$ extending from $(0, 0)$ to $(1, 1)$.

6. Find the area of the surface generated by revolving about the y-axis the arc of the curve $y = x^3$ extending from $(0, 0)$ to $(1, 1)$.

HINT: If x is taken as the variable of integration, the integral representing this area is of the form $\int_{x=0}^{x=1} \sqrt{u^2 + a^2} \, du$.

7. Find the area of the surface generated by revolving about the y-axis the arc of the parabola $4y = x^2$ extending from $(0, 0)$ to $(4, 4)$.

8. Revolve the arc described in Problem 7 about the line $x + 1 = 0$ and find the area of the surface generated.

9. Find the area of the surface generated by revolving the hypocycloid $x^{\frac{2}{3}} + y^{\frac{2}{3}} = a^{\frac{2}{3}}$ about the y-axis.

10. Find the area of the surface generated by revolving about the x-axis the arc of the parabola $y^2 = 4x$ extending from $y = 1$ to $y = 4$.

11. Find the area of the surface generated by revolving about the x-axis the arc of the catenary $y = \frac{a}{2}(e^{\frac{x}{a}} + e^{-\frac{x}{a}})$ extending from $x = 0$ to $x = a$.

12. Revolve the arc of Problem 11 about the y-axis and find the area of the surface generated.

13. Find the area of the surface generated by revolving about the x-axis the arc of the curve $x^4 + 3 = 6xy$ extending from $(1, \frac{2}{3})$ to $(2, \frac{19}{12})$.

14. Revolve the arc of Problem 13 about the y-axis and find the area of the surface generated.

15. Revolve the arc of Problem 13 about the line $y + 1 = 0$ and find the area of the surface generated.

16. Find the area of the surface generated by revolving about the x-axis one arch of the cycloid $x = a(\phi - \sin \phi)$, $y = a(1 - \cos \phi)$.

17. Find the area of the surface generated by revolving about the y-axis the arc of the curve $9y^2 = 4x^3$ extending from $(0, 0)$ to $(3, 2\sqrt{3})$.

18. Find the area of the surface generated by revolving about the y-axis the arc of the curve $y = 12 \ln x$ extending from $x = 5$ to $x = 9$.

19. Find the area of the surface generated by revolving about the x-axis the arc of the curve $y = e^x$ extending from $(0, 1)$ to $(1, e)$.

20. Find the area of the surface of infinite extent generated by revolving about the x-axis that part of the curve $y = e^{-x}$ lying in the first quadrant.

21. Find the area of the spherical surface generated by revolving the circle $r = 2a \cos \theta$ about the axis $\theta = 0$.

22. Find the area of the surface generated by revolving the cardioid $r = a(1 + \cos \theta)$ about the axis $\theta = 0$.

23. Find the area of the surface generated by revolving about the axis $\theta = \dfrac{\pi}{2}$ the arc of the logarithmic spiral $r = e^{a\theta}$ extending from $(1, 0)$ to $\left(e^{\frac{a\pi}{2}}, \dfrac{\pi}{2} \right)$.

24. Find the area of the surface generated by revolving the lemniscate $r^2 = 2a^2 \cos 2\theta$ about the axis $\theta = 0$.

25. Find the area of the surface generated by revolving the lemniscate $r^2 = 2a^2 \cos 2\theta$ about the axis $\theta = \dfrac{\pi}{2}$.

104. Center of Gravity, Centroid, Moment of Inertia.

In dynamics and the theory of elasticity there arise further applications of definite integration, as for example centers of gravity, centroids, and moments of inertia. These subjects will be treated in the ensuing articles.

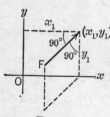

Fig. 105

105. Moment. In Fig. 105, let the force F be perpendicular to the xy-plane at the point (x_1, y_1). By the **moments** of the force with respect to the x- and y-axes are meant the products Fy_1 and Fx_1, respectively. The signs of these moments will depend on the signs of F, x_1, and y_1.

If F is the weight of a particle situated at the point (x_1, y_1), the xy-plane being horizontal, the above expressions are the moments of the weight of the particle.

If m_1 is the mass * of a particle, situated at (x_1, y_1), we define the

* For the relation between weight and mass see p. 172.

moments of the mass with respect to the coördinate axes (not necessarily assumed horizontal) as m_1y_1 and m_1x_1, where, since m_1 is essentially positive, the signs of these moments depend upon the signs of x_1 and y_1.

106. Center of Gravity of a System of Particles. In this article we shall consider systems of particles which are (a) coplanar and (b) non-coplanar.

(a) *Coplanar Particles.* Let us suppose that we have a system of n particles of masses $m_1, m_2, \cdots, m_n$, situated in the xy-plane at points $(x_1, y_1), (x_2, y_2), \cdots, (x_n, y_n)$, respectively. Then the algebraic sum M_x of the moments of the mass of the n particles with respect to the x-axis is

$$(1) \qquad M_x = m_1y_1 + m_2y_2 + \cdots + m_ny_n.$$

Similarly, the moment of the total mass with respect to the y-axis is

$$(2) \qquad M_y = m_1x_1 + m_2x_2 + \cdots + m_nx_n.$$

Now if a single particle of mass

$$m = m_1 + m_2 + \cdots + m_n$$

were located at such a position $(\bar{x}, \bar{y})$ that the moment of its mass with respect to the x-axis would be equal to the moment-sum (1), and with respect to the y-axis to the moment-sum (2), then the point $(\bar{x}, \bar{y})$ is called the **center of gravity** of the system of particles. We thus have

$$\bar{x}m = M_y \quad \text{and} \quad \bar{y}m = M_x.$$

Hence

$$(3) \qquad \bar{x} = \frac{M_y}{m} = \frac{m_1x_1 + m_2x_2 + \cdots + m_nx_n}{m_1 + m_2 + \cdots + m_n}$$

and

$$(4) \qquad \bar{y} = \frac{M_x}{m} = \frac{m_1y_1 + m_2y_2 + \cdots + m_ny_n}{m_1 + m_2 + \cdots + m_n}.$$

(b) *Non-coplanar Particles.* We shall now deduce formulas for the location of the center of gravity of a set of non-coplanar particles. For this purpose we shall find it necessary to consider the product of the mass of a particle by its perpendicular distance from a plane. This product will be called the moment of the mass of the particle with respect to the plane.

If n particles, of masses $m_1, m_2, \cdots, m_n$, are located with reference to three mutually perpendicular planes xy, yz, and xz, at the points $(x_1, y_1, z_1), (x_2, y_2, z_2), \cdots, (x_n, y_n, z_n)$, respectively, then the sum M_{yz} of the moments of the n masses with respect to the yz-plane is

$$(5) \qquad M_{yz} = m_1x_1 + m_2x_2 + \cdots + m_nx_n.$$

Similarly, the moment-sums with respect to the xz- and xy-planes are readily seen to be

(6)
$$M_{xz} = m_1y_1 + m_2y_2 + \cdots + m_ny_n$$

and

(7)
$$M_{xy} = m_1z_1 + m_2z_2 + \cdots + m_nz_n.$$

Now if a single particle of mass

$$m = m_1 + m_2 + \cdots + m_n$$

were located at such a position $(\bar{x}, \bar{y}, \bar{z})$ that the moments of its mass with respect to the coördinate planes are equal to M_{yz}, M_{xz}, and M_{xy} as given in (5), (6), and (7), then the point $(\bar{x}, \bar{y}, \bar{z})$ is called the center of gravity of the system of particles. We thus obtain

(8)
$$\bar{x} = \frac{M_{yz}}{m} = \frac{m_1x_1 + m_2x_2 + \cdots + m_nx_n}{m_1 + m_2 + \cdots + m_n},$$

(9)
$$\bar{y} = \frac{M_{xz}}{m} = \frac{m_1y_1 + m_2y_2 + \cdots + m_ny_n}{m_1 + m_2 + \cdots + m_n},$$

(10)
$$\bar{z} = \frac{M_{xy}}{m} = \frac{m_1z_1 + m_2z_2 + \cdots + m_nz_n}{m_1 + m_2 + \cdots + m_n}.$$

Although in the above discussion of coplanar and non-coplanar systems reference is made to coördinate axes, it can be shown that the center of gravity of a system of particles has a location which is independent of the choice of axes.

From a physical standpoint we may regard the center of gravity of a set of particles as follows:

Imagine a configuration composed of rigid wires of negligible weight joined at the center of gravity of the set, each wire being connected to one of the particles. Then, irrespective of its orientation, the system will balance when suspended at the center of gravity.

107. Center of Gravity of a Continuous Mass. The concepts and formulas of the preceding article on systems of particles readily admit of extension to solids of continuous mass distribution.

Let m be the mass of such a body and V its volume, and suppose that ΔV and Δm are the volume and mass of a small portion, or increment, of the body containing the point $P(x, y, z)$, as shown in Fig. 107a.   Then the ratio

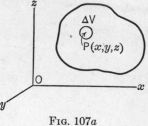

$$(1) \qquad \frac{\Delta m}{\Delta V}$$

is the **average density** of this increment.

Now if ΔV is allowed to approach zero in such a way that the corresponding portion of the body always contains the point P, the ratio (1) may or may not approach a limit.   If it does, this limit will be called

Fig. 107a

the **density** of the body at the point P, and will be denoted by ρ.   That is,

$$(2) \qquad \rho = \lim_{\Delta V \to 0} \frac{\Delta m}{\Delta V} = \frac{dm}{dV}.$$

The body is said to be **homogeneous** or **heterogeneous** according as ρ is a constant or is dependent on the position of the point P within the body.

By (2) we obtain for an element of mass

$$(3) \qquad dm = \rho\, dV,$$

so that the mass of the entire solid is given by

$$(4) \qquad m = \int \rho\, dV,$$

where the integral extends over the whole volume.

Since now the moment of the mass of the entire solid with respect to a plane may be regarded as the limit of the sum of the moments of its mass increments, and since m is given by (4), we may find the center of gravity $(\bar{x}, \bar{y}, \bar{z})$ of the mass of the solid by generalizations of (8), (9), and (10) of the preceding article, in which the sums are replaced by integrals extending over the whole volume.   Thus we obtain *

$$(5) \qquad \bar{x} = \frac{\int x\, dm}{m} = \frac{\int \rho x\, dV}{\int \rho\, dV},$$

---

* These equations may be derived rigorously by a rather involved use of Duhamel's Theorem.   It is deemed best, however, to omit details here.

(6)
$$\bar{y} = \frac{\int y \, dm}{m} = \frac{\int \rho y \, dV}{\int \rho \, dV},$$

(7)
$$\bar{z} = \frac{\int z \, dm}{m} = \frac{\int \rho z \, dV}{\int \rho \, dV},$$

where the integrals in the numerators give the moments of the mass of the body with respect to the yz-, the xz-, and the xy-planes.

In general, the evaluation of the integrals appearing in (5), (6), and (7) requires integration with respect to x, y, and z, corresponding to an implied element of volume $dV = dx \, dy \, dz$ (Fig. 107b). However, in many problems of theoretical and practical importance it is possible to choose volume elements in such a way as to avoid this difficulty. A similar remark applies to the use of the formulas (1) to (5) developed in the next article. The general method, requiring *multiple integration*, will be studied in Chapter XVII.

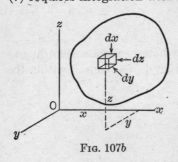

Fig. 107b

108. Centroid of a Volume and of a Plane Area. If a body is homogeneous, so that ρ is a constant, it follows from (5), (6), and (7) of the preceding article that

(1)
$$\bar{x} = \frac{\int x \, dV}{V}, \quad \text{whence} \quad V\bar{x} = \int x \, dV,$$

(2)
$$\bar{y} = \frac{\int y \, dV}{V}, \quad \text{whence} \quad V\bar{y} = \int y \, dV,$$

(3)
$$\bar{z} = \frac{\int z \, dV}{V}, \quad \text{whence} \quad V\bar{z} = \int z \, dV.$$

Here $\int x \, dV$ represents the limit of the sum of the moments of the elements of volume with respect to the yz-plane—that is, the moment of the entire volume with respect to this plane. Similarly $\int y \, dV$

and $\int z \, dV$ represent the moments of the volume with respect to the
other coördinate planes.   The point $(\bar{x}, \bar{y}, \bar{z})$ defined by (1), (2), and (3)
is called the **centroid** of the volume.   It
is customary to apply to volumes the
term centroid rather than center of gravity, because volumes, being mere geometrical figures, are not influenced by gravity.

If dA represents an element of an area
A lying in the xy-plane (Fig. 108a) we
define the centroid of the area, by analogy with (1), (2), and (3), as the point
whose coördinates are

Fig. 108a

$$(4) \qquad \bar{x} = \frac{\int x \, dA}{A}, \quad \text{whence} \quad A\bar{x} = \int x \, dA,$$

$$(5) \qquad \bar{y} = \frac{\int y \, dA}{A}, \quad \text{whence} \quad A\bar{y} = \int y \, dA,$$

where $\int x \, dA$ represents the limit of the sum of the moments of the
elements of area with respect to the y-axis—that is, the moment of the
entire area with respect to the y-axis.   Similarly $\int y \, dA$ represents
the moment of the entire area with respect to the x-axis.

The following remark may serve to render the concept of centroid of
a plane area more concrete.   Suppose a piece of thin cardboard cut into
the size and shape of the area.   Then, if placed in a horizontal position
with the centroid of the lower area resting on a needle point, the cardboard will balance, and the centroid of this area will be vertically below
the center of gravity of the cardboard.

As in the case of the center of gravity of a mass, the centroid of a
volume or area has a location which is fixed with reference to the volume
or area, and is independent of the choice of coördinate axes.

If an area consists of two or more portions for each of which the
centroid is known, or can be found, then the moment of the total area
with respect to a line in its plane is the algebraic sum of the products
obtained by multiplying the area of each portion by the distance (with
appropriate sign) from the line to the centroid of the portion.   For
example, if an area A consists of two parts A_1 and A_2, with centroids at
$(\bar{x}_1, \bar{y}_1,)$ and $(\bar{x}_2, \bar{y}_2)$, respectively, it follows from (4) and (5) that

$$(6) \quad \begin{cases} A\bar{x} = \int x\, dA = \int_{A_1} x\, dA + \int_{A_2} x\, dA = A_1\bar{x}_1 + A_2\bar{x}_2, \\[2mm] A\bar{y} = \int y\, dA = \int_{A_1} y\, dA + \int_{A_2} y\, dA = A_1\bar{y}_1 + A_2\bar{y}_2, \end{cases}$$

where the symbols $\int_{A_1}$ and $\int_{A_2}$ signify integrations over the respective portions of A.

Similarly, in the case of volumes,

$$(7) \quad \begin{cases} V\bar{x} = V_1\bar{x}_1 + V_2\bar{x}_2, \\ V\bar{y} = V_1\bar{y}_1 + V_2\bar{y}_2, \\ V\bar{z} = V_1\bar{z}_1 + V_2\bar{z}_2, \end{cases}$$

where the volume V consists of two portions, V_1 and V_2, with centroids at $(\bar{x}_1, \bar{y}_1, \bar{z}_1)$ and $(\bar{x}_2, \bar{y}_2, \bar{z}_2)$, respectively.

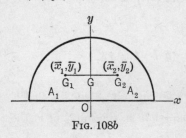

FIG. 108b

Considerations of symmetry may often be employed to simplify the determination of centroids. For example, since the y-axis is an axis of symmetry of the semicircular area shown in Fig. 108b, and divides it into two equal portions A_1 and A_2, the moments of A_1 and A_2 with respect to the y-axis are numerically equal but of opposite sign, so that $A_2\bar{x}_2 = - A_1\bar{x}_1$, and, by (6), $\bar{x} = 0$.

By reasoning in this manner we may prove that

(a) *If an area has an axis of symmetry the centroid of the area lies in that axis, and if it has two perpendicular axes of symmetry the centroid is at their point of intersection (i.e., at the geometrical center of the area).*

(b) *If a volume has a plane of symmetry the centroid of the volume lies in that plane; if it has two planes of symmetry the centroid lies in their line of intersection; and if it has three mutually perpendicular planes of symmetry the centroid is at their common point (i.e., at the geometrical center of the volume).*

109. Centroid by Integration. It was pointed out at the end of Art. 107 that the evaluation of the integrals in the formulas for centroids and centers of gravity developed in the last two articles in general requires multiple integration, but that in many problems the methods of integration hitherto explained are applicable. Accordingly, we shall now adapt these formulas to cases in which elements of area are taken as rectangular strips, and elements of volume as laminas (e.g., discs), or hollow cylinders.

(a) *Strips.* Let us now develop formulas for finding the centroid $(\bar{x}, \bar{y})$ of the area under the curve $y = f(x)$ from $x = a$ to $x = b$ (Fig. 109a). We have already seen that such an area may be considered as the limit of the sum of the areas of n rectangular strips (each of width $\Delta x = dx$) as n becomes infinite. Similarly, since the moment of the combined area of these strips with respect to the x-axis is (by the preceding article) the sum of the moments of the individual areas, the moment $A\bar{y}$ of the entire area A may be regarded as the limit of this sum as n becomes infinite; and since the moment of each strip is the product of its area $y\,dx$ by the distance $\frac{1}{2}y$ from the x-axis to its centroid, the limit of this sum is $\frac{1}{2}\int_a^b y^2 dx$. Hence

$$(1) \qquad A\bar{y} = \frac{1}{2}\int_a^b y^2 dx, \quad \text{and} \quad \bar{y} = \frac{\frac{1}{2}\int_a^b y^2 dx}{A}.$$

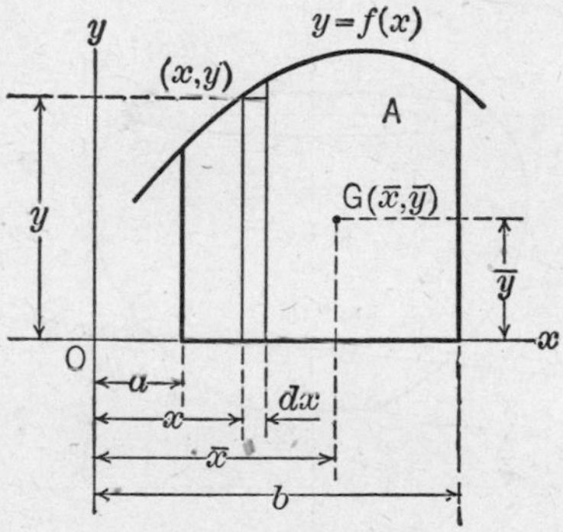

FIG. 109a   FIG. 109b

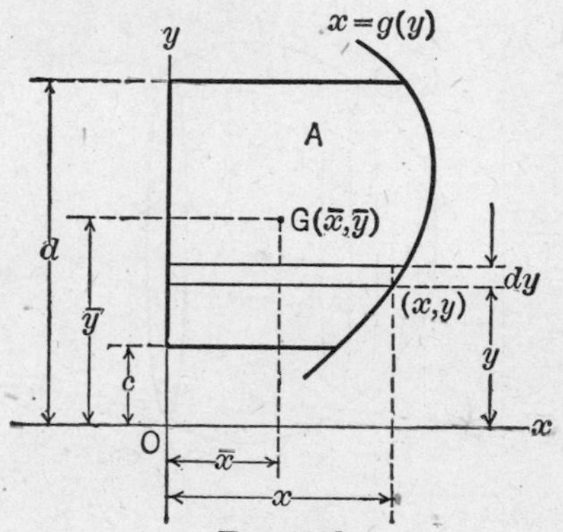

Similarly, since the moment of the strip with respect to the y-axis is $y\,dx(x + \frac{1}{2}dx)$ or $xy\,dx + \frac{1}{2}y(dx)^2$, and since by Duhamel's Theorem the term in $(dx)^2$ may be neglected, the moment of the area A with respect to the y-axis is

$$(2) \qquad A\bar{x} = \int_a^b xy\,dx, \quad \text{whence} \quad \bar{x} = \frac{\int_a^b xy\,dx}{A}.$$

For an area A such as that shown in Fig. 109b, bounded by the curve $x = g(y)$, the y-axis, and the lines $y = c$ and $y = d$, it is convenient to use horizontal strips. In this case the student may prove that

$$(3) \qquad A\bar{x} = \frac{1}{2}\int_c^d x^2 dy$$

and

(4) $$A\bar{y} = \int_c^d xy \, dy.$$

In Example 3 a method is given for locating the centroid of the area between two curves.

(*b*) *Laminas.* Let us now develop a formula for finding the centroid of the volume of revolution formed by revolving about the *x*-axis the area under the curve $y = f(x)$ from $x = a$ to $x = b$ (Fig. 109c).

As in Art. 36, the volume may be regarded as the limit of the sum of the volumes of *n* discs (each of thickness $\Delta x = dx$) as *n* becomes infinite. Likewise, since the moment of the total volume of these discs with respect to a plane through O perpendicular to the *x*-axis is (by the preceding article) the sum of the moments of the individual volumes, the moment $V\bar{x}$ of the entire volume V may be regarded as the limit of this

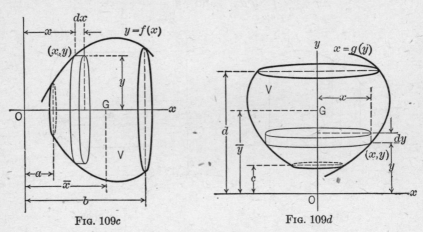

FIG. 109c   FIG. 109d

sum as *n* becomes infinite. Moreover, since the moment of each disc is the product $(\pi y^2 dx)(x + \frac{1}{2}dx)$ of its volume $\pi y^2 dx$ by the distance $(x + \frac{1}{2}dx)$, the aforementioned limit is $\int_a^b \pi y^2 x \, dx$, for by Duhamel's Theorem the terms in $(dx)^2$ may be neglected. Hence

(5) $$V\bar{x} = \pi \int_a^b y^2 x \, dx, \quad \text{whence} \quad \bar{x} = \frac{\pi \int_a^b y^2 x \, dx}{V}.$$

By symmetry $\bar{y} = \bar{z} = 0$.

Similarly, for a volume (Fig. 109d) generated by revolving about the

y-axis the area bounded by a curve $x = g(y)$, the y-axis, and the lines $y = c$ and $y = d$, we obtain

(6) $$V\bar{y} = \pi \int_c^d x^2 y \, dy, \quad \text{whence} \quad \bar{y} = \frac{\pi \int_c^d x^2 y \, dy}{V}.$$

Evidently $\bar{x} = \bar{z} = 0$.

A solid of revolution is but a special case of a solid for which the area of a section cut by a plane perpendicular to an axis is a function of the distance of the cutting plane from a fixed point on the axis. The centroids of many such solids may be found by use of laminar elements. (See Example 5.)

(c) *Hollow Cylinders.* Consider now the volume generated by revolving about the x-axis the area bounded by the curve $x = g(y)$, the y-axis, and the lines $y = c$ and $y = d$ (Fig. 109e). Since the solid thus formed is the limit of the sum of elementary hollow cylinders, the volume of each of which

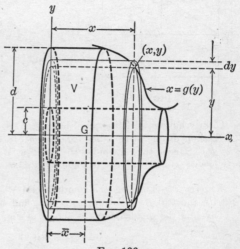

Fig. 109e

may be taken as $2\pi yx \, dy$ (cf. Art. 99), and since the centroids of these elements are on the x-axis at distances $\frac{x}{2}$ from the origin, the moment of the entire volume with respect to a plane through O and perpendicular to the x-axis is $\int_c^d 2\pi xy \, dy \frac{x}{2}$. Hence, if $\bar{x}$ is the distance along the x-axis from O to the centroid of the entire volume, we have

(7) $$V\bar{x} = \pi \int_c^d x^2 y \, dy, \quad \text{whence} \quad \bar{x} = \frac{\pi \int_c^d x^2 y \, dy}{V}.$$

Certain problems in the following list may be worked by obvious modifications of (7).

It is impossible to estimate the relative importance of the methods of discs (or washers) and hollow cylinders. In some problems the two methods can be used with equal facility; in others, one method may offer distinct advantages.

The center of gravity of a mass of variable density may be found by the use of elementary slices or hollow cylinders provided that the density is a function of the variable of integration.

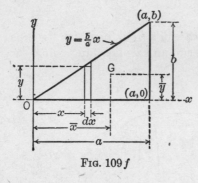

Fig. 109 f

Example 1. Find the centroid of the right triangle whose vertices are $(0, 0)$, $(a, 0)$, and (a, b). (See Fig. 109f.)

Using vertical strips we have by (2)

$$\bar{x} = \frac{\int_0^a xy\, dx}{\frac{1}{2}ab} = \frac{\frac{b}{a}\int_0^a x^2\, dx}{\frac{1}{2}ab} = \frac{2}{3}a,$$

and by (1)

$$\bar{y} = \frac{\int_0^a \frac{y}{2} y\, dx}{\frac{1}{2}ab} = \frac{\frac{b^2}{2a^2}\int_0^a x^2\, dx}{\frac{1}{2}ab} = \frac{1}{3}b.$$

Clearly horizontal strips could have been used.

Thus the distance from either leg of a right triangle to the centroid is one-third of the other leg. Hence the centroid is the point of intersection of the medians; this property is characteristic of any triangle (cf. Problem 22).

Example 2. Treating the quadrilateral whose vertices are $O(0, 0)$, $A(12, 0)$, $B(6, 9)$, and $C(0, 5)$ as a composite area, find its centroid.

Dividing the quadrilateral as shown in Fig. 109g into the rectangle $OEDC$ and

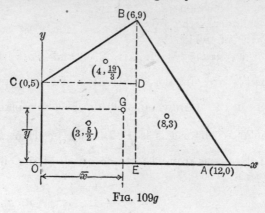

Fig. 109g

the two right triangles ABE and BCD, whose centroids are $(3, \frac{5}{2})$, $(8, 3)$, and $(4, \frac{19}{3})$, respectively, and using (6), Art. 108, we have

$$\bar{x} = \frac{3 \cdot 30 + 8 \cdot 27 + 4 \cdot 12}{30 + 27 + 12} = \frac{118}{23},$$

and

$$\bar{y} = \frac{\frac{5}{2} \cdot 30 + 3 \cdot 27 + \frac{19}{3} \cdot 12}{69} = \frac{232}{69}.$$

Example 3.   Find the centroid of the area bounded by the parabola $y^2 = 4x$ and the line $2x - y - 4 = 0$.

Choosing an element of area as shown in Fig. 109*h*, and noting that the horizontal dimension of this element, expressed as a positive quantity, is

$$\frac{y+4}{2} - \frac{y^2}{4},$$

and that the centroid of the element is at the distance $\dfrac{1}{2}\left(\dfrac{y+4}{2} + \dfrac{y^2}{4}\right)$ from the

y-axis, we have

$$A = \int_{-2}^{4}\left(\frac{y+4}{2} - \frac{y^2}{4}\right)dy = \frac{1}{4}\left[8y + y^2 - \frac{y^3}{3}\right]_{-2}^{4} = 9,$$

$$A\bar{x} = \int_{-2}^{4}\frac{1}{2}\left(\frac{y+4}{2} + \frac{y^2}{4}\right)\left(\frac{y+4}{2} - \frac{y^2}{4}\right)dy = \frac{1}{32}\int_{-2}^{4}(64 + 32y + 4y^2 - y^4)\,dy$$

$$= \tfrac{72}{5},$$

$$\bar{x} = \tfrac{8}{5},$$

$$A\bar{y} = \int_{-2}^{4}y\left(\frac{y+4}{2} - \frac{y^2}{4}\right)dy = \frac{1}{4}\int_{-2}^{4}(8y + 2y^2 - y^3)dy = 9,$$

and

$$\bar{y} = 1.$$

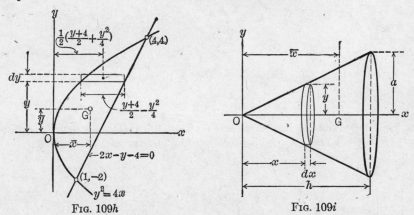

FIG. 109*h*   FIG. 109*i*

Example 4.   Locate the centroid of a right circular cone of altitude h and base-radius a.

Let the x-axis coincide with the axis of the cone and the vertex with the origin. (See Fig. 109*i*.)   Then taking as an element of volume a cylindrical disc whose left face is at a distance x from the origin and whose radius and thickness are respectively y and dx, and observing that $y = \dfrac{a}{h}x$, we have by (5)

$$V\bar{x} = \pi\int_{0}^{h}xy^2dx = \pi\frac{a^2}{h^2}\int_{0}^{h}x^3dx = \pi\frac{a^2h^2}{4},$$

and, since $V = \tfrac{1}{3}\pi a^2h$,

$$\bar{x} = \frac{\dfrac{\pi a^2h^2}{4}}{\dfrac{\pi a^2h}{3}} = \frac{3}{4}h.$$

Thus the centroid of a right circular cone lies on the axis at a distance from the vertex equal to three-fourths of the altitude.

Example 5. Find the centroid of the volume of Example 5, Art. 36.

Using the laminar element shown in Fig. 36h, the volume of which has been seen to be

$$dV = \tfrac{1}{2}x^2 dy = \tfrac{1}{2}(4 - y^2)dy,$$

and observing that the x-coördinate of the centroid of this element is $\tfrac{2}{3}x$ (cf. Example 1), we have for the moment of the entire volume with respect to the yz-plane

$$V\bar{x} = \int_{y=-2}^{y=2} \tfrac{2}{3}x \, dV = \tfrac{2}{3}\int_0^2 x^3 dy = \tfrac{2}{3}\int_0^2 (4 - y^2)^{\frac{3}{2}}dy.$$

Integrating this by the substitution $y = 2 \sin \theta$, and replacing V by the value $\tfrac{16}{3}$ previously found, we obtain

$$\tfrac{16}{3}\bar{x} = 2\pi,$$

whence

$$\bar{x} = \tfrac{3}{8}\pi.$$

Since the z-coördinate of the centroid of the element is $\tfrac{1}{3}x$, we have for the moment of the whole volume with respect to the xy-plane

$$V\bar{z} = \int_{y=-2}^{y=2} \tfrac{1}{3}x \, dV = \tfrac{1}{2}V\bar{x},$$

whence

$$\bar{z} = \tfrac{1}{2}\bar{x} = \tfrac{3}{16}\pi.$$

By symmetry $\bar{y} = 0$. Hence the centroid is the point $(\tfrac{3}{8}\pi, \, 0, \, \tfrac{3}{16}\pi)$.

PROBLEMS

Find the centroid of each of the areas described in Problems 1 to 21, inclusive, using integration unless the method suggested by (6), Art. 108, is applicable.

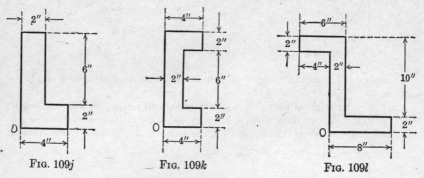

Fig. 109j Fig. 109k Fig. 109l

1. The area shown in Fig. 109j.
2. The area shown in Fig. 109k.
3. The area shown in Fig. 109l.
4. A trapezoid symmetrical with respect to the y-axis, with altitude h, upper base b, and lower base a, the lower base coinciding with the x-axis.

5. A semicircle of radius a with diameter on the x-axis and center at the origin.

6. The area cut from the second quadrant by the circle $x^2 + y^2 = a^2$.

7. The area in Fig. 109m in which a rectangle is shown surmounted by a semicircle.

8. The area enclosed by the semicircular arcs and straight lines shown in Fig. 109n.

9. The area of Fig. 109n with a hole of 1-in. radius having its center at O.

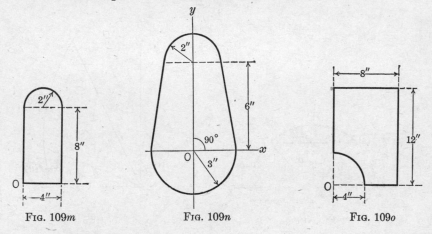

FIG. 109m FIG. 109n FIG. 109o

10. The area of Fig. 109n with a hole of 1-in. radius having its center at the point $(0, 2'')$.

11. The 8-in. by 12-in. rectangular area with a quarter circle of radius 4 in. removed from one corner as shown in Fig. 109o.

12. The area bounded by the parabola $4y = x^2$, the x-axis, and the line $x = 2$.

13. The area in the first quadrant bounded by the parabola $4y = x^2$, the y-axis, and the line $y = 4$.

14. The area in the first quadrant bounded by the curve $xy^2 = 1$, the x-axis, and the lines $x = 4$ and $x = 9$.

15. The area under the curve $y = \sin x$ from $x = 0$ to $x = \dfrac{\pi}{2}$.

16. The area bounded by the curve $y = e^x$, the coördinate axes, and the line $x = 1$.

17. The area bounded by the hyperbola $xy = 4$, the x-axis, and the lines $x = 1$ and $x = 4$.

18. The area bounded by the curve $y = \dfrac{8}{x^2 + 4}$, the coördinate axes, and the line $x = 2$.

19. The area in the first quadrant bounded by the y-axis and the curves $y = \dfrac{8}{x^2 + 4}$ and $4y = x^2$.

20. The area bounded by the parabolas $y^2 = 4x$ and $x^2 = 4y$.

21. The area bounded by the hyperbola $xy = 4$ and the line $x + y = 5$.

22. Prove that the centroid of any triangle coincides with the point of intersection of the medians.

23. Show that the total pressure on a plane surface of area A submerged in a fluid of weight w per unit volume is $w\bar{h}A$, where $\bar{h}$ is the depth of the centroid of the area.

24. Show that the moment with respect to the x-axis of the segment bounded by the circle $x^2 + y^2 = a^2$ and the line $y = b$ (Fig. 109p) is

$$\tfrac{2}{3}(a^2 - b^2)^{\frac{3}{2}} = \tfrac{2}{3}a^3 \sin^3 \alpha.$$

Combining this moment with that of the triangle OAB, show that, for the sector $OACB$,

$$\bar{y} = \frac{2a}{3} \cdot \frac{\sin \alpha}{\alpha}.$$

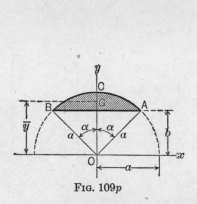

Fig. 109p

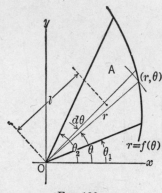

Fig. 109q

25. Show that the coördinates of the centroid of the area (Fig. 109q) bounded by the curve $r = f(\theta)$ and the lines $\theta = \theta_1$ and $\theta = \theta_2$ are given by the equations

$$A\bar{x} = \frac{1}{3}\int_{\theta_1}^{\theta_2} r^3 \cos \theta \, d\theta, \qquad A\bar{y} = \frac{1}{3}\int_{\theta_1}^{\theta_2} r^3 \sin \theta \, d\theta,$$

where by (3), Art. 98, $A = \dfrac{1}{2} \displaystyle\int_{\theta_1}^{\theta_2} r^2 d\theta$.

HINT: By the result of the preceding problem, the distance l from the origin to the centroid of the elementary sector is $\dfrac{2r}{3} \cdot \dfrac{\sin \dfrac{d\theta}{2}}{\dfrac{d\theta}{2}}$, where (cf. Arts. 46 and 25) the

fraction $\dfrac{\sin \dfrac{d\theta}{2}}{\dfrac{d\theta}{2}}$ differs from unity by an infinitesimal of at least the same order as $d\theta$.

Hence, by Duhamel's Theorem, this fraction can be replaced by 1 in the definite integrals representing the moments of the entire area with respect to the coördinate axes.

Using the formulas of Problem 25 find the centroids of the areas described in Problems 26 to 29, inclusive.

26. The area enclosed by the first-quadrant loop of the curve $r = a \sin 2\theta$.

27. The area in the first quadrant bounded by the curve $r = a \cos 2\theta$ and the line $\theta = 0$.

28. The semicircular area bounded by the upper half of the circle $r = a \cos \theta$, and the line $\theta = 0$.

29. The area bounded by the cardioid $r = a (1 - \cos \theta)$ and the lines $\theta = 0$ and $\theta = \dfrac{\pi}{2}$.

Find the centroid of each of the volumes described in Problems 30 to 42, inclusive, using integration unless the method suggested by (7), Art. 108, is applicable.

30. A concrete footing consisting of a 3 ft. by 3 ft. by 6 ft. rectangular parallelepiped resting on one of its long faces, surmounted centrally by a cube whose edge is 2 ft.

31. A right square pyramid with altitude h and edge of base a.

32. A concrete footing in the form of a truncated right square pyramid of altitude 4 ft., the edges of the upper and lower bases being respectively 6 ft. and 9 ft.

33. A monument consisting of a spherical ball of 2-ft. radius, resting on a right circular cylinder of radius 3 ft. and altitude 8 ft., the axis of the cylinder being vertical and passing through the center of the sphere.

34. A solid in the form of a right cylinder of radius 1 ft. and altitude 3 ft., surmounted by a coaxial cone of radius 1 ft. and altitude 3 ft.

35. A hemisphere of radius a.

36. A top whose lower portion is an inverted cone of radius $1\frac{1}{4}$ in. and altitude 2 in., the upper portion being a hemisphere of radius $1\frac{1}{4}$ in.

37. The volume generated by revolving about the x-axis the area in the first quadrant bounded by the parabola $y^2 = 4x$, the x-axis, and the line $x = 4$.

38. The volume generated by revolving about the y-axis the area bounded by the parabola $y^2 = 4x$, the y-axis, and the line $y = 4$.

39. The volume generated by revolving about the y-axis the area of Problem 37.

40. The volume generated by revolving about the x-axis the area under the curve $y = \dfrac{1}{x}$ from $x = 1$ to $x = 4$.

41. The volume generated by revolving about the x-axis the area under the curve $y = x^{-\frac{1}{2}}$ from $x = 4$ to $x = 9$.

42. The volume generated by revolving about the x-axis the area of Problem 16.

43. Find the center of gravity of a hemispherical mass of radius a, assuming that the density at any point is equal to kx, where x is the distance of the point from the plane of the base and k is a constant.

44. Find the center of gravity of the mass of a right circular cone of base-radius a and altitude h, if the density of the cone at any point is proportional to the distance of the point from the plane of the base.

The centroid of the arc of the curve $y = f(x)$ extending from (a, c) to (b, d) is defined as the point $(\bar{x}, \bar{y})$ such that

$$(8) \qquad s\bar{x} = \int_{x=a}^{x=b} x \, ds, \qquad s\bar{y} = \int_{x=a}^{x=b} y \, ds,$$

where s, the length of the arc, is given by (2) or (2′), Art. 101.

Find the centroids of the arcs described in Problems 45 to 47.

45. The semicircular arc $x = \sqrt{a^2 - y^2}$.

46. The first-quadrant arc of the circle $x^2 + y^2 = a^2$.

47. The first-quadrant arc of the hypocycloid $x^{\frac{2}{3}} + y^{\frac{2}{3}} = a^{\frac{2}{3}}$.

The centroid of the surface of revolution generated by revolving about the x-axis the arc of the curve $y = f(x)$ extending from (a, c) to (b, d) is defined as the point $(\bar{x}, 0, 0)$ for which

$$(9) \qquad S\bar{x} = 2\pi \int_{x=a}^{x=b} xy \, ds,$$

where S is the area of the surface, and ds is an element of arc.

Find the centroids of the surfaces described in Problems 48 and 49.

48. A hemispherical surface of radius a.

49. The lateral surface of the cone generated by revolving about the x-axis the right triangle whose vertices are $(0, 0)$, $(a, 0)$, and (a, b).

50. Prove the **First Theorem of Pappus:**

If a plane area is revolved (through a complete turn or any part thereof) about a coplanar axis not crossing the area, the volume thus generated is equal to the product of the area by the length of the circular path described by its centroid.

51. Prove the **Second Theorem of Pappus:**

If a plane arc is revolved (through a complete turn or any part thereof) about a coplanar axis not crossing the arc, the area of the surface thus generated is equal to the product of the length of the arc by the length of the circular path described by its centroid.

Solve the following problems by the use of the theorems of Pappus:

52. Referring to the result of Problem 45, find the surface of a sphere of radius a.

53. Find the lateral surface of the cone given in Problem 49.

54. Find the volume of the cone given in Problem 49.

55. Find the surface of a torus generated by revolving a circle of radius a about a coplanar axis, the center of the circle being at a distance b from the axis $(b > a)$.

56. Find the volume of the torus of Problem 55.

57. Show that the lateral area of a frustum of a right circular cone is equal to the product of its slant height by its average circumference.

110. Moment of Inertia (Masses and Volumes). The product of the mass of a particle by the square of its distance from a line, or from a plane, is called the **second moment,** or **moment of inertia,** of the mass with respect to the line (called an axis) or to the plane.

In the case of n particles of masses $m_1, m_2, \cdots, m_n$ situated at distances $p_1, p_2, \cdots, p_n$ respectively, from an axis a, we define the moment of inertia $_mI_a^*$ of the system of masses with respect to this axis as the sum of the moments of inertia of the individual masses. That is,

$$(1) \qquad {}_mI_a = m_1p_1^2 + m_2p_2^2 + \cdots + m_np_n^2.$$

Similarly, if the n particles are situated at distances $q_1, q_2, \cdots, q_n$, respectively, from a plane ab, the moment of inertia $_mI_{ab}$ of the system of masses with respect to the plane is defined as

$$(2) \qquad {}_mI_{ab} = m_1q_1^2 + m_2q_2^2 + \cdots + m_nq_n^2.$$

*An index m or V will be used to indicate that the symbol to which it is prefixed represents a quantity associated with a mass or a volume. When no confusion is likely to arise the index may be omitted.

If $m_1 + m_2 + \cdots + m_n = m$, and $_mk_a$ is a quantity such that

$$m(_mk_a)^2 = m_1p_1{}^2 + m_2p_2{}^2 + \cdots + m_np_n{}^2 = {}_mI_a,$$

whence

(3) $$_mk_a = \sqrt{\frac{{}_mI_a}{m}},$$

then $_mk_a$ is called the **radius of gyration** of the mass-system with respect to the axis a.

Similarly, if $_mk_{ab}$ satisfies the relation

$$m(_mk_{ab})^2 = m_1q_1{}^2 + m_2q_2{}^2 + \cdots + m_nq_n{}^2 = {}_mI_{ab},$$

whence

(4) $$_mk_{ab} = \sqrt{\frac{{}_mI_{ab}}{m}},$$

then $_mk_{ab}$ is called the radius of gyration of the mass-system with respect to the plane ab.

Let us now consider a continuous mass m and let dm be an element of mass containing the point (x, y, z). Then, denoting by dV and ρ the volume and density of the element, so that $dm = \rho \, dV$, as in Art. 107, and designating by $_mI_{xy}, {}_mI_{xz}$, and $_mI_{yz}$ the moments of inertia of the mass m with respect to the coördinate planes, we have,* by analogy with (2),

(5) $$_mI_{xy} = \int z^2 \, dm = \int \rho z^2 \, dV,$$

(6) $$_mI_{xz} = \int y^2 \, dm = \int \rho y^2 \, dV,$$

(7) $$_mI_{yz} = \int x^2 \, dm = \int \rho x^2 \, dV.$$

The radii of gyration of the continuous mass with respect to the coördinate planes are

(8) $$_mk_{xy} = \sqrt{\frac{{}_mI_{xy}}{m}}, \quad _mk_{xz} = \sqrt{\frac{{}_mI_{xz}}{m}}, \quad _mk_{yz} = \sqrt{\frac{{}_mI_{yz}}{m}},$$

where $m = \int \rho \, dV$.

If in (5), (6), and (7) we let $\rho = 1$, so that $dm = dV$ and $m = V$,

* See footnote, p. 293.

we obtain the following equations for the moments of inertia of the volume V with respect to the coördinate planes:

$$(9) \qquad _VI_{xy} = \int z^2 \, dV,$$

$$(10) \qquad _VI_{xz} = \int y^2 \, dV,$$

$$(11) \qquad _VI_{yz} = \int x^2 \, dV.$$

By analogy with (8), the radii of gyration of the volume with respect to the coördinate planes are defined as

$$(12) \qquad _Vk_{xy} = \sqrt{\frac{_VI_{xy}}{V}}, \quad _Vk_{xz} = \sqrt{\frac{_VI_{xz}}{V}}, \quad _Vk_{yz} = \sqrt{\frac{_VI_{yz}}{V}}.$$

It is left to the student to show that for a homogeneous mass (ρ constant) (8) gives the same radii of gyration with respect to the coördinate planes as (12) gives for the corresponding volume.

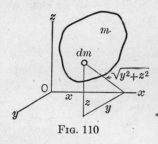

Fig. 110

The definition of the moment of inertia of a mass-particle with respect to an axis was given at the beginning of this article. Thus far, however, no mention has been made of the moment of inertia of a distributed mass or of a volume with respect to an axis. We shall now show that the latter concept may reasonably be based on the immediately preceding results for moments of inertia with respect to planes. We shall thereby be led to an important theorem.

Let the mass-element dm of a distributed mass m (Fig. 110) contain the point (x, y, z). Then by (5) and (6)

$$(13) \qquad _mI_{xy} + _mI_{xz} = \int (z^2 + y^2) \, dm.$$

But $z^2 + y^2$ is the square of the distance from the point (x, y, z) to the x-axis. Hence the integral in (13) may be regarded as defining the moment of inertia of the entire mass with respect to the x-axis, and will be denoted by $_mI_x$. That is,

$$(14) \qquad _mI_x = \int (z^2 + y^2) \, dm.$$

From (13) and (14) it follows that

$$(15) \qquad _mI_{xy} + _mI_{xz} = _mI_x.$$

Similarly, if we add both members of (9) and (10) we obtain

(16) $$_VI_{xy} + {}_VI_{xz} = {}_VI_x$$

where $_VI_x$, the moment of inertia of the volume V with respect to the x-axis, is defined by the equation

(17) $$_VI_x = \int (z^2 + y^2)\, dV.$$

Since any pair of perpendicular planes may be chosen as the xy- and xz-planes, and their line of intersection as the x-axis, the derivation of (15) and (16) constitutes a proof of the following

THEOREM. *The moment of inertia of a mass or a volume with respect to a line is the sum of its moments of inertia with respect to two perpendicular planes intersecting in the line.*

By analogy with (3) we define the radius of gyration of a continuous mass m, and of a volume V, with respect to an axis s, by the respective equations

(18) $$_mk_s = \sqrt{\frac{{}_mI_s}{m}}$$

and

(19) $$_Vk_s = \sqrt{\frac{{}_VI_s}{V}}.$$

Applications of the above theorem which do not involve multiple integration will be given in Art. 113, where, in addition, methods not based on this theorem will be developed for determining directly the moment of inertia of a solid of revolution with respect to its axis. It will be shown further that the theorem is particularly useful for finding the moment of inertia of the mass or volume of a solid with respect to an axis perpendicular to its geometric axis.

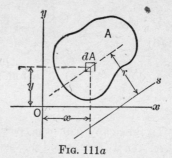

FIG. 111a

111. Moment of Inertia (Areas). The moment of inertia of an area is defined by analogy with the moment of inertia of a mass or a volume. Let r be the distance from any point of the element dA to an axis s in the plane of the area (Fig. 111a). Then regarding the whole area A as the limit of the sum of such elements, we define the moment of inertia of the area with respect to the axis as

(1) $$I_s = \int r^2 dA.$$

Thus, in particular, if the area lies in the xy-plane and the element dA contains the point (x, y), the moments of inertia of the area with respect to the coördinate axes are

(2) $$I_x = \int y^2 dA,$$

(3) $$I_y = \int x^2 dA.$$

By analogy with (8) and (12) of the preceding article the radii of gyration of the area with respect to the coördinate axes are

(4) $$k_x = \sqrt{\frac{I_x}{A}}, \quad k_y = \sqrt{\frac{I_y}{A}}.$$

We shall now prove a theorem analogous to that of the preceding article.

Adding both members of (2) and (3), we obtain

(5) $$I_x + I_y = \int (x^2 + y^2)\, dA.$$

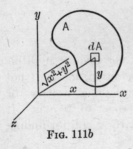

FIG. 111b

Since $x^2 + y^2$ is the square of the distance from the chosen point of the element dA to the origin, or to the z-axis which will be taken as perpendicular to the xy-plane at the origin (Fig. 111b), we shall regard the integral in (5) as representing the moment of inertia of the area A with respect to the z-axis, or, alternatively, as its **polar moment of inertia** with respect to the origin. Accordingly we write

(6) $$I_z = \int (x^2 + y^2)\, dA.$$

From (5) and (6) it follows that

(7) $$I_z = I_x + I_y.$$

Since any pair of perpendicular lines in the plane of the area may be chosen as the x- and y-axes, we have the following

THEOREM. *The moment of inertia of an area with respect to an axis perpendicular to the plane of the area is equal to the sum of its moments of inertia with respect to two perpendicular axes lying in the plane of the area and intersecting on the other axis.*

112. Parallel-Axis Theorem. We shall now derive an important relation between the moments of inertia of an area with respect to two parallel axes in its plane, one of which contains the centroid of the area.

In Fig. 112 let s and g be two parallel axes separated by a distance c, and lying in the plane of the area A; moreover let g pass through the centroid of the area and r represent the distance from this axis to any point of the element dA. Then, by the preceding article,

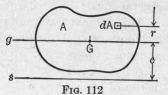

Fig. 112

$$I_s = \int (r + c)^2 dA = \int r^2 dA + 2c \int r\, dA + c^2 \int dA.$$

Since the g-axis passes through the centroid of the area, the moment of the area with respect to this axis, represented by $\int r\, dA$, is zero. Furthermore $\int r^2 dA$ is the moment of inertia I_g of the area with respect to the g-axis. Therefore

(1) $$I_s = I_g + Ac^2.$$

Thus we have proved the following

THEOREM. *The moment of inertia of an area with respect to an axis lying in its plane is equal to its moment of inertia with respect to a parallel axis through the centroid plus the product of the area by the square of the distance between the axes.*

It will be left to the student to show that the theorem holds if the words "lying in" are replaced by "perpendicular to."

The following equations, analogous to (1), may be shown to apply to volumes and masses:

(2) $$_mI_s = {_m}I_g + mc^2,$$

(3) $$_vI_s = {_v}I_g + Vc^2,$$

(4) $$_mI_{st} = {_m}I_{gh} + mc^2,$$

(5) $$_vI_{st} = {_v}I_{gh} + Vc^2,$$

where in (2) and (3) c represents the distance from a given axis s to a parallel axis g containing the centroid of the volume or the center of gravity of the mass, and where in (4) and (5) c is the distance from a given plane st to a parallel plane gh containing the centroid of the volume or center of gravity of the mass.

If m and V refer to a heterogeneous solid it should be observed that for the same choice of the s-axis the values of c in (2) and (3) are not in general equal. A similar remark holds for the values of c in (4) and (5).

113. Moment of Inertia by Integration. We shall now develop the technique of applying the formulas of the preceding articles to problems on moment of inertia.

(a) *Area.* The use of rectangular strips in determining moments of inertia of plane areas will be introduced by way of the basic problem of finding the moment of inertia of a rectangular area with respect to an

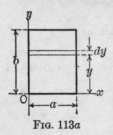

FIG. 113a

axis containing a side. For this purpose we take a rectangle of dimensions a and b (Fig. 113a), such that a side of length a lies on the x-axis, and proceed to compute the moment of inertia I_x of this rectangular area with respect to the x-axis.

Denoting by y the distance from the x-axis to the lower side of the strip, so that dy is its thickness, and observing that the ordinate of any point within the strip differs from y by a fractional part of dy, we have for an element of the required moment of inertia

(1) $$dI_x = y^2 dA = y^2 a\, dy,$$

whence

(2) $$I_x = a \int_0^b y^2 dy = \frac{ab^3}{3},$$

or

(3) $$I_x = A \frac{b^2}{3},$$

where A is the area of the rectangle.

Hence *the moment of inertia of the area of a rectangle with respect to an axis containing a side is the product of the area of the rectangle by one-third of the square of the dimension perpendicular to this side.*

By (4), Art. 111, and (3), the squared radius of gyration of the area of the rectangle with respect to the x-axis is

(4) $$k_x^2 = \frac{b^2}{3}.$$

Similarly, if a side of length b lies on the y-axis we have

(5) $$I_y = \frac{a^3 b}{3}$$

and

(6) $$k_y^2 = \frac{a^2}{3}.$$

Example 1. Find the moment of inertia and the radius of gyration, with respect to the x-axis, of the area cut from the first quadrant by the curve $y = 4 - x^2$. (See Fig. 113b.)

First Solution. Choosing a horizontal strip as an element of area we have (cf. (1))

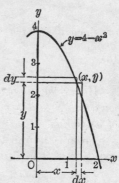

$$dI_x = y^2 x \, dy = y^2 \sqrt{4 - y} \, dy,$$

whence

$$I_x = \int_0^4 y^2 \sqrt{4 - y} \, dy.$$

Making the substitution $v = \sqrt{4 - y}$, we obtain

$$I_x = 2 \int_0^2 (4 - v^2)^2 v^2 dv = \tfrac{2048}{105}.$$

Second Solution. Choosing a vertical strip as an element of area we note that in accordance with (2) or (3) its moment of inertia is

$$dI_x = \tfrac{1}{3} y^3 dx = \tfrac{1}{3} (4 - x^2)^3 dx.$$

Fig. 113b

Hence

$$I_x = \tfrac{1}{3} \int_0^2 (4 - x^2)^3 dx = \tfrac{2048}{105},$$

in agreement with the previous result.

The area is readily found by integration to be $\tfrac{16}{3}$; therefore by (4), Art. 111, the radius of gyration with respect to the x-axis is

$$k_x = \sqrt{\tfrac{2048}{105} \cdot \tfrac{3}{16}} = \tfrac{8}{35} \sqrt{70}.$$

(b) Volume of Revolution. The use of cylindrical discs in determining moments of inertia of solids of revolution will be introduced through the problem of finding the moment of inertia of a right circular cylinder of radius a and altitude h with respect to its geometric axis.

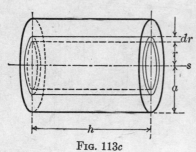

FIG. 113c

For this purpose let s represent the axis of the cylinder (Fig. 113c), V its volume, and dV the volume of a coaxial hollow cylindrical element of inner radius r and thickness dr. Then since the volume of the element may be taken as

$$dV = 2\pi r h \, dr,$$

and since the distance from the axis to any point of the element differs from r by a fractional part of dr, we have, for an element of the required moment of inertia,

(7)
$$dI_s = r^2 dV = 2\pi r^3 h \, dr.$$

whence

$$I_s = 2\pi h \int_0^a r^3 dr = \tfrac{1}{2}\pi a^4 h,$$

or, since $V = \pi a^2 h$,

(8) $$I_s = V \frac{a^2}{2}.$$

Hence *the moment of inertia of the volume of a right circular cylinder with respect to its axis is the product of its volume by one-half of the square of its radius.*

From this and (19), Art. 110, it follows that the squared radius of gyration of the cylinder with respect to its axis is

$$k_s{}^2 = \tfrac{1}{2}a^2.$$

Example 2. Find the moment of inertia and radius of gyration of the volume of a right circular cone with respect to its axis.

First Solution. Let the axis of the cone coincide with the x-axis and the vertex with the origin (Fig. 113d). Then, choosing as a volume element a coaxial cylindrical disc whose left face is at a distance x from the origin, and whose thickness is therefore dx, we have, by (8), for the moment of inertia of the disc,

$$dI_x = (\pi y^2 dx)\frac{y^2}{2},$$

whence

$$I_x = \frac{\pi}{2}\int_0^h y^4 dx,$$

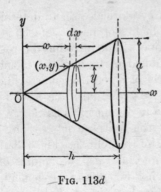

FIG. 113d

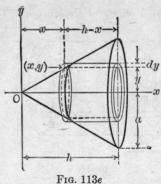

FIG. 113e

where h is the altitude of the cone. Now if a is the base-radius of the cone, it is evident from the figure that $y = \dfrac{a}{h}x$, so that

$$I_x = \frac{\pi a^4}{2h^4}\int_0^h x^4 dx = \frac{\pi}{10}a^4 h.$$

Second Solution. Using hollow cylindrical elements, a typical one of which is shown in Fig. 113e, and observing that the volume of this element may be taken as

$$dV = 2\pi y(h - x)dy,$$

we have (cf. (7)), for an element of the required moment of inertia,

$$dI_x = y^2 dV = 2\pi y(h - x)y^2 dy = 2\pi y\left(h - \frac{h}{a}y\right)y^2 dy,$$

where in the last step x is replaced by $\dfrac{h}{a}y$. Integrating, we find that

$$I_x = 2\pi \frac{h}{a} \int_0^a (ay^3 - y^4)dy = \frac{\pi}{10} a^4 h,$$

in agreement with the previous result.

Since the volume of the cone is $\dfrac{\pi}{3} a^2 h$, we find, by (19), Art. 110, that its radius of gyration is

$$k_x = \sqrt{\frac{\dfrac{\pi}{10} a^4 h}{\dfrac{\pi}{3} a^2 h}} = \frac{a}{10}\sqrt{30}.$$

(c) *Heterogeneous Mass.*   Moments of inertia of homogeneous masses present essentially the same situation as moments of inertia of volumes, and therefore call for no separate treatment. It is desirable, however, to illustrate the procedure involved in finding moments of inertia of heterogeneous masses. This is done in the next example, which has the additional features of dealing with a solid other than a solid of revolution, and of requiring its moment of inertia with respect to a plane instead of a line.

Example 3. The density ρ at any point within a pyramid whose altitude is h and whose base is a square of side a varies according to the law $\rho = cx$, where x is the distance from the apex to a plane through the point parallel to the base, and c is a constant. Find the moment of inertia and radius of gyration of the mass of the pyramid with respect to the plane of its base.

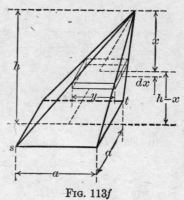

Choosing as an element of volume a lamina of thickness dx whose upper face is the square of side y cut from the pyramid by a plane parallel to that of the base (*st*, Fig. 113*f*) and at a distance x from the apex, we have, for its volume,

$$dV = y^2 dx$$

and, for its mass,

$$dm = cxy^2 dx,$$

where, by the geometry of the figure,

$$y = \frac{a}{h}x.$$

Fig. 113*f*

Since the corresponding element of moment of inertia with respect to the plane of the base is

$$dI_{st} = cxy^2dx(h - x)^2 = \frac{ca^2}{h^2} x^3(h - x)^2dx,$$

the required moment of inertia is

$$I_{st} = \frac{ca^2}{h^2} \int_0^h x^3(h - x)^2dx = \frac{ca^2h^4}{60}.$$

The mass of the pyramid being

$$m = \frac{ca^2}{h^2} \int_0^h x^3dx = \frac{ca^2h^2}{4},$$

it follows by (8), Art. 110, that the radius of gyration with respect to the plane of the base is

$$k_{st} = \sqrt{\frac{I_{st}}{m}} = \frac{h\sqrt{15}}{15}.$$

(d) *Applications of Theorems on Moment of Inertia* are illustrated in the following examples:

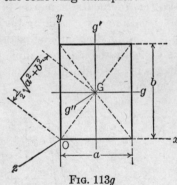

FIG. 113*g*

Example 4. Find the moments of inertia of the rectangular area shown in Fig. 113*g* with respect to the following axes: (i) an axis z through O perpendicular to the plane of the figure; (ii) axes g and g' through the centroid G parallel to the x- and y-axes, respectively; (iii) an axis g'' through G perpendicular to the plane of the area.

(i) Since by (2) and (5)

$$I_x = \frac{ab^3}{3}, \qquad I_y = \frac{a^3b}{3},$$

we have by the theorem of Art. 111

$$I_z = \frac{ab^3}{3} + \frac{a^3b}{3} = \frac{1}{3} ab(a^2 + b^2).$$

(ii) Since $I_x = \dfrac{ab^3}{3}$, we find by (1), Art. 112, that

$$I_g = \frac{ab^3}{3} - ab \left(\frac{b}{2}\right)^2 = \frac{1}{12} ab^3.$$

Similarly,

$$I_{g'} = \tfrac{1}{12}a^3b.$$

(iii) By the theorem of Art. 111,

$$I_{g''} = I_g + I_{g'} = \tfrac{1}{12}ab(a^2 + b^2).$$

Or, alternatively, by (1), Art. 112,

$$I_{g''} = I_z - ab(\tfrac{1}{2}\sqrt{a^2 + b^2})^2 = \tfrac{1}{12}ab(a^2 + b^2).$$

Example 5. Find the moment of inertia of the volume of a right circular cone of altitude h and base-radius a with respect to the following planes and axes parallel to the base: (i) a plane through the apex; (ii) an axis through the apex; (iii) an axis through the centroid; (iv) a plane through the centroid.

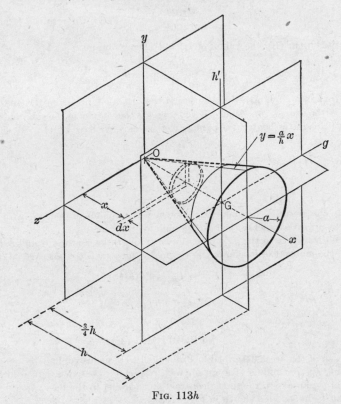

FIG. 113h

(i) Choosing three mutually perpendicular coördinate planes as shown in Fig. 113h, we proceed to find I_{yz} by integration. Using discs as elements of volume we have

$$(9) \qquad I_{yz} = \int_0^h \pi y^2 dx \cdot x^2 = \pi \frac{a^2}{h^2} \int_0^h x^4 dx$$

$$= \frac{\pi a^2 h^3}{5}.$$

(ii) By symmetry, the moment of inertia of the volume of the cone with respect to any axis through the apex and parallel to the base is equal to I_z, which by the theorem of Art. 110 may be expressed in the form

$$(10) \qquad I_z = I_{xz} + I_{yz},$$

where I_{yz} is given by (9) and I_{xz} remains to be found.

Evidently $I_{xz} = I_{xy}$, and hence

$$I_{xz} = \tfrac{1}{2}(I_{xy} + I_{xz})$$

$$= \tfrac{1}{2}I_x \qquad \text{(by (16), Art. 110)}$$

$$= \frac{\pi a^4 h}{20}. \qquad \text{(by the result of Example 2)}$$

Substituting in (10) the values of I_{xz} and I_{yz}, we obtain

(11) $$I_z = \frac{\pi a^2 h}{20}k(a^2 + 4h^2).$$

(iii) In Example 4, Art. 109, we found that the distance from the apex to the centroid of the cone is $\tfrac{3}{4}h$. Hence, if V represents the volume of the cone and a g-axis is drawn through the centroid G parallel to the z-axis, we have by (1), Art. 112,

$$I_g = I_z - V(\tfrac{3}{4}h)^2.$$

Therefore by (11)

$$I_g = \frac{\pi a^2 h}{80}(4a^2 + h^2).$$

Obviously this result is the moment of inertia of the volume of the cone with respect to any axis drawn parallel to the base through the centroid.

(iv) With respect to the gh'-plane, drawn through the centroid G and parallel to the base, the moment of inertia of the volume of the cone is (by (5), Art. 112)

$$I_{gh'} = I_{yz} - V(\tfrac{3}{4}h)^2$$

$$= \frac{\pi}{80}a^2 h^3.$$

PROBLEMS

For each of the areas described in Problems 1 to 8, inclusive, find the moment of inertia and squared radius of gyration with respect to: (a) an axis containing the base; and (b) an axis through the centroid and parallel to the base.

1. The T-shaped area shown in Fig. 113i.

2. The L-shaped area shown in Fig. 113j.

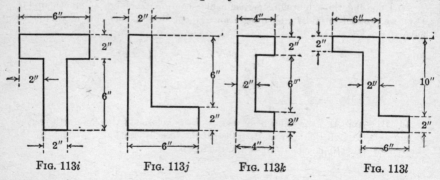

FIG. 113i FIG. 113j FIG. 113k FIG. 113l

3. The area shown in Fig. 113k.

4. The area shown in Fig. 113l.

5. A triangular area of base b and altitude h.

6. The area shown in Fig. 113m.

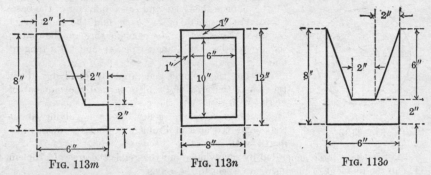

FIG. 113m FIG. 113n FIG. 113o

7. The 8-in. by 12-in. rectangular area with the 6-in. by 10-in. rectangle removed as shown in Fig. 113n.

8. The area shown in Fig. 113o.

9. For the area in the first quadrant bounded by the parabola $y^2 = 4x$, the x-axis, and the line $x = 4$, find the moment of inertia with respect to: (a) the x-axis; (b) the y-axis; and (c) an axis through the origin and perpendicular to the xy-plane.

10. Find the moment of inertia of the area of the ellipse $\dfrac{x^2}{a^2} + \dfrac{y^2}{b^2} = 1$ with respect to: (a) the x-axis; and (b) the axis $y = b$.

11. Find the moment of inertia of the area under the curve $xy = 4$ from $x = 2$ to $x = 6$ with respect to: (a) the x-axis; (b) the y-axis; and (c) an axis through the origin and perpendicular to the xy-plane.

12. For the area under the curve $y = x^3$ from $x = 0$ to $x = 2$, find the moment of inertia with respect to: (a) the x-axis; (b) the y-axis; and (c) an axis through the origin and perpendicular to the xy-plane.

13. For the area under the curve $y = e^x$ from $x = -1$ to $x = 1$, find the moment of inertia with respect to: (a) the x-axis; (b) the y-axis; and (c) an axis through the origin and perpendicular to the xy-plane.

14. For the area under the curve $y = \sin x$, from $x = 0$ to $x = \pi$, find the moment of inertia with respect to: (a) the x-axis; (b) the y-axis; and (c) an axis through the origin and perpendicular to the xy-plane.

15. For the area bounded by the curve $y = \dfrac{8}{x^2 + 4}$, the coördinate axes, and the line $x = 2$, find the moment of inertia and radius of gyration with respect to the y-axis.

16. For the area bounded by the curves $y^2 = 4x$ and $x^2 = 4y$, find the moment of inertia with respect to the x-axis.

17. For the area bounded by the curves $y^2 = 4x$ and $y = 2x^3$, find the moment of inertia with respect to: (a) the x-axis; (b) the y-axis; and (c) an axis through the origin and perpendicular to the xy-plane.

18. For the area bounded by the curve $xy = 4$ and the line $x + y = 5$, find the moment of inertia with respect to the y-axis.

19. Using as an element of area the annular ring shown in Fig. 113p find the polar moment of inertia of the area of a circle of radius a with respect to its center; thence by the theorem of Art. 111 find its moment of inertia with respect to a diameter.

20. For a right circular cylinder with altitude h and base-radius a, find the moment of inertia with respect to: (a) an axial plane; (b) the plane of the base; and (c) a diameter of the base.

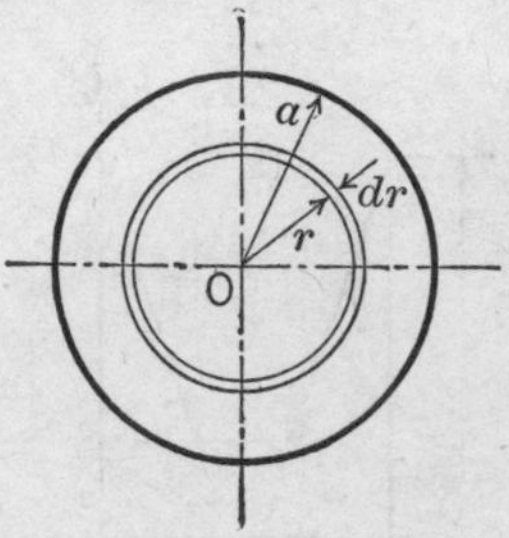

21. For a sphere of radius a find the moment of inertia with respect to: (a) a plane through the center; (b) a diameter; (c) a tangent plane; and (d) a tangent line.

22. For the volume generated by revolving about the x-axis the area of Problem 9, find the moment of inertia with respect to the x-axis.

23. For the volume generated by revolving about the y-axis the area of Problem 9, find the moment of inertia with respect to the y-axis.

FIG. 113p

24. For the volume generated by revolving about the x-axis the area of Problem 11, find the moment of inertia with respect to the x-axis.

25. For the volume generated by revolving about the y-axis the area of Problem 11, find the moment of inertia with respect to the y-axis.

26. For the volume generated by revolving about the x-axis the area of Problem 13, find the moment of inertia with respect to the x-axis.

27. For the volume generated by revolving about the x-axis the area of Problem 18, find the moment of inertia with respect to the x-axis.

The moments of inertia with respect to the coördinate axes of the arc of a curve extending from $x = a$ to $x = b$ are

$$I_x = \int_{x=a}^{x=b} y^2 ds, \qquad I_y = \int_{x=a}^{x=b} x^2 ds.$$

Find the moments of inertia of the arcs described in Problems 28 to 34, inclusive, with respect to the designated axes.

28. A straight line segment of length l with respect to a perpendicular through one end.

29. The arc of the curve $9y^2 = 4(1 + x^2)^3$ extending from $(0, \frac{2}{3})$ to $(3, \frac{20}{3}\sqrt{10})$ with respect to the y-axis.

30. The circumference of a circle of radius a with respect to a diameter.

31. The first-quadrant portion of the hypocycloid $x^{\frac{2}{3}} + y^{\frac{2}{3}} = a^{\frac{2}{3}}$ with respect to a coördinate axis.

32. The arc of the catenary $y = \dfrac{a}{2}(e^{\frac{x}{a}} + e^{-\frac{x}{a}})$ extending from $x = 0$ to $x = a$ with respect to the coördinate axes.

33. The arc of the curve $y = 12 \ln x$ extending from $x = 5$ to $x = 9$, with respect to the y-axis.

34. The arc of the curve $y = e^x$ extending from $x = 0$ to $x = 1$, with respect to the x-axis.

35. If the density at any point within a right circular cylinder of base-radius a and altitude h is proportional to the distance of the point from the axis, find the moment of inertia of the mass of the cylinder with respect to the axis.

36. If the density at any point within a hemisphere of radius a is proportional to the distance of the point from the base-plane, find the moment of inertia of the mass of the hemisphere with respect to; (a) the geometrical axis; and (b) the base-plane.

CHAPTER XI

APPROXIMATE INTEGRATION

114. Approximations. In practical applications of the definite integral to area, volume, pressure, work, etc., numerical values are usually required. When a result involves irrational quantities such as $\sqrt{2}$, π, log 17, or sin 31°, it can be evaluated only approximately, though to any required degree of accuracy. Furthermore, the accuracy of a computation which involves measured data is affected by the accuracy of the measurements. For example, the accuracy of the calculated area of a circle will depend upon the approximate value that is used for π and upon the accuracy with which the radius is measured.

Moreover, in the evaluation of a quantity represented by $\int_a^b f(x)\ dx$, two other difficulties may arise: First, the function $f(x)$ may not be known, and second, if it is, its indefinite integral may not be expressible in terms of elementary functions. In both cases, methods of approximation, some of which will be developed in the present chapter, must be resorted to.

Typical situations illustrating the first of these difficulties are readily cited. For instance, if a surveyor has to determine the area of a plot which has a river bank for one boundary, he will make no attempt to express this area as a definite integral because the equation of the curve followed by the bank is unknown; instead he will locate with reasonable accuracy a sufficient number of points of the river bank to enable him to calculate a satisfactory approximation to the area. Again, the volume of a railroad cut or fill, the area of a steam-engine indicator diagram, and the area under a curve whose ordinates have been obtained experimentally are types of quantities whose approximate values are frequently required. An acceptable solution need not have the same degree of accuracy in all types of problems. A larger percentage of error may be allowed in the calculation of the volume of a railroad cut than should be permitted in the area of a steam-engine indicator diagram.

In the following articles various methods will be developed for approximating quantities representable as definite integrals. No general discussion will be given, however, of the difficult question of estimating

321

the errors in the various approximations. For in many cases, more advanced calculus would be required than is available at this stage. Moreover, in other cases the amount of the error is inaccessible.

The examples and problems under the several formulas developed in this chapter deal with situations to which the respective formulas apply with sufficient accuracy.

115. Trapezoidal Rule. An approximation to the area under a curve from $x = a$ to $x = b$ (Fig. 115a) may be obtained by adding the areas of n trapezoids. For this purpose let us divide the inter-

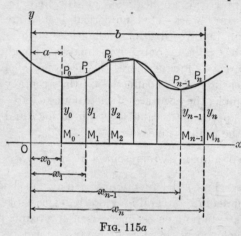

FIG. 115a

val from $x = a$ to $x = b$ into n parts (not necessarily equal), and through each point of division M_0, M_1, M_2, $\cdots$, M_n, draw vertical lines that intersect the curve in the points P_0, P_1, P_2, $\cdots$, P_n, respectively. By joining successive pairs of these points, as P_0P_1, P_1P_2, P_2P_3, $\cdots$, $P_{n-1}P_n$, we form n trapezoids, $M_0M_1P_1P_0$, $M_1M_2P_2P_1$, $\cdots$, $M_{n-1}M_nP_nP_{n-1}$. If we let $x_0 = a$, and denote the abscissas of the successive points of division on the x-axis by x_1, x_2, $\cdots$, x_n, where $x_n = b$, and the corresponding ordinates by y_0, y_1, y_2, $\cdots$, y_n, then

$$(1) \quad \left. \begin{array}{c} \text{sum of} \\ \text{trapezoidal} \\ \text{areas} \end{array} \right\} = \tfrac{1}{2}(y_0 + y_1)(x_1 - x_0) + \tfrac{1}{2}(y_1 + y_2)(x_2 - x_1) + \cdots + \tfrac{1}{2}(y_{n-1} + y_n)(x_n - x_{n-1}).$$

If we divide the interval from a to b into n equal parts Δx, so that $\Delta x = \dfrac{b - a}{n}$, then $x_1 - x_0 = x_2 - x_1 = \cdots = x_n - x_{n-1} = \Delta x$; hence the right member of (1) becomes

$$\tfrac{1}{2}(y_0 + y_1)\Delta x + \tfrac{1}{2}(y_1 + y_2)\Delta x + \cdots + \tfrac{1}{2}(y_{n-1} + y_n)\Delta x,$$

and we have

$$(2) \quad \left. \begin{array}{c} \text{sum of} \\ \text{trapezoidal} \\ \text{areas} \end{array} \right\} = \frac{\Delta x}{2} (y_0 + 2y_1 + 2y_2 + \cdots + 2y_{n-1} + y_n).$$

Clearly the area under a curve from $x = a$ to $x = b$ may be found approximately from either (1) or (2); the latter formula, when employed for this purpose, is known as the **trapezoidal rule.**

If the curve is of sufficient regularity to justify the use of equal divisions of the interval from $x = a$ to $x = b$, then (2) is preferable to (1).

If the equation of the curve is known, 'the ordinates $y_0, y_1, \cdots, y_n$ are found by computation; otherwise they must be measured.

Since a definite integral may be represented as an area under a curve its value may be found approximately by means of the trapezoidal rule.

Example 1. Find the area under the curve $y = \dfrac{e^x - 1}{x}$ from $x = 0.1$ to $x = 0.2$.

Applying the trapezoidal rule, with $n = 2$ and $\Delta x = 0.05$, we have for the definite integral which represents the desired area

$$\int_{0.1}^{0.2} \frac{e^x - 1}{x}\, dx = \frac{0.05}{2}\left[\frac{e^{0.1} - 1}{0.1} + 2\left(\frac{e^{0.15} - 1}{0.15}\right) + \frac{e^{0.2} - 1}{0.2}\right]$$

$$= \frac{0.05}{2}\left[\frac{1.1052 - 1}{0.1} + 2\left(\frac{1.1618 - 1}{0.15}\right) + \frac{1.2214 - 1}{0.2}\right]$$

$$= \frac{0.05}{2}\,(1.052 + 2.157 + 1.107)$$

$$= 0.1079, \text{ approximately.}$$

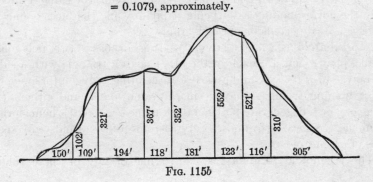

Fig. 115*b*

Example 2. Measurements are made as shown in Fig. 115*b* for determining the area of a field bounded by a straight road and the irregular outline of a wooded hill. Find the area.

Applying (1) we have

approximate area $= \frac{1}{2}(102)(150) + \frac{1}{2}(102 + 321)(109) + \frac{1}{2}(321 + 367)(194)$

$\quad + \frac{1}{2}(367 + 352)(118) + \frac{1}{2}(352 + 552)(181) + \frac{1}{2}(552 + 521)(123)$

$\quad + \frac{1}{2}(521 + 310)(116) + \frac{1}{2}(305)(310)$

$\quad = 383{,}135$ sq. ft.

Aside from any error caused by using straight-line segments along the curved boundary (the amount of such an error depending upon the judgment exercised by the surveyor), the question naturally arises as to the extent to which this result is reliable in view of errors or approximations in the field measurements. These measurements are given only to three significant figures; hence by rules to be given in Art. 144 we are justified in retaining no more than three significant figures in the result. Therefore we say that the

$$\text{area} = 383,000 \text{ sq. ft., approximately.}$$

116. Prismoidal Formula. In this article we shall consider two formulas which are widely used to obtain approximate values of volumes, areas, and definite integrals. One of these, the *prismoidal formula*, originated as an expression for the volume of any solid which may be suitably decomposed into prisms and related solids such as pyramids and frustums of pyramids. We shall give here the definitions of the three solids (the *prism*, the *prismoid*, and the *prismatoid*) which are most intimately connected with the formula.

A **prism** is a solid bounded by plane faces, two of which, called the ends or bases, are congruent and similarly situated polygons in parallel planes, while the faces connecting the ends are parallelograms equal in number to the sides of the polygons.

A **prismoid** is a solid bounded by plane faces, two of which, called the ends or bases, are dissimilar plane polygons having the same number of sides, the corresponding sides being parallel, while the faces connecting the ends are trapezoids or parallelograms.

A **prismatoid** is a solid having as ends or bases two polygons in parallel planes, and for each of the other faces a triangle with a side of one polygon for its base and a vertex of the other polygon for its vertex. Two adjoining triangles may lie in the same plane, and either of the bases may be a degenerate polygon (i. e., a line or a point); hence prisms, prismoids, wedges, pyramids, and frustums of pyramids are special cases of prismatoids.

The **prismoidal formula** for the volume of any of these solids is

$$(1) \qquad V = \frac{h}{6} (A_1 + 4 A_2 + A_3),$$

where A_1 and A_3 are the areas of the bases whose distance apart is h, and A_2 is the area of the cross-section of the solid in a plane parallel to the end planes and half way between them.* It is easy to verify the fact that this formula will give the volume of those solids (prisms, pyramids, and frustums of pyramids) into which a prismatoid may be decomposed.

* For the proof of (1) see, e.g., P. A. Lambert, *Computation and Mensuration* (Macmillan, 1907), p. 27.

The prismoidal formula will now be shown to give the exact volume of any solid, with parallel end areas, for which the area A of cross-section in any intermediate plane parallel to the end planes is a polynomial function, of the third degree or lower, of the distance x of the cutting plane from any parallel fixed plane of reference.

For this purpose let

$$(2) \qquad A = a_3x^3 + a_2x^2 + a_1x + a_0,$$

and let the distances from the fixed plane of reference to the end planes be x_1 and x_3, where $x_1 \leqq x \leqq x_3$. Then the volume V of the solid is (Art. 36)

$$V = \int_{x_1}^{x_3} (a_3x^3 + a_2x^2 + a_1x + a_0)dx$$

$$= \frac{a_3}{4}(x_3{}^4 - x_1{}^4) + \frac{a_2}{3}(x_3{}^3 - x_1{}^3) + \frac{a_1}{2}(x_3{}^2 - x_1{}^2) + a_0(x_3 - x_1)$$

$$= (x_3 - x_1)\left[\frac{a_3}{4}(x_3{}^3 + x_3{}^2x_1 + x_3x_1{}^2 + x_1{}^3) + \frac{a_2}{3}(x_3{}^2 + x_3x_1 + x_1{}^2)\right.$$

$$\left. + \frac{a_1}{2}(x_3 + x_1) + a_0\right].$$

We shall now show that the prismoidal formula gives the same result. Since $h = x_3 - x_1$ and $A_1, A_2,$ and A_3 are found by substituting $x_1, \dfrac{x_1 + x_3}{2}$, and x_3 in (2), we have for the right member of (1)

$$\frac{x_3 - x_1}{6}\left[(a_3x_1{}^3 + a_2x_1{}^2 + a_1x_1 + a_0) + 4\left\{a_3\left(\frac{x_1 + x_3}{2}\right)^3 \right.\right.$$

$$\left.\left. + a_2\left(\frac{x_1 + x_3}{2}\right)^2 + a_1\left(\frac{x_1 + x_3}{2}\right) + a_0\right\} + (a_3x_3{}^3 + a_2x_3{}^2 + a_1x_3 + a_0)\right]$$

$$= \frac{x_3 - x_1}{6}\left[(a_3x_1{}^3 + a_2x_1{}^2 + a_1x_1 + a_0) + 4\left\{\frac{a_3}{8}(x_1{}^3 + 3x_1{}^2x_3\right.\right.$$

$$\left.\left. + 3x_1x_3{}^2 + x_3{}^3) + \frac{a_2}{4}(x_1{}^2 + 2x_1x_3 + x_3{}^2) + \frac{a_1}{2}(x_1 + x_3) + a_0\right\}\right.$$

$$\left. + (a_3x_3{}^3 + a_2x_3{}^2 + a_1x_3 + a_0)\right]$$

$$= (x_3 - x_1)\left[\frac{a_3}{4}(x_3{}^3 + x_3{}^2x_1 + x_3x_1{}^2 + x_1{}^3) + \frac{a_2}{3}(x_3{}^2 + x_3x_1 + x_1{}^2)\right.$$

$$\left. + \frac{a_1}{2}(x_3 + x_1) + a_0\right],$$

which is seen to be the value of V obtained by integration.

Since a polynomial of degree lower than the third may be obtained from (2) by assigning the value zero to one or more of the coefficients, this proof is applicable to the case in which A is represented by any such polynomial.

From the above proof it follows that the prismoidal formula gives the exact volume of a prism, pyramid, frustum of a pyramid, wedge, cylinder, cone, frustum of a cone, sphere, ellipsoid, spherical segment, or, in general, any solid bounded by a quadric surface and two parallel planes. For in all these cases it may be shown that the area of cross-section in any intermediate plane parallel to the end planes is a quadratic function of x.

Example 1. Obtain by the prismoidal formula the volume of a spherical segment of altitude h and base-radii r_1 and r_3.

Denoting by a the radius of the corresponding sphere (Fig. 116a) and by x the

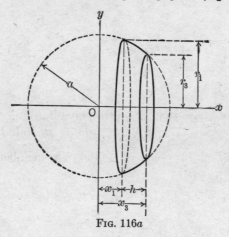

Fig. 116a

distance from its center to a cross-section of the segment in a plane parallel to the bases, we have for the area A of the cross-section

$$A = \pi(a^2 - x^2).$$

Since the right member is a quadratic function of x, the exact volume V of the segment is given by the prismoidal formula as

$$V = \frac{x_3 - x_1}{6}\left[\pi(a^2 - x_1^2) + 4\pi\left\{a^2 - \left(\frac{x_1 + x_3}{2}\right)^2\right\} + \pi(a^2 - x_3^2)\right]$$

$$= \frac{\pi(x_3 - x_1)}{6}[6a^2 - 2x_1^2 - 2x_3^2 - 2x_1x_3]$$

$$= \frac{\pi(x_3 - x_1)}{6}[3(a^2 - x_1^2) + 3(a^2 - x_3^2) + (x_3 - x_1)^2],$$

where x_1 and x_3 represent the distances from the center of the sphere to the bases of the segment. Observing that $x_3 - x_1 = h$, $a^2 - x_1^2 = r_1^2$, and $a^2 - x_3^2 = r_3^2$, we obtain the formula

$$(3) \qquad V = \frac{\pi h}{6}(3r_1^2 + 3r_3^2 + h^2).$$

Thus far we have shown how to apply the prismoidal formula to a solid for which the cross-sectional area is expressible as a function of the position of the cutting plane. However, in many important applications the cross-sectional area cannot be so expressed. In such cases the formula will give the volume to an approximation the closeness of which will depend upon the accuracy with which sectional areas are determined, and upon how nearly the solid approximates one for which the formula gives an exact result. When we consider the wide range of solids for which the formula holds, we readily see that it will apply with a fair degree of accuracy to almost any solid whose surface does not have sudden and extensive breaks and irregularities. If the surface is irregular it may be possible to divide the solid into portions which do approximate figures for which the formula holds. The procedure just described is extensively used in earthwork and masonry computations.

The prismoidal formula may be used also to evaluate a definite integral. For, by Art. 36, $\int_{x_1}^{x_3} f(x)\, dx$ represents the volume of a solid with end planes perpendicular to the x-axis at distances x_1 and x_3 from the origin and for which the cross-sectional area in a plane parallel to the ends is given by $f(x)$; hence the determination of the volume of the solid by the prismoidal formula is equivalent to the evaluation of the corresponding definite integral.

Therefore, in view of what has already been said, we conclude that

$$(4) \qquad \int_{x_1}^{x_3} f(x)\, dx = \frac{x_3 - x_1}{6}\,[f(x_1) + 4f(x_2) + f(x_3)], \quad x_2 = \frac{x_1 + x_3}{2},$$

exactly if $f(x)$ is a polynomial of the third or lower degree, and approximately otherwise.

From (4) it is at once apparent that the prismoidal formula may be used also to find the area under a curve. For $\int_{x_1}^{x_3} f(x)dx$ represents the area under the curve $y = f(x)$ from $x = x_1$ to $x = x_3$. Hence if this area is denoted by A we obtain from (4)

$$(5) \qquad A = \frac{x_3 - x_1}{6}(y_1 + 4y_2 + y_3),$$

where y_1, y_2, and y_3 are the ordinates corresponding to x_1, x_2, and x_3, respectively (Fig. 116b), and $x_2 = \dfrac{x_1 + x_3}{2}$.

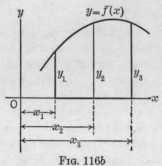

Fig. 116b

It is of course understood that (5) gives the exact area under the curve if y is a polynomial function of the third or lower degree, and otherwise only the approximate area. Moreover, if the equation of the bounding curve is not known so that no means are available for calculating the values of y_1, y_2, and y_3, these ordinates must be measured.

Example 2. Apply the prismoidal formula to the evaluation of the definite integral of Example 1, Art. 115.

By (4) we have

$$\int_{0.1}^{0.2} \frac{e^x - 1}{x}\, dx = \frac{0.1}{6}\left[\frac{e^{0.1} - 1}{0.1} + 4\left(\frac{e^{0.15} - 1}{0.15}\right) + \frac{e^{0.2} - 1}{0.2}\right]$$

$$= 0.1079, \text{ approximately.}$$

117. Simpson's Rule. We shall now develop an extension of the prismoidal formula whereby it is possible to approximate the value of a quantity which cannot be satisfactorily calculated by a single application of the prismoidal formula.

Consider for example the area A bounded by the curve of Fig. 117, the x-axis, and the lines $x = a$ and $x = b$. Let us divide the base of this area into an even number n of equal lengths Δx, and designate the abscissas of the points of division by x_0, $x_1, \cdots, x_n$, where $x_0 = a$ and $x_n = b$; the corresponding ordinates of the curve will be called $y_0, y_1, \cdots, y_n$. We shall

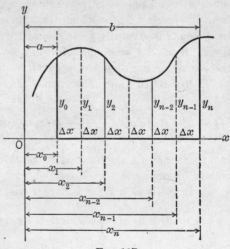

Fig. 117

regard the required area as divided by the ordinates $y_0, y_2, \cdots,$ y_{n-2}, y_n into $\dfrac{n}{2}$ double strips and apply the prismoidal formula as given by (5) of the preceding article. Thus we obtain the approximation

$$A = \frac{\Delta x}{3}(y_0 + 4y_1 + y_2) + \frac{\Delta x}{3}(y_2 + 4y_3 + y_4) + \cdots$$

$$+ \frac{\Delta x}{3}(y_{n-2} + 4y_{n-1} + y_n),$$

or

(1) $A = \dfrac{\Delta x}{3}(y_0 + 4y_1 + 2y_2 + 4y_3 + 2y_4 + \cdots + 2y_{n-2} + 4y_{n-1} + y_n).$

This formula is known as **Simpson's rule** for area.

Similarly, if a solid has two base-planes perpendicular to the x-axis, and it is divided by planes parallel to these bases into an even number n of slices, each of thickness Δx, its volume V is given approximately by

(2) $V = \dfrac{\Delta x}{3}(A_0 + 4A_1 + 2A_2 + 4A_3 + 2A_4 + \cdots + 2A_{n-2} + 4A_{n-1} + A_n),$

where A_0 and A_n are the base-areas and $A_1, \cdots, A_{n-1}$ are the cross-sectional areas in the auxiliary cutting planes. Formula (2) is known as Simpson's rule for volume.

Applied to a definite integral Simpson's rule becomes

(3) $\displaystyle\int_a^b f(x)\,dx = \dfrac{\Delta x}{3}[f(x_0) + 4f(x_1) + 2f(x_2) + 4f(x_3) + 2f(x_4) + \cdots$

$$+ 2f(x_{n-2}) + 4f(x_{n-1}) + f(x_n)],$$

where $\Delta x = \dfrac{b-a}{n}$, n is even, $x_0 = a$, $x_1 = a + \Delta x$, $x_2 = a + 2\Delta x$, $\cdots$, $x_{n-1} = b - \Delta x$, $x_n = b$.

Evidently (1), (2), and (3) reduce, for $n = 2$, to the corresponding forms of the prismoidal formula. Moreover, if the latter gives an exact result, so will Simpson's rule; in such a case it is needless to take $n > 2$.

Example. By Simpson's rule find the area under the *probability curve* $y = \dfrac{2}{\sqrt{\pi}}e^{-x^2}$ from $x = 0$ to $x = 0.6$.

Using $n = 6$ and $\Delta x = 0.1$, we have, by (1) or (3),

$$A = \frac{2}{\sqrt{\pi}}\int_0^{0.6} e^{-x^2}\,dx = \frac{2}{\sqrt{\pi}}\left(\frac{0.1}{3}\right)(e^0 + 4e^{-0.01} + 2e^{-0.04} + 4e^{-0.09}$$

$$+ 2e^{-0.16} + 4e^{-0.25} + e^{-0.36})$$

$$= \frac{2}{\sqrt{\pi}} \left(\frac{0.1}{3}\right) (1.00000 + 3.96020 + 1.92158 + 3.65572 + 1.70429$$

$$+ \ 3.11520 + 0.69768)$$

$$= 0.60386, \text{ approximately.}$$

A five-place table of probability integrals gives the same result.

118. Mechanical Integration.   Areas may be approximated not only by the methods described above but also by the use of instruments, known as *mechanical integrators*, which have been devised for this purpose.   The form in most common use is the *polar planimeter*.   This instrument has a stylus which is made to follow the boundary of the required area whose value is thereupon read on a graduated cylindrical drum.   Information concerning the theory and use of mechanical integrators may be found in books on engineering.*

PROBLEMS

1. Show that the prismoidal formula gives the exact value of

$$\int_{x_1}^{x_3} f(x)dx$$

if

(a) $f(x) = a_0$,

(b) $f(x) = a_1 x + a_0$,

(c) $f(x) = a_2 x^2 + a_1 x + a_0$.

2. Evaluate $\int_2^3 \frac{dx}{1 + x^3}$ by the trapezoidal rule, and by Simpson's rule, using $\Delta x = \frac{1}{4}$.   Check by the result of Problem 17, Art. 91.

3. Find the area under the curve $y = \frac{1}{1 + x}$ from $x = 1$ to $x = 3$, using the trapezoidal rule with $\Delta x = \frac{1}{4}$.   Check by integration.

4. Evaluate $\int_1^2 \sqrt{1 + x^3} \, dx$ by Simpson's rule, with $\Delta x = \frac{1}{4}$.

5. Evaluate $\int_0^{0.4} e^{-\frac{1}{2}x^2} \, dx$ by Simpson's rule, with $\Delta x = \frac{1}{10}$.

6. A smooth curve passes through the points (4, 5), (6, 6), (8, 6), (10, 5), (12, 4), (14, 5), (16, 8).   Calculate the area under the curve from $x = 4$ to $x = 16$ by the trapezoidal rule and by Simpson's rule.

7. Find the length of the arc of the ellipse $\frac{x^2}{16} + \frac{y^2}{9} = 1$ from (0, 3) to $(2, \frac{3}{2}\sqrt{3})$ by the prismoidal formula.

8. Show by the use of (3), Art. 116, that the volume of a spherical segment of one

* See, for example, Diederichs and Andrae, *Experimental Mechanical Engineering*, Vol. I, *Engineering Instruments* (John Wiley & Sons, Inc., 1930), p. 33.

base is $\dfrac{\pi h^2}{3}(3a - h)$, where h is the altitude of the segment and a is the radius of the corresponding sphere.

Find by the prismoidal formula the volumes of the solids described in Problems 9 to 14, inclusive.

9. A sphere of radius a.   (Check by (3), Art. 116, and also by the result of Problem 8.)

10. A right circular cone of altitude h and base-radius a.

11. A right pyramid of altitude h, whose base is a square of side a.

12. A frustum of a right circular cone of base-radii a and b and altitude h.

13. A frustum of a right pyramid with square bases of sides a and b and altitude h.

14. An ellipsoid of semi-axes a, b, and c.   (The area of an ellipse is π times the product of its semi-axes.)

15. Evaluate $\displaystyle\int_1^2 \dfrac{dx}{x}$ by Simpson's rule with $n = 8$ and thus compute ln 2 to five decimals.

16. Evaluate $\displaystyle\int_0^1 \dfrac{dx}{1 + x^2}$ by Simpson's rule with $n = 10$ and thence compute π to five decimals.

CHAPTER XII

INDETERMINATE FORMS

119. Indeterminate Forms. A function is said to be **indeterminate** for any value of x for which it assumes one of the forms

$$\frac{0}{0}, \ \frac{\infty}{\infty}, \ 0 \cdot \infty, \ \infty - \infty, \ 0^0, \ \infty^0, \ 1^\infty,$$

called **indeterminate forms.** For such a value of x the function is discontinuous. Yet it may be possible so to define the function for the exceptional value of x that the discontinuity is removed.

For example, the function

$$\frac{\sin x}{x}$$

is clearly discontinuous for $x = 0$, as it assumes for this value of x the indeterminate form $\frac{0}{0}$. However, since

$$\lim_{x \to 0} \frac{\sin x}{x} = 1 \quad \text{(Art. 46)},$$

the discontinuity may be removed by defining the function to be 1 for $x = 0$; for then the limiting value of $\dfrac{\sin x}{x}$ as x approaches zero is the same as the value assigned to it for $x = 0$. Thus by the definition of continuity (Art. 7) the function given by the equations

$$\begin{cases} \phi(x) = \dfrac{\sin x}{x}, & x \neq 0, \\ \phi(0) = 1 \end{cases}$$

is continuous for all values of x.

It should be noted here that we are at liberty to give $\phi(0)$ any value we please, but that, if complete continuity is desired, we must define it as 1.

In general, if a function $\phi(x)$ is indeterminate and hence discontinuous for $x = a$, but if $\lim\limits_{x \to a} \phi(x)$ exists, independently of the manner in which

332

x approaches a, it is customary to define $\phi(a)$ so that continuity is established, that is, so that

$$\phi(a) = \lim_{x \to a} \phi(x).$$

To provide a means of developing the general theory of indeterminate forms, we shall next establish two theorems of fundamental importance in mathematical analysis, known as *Rolle's Theorem* and the *Mean Value Theorem*.

120. Rolle's Theorem. *If a function $f(x)$ and its derivative $f'(x)$ are single-valued and continuous for all values of x throughout an interval $a \leqq x \leqq b$, and if $f(a) = f(b) = 0$, there exists at least one value x_1 of x such that $f'(x_1) = 0$, where $a < x_1 < b$.*

First we dispose of the case in which $f(x) = 0$ for all values of x from a to b. Obviously then if x_1 is any number between a and b, $f'(x_1) = 0$, and the theorem holds.

Next we observe that, if $f(x)$ is not identically zero when $a < x < b$, the function has, by virtue of its continuity, a greatest value M and a smallest value m, at least one of which differs from zero and corresponds to a value of x between a and b.

Suppose $M \neq 0$, so that $M > 0$. Now let x_1 be a value of x such that

$$f(x_1) = M, \quad a < x_1 < b.$$

Then since $f'(x)$ is continuous, $f'(x_1)$ exists, and it remains to show that $f'(x_1) = 0$.

To prove this we note that, if $f'(x_1)$ were not zero, it would be positive or negative, and hence $f(x)$ would be either an increasing or a decreasing function for $x = x_1$. This would require that $f(x)$ exceed its greatest value M for values of x near x_1, which is impossible. Hence

$$f'(x_1) = 0.$$

Next suppose $m \neq 0$, so that $m < 0$. Then a similar argument shows that there must exist a value x_1 of x such that

$$f'(x_1) = 0, \quad a < x_1 < b.$$

This completes the proof.

Geometrically, Rolle's Theorem signifies that the curve $y = f(x)$ has at least one tangent parallel to the x-axis between the points for which $x = a$ and $x = b$. (See Fig. 120a.)

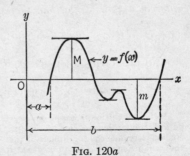

Fig. 120a

The theorem is likewise true if the condition $f(a) = f(b) = 0$ is generalized to read $f(a) = f(b) = k$, where k is a constant.

Although Rolle's Theorem as stated here is valid, it is noteworthy that the conclusion may or may not hold when $f(x)$ has a discontinuous derivative at one or more points within the interval. Fig. 120b shows the graph of a continuous function having a derivative which is infinite, and therefore discontinuous, for $x = a$, $x = b$, and $x = c$, and yet the conclusion of the theorem holds, for, at P, a tangent to the curve is

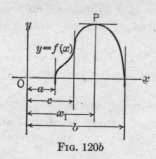

FIG. 120b

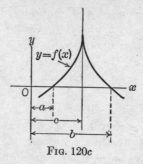

FIG. 120c

parallel to the x-axis. Fig. 120c shows the graph of a continuous function whose derivative is discontinuous for $x = c$. Clearly the theorem fails here, for at no point of the curve is a tangent parallel to the x-axis. Moreover, it should be remarked that the requirement that $f(x)$ be continuous is redundant, for it can be proved that the mere existence of a single-valued derivative $f'(x)$ guarantees the continuity of $f(x)$. Thus it appears that, though the conditions of the theorem are not completely *necessary*,* they are *sufficient* to guarantee the conclusion.

121. Mean Value Theorem. *If a function $f(x)$ and its derivative $f'(x)$ are single-valued and continuous for all values of x throughout an interval $a \leqq x \leqq b$, then there exists at least one value x_1 of x such that*

(1) $$f(b) - f(a) = (b - a)f'(x_1), \quad \text{where} \quad a < x_1 < b.$$

To prove this let us consider the function

$$\phi(x) = (b - a)[f(x) - f(a)] - (x - a)[f(b) - f(a)].$$

---

* If a conclusion is based on a certain hypothesized condition, the condition is said to be **sufficient**; that is, the condition guarantees the conclusion. Conversely, if the conclusion demands the fulfillment of the condition, that is, if the condition is deducible from the conclusion, the condition is said to be **necessary**. For example, a sufficient condition for the similarity of two triangles is the parallelism of corresponding sides. Obviously this condition is not necessary. However, a necessary condition is the equality of corresponding angles. This condition is also sufficient.

This function is single-valued and continuous throughout the interval $a \le x \le b$, since $f(x)$ has these properties. Moreover, $\phi(x)$ possesses throughout the interval a continuous derivative

$$\phi'(x) = (b - a)f'(x) - [f(b) - f(a)],$$

by virtue of the assumed continuity of $f'(x)$. Finally we note that

$$\phi(a) = \phi(b) = 0.$$

Thus $\phi(x)$ satisfies all the conditions of Rolle's Theorem. Hence there exists a value x_1 of x such that

$$\phi'(x_1) = (b - a)f'(x_1) - [f(b) - f(a)] = 0, \qquad a < x_1 < b,$$

which proves the theorem.

To establish a geometrical interpretation of the Mean Value Theorem let us write the last equation in the form

$$(2) \qquad \frac{f(b) - f(a)}{b - a} = f'(x_1).$$

The left member of this equation represents the slope of a chord of the curve $y = f(x)$, drawn between the points for which $x = a$ and $x = b$ (Fig. 121), while the right member rep-
resents the slope of a tangent to the curve at some intermediate point for which $x = x_1$. Thus the theorem states that there exists at least one point on the curve $y = f(x)$, with an abscissa between a and b, where a tangent line to the curve is parallel to the chord with extremities at the points for which $x = a$ and $x = b$.

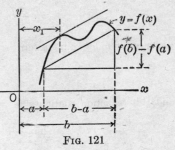

FIG. 121

The theorem and its geometrical interpretation are generalizations of Rolle's Theorem and its geometrical interpretation. This is made clear by placing $f(b) = f(a)$ in (2).

Equation (1) is sometimes called the **law of the mean**.

This law may be converted into another useful form by **letting** $b = a + h$ and $x_1 = a + \theta h$, where $0 < \theta < 1$. Thus by (1)

$$f(a + h) = f(a) + hf'(a + \theta h), \quad 0 < \theta < 1.$$

122. The Indeterminate Forms $\frac{0}{0}$ and $\frac{\infty}{\infty}$. If two functions $f(x)$ and $g(x)$ both vanish for $x = a$, or if both become infinite as x approaches a, their quotient $\dfrac{f(x)}{g(x)}$ is without meaning when $x = a$. In the former case the fraction is said to assume the indeterminate form $\frac{0}{0}$ — in the latter the indeterminate form $\frac{\infty}{\infty}$ — when $x = a$. Even though no value of the quotient then exists in either case, a definite value of $\lim\limits_{x \to a} \dfrac{f(x)}{g(x)}$ may exist. An example of frequent occurrence is the indeterminate form $\frac{0}{0}$ assumed by $\dfrac{\Delta y}{\Delta x}$ for $\Delta x = 0$.

The indeterminate forms $\frac{0}{0}$ and $\frac{\infty}{\infty}$ may arise when x becomes infinite as well as for some finite value of x. Thus if $f(x)$ and $g(x)$ both vanish or both become infinite as x becomes infinite, the fraction $\dfrac{f(x)}{g(x)}$ assumes one of the indeterminate forms $\frac{0}{0}$ or $\frac{\infty}{\infty}$. Even though no value of this quotient then exists, it is possible that a definite value of $\lim\limits_{x \to \infty} \dfrac{f(x)}{g(x)}$ may exist.

The following examples illustrate how an indeterminate form may arise for a finite value of x, or when x becomes infinite.

Example 1. The fraction

$$\frac{x^2 - 9}{x - 3}$$

assumes the indeterminate form $\frac{0}{0}$ when $x = 3$. For all other values of x

$$\frac{x^2 - 9}{x - 3} = x + 3,$$

and this reduction continues to be valid as x approaches 3. Hence

$$\lim_{x \to 3} \frac{x^2 - 9}{x - 3} = \lim_{x \to 3} (x + 3) = 6.$$

It should be noted that the function

$$\frac{x^2 - 9}{x - 3}$$

is discontinuous for $x = 3$, but that the discontinuity may be removed by assigning the value 6 to the function when $x = 3$. (See Art. 7.)

Example 2. The fraction

$$\frac{2x^2 + x - 1}{x^2 + 2x + 3}$$

assumes the indeterminate form $\frac{\infty}{\infty}$ as x becomes infinite. However, from the fact that

$$\frac{2x^2 + x - 1}{x^2 + 2x + 3} = \frac{2 + \dfrac{1}{x} - \dfrac{1}{x^2}}{1 + \dfrac{2}{x} + \dfrac{3}{x^2}}$$

for all finite values of x (except $x = 0$), it follows that

$$\lim_{x \to \infty} \frac{2x^2 + x - 1}{x^2 + 2x + 3} = \lim_{x \to \infty} \frac{2 + \dfrac{1}{x} - \dfrac{1}{x^2}}{1 + \dfrac{2}{x} + \dfrac{3}{x^2}} = 2.$$

The procedure followed in these examples, and often other simple devices, may be used to investigate elementary indeterminate forms. However, a general method is needed. Accordingly we give the following

THEOREM. *L'Hospital's Rule. If the fraction* $\dfrac{f(x)}{g(x)}$ *assumes one of the indeterminate forms* $\frac{0}{0}$ *or* $\frac{\infty}{\infty}$ *when* $x = a$, *while for* $x = a$ *the fraction* $\dfrac{f'(x)}{g'(x)}$ *does not assume an indeterminate form, then*

$$\lim_{x \to a} \frac{f(x)}{g(x)} = \frac{f'(a)}{g'(a)},$$

provided $\dfrac{f'(a)}{g'(a)}$ *exists; and if this does not exist,* $\dfrac{f(x)}{g(x)}$ *will become positively or negatively infinite as x approaches a, according as* $\dfrac{f'(x)}{g'(x)}$ *becomes positively or negatively infinite.*

A similar statement holds if the indeterminate form arises when x becomes infinite instead of when $x = a$.

The student should be informed here that the functions $f(x)$ and $g(x)$ are subject to further restrictions not included in the above statement of the theorem. A thorough analysis of all the conditions of the rule is beyond the scope of this book. Accordingly a complete proof will not be attempted.

Let us consider, however, the instructive case in which $f(a) = g(a) = 0$. Then by the law of the mean (Art. 121),

$$f(x) - f(a) = (x - a)f'(x_1), \qquad a < x_1 < x,$$

and

$$g(x) - g(a) = (x - a)g'(x_2), \qquad a < x_2 < x.$$

Therefore, since $f(a) = g(a) = 0$,

$$\frac{f(x)}{g(x)} = \frac{(x-a)f'(x_1)}{(x-a)g'(x_2)} = \frac{f'(x_1)}{g'(x_2)},$$

provided $x \neq a$. Now as x approaches a, x_1 and x_2 do likewise, and the last equation is valid during the process. Hence

$$\lim_{x \to a} \frac{f(x)}{g(x)} = \lim_{x \to a} \frac{f'(x_1)}{g'(x_2)} = \frac{f'(a)}{g'(a)},$$

provided the last fraction exists. This demonstrates the truth of a part of the theorem relating to indeterminate forms of the type $\frac{0}{0}$ arising when $x = a$. The proof of the rest of the theorem is omitted.

If $\frac{f'(x)}{g'(x)}$ also assumes an indeterminate form of the type $\frac{0}{0}$ or $\frac{\infty}{\infty}$, the theorem may be applied likewise to it; in fact, the process may be repeated as many times as may be necessary to yield a fraction $\frac{f^{(n)}(a)}{g^{(n)}(a)}$ which is not indeterminate. A similar statement holds in case the given indeterminate form arises when x becomes infinite, instead of when $x = a$. Thus our findings may be summarized in the following rules:

RULE 1. *If the fraction* $\frac{f(x)}{g(x)}$ *assumes an indeterminate form of the type* $\frac{0}{0}$ *or* $\frac{\infty}{\infty}$ *when* $x = a$, *then*

$$\lim_{x \to a} \frac{f(x)}{g(x)}$$

will be equal to the first of the expressions

$$\frac{f'(a)}{g'(a)}, \ \frac{f''(a)}{g''(a)}, \ \frac{f'''(a)}{g'''(a)}, \ etc.,$$

which is not indeterminate, provided this expression exists; and if it fails to exist, the limit sought does likewise.

RULE 2. *If the fraction* $\frac{f(x)}{g(x)}$ *becomes an indeterminate form of the type* $\frac{0}{0}$ *or* $\frac{\infty}{\infty}$ *when* x *becomes infinite, then*

$$\lim_{x \to \infty} \frac{f(x)}{g(x)}$$

will be equal to the first of the expressions

$$\frac{\lim\limits_{x \to \infty} f'(x)}{\lim\limits_{x \to \infty} g'(x)}, \quad \frac{\lim\limits_{x \to \infty} f''(x)}{\lim\limits_{x \to \infty} g''(x)}, \quad \frac{\lim\limits_{x \to \infty} f'''(x)}{\lim\limits_{x \to \infty} g'''(x)}, \text{ etc.,}$$

which is not indeterminate, provided this expression exists; and if it fails to exist, the limit sought does likewise.

Example 3. Evaluate $\lim\limits_{\theta \to 0} \dfrac{\sin \theta}{\theta}$.

This limit was obtained in Art. 46 and considered further in Art. 119. In the light of Rule 1 we have

$$\lim_{\theta \to 0} \frac{\sin \theta}{\theta} = \lim_{\theta \to 0} \frac{\cos \theta}{1} = 1.$$

Example 4. Evaluate $\lim\limits_{x \to \frac{\pi}{2}} \dfrac{\ln\left(x - \dfrac{\pi}{2}\right)}{\sec x}$, assuming that $x > \dfrac{\pi}{2}$.

Since the fraction

$$\frac{f(x)}{g(x)} = \frac{\ln\left(x - \dfrac{\pi}{2}\right)}{\sec x}$$

assumes the indeterminate form $\dfrac{\infty}{\infty}$ when $x = \dfrac{\pi}{2}$, we differentiate the numerator and denominator separately in accordance with Rule 1 and form

$$\frac{f'(x)}{g'(x)} = \frac{\dfrac{1}{x - \dfrac{\pi}{2}}}{\sec x \tan x} = \frac{\cos^2 x}{\left(x - \dfrac{\pi}{2}\right) \sin x}.$$

As this assumes the indeterminate form $\dfrac{0}{0}$ when $x = \dfrac{\pi}{2}$, we repeat the process and find that

$$\frac{f''(x)}{g''(x)} = \frac{-2 \sin x \cos x}{\left(x - \dfrac{\pi}{2}\right) \cos x + \sin x}.$$

Clearly this has the value zero when $x = \dfrac{\pi}{2}$. We conclude therefore that

$$\lim_{x \to \frac{\pi}{2}} \frac{\ln\left(x - \dfrac{\pi}{2}\right)}{\sec x} = \lim_{x \to \frac{\pi}{2}} \frac{-2 \sin x \cos x}{\left(x - \dfrac{\pi}{2}\right) \cos x + \sin x} = 0.$$

Example 5. Evaluate $\lim\limits_{x \to \infty} \dfrac{e^x}{x^4}$.

Since $\dfrac{e^x}{x^4}$ assumes the indeterminate form $\dfrac{\infty}{\infty}$ as x becomes infinite, we differentiate the numerator and denominator separately as many times as are necessary to arrive at a fraction which does not assume an indeterminate form as x becomes infinite (Rule 2). Thus we obtain the fractions

$$\frac{\lim\limits_{x \to \infty} e^x}{\lim\limits_{x \to \infty} 4x^3}, \quad \frac{\lim\limits_{x \to \infty} e^x}{\lim\limits_{x \to \infty} 12x^2}, \quad \frac{\lim\limits_{x \to \infty} e^x}{\lim\limits_{x \to \infty} 24x}, \quad \lim\limits_{x \to \infty} \frac{e^x}{24}.$$

All except the last of these are indeterminate. However, since the last fraction becomes infinite with x, we conclude that

$$\lim_{x \to \infty} \frac{e^x}{x^4}$$

does not exist.

123. The Indeterminate Form $0 \cdot \infty$. If $f(x) \cdot g(x)$ assumes the indeterminate form $0 \cdot \infty$ when x has a finite value a, or when x becomes positively or negatively infinite, the product may be converted to one of the indeterminate forms $\dfrac{0}{0}$ or $\dfrac{\infty}{\infty}$ by use of the identities

$$f(x) \cdot g(x) = \frac{f(x)}{\dfrac{1}{g(x)}} = \frac{g(x)}{\dfrac{1}{f(x)}},$$

and hence may be investigated by one of the foregoing rules.

Example. Evaluate $\lim\limits_{x \to 0} [\csc x \cdot \ln (x + 1)]$.

Since $\csc x \cdot \ln (x + 1)$ assumes the form $\infty \cdot 0$ for $x = 0$, we write

$$\csc x \cdot \ln (x + 1) = \frac{\ln (x + 1)}{\sin x}.$$

This assumes the form $\dfrac{0}{0}$ for $x = 0$. Hence by Rule 1 (Art. 122),

$$\lim_{x \to 0} [\csc x \cdot \ln (x + 1)] = \lim_{x \to 0} \frac{\ln (x + 1)}{\sin x} = \lim_{x \to 0} \frac{\dfrac{1}{x + 1}}{\cos x} = 1.$$

124. The Indeterminate Form $\infty - \infty$. If $f(x) - g(x)$ assumes the indeterminate form $\infty - \infty$ when x has a finite value a, or when x becomes positively or negatively infinite, it is generally possible by algebraic reduction to transform $f(x) - g(x)$ into a fraction which will assume either the form $\dfrac{0}{0}$ or $\dfrac{\infty}{\infty}$.

Example. Evaluate $\lim\limits_{x \to 1} \left[\dfrac{1}{\ln x} - \dfrac{1}{x - 1} \right]$.

The quantity within the bracket assumes the form $\infty - \infty$ for $x = 1$. However, when written as

$$\frac{x - 1 - \ln x}{(x - 1) \ln x},$$

it assumes the form $\frac{0}{0}$ for $x = 1$, and hence may be investigated as follows:

$$\lim_{x \to 1} \left[\frac{1}{\ln x} - \frac{1}{x - 1} \right] = \lim_{x \to 1} \frac{x - 1 - \ln x}{(x - 1) \ln x}$$

$$= \lim_{x \to 1} \frac{1 - \dfrac{1}{x}}{\dfrac{x - 1}{x} + \ln x}$$

$$= \lim_{x \to 1} \frac{x - 1}{x - 1 + x \ln x}$$

$$= \lim_{x \to 1} \frac{1}{1 + 1 + \ln x}$$

$$= \tfrac{1}{2}.$$

PROBLEMS

Evaluate the limits in Problems 1 to 31 inclusive, or show that they do not exist.

1. $\lim\limits_{\theta \to \frac{\pi}{2}} \dfrac{1 - \sin \theta}{\cos \theta}$.

2. $\lim\limits_{x \to 0} \dfrac{x}{\sqrt{x + 1} - 1}$.

3. $\lim\limits_{\theta \to 0} \dfrac{\tan 2\theta}{\ln (1 + \theta)}$.

4. $\lim\limits_{x \to 4} \dfrac{\sqrt{x} - 2}{x - 4}$.

5. $\lim\limits_{x \to 0} \dfrac{\ln (1 - x)}{e^x - 1}$.

6. $\lim\limits_{x \to \frac{1}{2}} \dfrac{\tan^{-1}(2x - 1)}{\ln 2x}$.

7. $\lim\limits_{\theta \to 0} \dfrac{\sin 2\theta - \sin \theta}{\tan 3\theta}$.

8. $\lim\limits_{\theta \to \frac{\pi}{2}} \dfrac{\ln \sin \theta}{e^{\cos \theta} - 1}$.

9. $\lim\limits_{\theta \to \frac{\pi}{2}} \dfrac{2(e^{\cos \theta} + \theta - 1) - \pi}{\ln \sin (-3\theta)}$.

10. $\lim\limits_{\theta \to 0} \dfrac{\cos \theta - 1}{\cos 2\theta - 1}$.

11. $\lim\limits_{x \to 0} \dfrac{\tan^{-1} x}{\sin^{-1} x}$.

12. $\lim\limits_{\theta \to 0} \dfrac{e^\theta - \cos \theta}{1 - \sqrt{1 - \theta}}$.

13. $\lim\limits_{x \to 5} \dfrac{\ln (3x - 14)}{\cos (5 - x) - e^{x - 5}}$.

14. $\lim\limits_{x \to \infty} \lfloor x(e^{\frac{1}{x}} - 1) \rfloor$.

15. $\lim\limits_{x \to \infty} [x^2(a^{\frac{1}{x}} - b^{\frac{1}{x}})]$.

16. $\lim\limits_{x \to 0} \dfrac{a^x - 1}{x}$.

17. $\lim\limits_{x \to \frac{\pi}{2}} (\cos x \ln \tan x)$, $x < \dfrac{\pi}{2}$.

18. $\lim\limits_{x \to 0} \dfrac{1 - e^x \sec x}{x}$.

19. $\lim\limits_{x \to \frac{\pi}{2}} (\sec x - \tan x)$.

20. $\lim\limits_{\theta \to 0} (\cot \theta - \csc \theta)$.

21. $\lim\limits_{x \to 0} \dfrac{\ln (1 - x)}{\sin x}$.

22. $\lim\limits_{x \to \infty} \dfrac{\ln x}{x}$.

23. $\lim\limits_{x \to 0} (x \cot x)$.

24. $\lim\limits_{x \to \frac{\pi}{2}} \left[\left(\dfrac{\pi}{2} - x \right) \tan x \right]$.

25. $\lim\limits_{x \to \infty} \dfrac{e^{x - 2}}{x - 2}$.

26. $\lim\limits_{x \to \infty} \dfrac{x^n}{e^x}$, $n > 0$.

27. $\lim\limits_{x \to \infty} [\ln (x + 1) - \ln (x - 1)]$.

28. $\lim\limits_{x \to \infty} [(x - 1)e^{-x^2}]$.

29. $\lim\limits_{x \to a} \dfrac{x - a}{\ln x - \ln a}$.

30. $\lim\limits_{x \to 1} \left(\dfrac{1}{\ln x} - \dfrac{x}{1 - x} \right)$.

31. $\lim\limits_{x \to 0} (x^n \ln x)$, $n > 0$, $x > 0$.

Evaluate the following definite integrals:

32. $\displaystyle\int_0^\infty x e^{-x} dx$.

33. $\displaystyle\int_0^1 x \ln x \, dx$.

CHAPTER XIII

INFINITE SERIES

A. GENERAL DISCUSSION

125. Series. The indicated sum

$$u_1 + u_2 + u_3 + \cdots + u_n$$

of n constant or variable terms, each formed according to a definite law, is called a **finite series.** If the number of terms is unlimited, the series is written in the form

$$u_1 + u_2 + u_3 + \cdots,$$

or

$$u_1 + u_2 + u_3 + \cdots + u_n + \cdots,$$

and is called an **infinite series.** The arithmetic series

$$a + (a + d) + (a + 2d) + \cdots + [a + (n - 1)d],$$

in which each of the n terms is formed by adding a fixed amount d to the preceding term, is a familiar example of a finite series. The indicated sum of an unlimited number of terms in geometric progression, such as

$$a + ar + ar^2 + ar^3 + \cdots + ar^{n-1} + \cdots,$$

in which each term bears the ratio r to the preceding term, is an infinite series. Likewise the binomial expansion

$$1 + \frac{k}{1!} x + \frac{k(k - 1)}{2!} x^2 + \frac{k(k - 1)(k - 2)}{3!} x^3 + \cdots$$

of $(1 + x)^k$ is an infinite series for all except positive integral values of k and $k = 0$. If k is a positive integer or zero, the expansion reduces to a finite series of $k + 1$ terms ending with x^k.

The **general term** of a series (usually taken as the nth term) defines the law of formation of its terms. No positive information concerning the law is presented unless the general term is given. If, however, the law suggested by the first few terms holds throughout, the general term may be formulated. Thus if the law of formation suggested by the terms of the infinite series

$$1 - \frac{3}{2!} + \frac{5}{4!} - \frac{7}{6!} + \cdots$$

holds likewise for all the terms omitted, the nth term is

$$(-1)^{n+1}\frac{2n-1}{(2n-2)!},$$

for all values of n except $n = 1$.*

PROBLEMS

Assuming that the law of formation of the terms of each of the following series holds throughout, find the nth term.

1. $1 + \dfrac{1}{1!} + \dfrac{1}{2!} + \dfrac{1}{3!} + \cdots$.

5. $1 + \dfrac{2}{1!} + \dfrac{3}{2!} + \dfrac{4}{3!} + \cdots$.

2. $1 - \dfrac{x^2}{2!} + \dfrac{x^4}{4!} - \dfrac{x^6}{6!} + \cdots$.

6. $1 + \dfrac{2}{3!} + \dfrac{3}{5!} + \dfrac{4}{7!} + \cdots$.

3. $x - \dfrac{x^3}{3!} + \dfrac{x^5}{5!} - \dfrac{x^7}{7!} + \cdots$.

7. $\dfrac{1}{2} - \dfrac{2}{3\cdot4} + \dfrac{3}{4\cdot5\cdot6} - \dfrac{4}{5\cdot6\cdot7\cdot8} + \cdots$.

4. $1 + \dfrac{3}{2!} + \dfrac{5}{4!} + \dfrac{7}{6!} + \cdots$.

8. $\dfrac{1}{2} - \dfrac{2}{9} + \dfrac{3}{28} - \dfrac{4}{65} + \cdots$.

9. $1 - \dfrac{5}{2!+3} + \dfrac{10}{3!+4} - \dfrac{17}{4!+5} + \cdots$.

10. $\dfrac{1}{3} + \dfrac{4}{4\cdot5\cdot6} + \dfrac{9}{5\cdot6\cdot7\cdot8\cdot9} + \dfrac{16}{6\cdot7\cdot8\cdots12} + \cdots$.

11. $1 + kx + \dfrac{k(k-1)}{2!}x^2 + \dfrac{k(k-1)(k-2)}{3!}x^3 + \cdots$.

12. $x + \dfrac{1}{2}\dfrac{x^3}{3} + \dfrac{1\cdot3}{2\cdot4}\dfrac{x^5}{5} + \dfrac{1\cdot3\cdot5}{2\cdot4\cdot6}\dfrac{x^7}{7} + \cdots$.

13. $\dfrac{3}{1\cdot2!} - \dfrac{4}{2\cdot3!} + \dfrac{5}{3\cdot4!} - \dfrac{6}{4\cdot5!} + \cdots$.

14. $\dfrac{1}{6}x - \dfrac{8}{2\cdot3\cdot4\cdot5\cdot6}x^3 + \dfrac{27}{3\cdot4\cdot5\cdots9}x^5 - \dfrac{64}{4\cdot5\cdot6\cdots12}x^7 + \cdots$.

126. Sum of an Infinite Series.
The sum of a finite series has an obvious meaning. It is necessary, however, to define the *sum of an infinite series*.

---

* This incompatibility between the first and nth terms is characteristic of many important series. Complete harmony may often be effected (as in this example) by defining 0! to be 1.

Definition: If $\quad S_n = u_1 + u_2 + u_3 + \cdots + u_n$

is the sum of the first n terms of the infinite series

$$u_1 + u_2 + u_3 + \cdots + u_n + \cdots,$$

and if the limit of S_n exists as n becomes infinite, this limit is called the sum S of the series; that is,

$$S = \lim_{n \to \infty} S_n.$$

If this limit does not exist, the series has no sum.

For example, as n becomes infinite, the sum

$$S_n = a + ar + ar^2 + \cdots + ar^{n-1} = \frac{a(1 - r^n)}{1 - r}$$

of the first n terms of the infinite geometric series

$$(1) \qquad\qquad a + ar + ar^2 + \cdots + ar^{n-1} + \cdots$$

approaches a definite limit if $|r| < 1$. This limit is

$$(2) \qquad\qquad S = \lim_{n \to \infty} \frac{a(1 - r^n)}{1 - r} = \frac{a}{1 - r},$$

since r^n approaches zero as n becomes infinite. Therefore if $|r| < 1$ the series has the sum S. However, if in (1) $|r| > 1$, r^n becomes infinite with n; hence in this case the limit of S_n does not exist, and the series has no sum. Moreover, it is evident that (1) has no sum when $r = 1$, and it will become clear in the light of the next article that no sum exists when $r = -1$.

127. Convergent and Divergent Series. An infinite series is said to be **convergent** or **divergent** according as it has or has not a sum, that is, according as $\lim_{n \to \infty} S_n$ does or does not exist. If this limit exists, and equals S, the series is said to **converge to** (or **have**) **the value S**. A divergent series has no sum. The infinite geometric series of the foregoing article converges to the value $S = \dfrac{a}{1 - r}$ when $|r| < 1$, and diverges when $|r| \geqq 1$.

A series diverges if the limit of S_n fails to exist either because S_n becomes positively or negatively infinite, or increases or decreases alternately without approaching a definite limit, as n becomes infinite. In the latter case we have an **oscillatory** series. Thus

$$1 + 3 + 5 + 7 + \cdots$$

and

$$1 - 1 + 1 - 1 + \cdots$$

are divergent series, the latter being oscillatory.

For practical use a series must be convergent. A divergent series is of no elementary importance.* Therefore it becomes pertinent to establish conditions and tests for convergence. The method employed in Art. 126 to investigate the convergence of the geometric series is in general impractical, for the process requires the determination of S_n as a function of n, and no general method is available by which S_n may always be so expressed. The student will appreciate the truth of this statement by attempting to evaluate S_n for the series given in the problems of Art. 125. In the following articles tests for convergence will be established which depend not on S_n but on the general term u_n.

B. SERIES OF CONSTANT TERMS

128. The Maclaurin-Cauchy Integral Test. *If a function $f(x)$ can be found such that $f(n)$ is the general term u_n of an infinite series*

$$(1) \qquad u_1 + u_2 + u_3 + \cdots$$

of finite constant terms, and if for all values of x not less than some positive number a (i.e., for $x \geqq a > 0$) the function $f(x)$ is defined, is positive, and never increases as x increases continuously, then the series converges or diverges according as

$$(2) \qquad \int_a^\infty f(x)dx$$

does or does not exist.

We assume that the integral is finite and show that the series (1) then converges. To prove this, consider the curve $y = f(x)$ (Fig. 128a),

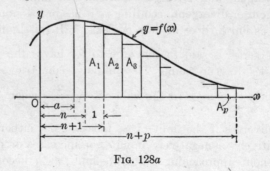

Fig. 128a

and imagine p rectangles of unit width to be inscribed as shown, between the x-axis and the curve, from $x = n$ to $x = n + p$, n being the least

* Except as a means established later by which other series under investigation may be recognized as divergent by comparison with it. However, a comparatively recent advanced theory of summability of divergent series attaches considerable inherent importance to a class of divergent series which in certain defined senses are summable.

integer greater than a. Then since the heights of the successive rectangles are

$$f(n+1) = u_{n+1}, \qquad f(n+2) = u_{n+2}, \cdots, \qquad f(n+p) = u_{n+p},$$

their areas are

$$A_1 = u_{n+1}, \qquad A_2 = u_{n+2}, \cdots, \qquad A_p = u_{n+p}.$$

The sum S_p of these areas does not exceed the area between the x-axis and the curve from $x = n$ to $x = n + p$; that is,

$$S_p = u_{n+1} + u_{n+2} + \cdots + u_{n+p} \leqq \int_n^{n+p} f(x)dx < \int_a^{n+p} f(x)dx.$$

If p is allowed to become infinite, the last integral becomes (2), which by hypothesis has a finite value, say A. Hence, for all values of p, $S_p < A$. Thus, as p increases, S_p is a variable quantity which never decreases and always remains less than the fixed number A. Therefore (Theorem 5, Art. 5) S_p approaches a limit $S' \leqq A$ as p becomes infinite. Hence the infinite series

$$u_{n+1} + u_{n+2} + \cdots + u_{n+p} + \cdots$$

has a finite sum S'. But this series is precisely the original series (1) except for the finite sum $u_1 + u_2 + \cdots + u_n$. Hence (1) converges, and has the sum $S = u_1 + u_2 + \cdots + u_n + S'$.

The proof is readily modified for the case of divergence.

It should be noted that the condition that $f(x)$ be positive for all values of $x \geqq a > 0$ requires that the terms of the series be positive for all values of $n > a$. *Thus the test is essentially one for series of positive terms*, since any negative terms which occur for $n \leqq a$ have a finite sum which cannot affect the convergence or divergence of the series. However, if beyond a certain point the terms of a series are all negative, and yet when the minus signs are ignored the conditions of the test are fulfilled, it is clear that the test is applicable.

Example 1. Test for convergence the k series

$$1 + \frac{1}{2^k} + \frac{1}{3^k} + \frac{1}{4^k} + \cdots + \frac{1}{n^k} + \cdots, \qquad k > 0.$$

Here $u_n = f(n) = \dfrac{1}{n^k}$. Hence $f(x) = \dfrac{1}{x^k}$. This is a positive decreasing function for all positive values of x. Thus, for $x \geqq 1$, $f(x)$ satisfies the conditions of the test. Accordingly we take $a = 1$. Then

$$\int_1^\infty \frac{dx}{x^k} = \lim_{p \to \infty} \int_1^p \frac{dx}{x^k} = \lim_{p \to \infty} \left[\frac{x^{1-k}}{1-k} \right]_1^p = \frac{1}{1-k} \lim_{p \to \infty} (p^{1-k} - 1),$$

provided $k \neq 1$.

If $k > 1$, $1 - k$ is negative, and p^{1-k} approaches zero as p becomes infinite, so that the integral has the finite value $\dfrac{1}{k-1}$, and the series converges.

If $k < 1$, $1 - k$ is positive, so that p^{1-k} becomes infinite with p, and the series diverges.

If $k = 1$, the k-series reduces to the **harmonic series**.

$$1 + \frac{1}{2} + \frac{1}{3} + \frac{1}{4} + \cdots + \frac{1}{n} + \cdots,$$

and the evaluation of the foregoing integral must be modified as follows:

$$\int_1^\infty \frac{dx}{x} = \lim_{p \to \infty} \int_1^p \frac{dx}{x} = \lim_{p \to \infty} (\ln p).$$

Since $\ln p$ becomes infinite with p, the harmonic series diverges.

These important results are summarized for future reference.

The k-series

$$1 + \frac{1}{2^k} + \frac{1}{3^k} + \frac{1}{4^k} + \cdots + \frac{1}{n^k} + \cdots$$

converges when $k > 1$, and diverges when $k \leq 1$.

Example 2. Test for convergence the series

$$\tan \frac{7\pi}{3} + \frac{1}{4} \tan \frac{7\pi}{6} + \frac{1}{9} \tan \frac{7\pi}{9} + \cdots + \frac{1}{n^2} \tan \frac{7\pi}{3n} + \cdots.$$

As x increases continuously, the function

$$f(x) = \frac{1}{x^2} \tan \frac{7\pi}{3x}, \qquad x > 0,$$

becomes and remains a positive decreasing function for all values of x which reduce $\dfrac{7\pi}{3x}$ to an acute angle; i.e., for values of x such that

$$\frac{7\pi}{3x} < \frac{\pi}{2}, \qquad \text{whence} \qquad x > \frac{14}{3}.$$

Hence, for $x \geq 5$, $f(x)$ satisfies the conditions of the test. Accordingly we take $a = 5$ and proceed to evaluate

$$\int_5^\infty \frac{1}{x^2} \tan \frac{7\pi}{3x}\, dx = -\frac{3}{7\pi} \lim_{p \to \infty} \int_5^p \tan \frac{7\pi}{3x} \left(-\frac{7\pi}{3x^2}\, dx \right)$$

$$= -\frac{3}{7\pi} \lim_{p \to \infty} \left[\ln \sec \frac{7\pi}{3x} \right]_5^p$$

$$= \frac{3}{7\pi} \ln \sec \frac{7\pi}{15}.$$

Since the result is finite the given series converges.

It is noteworthy that the test is not invalidated, nor is convergence affected, by the fact that the third and fourth terms of the series are negative. Furthermore it is of no consequence that $f(x)$ changes sign infinitely many times as x increases from zero to $\frac{14}{3}$, and even fails to exist when x has any one of the infinite sequence of values,

$$\frac{14}{3}, \ \frac{14}{9}, \ \frac{14}{15}, \ \frac{14}{21}, \ \frac{14}{27}, \ \cdots.$$

A requirement of the test is that $f(x)$ *must ultimately become and remain a positive non-increasing function as x increases continuously*; and this condition is satisfied for all values of x greater than $\frac{14}{3}$.

The graph of the equation $y = \dfrac{1}{x^2} \tan \dfrac{7\pi}{3x}$ is shown in Fig. 128b.   Clearly the

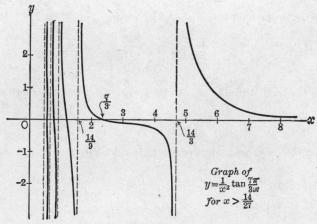

Graph of
$$y = \frac{1}{x^2} \tan \frac{7\pi}{3x}$$
for $x > \frac{14}{27}$

FIG. 128b

ordinates of this curve, corresponding to positive integral values of x, represent the terms of the given series.

129. A Necessary Condition for Convergence.   Consider a series $u_1 + u_2 + u_3 + \cdots + u_n + \cdots$ of constant terms (with mixed or like signs) which converges to the value S.   Then

$$\lim_{n \to \infty} S_n = S, \qquad \lim_{n \to \infty} S_{n+1} = S.$$

Hence (Theorem 1, Art. 5),

$$\lim_{n \to \infty} (S_{n+1} - S_n) = 0.$$

But $S_{n+1} - S_n = u_{n+1}$; hence $\lim\limits_{n \to \infty} u_{n+1} = 0$.   Therefore

A necessary condition for the convergence of an infinite series is that its general term approach zero as n becomes infinite.

This condition, though necessary, is not sufficient to guarantee the convergence of a series, for, by the foregoing article, the harmonic series diverges although its nth term $\dfrac{1}{n}$ approaches zero as n becomes infinite.

Example. The series

$$\tfrac{1}{3} + \tfrac{2}{5} + \tfrac{3}{7} + \tfrac{4}{9} + \cdots$$

diverges since the limit of the nth term $\dfrac{n}{2n+1}$, as n becomes infinite, is $\tfrac{1}{2}$. This may be shown by the method of Art. 122 for evaluating indeterminate forms of the type $\dfrac{\infty}{\infty}$, even though n assumes only positive integral values instead of varying continuously. Or the limit may be found by writing

$$\frac{n}{2n+1} = \frac{1}{2 + \dfrac{1}{n}},$$

from which the limit is readily seen to be $\tfrac{1}{2}$ as n becomes infinite (cf. Example 2, Art. 122).

PROBLEMS

Establish the convergence or divergence of each of the following series:

1. $\tfrac{1}{2} + \tfrac{1}{5} + \tfrac{1}{10} + \tfrac{1}{17} + \cdots + \dfrac{1}{n^2+1} + \cdots$.

2. $1 + \tfrac{1}{4} + \tfrac{1}{9} + \tfrac{1}{16} + \cdots$.

3. $\dfrac{1}{\sqrt{5}} + \dfrac{1}{\sqrt{6}} + \dfrac{1}{\sqrt{7}} + \dfrac{1}{\sqrt{8}} + \cdots$.

4. $1 - \tfrac{2}{3} + \tfrac{3}{5} - \tfrac{4}{7} + \cdots + (-1)^{n+1}\dfrac{n}{2n-1} + \cdots$.

5. $1 + \dfrac{1}{3^2} + \dfrac{1}{5^2} + \dfrac{1}{7^2} + \cdots$.

6. $1 + \dfrac{1}{e} + \dfrac{1}{e^2} + \dfrac{1}{e^3} + \cdots$.

7. $\dfrac{1}{e} + \dfrac{2}{e^4} + \dfrac{3}{e^9} + \dfrac{4}{e^{16}} + \cdots$.

8. $1 + \dfrac{1}{2^2-1} + \dfrac{2}{3^2-1} + \dfrac{3}{4^2-1} + \cdots$.

9. $\tfrac{1}{2} + \tfrac{2}{5} + \tfrac{3}{10} + \tfrac{4}{17} + \cdots$.

10. $1 + \tfrac{1}{6} + \tfrac{1}{9} + \tfrac{1}{12} + \tfrac{1}{15} + \cdots$.

11. $\dfrac{1}{\sqrt{2}} + \dfrac{2}{\sqrt{5}} + \dfrac{3}{\sqrt{10}} + \dfrac{4}{\sqrt{17}} + \cdots$.

12. $\dfrac{1}{\sqrt{2}} - \dfrac{2}{\sqrt{5}} + \dfrac{3}{\sqrt{10}} - \dfrac{4}{\sqrt{17}} + \cdots$.

13. $1 - \dfrac{1}{\sqrt{2^2-1}} + \dfrac{2}{\sqrt{3^2-1}} - \dfrac{3}{\sqrt{4^2-1}} + \cdots$.

14. $\dfrac{5}{1\cdot2} + \dfrac{5}{3\cdot4} + \dfrac{5}{5\cdot6} + \dfrac{5}{7\cdot8} + \cdots$.

15. $\frac{1}{3} + \frac{1}{15} + \frac{1}{35} + \frac{1}{63} + \cdots$.

16. $\dfrac{1}{2} + \dfrac{4}{2^3+1} + \dfrac{9}{3^3+1} + \dfrac{16}{4^3+1} + \cdots$.

17. $1 + \dfrac{4}{2^4+1} + \dfrac{6}{3^4+1} + \dfrac{8}{4^4+1} + \cdots$.

18. $\frac{1}{101} - \frac{2}{201} + \frac{3}{301} - \frac{4}{401} + \cdots$.

19. $\frac{1}{101} + \frac{1}{201} + \frac{1}{301} + \frac{1}{401} + \cdots$.

20. $100 + \frac{4}{7} + \frac{9}{26} + \frac{16}{63} + \cdots$.

21. $\dfrac{1}{e} + \dfrac{2}{e^2} + \dfrac{3}{e^3} + \dfrac{4}{e^4} + \cdots$.

22. $\dfrac{1}{3} + \dfrac{2\cdot2^2-1}{2\cdot2^2+1} + \dfrac{2\cdot3^2-1}{2\cdot3^2+1} + \dfrac{2\cdot4^2-1}{2\cdot4^2+1} + \cdots$.

23. $\dfrac{1}{5} - \dfrac{3\sqrt{2}-2}{3\sqrt{2}+2} + \dfrac{3\sqrt{3}-2}{3\sqrt{3}+2} - \dfrac{3\sqrt{4}-2}{3\sqrt{4}+2} + \cdots$.

24. $\dfrac{3}{2} + \dfrac{1+2\cdot2}{2\cdot3} + \dfrac{1+2\cdot3}{3\cdot4} + \dfrac{1+2\cdot4}{4\cdot5} + \cdots$.

25. $0.05 + \dfrac{0.02}{0.3} + \dfrac{0.03}{0.4} + \dfrac{0.04}{0.5} + \cdots$.

26. $1 + \dfrac{1}{3^{\frac{4}{3}}} + \dfrac{1}{4^{\frac{4}{3}}} + \dfrac{1}{5^{\frac{4}{3}}} + \cdots$.

27. $\dfrac{\ln 2}{2} + \dfrac{\ln 3}{3} + \dfrac{\ln 4}{4} + \cdots$.

28. $\sin \pi + \dfrac{1}{4}\sin\dfrac{\pi}{2} + \dfrac{1}{9}\sin\dfrac{\pi}{3} + \dfrac{1}{16}\sin\dfrac{\pi}{4} + \cdots$.

29. $\cos \pi + \dfrac{1}{4}\cos\dfrac{\pi}{2} + \dfrac{1}{9}\cos\dfrac{\pi}{3} + \dfrac{1}{16}\cos\dfrac{\pi}{4} + \cdots$.

30. $\tan 2\pi + \dfrac{1}{3^2}\tan\dfrac{2\pi}{3} + \dfrac{1}{5^2}\tan\dfrac{2\pi}{5} + \dfrac{1}{7^2}\tan\dfrac{2\pi}{7} + \cdots$.

130. The Comparison Test. (a) *A series of constant positive terms is convergent if each of its terms is either equal to or less than the corresponding term of a series known to be convergent.*

(b) *A series of constant positive terms is divergent if each of its terms is either equal to or greater than the corresponding term of a series known to be divergent.*

To prove (a), consider the two series

(1) $$u_1 + u_2 + u_3 + \cdots + u_n + \cdots,$$

(2) $$a_1 + a_2 + a_3 + \cdots + a_n + \cdots$$

of constant positive terms. Suppose that (2) is convergent and that

$u_n \leqq a_n$ for $n = 1, 2, 3, \cdots$. Let S_n and S'_n be the sums of the first n terms of (1) and (2), respectively. Then since (2) is composed of positive terms, S'_n approaches a limit $S' > S'_n$ as n becomes infinite. Hence

$$S_n \leqq S'_n < S'.$$

Thus, as n increases, S_n is a variable quantity which never decreases (since no terms of (1) are negative) and is always less than the number S'. Therefore (Theorem 5, Art. 5) S_n approaches a limit $S \leq S'$ as n becomes infinite. Hence the series (1) converges, and has a sum no greater than that of (2).

The proof of (b) depends on a similar argument.

This test makes it possible to establish the convergence of a given series, provided a convergent series can be found whose terms are no less than the corresponding terms of the given series, or to establish its divergence, provided a divergent series can be found whose terms are no greater than the corresponding terms of the given series. Nothing is gained by showing that the terms of a series under investigation are greater than those of some convergent series, or less than those of some divergent series.

If a given series and some series used for comparison are modified by dropping or adding a finite number of terms, and the resulting pair of series admit of the comparison test, the conclusion drawn from this test, regarding the convergence or divergence of the modified given series, obtains also for the series in its original form, for the convergence or divergence of the latter is not affected by dropping or adding a finite number of terms. A similar remark holds if only one of the two series is so modified.

The geometric series, and the k-series discussed in Example 1, Art. 128, are useful for comparison.

Example 1. All the terms (except the first) of the series

$$100 + \frac{100}{3^2} + \frac{100}{5^2} + \frac{100}{7^2} + \cdots$$

are obviously less than the corresponding terms of the series

$$100 \left(1 + \frac{1}{2^2} + \frac{1}{3^2} + \frac{1}{4^2} + \cdots \right),$$

which, by the result of Example 1, Art. 128, is convergent. Hence the first series converges.

Example 2. The series

$$\frac{1}{\sqrt[5]{5} \cdot 3} + \frac{1}{\sqrt[6]{6} \cdot 3} + \frac{1}{\sqrt[7]{7} \cdot 3} + \cdots$$

diverges; for its terms are obviously greater than the corresponding terms of the series

$$\tfrac{1}{3}\left(\tfrac{1}{5} + \tfrac{1}{6} + \tfrac{1}{7} + \cdots\right),$$

which, by Example 1, Art. 128, is known to diverge.

Example 3. By comparison with the convergent series

$$\tan\frac{7\pi}{3} + \frac{1}{4}\tan\frac{7\pi}{6} + \frac{1}{9}\tan\frac{7\pi}{9} + \cdots + \frac{1}{n^2}\tan\frac{7\pi}{3n} + \cdots$$

of Example 2, Art. 128, the series

$$\sin\frac{7\pi}{3} + \frac{1}{8}\sin\frac{7\pi}{6} + \frac{1}{27}\sin\frac{7\pi}{9} + \cdots + \frac{1}{n^3}\sin\frac{7\pi}{3n} + \cdots$$

may be shown to converge; for the condition

$$\frac{1}{n^3}\sin\frac{7\pi}{3n} < \frac{1}{n^2}\tan\frac{7\pi}{3n}, \qquad \text{or} \qquad \sin\frac{7\pi}{3n} < n\tan\frac{7\pi}{3n},$$

is satisfied for $n = 5, 6, 7, \cdots$. The test is not invalidated by the fact that the conditions for comparison hold only from the fifth term on, for the first four terms of the sine series have a finite sum.

PROBLEMS

By comparison with either the harmonic, geometric, or k-series investigate the convergence of the following series.

1. The series of Problem 1, Art. 129.
2. The series of Problem 5, Art. 129.
3. The series of Problem 6, Art. 129.
4. The series of Problem 8, Art. 129.

5. $1 + \dfrac{4}{3^2 - 1} + \dfrac{5}{4^2 - 1} + \dfrac{6}{5^2 - 1} + \cdots.$

6. The series of Problem 10, Art. 129.
7. The series of Problem 27, Art. 129.

8. $\dfrac{1}{1 + 3^2} + \dfrac{1}{1 + 4^2} + \dfrac{1}{1 + 5^2} + \dfrac{1}{1 + 6^2} + \cdots.$

9. $\dfrac{1}{1000} + \dfrac{1}{2000} + \dfrac{1}{3000} + \dfrac{1}{4000} + \cdots.$

10. $\dfrac{1}{\ln 2} + \dfrac{1}{\ln 3} + \dfrac{1}{\ln 4} + \dfrac{1}{\ln 5} + \cdots.$

11. $1 + \dfrac{\sqrt{1}}{2} + \dfrac{\sqrt{2}}{3} + \dfrac{\sqrt{3}}{4} + \cdots.$

12. $\dfrac{3}{1 \cdot 2} + \dfrac{3}{2 \cdot 3} + \dfrac{3}{3 \cdot 4} + \dfrac{3}{4 \cdot 5} + \cdots.$

13. $1 + \tfrac{1}{4} + \tfrac{1}{7} + \tfrac{1}{10} + \cdots.$

HINT: Convert the terms to the form $\dfrac{1}{3(n - \frac{2}{3})}$.

14. $\dfrac{1}{1\cdot 2^2} + \dfrac{1}{2\cdot 3^2} + \dfrac{1}{3\cdot 4^2} + \dfrac{1}{4\cdot 5^2} + \cdots.$

15. $\dfrac{1}{2\cdot 3} + \dfrac{1}{4\cdot 5} + \dfrac{1}{6\cdot 7} + \dfrac{1}{8\cdot 9} + \cdots.$

16. $\dfrac{1}{1\cdot 2\cdot 3} + \dfrac{1}{2\cdot 3\cdot 4} + \dfrac{1}{3\cdot 4\cdot 5} + \cdots.$

17. $\dfrac{1}{1\cdot 2\cdot 3} + \dfrac{1}{4\cdot 5\cdot 6} + \dfrac{1}{7\cdot 8\cdot 9} + \cdots.$

18. $\dfrac{1}{\sqrt{1}\cdot\sqrt{2}\cdot\sqrt{3}} + \dfrac{1}{\sqrt{4}\cdot\sqrt{5}\cdot\sqrt{6}} + \dfrac{1}{\sqrt{7}\cdot\sqrt{8}\cdot\sqrt{9}} + \cdots.$

19. $\dfrac{1}{2\cdot 4\cdot 5\cdot 7} + \dfrac{1}{4\cdot 6\cdot 7\cdot 9} + \dfrac{1}{6\cdot 8\cdot 9\cdot 11} + \cdots.$

20. $\dfrac{1}{\sqrt[3]{2}\cdot\sqrt[3]{4}\cdot\sqrt[3]{5}\cdot\sqrt[3]{7}} + \dfrac{1}{\sqrt[3]{4}\cdot\sqrt[3]{6}\cdot\sqrt[3]{7}\cdot\sqrt[3]{9}} + \dfrac{1}{\sqrt[3]{6}\cdot\sqrt[3]{8}\cdot\sqrt[3]{9}\cdot\sqrt[3]{11}} + \cdots.$

21. $\dfrac{1}{3} + \dfrac{1}{4^2} + \dfrac{1}{5^3} + \dfrac{1}{6^4} + \cdots.$

22. $1 + \dfrac{1}{3^2} + \dfrac{1}{5^3} + \dfrac{1}{7^4} + \cdots.$

23. $1 + \dfrac{1}{5^4} + \dfrac{1}{9^6} + \dfrac{1}{13^8} + \dfrac{1}{17^{10}} + \cdots.$

131. The Ratio Test. *The infinite series*

(1) $$u_1 + u_2 + u_3 + \cdots + u_n + \cdots$$

of finite positive* terms converges if

$$\lim_{n \to \infty} \frac{u_{n+1}}{u_n} < 1,$$

and diverges either if

$$\lim_{n \to \infty} \frac{u_{n+1}}{u_n} > 1,$$

or if $\dfrac{u_{n+1}}{u_n}$ *becomes infinite with n. The test fails if the limit equals 1.*

For convenience in the proof let $\lim\limits_{n \to \infty} \dfrac{u_{n+1}}{u_n} = L$, if the limit exists. Three cases must be considered.

Case 1. $L < 1$. Let r be a number between L and 1: $L < r < 1$. From the definition of a limit it follows that, as n increases, the difference between $\dfrac{u_{n+1}}{u_n}$ and L becomes and remains smaller in absolute value than

---

*A generalization of this test will be given in Art. 135 for series of positive and negative terms.

any preassigned positive constant, however small. Hence a number k can be found such that

$$\frac{u_{n+1}}{u_n} < r, \text{ or } u_{n+1} < ru_n,$$

for all values of $n \geqq k$. Hence

$$u_{k+1} < ru_k,$$

$$u_{k+2} < ru_{k+1} < r^2 u_k,$$

$$u_{k+3} < ru_{k+2} < r^3 u_k,$$

$$\begin{matrix} \cdot & \cdot & \cdot \\ \cdot & \cdot & \cdot \\ \cdot & \cdot & \cdot \end{matrix}$$

Thus the terms of the series

(2) $$u_{k+1} + u_{k+2} + u_{k+3} + \cdots$$

are less than the corresponding terms of the series

$$ru_k + r^2 u_k + r^3 u_k + \cdots .$$

But the latter is a geometric series of ratio $r < 1$, which by Art. 126 has the finite sum $\dfrac{ru_k}{1-r}$. Hence by the comparison test (2) converges. But (1) differs from (2) by the finite sum $u_1 + u_2 + \cdots + u_k$; therefore (1) converges.

　　Case 2. Either $L > 1$ or $\dfrac{u_{n+1}}{u_n}$ becomes infinite with n. In either of these situations a number k can be found such that

$$\frac{u_{n+1}}{u_n} > 1, \text{ or } u_{n+1} > u_n,$$

for all values of $n \geqq k$. Thus every term following u_k is larger than its predecessor. Hence the general term fails to approach zero as n becomes infinite and (by Art. 129) the series diverges.

　　Case 3. $L = 1$. To show that the test fails when $L = 1$, it is sufficient to exhibit a single series which converges and another which diverges, for each of which $L = \lim\limits_{n \to \infty} \dfrac{u_{n+1}}{u_n} = 1$.

　　For the divergent harmonic series

$$1 + \frac{1}{2} + \frac{1}{3} + \frac{1}{4} + \cdots + \frac{1}{n} + \cdots$$

(Art. 128) the value of L is

$$\lim_{n \to \infty} \frac{\dfrac{1}{n+1}}{\dfrac{1}{n}} = \lim_{n \to \infty} \frac{n}{n+1} = \lim_{n \to \infty} \frac{1}{1+\dfrac{1}{n}} = 1.$$

Likewise the value of L for the convergent k-series

$$1 + \frac{1}{2^2} + \frac{1}{3^2} + \cdots + \frac{1}{n^2} + \cdots$$

is

$$\lim_{n \to \infty} \frac{\dfrac{1}{(n+1)^2}}{\dfrac{1}{n^2}} = \lim_{n \to \infty} \left(\frac{n}{n+1}\right)^2 = 1.$$

Caution. The test for convergence requires that the limit of $\frac{u_{n+1}}{u_n}$ shall be less than 1. It is not sufficient that $\frac{u_{n+1}}{u_n}$ shall be less than 1 for all positive integral values of n, or for all values no less than a certain number m, for in the case of the harmonic series the ratio

$$\frac{u_{n+1}}{u_n} = \frac{n}{n+1}$$

is less than 1 for all positive integral values of n, yet the series diverges. However, the limit of this ratio as n becomes infinite is actually 1, and the test fails.*

Example. The $(n+1)$th term of the series

$$1 + \frac{2^2}{2!} + \frac{3^3}{3!} + \cdots + \frac{n^n}{n!} + \cdots$$

is $\frac{(n+1)^{n+1}}{(n+1)!}$. Therefore

$$\frac{u_{n+1}}{u_n} = \frac{(n+1)^{n+1}}{(n+1)!} \cdot \frac{n!}{n^n} = \left(\frac{n+1}{n}\right)^n$$

whence

$$\lim_{n \to \infty} \frac{u_{n+1}}{u_n} = \lim_{n \to \infty} \left(1 + \frac{1}{n}\right)^n = e = 2.718 \cdots \text{ (Art. 52).}$$

Since this limit exceeds 1 the series diverges.

* It can be shown that a series converges provided $\frac{u_{n+1}}{u_n}$ ultimately becomes and remains no greater than a certain number r which is itself less than 1, and diverges if the ratio ultimately becomes and remains greater than or equal to 1.

PROBLEMS

Investigate the convergence of each of the following series by the ratio test. If this fails use another test.

1. $1 + \frac{1}{3} + \frac{1}{9} + \frac{1}{27} + \cdots$.

2. $\frac{1}{2^2} + \frac{2}{2^3} + \frac{3}{2^4} + \frac{4}{2^5} + \cdots$.

3. $1 + \frac{1!}{4} + \frac{3!}{4^3} + \frac{5!}{4^5} + \cdots$.

4. $\frac{3}{2} + \frac{4}{3} \cdot \frac{1}{3} + \frac{5}{4} \cdot \frac{1}{3^2} + \frac{6}{5} \cdot \frac{1}{3^3} + \cdots$.

5. $1 + \frac{100}{1!} + \frac{10,000}{2!} + \frac{1,000,000}{3!} + \cdots$.

6. $\frac{1}{3} + \frac{1 \cdot 2}{3 \cdot 5} + \frac{1 \cdot 2 \cdot 3}{3 \cdot 5 \cdot 7} + \frac{1 \cdot 2 \cdot 3 \cdot 4}{3 \cdot 5 \cdot 7 \cdot 9} + \cdots$.

7. $\frac{5}{2!} + \frac{5}{4!} + \frac{5}{6!} + \frac{5}{8!} + \cdots$.

8. $\frac{2}{1^{1.2}} + \frac{2}{2^{1.2}} + \frac{2}{3^{1.2}} + \frac{2}{4^{1.2}} + \cdots$.

9. $\frac{1}{2 + 1^2} + \frac{1}{2 + 2^2} + \frac{1}{2 + 3^2} + \frac{1}{2 + 4^2} + \cdots$.

10. $\frac{1 \cdot 3}{2!} + \frac{2 \cdot 4}{3!} + \frac{3 \cdot 5}{4!} + \frac{4 \cdot 6}{5!} + \cdots$.

11. $1 + \frac{2}{5} + \frac{3}{5^2} + \frac{4}{5^3} + \cdots$.

12. $\frac{2}{1 \cdot 2} + \frac{2^2}{2 \cdot 3} + \frac{2^3}{3 \cdot 4} + \frac{2^4}{4 \cdot 5} + \cdots$.

13. $\frac{1}{3.3} + \frac{1}{4.4} + \frac{1}{5.5} + \frac{1}{6.6} + \cdots$.

14. $1 + \frac{1}{5} \cdot \frac{3}{2^2} + \frac{1}{5^2} \cdot \frac{3^2}{3^2} + \cdots + \frac{1}{5^{n-1}} \cdot \frac{3^{n-1}}{n^2} + \cdots$.

15. $\frac{1!}{1^2 \cdot 2^2} + \frac{2!}{2^2 \cdot 3^2} + \frac{3!}{3^2 \cdot 4^2} + \frac{4!}{4^2 \cdot 5^2} + \cdots$.

16. $\frac{1}{3} + \frac{1 \cdot 3}{3 \cdot 6} + \frac{1 \cdot 3 \cdot 5}{3 \cdot 6 \cdot 9} + \frac{1 \cdot 3 \cdot 5 \cdot 7}{3 \cdot 6 \cdot 9 \cdot 12} + \cdots$.

17. $1 + \frac{5}{1!} + \frac{5^2}{2!} + \frac{5^3}{3!} + \cdots$.

18. $2^2 + \frac{4^2}{5} + \frac{6^2}{5^2} + \frac{8^2}{5^3} + \cdots$.

19. $\frac{1}{\ln 10} + \frac{1}{\ln 11} + \frac{1}{\ln 12} + \frac{1}{\ln 13} + \cdots$.

20. $\frac{2 + \sqrt{1}}{1!} + \frac{2 + \sqrt{2}}{2!} + \frac{2 + \sqrt{3}}{3!} + \frac{2 + \sqrt{4}}{4!} + \cdots$.

132. Alternating Series. A series whose terms are alternately positive and negative is called an **alternating series.** For such a series we have the following simple convergence test.

THEOREM 1. *An alternating series*

(1) $$u_1 - u_2 + u_3 - u_4 + \cdots$$

in which the u's are all positive,* converges if

    (a) the terms beyond a certain (kth) term never increase in numerical value, i.e., $u_n \geqq u_{n+1}$ for $n = k,\ k + 1,\ k + 2, \cdots$, and if

    (b) the general term approaches zero: $\lim\limits_{n \to \infty} u_n = 0$.

To prove this assume that (a) holds throughout (1); that is, let $k = 1$. Clearly this effects no loss of generality, for, if $k > 1$, we may neglect as many terms as may be necessary to obtain an alternating series which begins with a positive term and for which (a) holds.

Write the sum of an *even* number ($2n$) of terms in the two forms

(2) $$S_{2n} = (u_1 - u_2) + (u_3 - u_4) + \cdots + (u_{2n-1} - u_{2n}),$$

(3) $$S_{2n} = u_1 - (u_2 - u_3) - (u_4 - u_5) - \cdots$$
$$- (u_{2n-2} - u_{2n-1}) - u_{2n}.$$

Since no term of (2) is negative (by hypothesis (a)), S_{2n} is a positive increasing function of n, which by (3) always remains less than u_1. Hence as n becomes infinite S_{2n} approaches a limit S (Theorem 5, Art. 5); that is,

(4) $$\lim_{n \to \infty} S_{2n} = S.$$

Moreover,† the sum S_{2n+1} of an *odd* number of terms may be written in the form

$$S_{2n+1} = S_{2n} + u_{2n+1},$$

so that, by (4),

(5) $$\lim_{n \to \infty} S_{2n+1} = \lim_{n \to \infty} S_{2n} + \lim_{n \to \infty} u_{2n+1} = S,$$

since $\lim\limits_{n \to \infty} u_{2n+1} = 0$ by hypothesis (b). Thus (4) and (5) show that

---

* Clearly there is no essential restriction in writing the first term with a positive sign.

† For convergence it is not enough that the sum S_{2n} of an even number of terms of a series shall approach a limit as n becomes infinite. If it were, the divergent oscillatory series $1 - 1 + 1 - 1 + \cdots$ could be shown to converge, for S_{2n} is zero for all positive integral values of n and hence has the limit zero as n becomes infinite.

the sum S_m of *any number* (m) *of terms, either even or odd,* approaches a definite limit S as m becomes infinite.   Hence (1) converges.

Generally it is impossible to find the exact sum of a convergent infinite series.   However, it may be satisfactorily approximated by summing a sufficiently large number of terms.   It is desirable to know to what degree of accuracy this sum represents the true sum of the series. In the case of an alternating series this question is answered by

THEOREM 2.   *The error committed in approximating the sum of a convergent alternating series* * *by summing the first n terms is numerically less than the* $(n + 1)$*th term.*

To prove this we note that, if n is even,

$$S - S_n = u_{n+1} - (u_{n+2} - u_{n+3}) - (u_{n+4} - u_{n+5}) - \cdots < u_{n+1},$$

while if n is odd,

$$S_n - S = u_{n+1} - (u_{n+2} - u_{n+3}) - (u_{n+4} - u_{n+5}) - \cdots < u_{n+1},$$

and in either case $|S - S_n| < u_{n+1}$.

Example.   Since the terms of the series

$$1 - \frac{1}{3!} + \frac{1}{5!} - \frac{1}{7!} + \cdots$$

do not increase in numerical value, and since

$$\lim_{n \to \infty} u_n = \lim_{n \to \infty} \frac{1}{(2n - 1)!} = 0,$$

the series converges.   The first four terms have to five decimals the sum 0.84147, which is smaller than the sum of the series by an amount less than the fifth term $\frac{1}{9!} = 0.000003$.

A more detailed discussion of computations involving series is given in the text and examples of Art. 145.

133. Series of Positive and Negative Terms; Absolute Convergence.
We shall now consider a more general type of series in which both positive and negative constant terms occur in any order and in unlimited number.

THEOREM.   *A series converges, and is said to* **converge absolutely,** *if the absolute values of its terms form a convergent series.*

To prove this let

(1) $$u_1 + u_2 + u_3 + \cdots + u_n + \cdots$$

---
* Fulfilling the conditions of the preceding theorem.

be a series of the type described above, in which some of the u's are positive and some negative. Construct the positive-term series

$$v_1 + v_2 + v_3 + \cdots + v_p + \cdots$$

and

$$w_1 + w_2 + w_3 + \cdots + w_q + \cdots$$

from the numerical values of the positive and negative terms of (1) in the order in which they occur. Thus v_p is the pth positive term and w_q the numerical value of the qth negative term of (1). Now suppose that the first n terms of (1) contain p positive and q negative terms, so that $n = p + q$, and write

$$(2) \qquad S'_p = v_1 + v_2 + \cdots + v_p, \qquad S''_q = w_1 + w_2 + \cdots + w_q;$$

then

$$(3) \qquad S_n = S'_p - S''_q.$$

Finally designate the sum of the absolute values of n terms of (1) by

$$T_n = |u_1| + |u_2| + \cdots + |u_n|;$$

then since $n = p + q$,

$$(4) \qquad T_n = S'_p + S''_q.$$

Now by hypothesis the series composed of the absolute values of the terms of (1) is convergent; hence we may write

$$\lim_{n \to \infty} T_n = T.$$

With (4) this shows that

$$(5) \qquad S'_p < T_n < T, \qquad S''_q < T_n < T.$$

Thus as p and q increase S'_p and S''_q are variable quantities which by (2) never decrease and by (5) always remain less than T. Hence (Theorem 5, Art. 5) S'_p and S''_q approach limits, say S' and S'', as p and q become infinite:

$$(6) \qquad \lim_{p \to \infty} S'_p = S', \qquad \lim_{q \to \infty} S''_q = S''.$$

Since p and q both become infinite with n, (3) and (6) show that S_n approaches a limit as n becomes infinite, and that

$$\lim_{n \to \infty} S_n = \lim_{p \to \infty} S'_p - \lim_{q \to \infty} S''_q = S' - S''.$$

Hence (1) converges.

Example.   If $k > 1$ the series

(7)
$$1 + \frac{1}{2^k} - \frac{1}{3^k} + \frac{1}{4^k} + \frac{1}{5^k} - \frac{1}{6^k} + \cdots,$$

in which every third term is negative, converges absolutely; for the k-series

$$1 + \frac{1}{2^k} + \frac{1}{3^k} + \frac{1}{4^k} + \frac{1}{5^k} + \frac{1}{6^k} + \cdots,$$

formed of the absolute values of the terms of (7), converges if $k > 1$ (Example 1, Art. 128).

134. Conditional Convergence.   A convergent series of positive and negative constant terms is said to be **conditionally convergent** if it becomes divergent when all its terms are made positive.

Example.   It follows from Theorem 1, Art. 132, that the alternating series

$$1 - \tfrac{1}{2} + \tfrac{1}{3} - \tfrac{1}{4} + \cdots$$

is convergent. However, it is conditionally convergent; for it becomes the divergent harmonic series when all its terms are made positive.

135. Ratio Test for Series of Positive and Negative Terms.   *The infinite series*

(1)
$$u_1 + u_2 + u_3 + \cdots + u_n + \cdots$$

of finite terms, with mixed or like signs, converges if

$$\lim_{n \to \infty} \left| \frac{u_{n+1}}{u_n} \right| < 1,$$

and diverges either if

$$\lim_{n \to \infty} \left| \frac{u_{n+1}}{u_n} \right| > 1,$$

or if $\left| \dfrac{u_{n+1}}{u_n} \right|$ *becomes infinite with n.   The test fails if the limit equals* 1.

The proof pertaining to convergence consists in applying the ratio test of Art. 131 to the positive-term series

$$|u_1| + |u_2| + |u_3| + \cdots,$$

and making use of the theorem of Art. 133.

The proof for divergence consists in replacing $\dfrac{u_{n+1}}{u_n}$ by $\dfrac{|u_{n+1}|}{|u_n|}$ in Case 2, Art. 131.

We readily see that the test fails when $\lim\limits_{n \to \infty} \left| \dfrac{u_{n+1}}{u_n} \right| = 1$,   for this condition is fulfilled by the convergent series

$$1 - \tfrac{1}{2} + \tfrac{1}{3} - \tfrac{1}{4} + \cdots$$

in the example of Art. 134, as well by the obviously divergent series

$$1 - 2 + 3 - 4 + \cdots.$$

Example. The $(n + 1)$th term of the series

$$1 - \frac{1}{1!} + \frac{1}{2!} - \frac{1}{3!} + \cdots + (-1)^{n-1} \frac{1}{(n-1)!} + \cdots$$

is $(-1)^n \dfrac{1}{n!}$.   Therefore

$$\lim_{n \to \infty} \left| \frac{u_{n+1}}{u_n} \right| = \lim_{n \to \infty} \frac{(n-1)!}{n!} = \lim_{n \to \infty} \frac{1}{n} = 0.$$

Hence the series is convergent.

PROBLEMS

By the alternating-series test show that the series in Problems 1 to 10 inclusive are convergent.

1. $1 - \frac{1}{3} + \frac{1}{9} - \frac{1}{27} + \cdots.$

2. $\dfrac{1}{2^2} - \dfrac{2}{2^3} + \dfrac{3}{2^4} - \dfrac{4}{2^5} + \cdots.$

3. $\dfrac{3}{2} - \dfrac{4}{3} \cdot \dfrac{1}{3} + \dfrac{5}{4} \cdot \dfrac{1}{3^2} - \dfrac{6}{5} \cdot \dfrac{1}{3^3} + \cdots.$

4. $\dfrac{1}{3} - \dfrac{1 \cdot 2}{3 \cdot 5} + \dfrac{1 \cdot 2 \cdot 3}{3 \cdot 5 \cdot 7} - \dfrac{1 \cdot 2 \cdot 3 \cdot 4}{3 \cdot 5 \cdot 7 \cdot 9} + \cdots.$

5. $\dfrac{3}{1^{1.3}} - \dfrac{3}{2^{1.3}} + \dfrac{3}{3^{1.3}} - \dfrac{3}{4^{1.3}} + \cdots.$

6. $e^{-1} - 2e^{-2} + 3e^{-3} - 4e^{-4} + \cdots.$

7. $\dfrac{1}{4 + 1^2} - \dfrac{1}{4 + 2^2} + \dfrac{1}{4 + 3^2} - \dfrac{1}{4 + 4^2} + \cdots.$

8. $1 - \dfrac{2}{7} + \dfrac{3}{7^2} - \dfrac{4}{7^3} + \cdots.$

9. $\dfrac{1}{3} - \dfrac{1 \cdot 3}{3 \cdot 6} + \dfrac{1 \cdot 3 \cdot 5}{3 \cdot 6 \cdot 9} - \dfrac{1 \cdot 3 \cdot 5 \cdot 7}{3 \cdot 6 \cdot 9 \cdot 12} + \cdots.$

10. $2^2 - \dfrac{4^2}{7} + \dfrac{6^2}{7^2} - \dfrac{8^2}{7^3} + \cdots.$

11–20. Show that the series in Problems 1 to 10 inclusive are absolutely convergent.   Use the ratio test where possible.

Show that the following series are conditionally convergent:

21. $\dfrac{1}{\ln 2} - \dfrac{1}{\ln 3} + \dfrac{1}{\ln 4} - \dfrac{1}{\ln 5} + \cdots.$

22. $\dfrac{1}{1.2} - \dfrac{1}{2.4} + \dfrac{1}{3.6} - \dfrac{1}{4.8} + \cdots.$

23. $1 - \dfrac{1}{\sqrt{2}} + \dfrac{1}{\sqrt{3}} - \dfrac{1}{\sqrt{4}} + \cdots.$

24. $1 - \dfrac{1}{2^2 - 1} + \dfrac{2}{3^2 - 1} - \dfrac{3}{4^2 - 1} + \cdots$.

25. $\frac{1}{2} - \frac{2}{5} + \frac{3}{10} - \frac{4}{17} + \cdots$.

26. $1 - \dfrac{1}{2^k} + \dfrac{1}{3^k} - \dfrac{1}{4^k} + \cdots, \qquad 0 < k \leqq 1$.

C. SERIES OF VARIABLE TERMS

136. Power Series.   Such infinite series as

$$(1) \qquad c_0 + c_1(x - a) + c_2(x - a)^2 + \cdots + c_n(x - a)^n + \cdots,$$

in which x is a variable and the c's and a are constants, are called **power series**.   It is conceivable that among such series may be found some which converge for all values of x, and others which converge for only a limited range of values or for only one value of x.   In what follows an investigation of these matters will be made.

THEOREM.   *If a positive number can be found which exceeds the absolute value of each term of* (1) *when* $x = x_0$, *the series converges for all values of x within an interval of length* $2|x_0 - a|$ *with center at* $x = a$.

To prove this, let x have any fixed value x' within the interval defined in the theorem (see Fig. 136), and for $x = x'$ express the

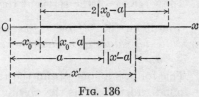

FIG. 136

series formed of the absolute values of the terms of (1) in the form

$$(2) \qquad |c_0| + \left| c_1(x_0 - a)\,\frac{x' - a}{x_0 - a} \right| + \left| c_2(x_0 - a)^2 \left(\frac{x' - a}{x_0 - a} \right)^2 \right| + \cdots$$
$$+ \left| c_n(x_0 - a)^n \left(\frac{x' - a}{x_0 - a} \right)^n \right| + \cdots.$$

As the absolute value of the product of any number of real quantities is the product of their absolute values, (2) may be written in the abbreviated form

$$(3) \qquad |c_0| + |c_1(x_0 - a)|r + |c_2(x_0 - a)^2|r^2 + \cdots + |c_n(x_0 - a)^n|r^n + \cdots,$$

where

$$r = \frac{|x' - a|}{|x_0 - a|}, \qquad 0 < r < 1,$$

the inequality resulting from the fact that $|x' - a| < |x_0 - a|$.

Now, by hypothesis, a positive number M can be found which exceeds the absolute value of any term of (1) when $x = x_0$; that is,

$$|c_n(x_0 - a)^n| < M,$$

whence

(4) $$|c_n(x_0 - a)^n|r^n < Mr^n,$$

for $n = 0, 1, 2, 3, \cdots$. But (4) shows that each term of (3) is less than the corresponding term of the geometric series

$$M + Mr + Mr^2 + \cdots + Mr^n + \cdots,$$

which converges because $0 < r < 1$ (Art. 127). Hence by the comparison test (3) and its equivalent (2) are convergent. But (2) is a series of constant terms composed of the absolute values of the terms of (1) for $x = x'$. Therefore (1) is absolutely convergent for $x = x'$ (Art. 133); and, since x' is any value of x within the interval defined in the theorem, (1) is absolutely convergent for all values of x within this interval.

It should be observed that the theorem guarantees nothing regarding the convergence of the series at the end-points of the interval.

COROLLARY 1. *If the power series* (1) *converges for $x = x_0$, it converges for all values of x within an interval of length $2|x_0 - a|$ with center at $x = a$.*

This follows at once from the theorem, since a positive number can be found which exceeds the absolute value of any term of a convergent series.

COROLLARY 2. *If the power series* (1) *diverges for $x = x_1$, it diverges for all values of x outside an interval of length $2|x_1 - a|$ with center at $x = a$.*

For suppose that the series converges when x has a value x_2 outside the interval; then, by the foregoing corollary, it converges for $x = x_1$, contrary to hypothesis. Therefore the series cannot converge, and hence must diverge, for all values of x outside the interval.

137. Interval of Convergence of a Power Series. It may now be considered evident* that if a power series of the type (1), Art. 136, converges for $x = x_0$ and diverges for $x = x_1$, it converges for all values of x within an interval with center at $x = a$ and of fixed length l (see Fig. 137) such that

$$2|x_0 - a| \leqq l \leqq 2|x_1 - a|,$$

and diverges for all values of x outside the interval, while at the end-points of the interval the series may either converge or diverge.

* Though a formal demonstration is considered necessary in more advanced works.

The totality of values of x for which a power series converges is called its **interval of convergence.** Except for its end-points this interval may be found by the ratio test. Other methods must be employed to determine the behavior of the series at the end-points of the interval.

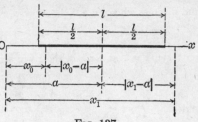

FIG. 137

Any series of the form of (1), Art. 136, necessarily converges to c_0 when $x = a$. Thus every power series has an interval of convergence, which in some cases consists solely of the value $x = a$. No power series can diverge (though some may converge) for all values of x.

Example 1. Find the interval of convergence of the power series

$$x + \frac{x^2}{2} + \frac{x^3}{3} + \cdots + \frac{x^n}{n} + \cdots.$$

Employing the ratio test for series of positive and negative terms we find that

$$\lim_{n \to \infty} \left| \frac{u_{n+1}}{u_n} \right| = \lim_{n \to \infty} \left| \frac{x^{n+1}}{n+1} \cdot \frac{n}{x^n} \right| = \lim_{n \to \infty} \left| \frac{n}{n+1} x \right| = |x|.$$

Hence the series converges when $|x| < 1$ and diverges when $|x| > 1$. The ratio test fails, however, when $|x| = 1$, that is, when $x = \pm 1$. Accordingly we must test separately the series

$$1 + \tfrac{1}{2} + \tfrac{1}{3} + \tfrac{1}{4} + \tfrac{1}{5} + \cdots$$

and

$$-1 + \tfrac{1}{2} - \tfrac{1}{3} + \tfrac{1}{4} - \tfrac{1}{5} + \cdots,$$

obtained from the original series for $x = 1$ and $x = -1$, respectively. The first of these is the divergent harmonic series (Art. 128). The second is a convergent alternating series; for the nth term approaches zero as n becomes infinite, and each term is numerically less than its predecessor.

Hence the given series has the interval of convergence $-1 \leqq x < 1$.

In accordance with the statement at the beginning of this article, the interval extends equally far on either side of the point for which $x = 0$, this being the value of a for the series under consideration.

Example 2. Find the interval of convergence of the series

$$(x - 2) - \tfrac{1}{4}(x - 2)^2 + \tfrac{1}{9}(x - 2)^3 - \tfrac{1}{16}(x - 2)^4 + \cdots.$$

Disregarding signs, we form the test-ratio

$$\frac{(x - 2)^{n+1}}{(n + 1)^2} \cdot \frac{n^2}{(x - 2)^n} = \left(\frac{n}{n + 1} \right)^2 (x - 2).$$

The limit of the absolute value of this ratio is

$$\lim_{n \to \infty} \left| \left(\frac{n}{n + 1} \right)^2 (x - 2) \right| = |x - 2|.$$

Hence the series converges when $|x - 2| < 1$; that is, when

$$-1 < (x - 2) < 1, \quad \text{or} \quad 1 < x < 3,$$

and diverges when $|x - 2| > 1$, or when

$$x < 1 \quad \text{and} \quad x > 3.$$

When $x = 1$ and $x = 3$ the given series becomes, respectively,

$$-\left(1 + \frac{1}{2^2} + \frac{1}{3^2} + \frac{1}{4^2} + \cdots\right),$$

and

$$1 - \frac{1}{2^2} + \frac{1}{3^2} - \frac{1}{4^2} + \cdots,$$

both of which converge (see Example 1, Art. 128, and the theorem of Art. 133).

Hence the interval of convergence is $1 \leqq x \leqq 3$. This interval extends equally far on either side of the point for which $x = 2$, this being the value of a for the given series.

PROBLEMS

Find the interval of convergence of each of the power series in Problems 1 to 17 inclusive.

1. $1 + x + 2x^2 + 3x^3 + \cdots$.

2. $x - \dfrac{x^3}{3!} + \dfrac{x^5}{5!} - \dfrac{x^7}{7!} + \cdots$.

3. $1 - \dfrac{x^2}{2!} + \dfrac{x^4}{4!} - \dfrac{x^6}{6!} + \cdots$.

4. $1 + x + \dfrac{x^2}{2!} + \dfrac{x^3}{3!} + \dfrac{x^4}{4!} + \cdots$.

5. $1 + (x - 4) \ln a + \dfrac{(x - 4)^2 (\ln a)^2}{2!} + \dfrac{(x - 4)^3 (\ln a)^3}{3!} + \cdots$, $a > 0$.

6. $x - \dfrac{x^3}{3} + \dfrac{x^5}{5} - \dfrac{x^7}{7} + \cdots$.

7. $(x - 5) - 2(x - 5)^2 + 3(x - 5)^3 - 4(x - 5)^4 + \cdots$.

8. $1 - 3x + 5x^2 - 7x^3 + \cdots$.

9. $1 + x + 2! \, x^2 + 3! \, x^3 + \cdots$.

10. $x - \dfrac{x^2}{2} + \dfrac{x^3}{3} - \dfrac{x^4}{4} + \cdots$.

11. $1 + \dfrac{2x}{3} + \dfrac{3x^2}{9} + \dfrac{4x^3}{27} + \cdots$.

12. $1 + \dfrac{x}{2} + \dfrac{x^2}{3^2 \cdot 2^2} + \dfrac{x^3}{5^2 \cdot 2^3} + \dfrac{x^4}{7^2 \cdot 2^4} + \cdots$.

13. $(x + 2) - \frac{1}{2}(x + 2)^2 + \frac{1}{3}(x + 2)^3 - \frac{1}{4}(x + 2)^4 + \cdots$.

14. $(x + 6) - \left(\dfrac{x + 6}{2}\right)^2 + \left(\dfrac{x + 6}{3}\right)^3 - \left(\dfrac{x + 6}{4}\right)^4 + \cdots$.

15. $(x - 3) + \dfrac{(x - 3)^2}{2 \cdot 2!} + \dfrac{(x - 3)^3}{3 \cdot 3!} + \cdots.$

16. $\dfrac{x}{4 + 1^2} + \dfrac{x^2}{4 + 2^2} + \dfrac{x^3}{4 + 3^2} + \dfrac{x^4}{4 + 4^2} + \cdots.$

17. $x + 2^2 x^2 + 3^3 x^3 + 4^4 x^4 + \cdots.$

Show that each of the following series converges except for a finite interval of divergence, and determine this interval.

18. $1 - \dfrac{1}{x} + \dfrac{1}{2x^2} - \dfrac{1}{3x^3} + \cdots.$

19. $5 + \dfrac{5}{x - 2} + \dfrac{5}{2(x - 2)^2} + \dfrac{5}{3(x - 2)^3} + \cdots.$

20. $1 - \dfrac{1}{2x} + \dfrac{2}{4x^2} - \dfrac{3}{8x^3} + \cdots.$

21. $2 + \dfrac{3}{3(x + 1)} + \dfrac{4}{9(x + 1)^2} + \dfrac{5}{27(x + 1)^3} + \cdots.$

138. Operations with Infinite Series.

We have no assurance that the rules governing such operations as addition, multiplication, grouping of terms, differentiation, integration, etc., of finite series, hold unreservedly for infinite series. In fact the following examples will make it clear that caution must be exercised in forming conclusions regarding operations with infinite series.

If the two divergent series

$$1 + \tfrac{1}{3} + \tfrac{1}{5} + \tfrac{1}{7} + \cdots$$

and

$$- \tfrac{1}{2} - \tfrac{1}{4} - \tfrac{1}{6} - \tfrac{1}{8} - \cdots$$

are combined to yield

$$(1) \qquad 1 - \tfrac{1}{2} + \tfrac{1}{3} - \tfrac{1}{4} + \tfrac{1}{5} - \tfrac{1}{6} + \tfrac{1}{7} - \tfrac{1}{8} + \cdots,$$

the result is a conditionally convergent series, as shown in the example of Art. 134. Now if the terms of (1) are grouped in pairs, the series takes the form

$$(2) \qquad \dfrac{1}{1 \cdot 2} + \dfrac{1}{3 \cdot 4} + \dfrac{1}{5 \cdot 6} + \dfrac{1}{7 \cdot 8} + \cdots.$$

By comparison with the k-series (for $k = 2$) this is clearly a convergent series, to which the term conditional is no longer applicable.

Again consider the series

$$\tfrac{2}{1} - \tfrac{3}{2} + \tfrac{4}{3} - \tfrac{5}{4} + \tfrac{6}{5} - \tfrac{7}{6} + \tfrac{8}{7} - \tfrac{9}{8} + \cdots.$$

Since the general term does not approach zero as a limit, the series is

.divergent. However, if the terms are grouped in pairs, the series takes the form of the convergent series (2).

Thus it is desirable to know the conditions under which various operations with infinite series are admissible. As a complete discussion of these matters is beyond the scope of this book, the following theorems will be stated without proof.

THEOREM 1. *The terms of a convergent series of constant terms may be grouped in parentheses at pleasure without introducing divergence or changing the value of the series.*

THEOREM 2. *Two convergent series of constant terms having sums U and V may be added term by term to produce a series converging to the sum U + V.*

We shall now illustrate the connection between power series and functions, and give some theorems relating to operations with power series.

For example, consider the identity

$$\frac{1}{1-x} = 1 + x + x^2 + x^3 + \cdots + x^{n-1} + \frac{x^n}{1-x},$$

obtained by division. For a fixed value of x, the finite series

$$1 + x + x^2 + \cdots + x^{n-1},$$

of n terms, will represent the approximate value of the function $\frac{1}{1-x}$ only in case $\frac{x^n}{1-x}$ is negligible for sufficiently large values of n, and in fact approaches zero as n becomes infinite. Hence, provided $|x| < 1$, there is no error in representing $\frac{1}{1-x}$ by an infinite series as follows:

(3) $$\frac{1}{1-x} = 1 + x + x^2 + x^3 + x^4 + \cdots.$$

Accordingly we say that (3) is a power-series **expansion** or **development** of $\frac{1}{1-x}$ for values of x in the interval $-1 < x < 1$. By the ratio test this is the interval of convergence. The student should observe that (3) is false if x has a value (say 2) outside this interval, and by (2), Art. 126, is clearly true if, for example, $x = \frac{1}{2}$.

Now to illustrate the use of termwise differentiation of a series, we differentiate both sides of (3):

$$\frac{d}{dx}\left(\frac{1}{1-x}\right) = \left(\frac{1}{1-x}\right)^2 = 1 + 2x + 3x^2 + 4x^3 + \cdots.$$

This series can be shown (by a method developed later in Art. 142) to represent $\dfrac{1}{(1-x)^2}$ for all values of x in the interval of convergence $-1 < x < 1$.

It is of interest to note that the series in (3) has been squared by differentiation.

Again, by division we obtain

$$\frac{1}{1+x} = 1 - x + x^2 - x^3 + \cdots$$

and

$$\frac{1}{1+x^2} = 1 - x^2 + x^4 - x^6 + \cdots.$$

Hence by integration we find that

$$\int_0^x \frac{dx}{1+x} = \ln(1+x) = x - \frac{x^2}{2} + \frac{x^3}{3} - \frac{x^4}{4} + \cdots,$$

and

$$\int_0^x \frac{dx}{1+x^2} = \tan^{-1}x = x - \frac{x^3}{3} + \frac{x^5}{5} - \frac{x^7}{7} + \cdots.$$

The intervals of convergence * within which these series represent the corresponding functions are respectively $-1 < x \leqq 1$, $-1 \leqq x \leqq 1$. The first series is useful in evaluating the natural logarithms of numbers near 1, such as 1.02 (Example 2, Art. 145); the second may be used to evaluate π (Example 3, Art. 145).

A series for $\ln x$ may be obtained from that for $\ln(1+x)$ by letting $x' = 1 + x$, whence $x = x' - 1$. Thus, dropping primes, we have

$$\ln x = (x-1) - \frac{(x-1)^2}{2} + \frac{(x-1)^3}{3} - \frac{(x-1)^4}{4} + \cdots.$$

General methods by which a function may be expanded into a power series will be developed in the next chapter. Often, however, the use of special operations such as those illustrated above provides simpler means than the general method of expanding the function. The conditions under which such operations may be employed are contained in the following theorems which are stated without proof.

THEOREM 3. *Two power series may be added for all values of x for which both series converge.*

* See Problems 10 and 6, Art. 137.

Thus if the series

(4) $c_0 + c_1(x - a) + c_2(x - a)^2 + \cdots$

and

(5) $c'_0 + c'_1(x - a) + c'_2(x - a)^2 + \cdots$

represent two functions $f(x)$ and $g(x)$, respectively, the series

$$(c_0 + c'_0) + (c_1 + c'_1)(x - a) + (c_2 + c'_2)(x - a)^2 + \cdots$$

converges and represents $f(x) + g(x)$ for all values of x common to the intervals of convergence of the given series.

THEOREM 4. *If (4) and (5) represent two functions $f(x)$ and $g(x)$, respectively, the product series*

$$c_0 c'_0 + (c_1 c'_0 + c_0 c'_1)(x - a) + (c_2 c'_0 + c_1 c'_1 + c_0 c'_2)(x - a)^2 + \cdots$$

converges and represents $f(x) \cdot g(x)$ for all values of x for which both (4) and (5) are absolutely convergent.

THEOREM 5. *If (4) and (5) represent two functions $f(x)$ and $g(x)$, respectively, the quotient of (4) by (5) represents $\dfrac{f(x)}{g(x)}$, provided $c'_0 \neq 0$.*

No simple general method of determining the interval of convergence of the quotient series is available.

THEOREM 6. *A power series may be differentiated term by term for all values of x within its interval of convergence.*

THEOREM 7. *A power series may be integrated term by term between any limits lying within its interval of convergence.*

PROBLEMS

1. Expand $\sqrt{1 + x}$ by the binomial theorem (Art. 125). By differentiation find a series for

$$\frac{1}{\sqrt{1 + x}}.$$

Check the result by the binomial theorem.

2. Expand $\sqrt{1 - x^2}$ by the binomial theorem. Show that the same series is obtained by replacing x by $-x^2$ in the series for $\sqrt{1 + x}$ found in Problem 1. Use the result to obtain by differentiation a series for

$$\frac{x}{\sqrt{1 - x^2}}.$$

3. From the fact that the series

$$1 + x + \frac{x^2}{2!} + \frac{x^3}{3!} + \frac{x^4}{4!} + \cdots$$

is unaltered by termwise differentiation, what function would you say it represents?

4. Replace x by $-x^2$ in the series of Problem 3, and obtain a series for

$$\int_0^x e^{-x^2}\, dx.$$

5. Expand $(1 - x^2)^{-\frac{1}{2}}$ by the binomial theorem. Show that the result is obtainable from the series of Problem 2 for

$$\frac{x}{\sqrt{1 - x^2}}.$$

Use this result to obtain a series for $\sin^{-1} x$.

6. From the series for $\ln (1 + x)$, obtained in the text, find a series for

$$\ln \frac{1 + x}{1 - x}.$$

7. Show that the series found in Problem 6 is obtainable by integration from the series for

$$\frac{1}{1 - x^2}.$$

8. From the series for $\ln x$ given in this article find $\ln 1.02$ to four decimal places.

9. From the series obtained in Problem 6 find $\ln 1.5$ to four decimal places.

CHAPTER XIV

EXPANSION OF FUNCTIONS

139. Maclaurin's Series. In the preceding article special methods were given for expressing a few functions in the form of convergent power series, and the importance of such series for purposes of computation was indicated. Though (as we have seen) certain functions can be represented by power series of a given type, it is by no means certain that every function can be so expressed. To provide a start for our investigations, let us consider a function $f(x)$, having derivatives of all orders for $x = 0$, which can be represented within a certain interval of convergence (including $x = 0$) by a power series of the form

$$(1) \qquad f(x) = c_0 + c_1 x + c_2 x^2 + c_3 x^3 + \cdots + c_{n-1} x^{n-1} + \cdots$$

in which the c's are constants to be determined. Let us find these constants and thereby see how they are related to the function $f(x)$ whose expansion they characterize.

Clearly for $x = 0$ (1) shows that

$$c_0 = f(0).$$

Since by hypothesis (1) is convergent we may differentiate it term by term any number of times (Theorem 6, Art. 138), obtaining the following equations from which the rest of the coefficients may be found:

$$f'(x) = c_1 + 2c_2 x + 3c_3 x^2 + 4c_4 x^3 + \cdots$$

$$f''(x) = 2! c_2 + 3! c_3 x + 4 \cdot 3 \cdot c_4 x^2 + \cdots,$$

$$f'''(x) = 3! c_3 + 4! c_4 x + \cdots,$$

$$\cdot \qquad \cdot \qquad \cdot$$
$$\cdot \qquad \cdot \qquad \cdot$$
$$\cdot \qquad \cdot \qquad \cdot$$

$$f^{(n-1)}(x) = (n - 1)! c_{n-1} + n! c_n x + \cdots,$$

$$\cdot \qquad \cdot$$
$$\cdot \qquad \cdot$$
$$\cdot \qquad \cdot$$

Placing $x = 0$ in these equations and solving for the c's we find that

$$c_1 = f'(0), \qquad c_2 = \frac{f''(0)}{2!}, \cdots, \qquad c_{n-1} = \frac{f^{(n-1)}(0)}{(n-1)!}, \cdots.$$

Hence if $f(x)$ can be represented by a convergent series of the type (1), that series necessarily has the form

$$(2) \quad f(x) = f(0) + f'(0)x + \frac{f''(0)}{2!}x^2 + \frac{f'''(0)}{3!}x^3 + \cdots$$
$$+ \frac{f^{(n-1)}(0)}{(n-1)!}x^{n-1} + \cdots.$$

This is known as **Maclaurin's series.**[*] It is also called *the expansion (or development) of $f(x)$ in powers of x, or its expansion in the neighborhood of zero.* The latter designation arises from the fact that the series is especially useful in determining the value of $f(x)$ for a value of x in the neighborhood of zero. For if the values of $f(x)$ and its derivatives are known for $x = 0$, and if x has a value sufficiently near zero, the successive powers of x occurring in the expansion grow rapidly smaller, and the value of $f(x)$ can often be approximated by summing only the first few terms of (2).

Unless a function and all its derivatives exist for $x = 0$, the function cannot be represented by a Maclaurin series. Examples of functions which cannot be so represented are $\ln x$, $\cot x$, and $x^{\frac{7}{2}}$.

The conditions under which (2) may be used to develop a given function, and the related question of convergence of the corresponding series, will be treated in Art. 142. For the present we accept the validity of (2) for the representation of certain functions and confine our attention to its application to their formal expansion.

Example 1. Assuming that e^x can be expanded in a convergent power series in x obtain the expansion, giving the nth term.

Here $f(x) = e^x$. Therefore

$$f'(x) = e^x, \qquad f''(x) = e^x, \qquad f'''(x) = e^x, \cdots, \qquad f^{(n-1)}(x) = e^x, \cdots,$$

and

$$f(0) = 1, \qquad f'(0) = 1, \qquad f''(0) = 1, \qquad f'''(0) = 1, \cdots, \qquad f^{(n-1)}(0) = 1, \cdots.$$

Hence by (2)

$$e^x = 1 + x + \frac{x^2}{2!} + \frac{x^3}{3!} + \cdots + \frac{x^{n-1}}{(n-1)!} + \cdots.$$

We note that the series for e ((2), Art. 52) is obtained by placing $x = 1$.

Example 2. Assuming that $\ln(1 + x^2)$ can be represented by a convergent power series in x, expand it, giving the nth term.

*After Colin Maclaurin (1698–1746).

The work may be simplified by letting $y = x^2$ and expanding $\ln (1 + y)$. Accordingly we let

$$f(y) = \ln (1 + y), \qquad \text{whence} \qquad f(0) = \ln 1 = 0.$$

Then

$$f'(y) = (1 + y)^{-1}, \qquad\qquad f'(0) = 1,$$

$$f''(y) = - (1 + y)^{-2}, \qquad\qquad f''(0) = - 1,$$

$$f'''(y) = 2!(1 + y)^{-3}, \qquad\qquad f'''(0) = 2!,$$

$$f^{\text{iv}}(y) = - 3!(1 + y)^{-4}, \qquad\qquad f^{\text{iv}}(0) = - 3!,$$

$$\cdot \quad\quad \cdot \qquad\qquad\qquad \cdot \quad\quad \cdot$$

$$\cdot \quad\quad \cdot \qquad\qquad\qquad \cdot \quad\quad \cdot$$

Hence by (2)

$$\ln (1 + y) = 0 + y - \frac{1}{2!} y^2 + \frac{2!}{3!} y^3 - \frac{3!}{4!} y^4 + \cdots$$

$$= y - \frac{y^2}{2} + \frac{y^3}{3} - \frac{y^4}{4} + \cdots + (-1)^{n-1} \frac{y^n}{n} + \cdots,$$

in which n is the number of the term in which it occurs in the final form of the series, the term which vanishes not being counted.

This series was obtained by another method in Art. 138.

Replacing y by x^2 we obtain *

$$\ln (1 + x^2) = x^2 - \frac{x^4}{2} + \frac{x^6}{3} - \frac{x^8}{4} + \cdots + (-1)^{n-1} \frac{x^{2n}}{n} + \cdots.$$

The same result may be obtained, though with considerably more labor, by expanding the given function directly.

PROBLEMS

In the following problems assume where necessary that the given functions have convergent Maclaurin developments and obtain them.

In each of the first eleven problems give the nth term.

1. $\sin x = x - \dfrac{x^3}{3!} + \dfrac{x^5}{5!} - \cdots + \dfrac{(-1)^{n-1} x^{2n-1}}{(2n - 1)!} + \cdots;$

2. $\cos x = 1 - \dfrac{x^2}{2!} + \dfrac{x^4}{4!} - \cdots + \dfrac{(-1)^{n-1} x^{2n-2}}{(2n - 2)!} + \cdots;$

3. $\sin \left(\dfrac{\pi}{4} + x \right).$ **6.** $e^{-x}.$ **9.** $a^x.$

4. $\cos \left(\dfrac{\pi}{4} - x \right).$ **7.** $\sin ax.$ **10.** $\frac{1}{2}(e^x + e^{-x}).$

5. $\ln (1 - x).$ **8.** $\cos ax.$ **11.** $\frac{1}{2}(e^x - e^{-x}).$

* The general question of the expansion of a function of a function, involved in such a replacement, is beyond the scope of this book.

Frequently the nth term cannot be formulated easily. In the expansion of the following six functions it may be omitted. Find three non-vanishing terms in each case.

12. $\tan x$.   **14.** $\tan \left(\dfrac{\pi}{4} + x \right)$.   **16.** $e^{\sin x}$.

13. $\sec x$.   **15.** $\ln \cos x$.   **17.** $\ln \left(x + \sqrt{1 + x^2} \right)$.

Give six terms in the expansion of each of the following three functions. Express each series as the sum of two series, one including only even powers of x, the other odd powers, and compare this series with the result obtained by use of the trigonometric formula for $\sin (\alpha - \beta)$ or $\cos (\alpha - \beta)$ and the series for $\sin x$ and $\cos x$ given in Problems 1 and 2.

18. $\sin \left(x - \dfrac{\pi}{3} \right)$.   **19.** $\cos \left(x - \dfrac{\pi}{6} \right)$.   **20.** $\sin \left(\dfrac{\pi}{6} - x \right)$.

21. Verify the binomial expansion:

$$(a + x)^n = a^n + na^{n-1} x + \frac{n(n - 1)}{2!} a^{n-2} x^2 + \frac{n(n - 1)(n - 2)}{3!} a^{n-3} x^3 + \cdots .$$

Find four terms of the Maclaurin series for each of the following three functions:

22. $\sqrt{4 + x}$.   **23.** $\sqrt[3]{(1 - x)^2}$.   **24.** $\dfrac{1}{\sqrt{9 - x}}$.

25. From the series for e^x (Example 1) obtain the Maclaurin series for e^{-kx^2}.

26. From the series obtained in Problem 23, find the Maclaurin series for $(1 - x^2)^{-\frac{1}{3}}$.

27. From the series in Problems 1 and 2 obtain series for $\sin x^2$ and $\cos x^2$.

28. From the series for $\ln (1 + y)$ found in Example 2 obtain series for

$$\ln (1 - x) \quad \text{and} \quad \ln \frac{1 + x}{1 - x}.$$

29. By use of the identities

$$2 \sin^2 \theta = 1 - \cos 2\theta, \qquad 2 \cos^2 \theta = 1 + \cos 2\theta$$

and the series of Problem 2, obtain series for $\sin^2 \theta$ and $\cos^2 \theta$. Check the results by adding these series.

30. Show that the series of Problems 10 and 11 may be obtained one from the other by differentiation.

140. Taylor's Series. We have seen that certain functions such as $\ln x$, $\cot x$, and $x^{\frac{7}{2}}$ cannot be represented by Maclaurin series. Moreover, it has been indicated that Maclaurin's series is useful in computing the value of a function only when x is small (near zero). We now derive a formula for the expansion of a function in powers of $x - a$ (a being a constant), which will be useful in computing the value of the function for values of x near a.

We suppose now that a function $f(x)$ having derivatives of all orders for some value of x, say $x = a$, can be represented within a certain interval of convergence (including $x = a$) by a power series of the form

(1) $\quad f(x) = c_0 + c_1(x - a) + c_2(x - a)^2 + \cdots + c_{n-1}(x - a)^{n-1} + \cdots,$

in which the c's are constants to be determined. Since by hypothesis (1) is convergent, we may differentiate it term by term any number of times (Theorem 6, Art. 138), obtaining the following equations:

$$f'(x) = c_1 + 2c_2(x - a) + 3c_3(x - a)^2 + 4c_4(x - a)^3 + \cdots,$$

$$f''(x) = 2!c_2 + 3!c_3(x - a) + 4\cdot3c_4(x - a)^2 + \cdots,$$

$$f'''(x) = 3!c_3 + 4!c_4(x - a) + \cdots,$$

$$f^{n-1}(x) = (n - 1)!c_{n-1} + n!c_n(x - a) + \cdots,$$

Substituting $x = a$ in these equations and in (1), and solving for the c's, we find that

$$c_0 = f(a), \quad c_1 = f'(a), \quad c_2 = \frac{f''(a)}{2!}, \cdots, \quad c_{n-1} = \frac{f^{(n-1)}(a)}{(n - 1)!}, \cdots.$$

Thus if $f(x)$ can be represented by a convergent series of the type (1), that series necessarily has the form

(2) $\quad f(x) = f(a) + f'(a)(x - a) + \dfrac{f''(a)}{2!}(x - a)^2 + \dfrac{f'''(a)}{3!}(x - a)^3 +$

$$\cdots + \frac{f^{(n-1)}(a)}{(n - 1)!}(x - a)^{n-1} + \cdots.$$

This is known as **Taylor's Series.**[*]

Placing $x = a + h$ in (2), we obtain another useful form of Taylor's series:

(3) $\quad f(a + h) = f(a) + hf'(a) + \dfrac{h^2}{2!}f''(a) + \cdots + \dfrac{h^{n-1}}{(n - 1)!}f^{(n-1)}(a) + \cdots.$

In terms analogous to those describing Maclaurin's expansion, Taylor's series is called *the development of $f(x)$ in powers of $x - a$ (or h), or its expansion in the neighborhood of a.*

It should be observed that either form of Taylor's expansion reduces to Maclaurin's if $a = 0$. Thus Maclaurin's series is a special case of Taylor's.

[*] Due to Brook Taylor (1685–1731).

The conditions under which (2) and (3) may be used to expand a given function, and the closely allied question of the convergence of the corresponding series, will be treated in Art. 141. For the present we accept the validity of Taylor's series for the representation of certain functions, and proceed with its application to the formal expansion of such functions.

Example 1. Assuming that cos x can be expanded into a convergent series of powers of $x - \dfrac{\pi}{4}$, expand it to four terms.

We take $a = \dfrac{\pi}{4}$ and let

$$f(x) = \cos x, \quad \text{whence} \quad f(a) = \cos \frac{\pi}{4} = \frac{1}{\sqrt{2}}.$$

Then

$$f'(x) = -\sin x, \qquad f'(a) = -\sin \frac{\pi}{4} = -\frac{1}{\sqrt{2}},$$

$$f''(x) = -\cos x, \qquad f''(a) = -\cos \frac{\pi}{4} = -\frac{1}{\sqrt{2}},$$

$$f'''(x) = \sin x, \qquad f'''(a) = \sin \frac{\pi}{4} = \frac{1}{\sqrt{2}},$$

Hence by (2)

$$(4) \qquad \cos x = \frac{1}{\sqrt{2}} \left[1 - \left(x - \frac{\pi}{4}\right) - \frac{\left(x - \frac{\pi}{4}\right)^2}{2!} + \frac{\left(x - \frac{\pi}{4}\right)^3}{3!} + \cdots \right].$$

This can be expressed in the form of (3) by letting $x - \dfrac{\pi}{4} = h$, whence $x = \dfrac{\pi}{4} + h$; thus (4) becomes

$$\cos\left(\frac{\pi}{4} + h\right) = \frac{1}{\sqrt{2}} \left(1 - h - \frac{h^2}{2!} + \frac{h^3}{3!} + \cdots \right).$$

Example 2. Assuming that ln x admits of a convergent expansion in powers of $x - 1$, expand it, giving the nth term.

We take $a = 1$ and let

$$f(x) = \ln x, \qquad \text{whence} \qquad f(1) = \ln 1 = 0.$$

Then

$$f'(x) = x^{-1}, \qquad\qquad f'(1) = 1,$$

$$f''(x) = -x^{-2}, \qquad\qquad f''(1) = -1,$$

$$f'''(x) = 2! \, x^{-3}, \qquad\qquad f'''(1) = 2!,$$

$$f^{\text{iv}}(x) = -\,3!\,x^{-4}, \qquad\qquad f^{\text{iv}}(1) = -\,3!,$$

$$
\begin{array}{cccc}
\cdot & \cdot & \cdot & \cdot \\
\cdot & \cdot & \cdot & \cdot \\
\cdot & \cdot & \cdot & \cdot
\end{array}
$$

Hence by (2)

$$\ln x = 0 + (x - 1) - \frac{(x-1)^2}{2!} + \frac{2!(x-1)^3}{3!} - \frac{3!(x-1)^4}{4!} + \cdots$$

$$= (x - 1) - \frac{(x-1)^2}{2} + \frac{(x-1)^3}{3} - \cdots + (-1)^{n-1}\frac{(x-1)^n}{n} + \cdots.$$

If we let $x - 1 = h$, whence $x = 1 + h$, this series may be written alternatively in the form of (3):

$$\ln (1 + h) = h - \frac{h^2}{2} + \frac{h^3}{3} - \frac{h^4}{4} + \cdots + (-1)^{n-1}\frac{h^n}{n} + \cdots.$$

The same result was obtained as a Maclaurin expansion in Example 2 of the last article.

PROBLEMS

Assuming that the functions in Problems 1–11 have convergent Taylor developments express each one in two forms.

In each of the first five problems give the nth term.

1. e^x, $a = 1$.   **2.** k^x, $a = 2$.   **3.** $\ln x$, $a = k$.

4. $\sin x$, $a = \dfrac{\pi}{2}$. Compare with the series of Problem 2, Art. 139.

5. $\cos x$, $a = \dfrac{\pi}{2}$. Compare with the series of Problem 1, Art. 139.

6. Expand $\sin x$ in powers of $x - \dfrac{\pi}{6}$ to four terms.

7. Expand $\cos x$ in the neighborhood of $\dfrac{\pi}{3}$. Find four terms.

8. Expand $x^{\frac{3}{2}}$ in powers of $x - 4$ to four terms.

9. Expand $\tan x$ in the neighborhood of $x = \dfrac{\pi}{4}$. Find three terms.

10. Expand $\sqrt{x}$ in powers of $x - 9$ to four terms.
11. Expand $\sqrt[3]{x}$ in powers of $x - 8$ to four terms.
12. If $P(x)$ is a polynomial in x of degree n, show that

$$P(x) = P(a) + P'(a)(x - a) + \frac{P''(a)}{2!}(x - a)^2 + \cdots + \frac{P^{(n)}(a)}{n!}(x - a)^n.$$

13. Expand $x^3 - 2x^2 + 3x - 1$ in powers of $x - 1$. Use the result to determine

$$\int \frac{x^3 - 2x^2 + 3x - 1}{(x-1)^4}\,dx.$$

14. Expand $x^4 - 3x^3 - x - 5$ in powers of $x - 3$. Use the result to evaluate

$$\int_0^1 \frac{x^4 - 3x^3 - x - 5}{(x-3)^5}\,dx.$$

141. Taylor's Formula with the Remainder.   We have already seen that, if a function $f(x)$, with derivatives of all orders, can be expanded into a convergent power series in x or $x - a$, the expansion necessarily has the form of a Maclaurin or Taylor series.   We now abandon the assumption that $f(x)$ can be represented by a convergent power series, and investigate the conditions under which a Maclaurin or Taylor series will represent a given function.   For this purpose we shall now establish two important theorems.

THEOREM 1.   *If $f(x)$ and its first n derivatives are single-valued and continuous in the interval from $x = a$ to $x = a + h$ including the end-points, then*

$$f(a + h) = f(a) + hf'(a) + \frac{h^2}{2!}f''(a) + \cdots + \frac{h^{n-1}}{(n-1)!}f^{(n-1)}(a) + R_n,$$

in which R_n, known as the remainder after n terms, is given by the formula *

$$R_n = \frac{h^n}{n!}f^{(n)}(a + \theta h) \quad where \quad 0 < \theta < 1.$$

This is known as **Taylor's Theorem.**   To prove it let R_n be a number such that

(1) $f(a + h) = f(a) + hf'(a) + \dfrac{h^2}{2!}f''(a) + \cdots$

$$+ \frac{h^{n-1}}{(n-1)!}f^{(n-1)}(a) + R_n.$$

It should be observed that this equation is not based on the assumption referred to above, but simply defines R_n as the error involved in using the first n terms of Taylor's infinite series to represent $f(a + h)$.   It is now our purpose to evaluate R_n.

For convenience let

(2) $$R_n = \frac{h^n}{n!}P_n,$$

where now P_n is the number to be determined.   Then by transposition of terms (1) becomes

(3) $f(a + h) - f(a) - hf'(a) - \dfrac{h^2}{2!}f''(a) - \cdots$

$$- \frac{h^{n-1}}{(n-1)!}f^{(n-1)}(a) - \frac{h^n}{n!}P_n = 0.$$

---

* Other forms of R_n are known. This form was first established by Joseph Louis Lagrange (1736–1813), a French mathematician.

Now consider the function

(4) $\quad \phi(x) = f(a + h) - f(x) - \dfrac{a + h - x}{1!} f'(x) - \dfrac{(a + h - x)^2}{2!} f''(x) -$

$$\cdots - \dfrac{(a + h - x)^{n-1}}{(n - 1)!} f^{(n-1)}(x) - \dfrac{(a + h - x)^n}{n!} P_n.$$

It follows from the hypothesis regarding $f(x)$ and its first n derivatives that $\phi(x)$ and its derivative $\phi'(x)$ exist and are single-valued and continuous at each point of the interval $a \leq x \leq a + h$. Moreover, by inspection, $\phi(a + h) = 0$, and, by (3), $\phi(a) = 0$. Thus $\phi(x)$ satisfies all the conditions of Rolle's Theorem (Art. 120); hence $\phi'(x)$ must vanish at some point within the interval. Differentiating (4) we have

$$\phi'(x) = - f'(x) + f'(x) - \dfrac{(a + h - x)}{1!} f''(x) + \dfrac{(a + h - x)}{1!} f''(x)$$

$$- \dfrac{(a + h - x)^2}{2!} f'''(x) + \dfrac{(a + h - x)^2}{2!} f'''(x) - \cdots$$

$$- \dfrac{(a + h - x)^{n-1}}{(n - 1)!} f^{(n)}(x) + \dfrac{(a + h - x)^{n-1}}{(n - 1)!} P_n.$$

Observing now that all except the last two terms cancel in pairs, we find that

(5) $\qquad \phi'(x) = \dfrac{(a + h - x)^{n-1}}{(n - 1)!} [P_n - f^{(n)}(x)].$

By Rolle's Theorem (as noted above) there exists within the interval a value x_1, say $x_1 = a + \theta h$, where $0 < \theta < 1$, such that $\phi'(x_1) = \phi'(a + \theta h) = 0$. Hence by (5) and (2)

(6) $\qquad P_n = f^{(n)}(a + \theta h), \quad R_n = \dfrac{h^n}{n!} f^{(n)}(a + \theta h), \quad 0 < \theta < 1.$

Therefore by (1)

(7) $\quad f(a + h) = f(a) + hf'(a) + \dfrac{h^2}{2!} f''(a) + \cdots + \dfrac{h^{n-1}}{(n - 1)!} f^{(n-1)}(a)$

$$+ \dfrac{h^n}{n!} f^{(n)}(a + \theta h), \quad 0 < \theta < 1.$$

Thus we have derived one of the most important formulas of calculus known as **Taylor's formula with the remainder**.

The proof of the theorem is now complete.

It is of interest to note that (7) becomes the Law of the Mean (Art. 121) for $n = 1$:

$$f(a + h) = f(a) + hf'(a + \theta h), \quad 0 < \theta < 1.$$

Another useful form of (7) is obtained by letting $h = x - a$:

(8) $f(x) = f(a) + f'(a)(x - a) + \dfrac{f''(a)}{2!} (x - a)^2 + \cdots$

$$+ \dfrac{f^{(n-1)}(a)}{(n - 1)!} (x - a)^{n-1} + \dfrac{(x - a)^n}{n!} f^{(n)}[a + \theta(x - a)], \quad 0 < \theta < 1.$$

We are now in a position to establish an important theorem giving the conditions under which Taylor's series will represent a given function.

THEOREM 2.   *The Taylor series*

(9) $f(x) = f(a) + f'(a)(x - a) + \dfrac{f''(a)}{2!} (x - a)^2 + \cdots$

$$+ \dfrac{f^{(n-1)}(a)}{(n - 1)!} (x - a)^{n-1} + \cdots$$

represents $f(x)$ for those values of x, and those only, for which the remainder *

(10) $R_n(x) = \dfrac{(x - a)^n}{n!} f^{(n)}[a + \theta(x - a)], \quad 0 < \theta < 1,$

approaches zero as n becomes infinite.

Let x_0 be any value of x such that

(11) $$\lim_{n \to \infty} R_n(x_0) = 0,$$

and denote the sum of the first n terms of (8) or (9) for $x = x_0$ by $S_n(x_0)$. Then by (8)

$$f(x_0) = S_n(x_0) + R_n(x_0), \quad \text{or} \quad S_n(x_0) = f(x_0) - R_n(x_0).$$

Therefore, by virtue of (11),

$$\lim_{n \to \infty} S_n(x_0) = f(x_0),$$

and the series in (9) converges for $x = x_0$ and has the value $f(x_0)$.

Conversely, let x_1 be any value of x for which the series in (9) converges to $f(x_1)$. Now by (8)

$$f(x_1) = S_n(x_1) + R_n(x_1), \quad \text{or} \quad R_n(x_1) = f(x_1) - S_n(x_1).$$

* For convenience R_n is designated as a function $R_n(x)$.

Hence finally,

$$\lim_{n \to \infty} R_n(x_1) = \lim_{n \to \infty} [f(x_1) - S_n(x_1)] = f(x_1) - f(x_1) = 0,$$

since by hypothesis $\lim_{n \to \infty} S_n(x_1) = f(x_1)$.

It is possible for Taylor's series to converge for values of x for which the limit of the remainder is not zero; for such values of x, however, the series does not represent the function. In most cases the interval of convergence is identical with that for which the remainder approaches zero, and usually the former is more easily determined.

It will be shown in Art. 146 that the remainder is frequently useful in computations involving series.

142. Maclaurin's Formula with the Remainder. Important results are obtained from the theorems of the foregoing article by letting $a = 0$.

THEOREM 1. *If $f(x)$ and its first n derivatives are single-valued and continuous in an interval including the value $x = 0$, then*

$$(1) \qquad f(x) = f(0) + f'(0)x + \frac{f''(0)}{2!} x^2 + \frac{f'''(0)}{3!} x^3 +$$

$$\cdots + \frac{f^{(n-1)}(0)}{(n-1)!} x^{n-1} + \frac{x^n}{n!} f^{(n)}(\theta x), \quad 0 < \theta < 1.$$

This is known as **Maclaurin's formula with the remainder**; it is, of course, only a special case of Taylor's formula.

THEOREM 2. *The Maclaurin series*

$$f(x) = f(0) + f'(0)x + \frac{f''(0)}{2!} x^2 + \cdots + \frac{f^{(n-1)}(0)}{(n-1)!} x^{n-1} + \cdots$$

represents $f(x)$ for those values of x, and those only, for which the remainder

$$(2) \qquad R_n = \frac{x^n}{n!} f^{(n)}(\theta x), \quad 0 < \theta < 1,$$

approaches zero as n becomes infinite.

Example 1. Find the interval in which e^x may be represented by a Maclaurin series.

By Example 1, Art. 139,

$$(3) \qquad e^x = 1 + x + \frac{x^2}{2!} + \frac{x^3}{3!} + \cdots + \frac{x^{n-1}}{(n-1)!} + \frac{x^n}{n!} + \cdots.$$

Let us first find the interval of convergence of the series. By the ratio test (Art. 135),

$$\lim_{n \to \infty} \left| \frac{u_{n+1}}{u_n} \right| = \lim_{n \to \infty} \left| \frac{x^n}{n!} \cdot \frac{(n-1)!}{x^{n-1}} \right| = \lim_{n \to \infty} \left| \frac{x}{n} \right| = 0,$$

regardless of the value of x. Hence the series converges for all values of x.

Let us now find the interval within which the series represents e^x. Setting $f(x) = e^x$, so that

$$f^{(n)}(x) = e^x,$$

we have by (2)

$$R_n = \frac{x^n}{n!} e^{\theta x}, \quad 0 < \theta < 1.$$

We must investigate the behavior of R_n as n becomes infinite.

Consider first the factor $e^{\theta x}$. For a given value of x not less than zero, $\theta x \leqq x$, since $0 < \theta < 1$; hence $e^{\theta x}$ is finite. Moreover, if $x < 0$, then $\theta x < 0$, so that $e^{\theta x}$ lies between 0 and 1 and hence is finite. Thus for any assigned value of x, $e^{\theta x}$ is finite, and remains so as n becomes infinite.

The factor $\dfrac{x^n}{n!}$ is a general term of the series (3), which has just been shown to converge for all values of x. Hence (Art. 129) $\dfrac{x^n}{n!}$ approaches zero as n becomes infinite. We conclude therefore that

$$\lim_{n \to \infty} R_n = 0,$$

whatever be the value of x.

Thus the series represents e^x for all values of x.

As in most simple cases the series represents the function for those values of x for which it converges.

Example 2. For what values of x can sin x be represented by a Taylor expansion in the neighborhood of a?

We let $f(x) = \sin x$, whence $f(a) = \sin a$; then

$$f'(x) = \cos x, \qquad\qquad f'(a) = \cos a,$$

$$f''(x) = -\sin x, \qquad\qquad f''(a) = -\sin a,$$

$$f'''(x) = -\cos x, \qquad\qquad f'''(a) = -\cos a,$$

$$\cdot \qquad\qquad\qquad \cdot$$
$$\cdot \qquad\qquad\qquad \cdot$$
$$\cdot \qquad\qquad\qquad \cdot$$

Hence by (2), Art. 140,

$$(4) \quad \sin x = \sin a + (x - a) \cos a - \frac{(x-a)^2}{2!} \sin a - \frac{(x-a)^3}{3!} \cos a + \cdots.$$

For convenience we write the nth derivative of sin x in the form

$$f^{(n)}(x) = \sin\left(x + \frac{n\pi}{2}\right),$$

so that by (10), Art. 141,

$$(5) \quad R_n = \frac{(x-a)^n}{n!} \sin\left[a + \theta(x-a) + \frac{n\pi}{2}\right], \quad 0 < \theta < 1:$$

Since the numerical value of the sine of an angle cannot exceed unity, the limit of R_n as n becomes infinite depends on the limit of

$$\frac{(x-a)^n}{n!}.$$

We now show that this approaches zero as n becomes infinite.

By the foregoing example, the series

$$1 + u + \frac{u^2}{2!} + \frac{u^3}{3!} + \cdots$$

converges and represents e^u for all values of u. Therefore the series

$$1 + (x-a) + \frac{(x-a)^2}{2!} + \frac{(x-a)^3}{3!} + \cdots$$

converges and represents e^{x-a} for all values of x.* Hence by Art. 129 the general term

$$\frac{(x-a)^n}{n!}$$

approaches zero as n becomes infinite. We conclude from (5), therefore, that

$$\lim_{n \to \infty} R_n = 0.$$

Hence (4) converges and represents $\sin x$ for all values of x.

143. Some Important Series. Below are listed for reference a number of important series, together with the intervals in which they represent the corresponding functions.

The student should verify a few of these series and show that the intervals of convergence are identical with those given.

Some of these series may be derived by the special methods suggested in the text and problems of Art. 138.

(1) $\quad e^x = 1 + x + \dfrac{x^2}{2!} + \dfrac{x^3}{3!} + \cdots + \dfrac{x^{n-1}}{(n-1)!} + \cdots.$ All values.

(2) $\quad \sin x = x - \dfrac{x^3}{3!} + \dfrac{x^5}{5!} - \dfrac{x^7}{7!} + \cdots$

$$+(-1)^{n-1}\frac{x^{2n-1}}{(2n-1)!} + \cdots.$$ All values.

(3) $\quad \cos x = 1 - \dfrac{x^2}{2!} + \dfrac{x^4}{4!} - \dfrac{x^6}{6!} + \cdots$

$$+ (-1)^{n-1}\frac{x^{2n-2}}{(2n-2)!} + \cdots.$$ All values.

*A formal proof of this statement is given in Wilson's *Advanced Calculus*, p. 444.

(4) $\ln(1 + x) = x - \dfrac{x^2}{2} + \dfrac{x^3}{3} - \dfrac{x^4}{4} + \cdots + (-1)^{n-1}\dfrac{x^n}{n} + \cdots.$

$$-1 < x \leqq 1.$$

(5) $\ln(1 - x) = -x - \dfrac{x^2}{2} - \dfrac{x^3}{3} - \dfrac{x^4}{4} - \cdots - \dfrac{x^n}{n} - \cdots. \quad -1 \leqq x < 1.$

(6) $\ln\dfrac{1 + x}{1 - x} = 2\left(x + \dfrac{x^3}{3} + \dfrac{x^5}{5} + \cdots + \dfrac{x^{2n-1}}{2n - 1} + \cdots \right).$

$$-1 < x < 1.$$

(7) $\tan^{-1} x = x - \dfrac{x^3}{3} + \dfrac{x^5}{5} - \dfrac{x^7}{7} + \cdots + (-1)^{n-1}\dfrac{x^{2n-1}}{2n - 1} + \cdots.$

$$-1 \leqq x \leqq 1.$$

(8) $\sin^{-1} x = x + \dfrac{1 \cdot x^3}{2 \cdot 3} + \dfrac{1 \cdot 3 \cdot x^5}{2 \cdot 4 \cdot 5} + \cdots$

$$+ \dfrac{1 \cdot 3 \cdots (2n - 3)\, x^{2n-1}}{2 \cdot 4 \cdots (2n - 2)(2n - 1)} + \cdots. \quad -1 \leqq x \leqq 1.$$

(9) $a^x = 1 + x \ln a + \dfrac{x^2}{2!}(\ln a)^2 + \cdots$

$$+ \dfrac{x^{n-1}}{(n - 1)!}(\ln a)^{n-1} + \cdots, \; a > 0. \qquad \text{All values.}$$

(10) $\sin ax = ax - \dfrac{(ax)^3}{3!} + \dfrac{(ax)^5}{5!} - \dfrac{(ax)^7}{7!} + \cdots$

$$+ (-1)^{n-1}\dfrac{(ax)^{2n-1}}{(2n - 1)!} + \cdots. \qquad \text{All values.}$$

(11) $\cos ax = 1 - \dfrac{(ax)^2}{2!} + \dfrac{(ax)^4}{4!} - \dfrac{(ax)^6}{6!} + \cdots$

$$+ (-1)^{n-1}\dfrac{(ax)^{2n-2}}{(2n - 2)!} + \cdots. \qquad \text{All values.}$$

(12) $\ln(a + x) = \ln a + \dfrac{x}{a} - \dfrac{x^2}{2a^2} + \dfrac{x^3}{3a^3} - \cdots$

$$+ \dfrac{(-1)^n x^{n-1}}{(n - 1)\, a^{n-1}} + \cdots, \; a > 0. \qquad -a < x \leqq a.$$

(13) $\ln\dfrac{a + x}{a - x} = 2\left(\dfrac{x}{a} + \dfrac{x^3}{3a^3} + \dfrac{x^5}{5a^5} + \cdots \right.$

$$\left. + \dfrac{x^{2n-1}}{(2n - 1)\, a^{2n-1}} + \cdots \right). \qquad |x| < |a|.$$

(14) $\quad \dfrac{1}{2}\,(e^x - e^{-x}) = x + \dfrac{x^3}{3!} + \dfrac{x^5}{5!} + \cdots$

$$+ \dfrac{x^{2n-1}}{(2n-1)!} + \cdots. \qquad \text{All values.}$$

(15) $\quad \dfrac{1}{2}\,(e^x + e^{-x}) = 1 + \dfrac{x^2}{2!} + \dfrac{x^4}{4!} + \cdots$

$$+ \dfrac{x^{2n-2}}{(2n-2)!} + \cdots. \qquad \text{All values.}$$

(16) *The binomial series:*

$$(a + x)^k = a^k + k a^{k-1} x + \dfrac{k(k-1)}{2!}\, a^{k-2} x^2 + \cdots$$

$$+ \dfrac{k(k-1)(k-2)\cdots(k-n+2)}{(n-1)!}\, a^{k-n+1} x^{n-1} + \cdots.$$

This is a finite series if k is a positive integer or zero, and holds for all values of x. For all other real values of k it becomes an infinite series, valid only when $-a < x < a$.*

(17) $\quad \ln x = \ln a + \dfrac{1}{a}\,(x - a) - \dfrac{1}{2a^2}\,(x - a)^2 + \cdots$

$$+ \dfrac{(-1)^n}{(n-1)\,a^{n-1}}\,(x - a)^{n-1} + \cdots, \quad a > 0. \quad 0 < x \leqq 2a.$$

(18) $\quad e^x = e^a \left[1 + (x - a) + \dfrac{(x - a)^2}{2!} + \cdots \right.$

$$\left. + \dfrac{(x - a)^{n-1}}{(n-1)!} + \cdots \right]. \qquad \text{All values.}$$

(19) $\quad \sin x = \sin a + (x - a)\cos a - \dfrac{(x - a)^2}{2!}\,\sin a$

$$- \dfrac{(x - a)^3}{3!}\,\cos a + \cdots. \qquad \text{All values.}$$

(20) $\quad \cos x = \cos a - (x - a)\sin a - \dfrac{(x - a)^2}{2!}\,\cos a$

$$+ \dfrac{(x - a)^3}{3!}\,\sin a + \cdots. \qquad \text{All values.}$$

---

* It is important to observe that the expansion of $(a + x)^k$ in a Maclaurin series constitutes a proof that the binomial theorem holds within the interval of convergence for all real values of k. In standard books on algebra the proof is given only for positive integral values of k.

$$(21) \quad \sin (a \pm x) = \sin a \pm x \cos a - \frac{x^2}{2!} \sin a$$

$$\mp \frac{x^3}{3!} \cos a + \cdots. \qquad \text{All values.}$$

$$(22) \quad \cos (a \pm x) = \cos a \mp x \sin a - \frac{x^2}{2!} \cos a$$

$$\pm \frac{x^3}{3!} \sin a + \cdots. \qquad \text{All values.}$$

144. Accuracy in Computations. Before proceeding with the application of series to numerical computations, the student should have some knowledge of the extent to which he may rely upon a computed result. In calculations involving approximate or measured data—measurements being at best only approximations—care should be taken to retain no more significant figures in the result than are warranted by the data. This fact is best made clear by examples involving various arithmetical operations.

(a) *Multiplication and Division.* Suppose that the dimensions of a rectangular roof are found to be 120.3 ft. and 50.2 ft., it being implied that each measurement was made to the nearest tenth of a foot. Then one might thoughtlessly assert that the product

$$120.3 \times 50.2 = 6039.06$$

represents the area of the roof, correct to the nearest hundredth of a square foot. Of this, however, we have no assurance; for since we know only that the number of feet of length lies somewhere between

$$120.25 \quad \text{and} \quad 120.35,$$

and that of width somewhere between

$$50.15 \quad \text{and} \quad 50.25,$$

we can with certainty say only that the number of square feet of area lies somewhere between the products

$$120.25 \times 50.15 = 6030.5375$$

and

$$120.35 \times 50.25 = 6047.5875,$$

which differ by more than 17 sq. ft. Thus it is not only futile but misleading to state that the area is 6039.06 sq. ft., as this result would imply complete accuracy to the last significant figure given. Indeed we are justified in saying only that the area is approximately

$$6040 \text{ sq. ft.,}$$

and that even this may be in error in the third place.

It is important to observe here that the product (6039.06) of the given dimensions is not reliable beyond the number (three) of significant figures occurring in that one of the given numbers (50.2) which contains the fewer significant figures—it being agreed that 6039.06, when rounded off to three significant figures, becomes 6040.

Let us go one step further and suppose that the person who made these measurements contends that they are in reality accurate to the nearest hundredth of a foot. Then we have the right to insist that he should have given the measurements as

$$120.30 \text{ ft.} \quad \text{and} \quad 50.20 \text{ ft.,}$$

thereby indicating the degree of accuracy of his work through the use of *final significant zeros.*

Here it is found similarly that we are justified in retaining in the product representing the area no more than four significant figures—precisely the same number which occur in that one of the given measurements which contains the fewer significant figures. Thus even now we cannot commit ourselves beyond the statement that the area is approximately

$$6039 \text{ sq. ft.,}$$

and that even this may be in error by as much as 1 in the last place.

Let us now reverse the situation and consider the question of accuracy in division.

Suppose that the area and width of the roof are known to be approximately 6040 sq. ft. and 50.2 ft., respectively, it being understood that the last zero in the number 6040 is not significant.* Clearly then the number of feet of length lies somewhere between the quotients

$$\frac{6035}{50.25} = 120.10 \quad \text{and} \quad \frac{6045}{50.15} = 120.54.$$

Thus we can say only that the length is approximately 120 ft., and that this may be in error by 1 in the last place. In the number of significant figures it contains, this result agrees with the data.

* Significant zeros at the end of a *whole* number are sometimes underscored to indicate their character. Thus if the area had been expressed to four significant figures as 6040, this number would be understood to be accurate to the nearest square foot.

The inference to be drawn from these examples admits of extension to computations involving both multiplication and division. Accordingly we may state that

The result of a computation involving multiplications and divisions of approximate values of quantities is not in general reliable (and hence should not be given) beyond the number of significant figures occurring in that one of the given numbers which contains the fewest significant figures.

Even though experience has established the worth of this principle as a working rule, it should be remembered that it implies an upper limit of accuracy which is not always realized.

From the fact that an integer may be written with indefinitely many significant zeros, it follows that the rule applies without change to operations involving rational numbers as factors or divisors. Thus in a product such as $12\sqrt{5}$ one may ordinarily retain as many significant figures as are used to express the radical.

(*b*)   *Addition and Subtraction.* . The sum of any number of approximate values cannot be accurate beyond that digit which corresponds to the last significant figure of the least accurately expressed summand.

A similar statement applies to the difference of two numbers.

We agree, therefore, to express a sum or difference of approximate values of quantities to no greater degree of accuracy than occurs in that one which is least accurately expressed.

The use of this convention is illustrated in the following sums and differences, where the data represent approximate values which are not accurate beyond the last digit given.

22.65	467.5	0.053674	15600
3.1416	22.38	0.0248	16
25.79	445.1	0.0289	15620

If the sum of several quantities is to be found within a specified degree of accuracy, it is usually necessary to express each one with greater accuracy than is required in the result, so as to protect the result against cumulative errors. This presupposes that it is possible to express all terms of the sum to the same degree of accuracy.

For example, in evaluating

$$\sqrt{3} + \sqrt{5} + \sqrt{7} + \sqrt{11} + \sqrt{13},$$

it is necessary to carry each term to four decimal places in order to secure accuracy to three decimal places in the result:

$\sqrt{3} = 1.732$	$\sqrt{3} = 1.7321$
$\sqrt{5} = 2.236$	$\sqrt{5} = 2.2361$
$\sqrt{7} = 2.646$	$\sqrt{7} = 2.6458$
$\sqrt{11} = 3.317$	$\sqrt{11} = 3.3166$
$\sqrt{13} = 3.606$	$\sqrt{13} = 3.6056$
13.537 (incorrect)	13.536

In summing a large number of terms it is frequently necessary to carry the individual terms to two or more digits beyond the last one required in the result.

In conclusion it should be said that, as questions of accuracy do not in general lend themselves to rigorous treatment or infallible rules, the judgment of the computer plays an important rôle.

PROBLEMS

In the following problems give the results to the degree of accuracy warranted by the data.

1. Find the area of a circle whose diameter is 12.3 in.

2. The measured height and circumference of a cylindrical tank are 30.2 ft. and 157.0 ft. respectively. Compute its capacity.

3. A 1.6-oz. bullet has an estimated speed of 1200 ft./sec. Compute its kinetic energy in foot-pounds from the formula

$$E = \frac{1}{2} \frac{W}{g} v^2,$$

where W is its weight in pounds, v its speed in feet per second, and $g = 32.2$ ft./sec.²

4. A locomotive exerts an estimated draw-bar pull of 3.2 tons while moving at 36 mi./hr. Compute the horsepower which it generates, using the formula

$$\text{hp.} = \frac{Fv}{550},$$

F being the draw-bar pull in pounds, and v the speed in feet per second.

5. The correction C to be subtracted from the measured length of a survey base line to obtain its equivalent length at sea level is given by the formula

$$C = \frac{LE}{R},$$

in which L is the measured length, E is the mean elevation above sea level, and R is the mean radius of the earth (20,890,600 ft.). Above what elevation will this correction exceed 0.10 ft. in the measurement of a base line 408.26 ft. long?

6. The vertical distance between the balls of a Watt governor and their point of suspension is

$$h = \frac{g}{\omega^2};$$

where ω is the angular speed of the governor in radians per second and $g = 32.2$ ft./sec.^{2} If h is found by measurement to be 8.2 in., what is the angular speed of the governor in revolutions per minute?

7. The period of a simple pendulum is

$$T = 2\pi \sqrt{\frac{l}{g}} \text{ seconds,}$$

where l is the length in feet and g is the acceleration of gravity in feet per second per second. By experiment T and l are found to be 2.00 sec. and 3.26 ft., approximately. Find g.

8. Evaluate the sum of the series

$$1 - \frac{1}{5} + \frac{1}{5^2} - \frac{1}{5^3} + \cdots$$

to five decimal places from the values of the individual terms. Compare the result with the exact sum of the series.

9. The length of the edge of a cube is found to be 3.10 in. Between what limits does its volume lie? Its total surface? Solve by the method of this article and by the use of differentials.

10. By Ohm's Law the strength I (amperes) of an electric current due to an electromotive force E (volts) along a circuit of resistance R (ohms) is

$$I = \frac{E}{R}.$$

If I and E are found by measurement to be 10.0 amperes and 100 volts respectively, between what limits must the resistance lie?

145. Computation by Series. The value of a function $f(x)$ for a given value of x cannot always be computed by direct substitution. For example, sin 29° cannot be computed merely by substituting $x = 29°$ in the function sin x. In the evaluation of such functions Taylor's and Maclaurin's series are especially useful.

Since Taylor's series is an expansion in powers of $(x - a)$, the rapidity of the convergence of such a series (provided it does converge) depends on the numerical value of $(x - a)$. The smaller this is the more rapidly the series converges, i.e., the more rapidly the terms diminish in numerical value. Hence if the value of a function $f(x)$ is desired for a given value of x, and if a can be chosen so that $f(a)$, $f'(a)$, $f''(a)$, $\cdots$, are easily computed, and $|x - a|$ is small, the corresponding Taylor series will usually afford a simple means of computing the value of $f(x)$.

If, for a specified value of x, $f(x)$ is to be computed to k decimal places, then by the preceding article each term should be calculated to at least $k + 1$ decimal places. No general rule can be given regarding the accuracy of expressing individual terms. In the case of a slowly converging series in which many terms must be computed, it may be necessary to carry each one to several decimal places more than are required in the result. Special methods, beyond the scope of this book, have been devised for the purpose of minimizing the work involved in summing certain slowly converging series.

It is desirable to know the degree of accuracy with which the sum of n terms of a series represents the value of the corresponding function for a given value of x. In the case of convergent alternating series it follows from Theorem 2, Art. 132, that the error is numerically less than the $(n + 1)$th term.

The limit of error for power series in general will be treated in the next article.

Example 1. Evaluate sin 29° to five decimal places.

Solution by Taylor's series. Since 29° is near 30°, or $\dfrac{\pi}{6}$ radians, and sin x and its successive derivatives are readily found for the angle 30°, we use Taylor's series with $a = \dfrac{\pi}{6}$. The differentiations performed in the following work demand that x and a be expressed in radians. We now let

$$f(x) = \sin x, \qquad \text{whence} \qquad f(a) = \sin \frac{\pi}{6} = \frac{1}{2};$$

then

$$f'(x) = \cos x, \qquad\qquad f'(a) = \cos \frac{\pi}{6} = \frac{\sqrt{3}}{2},$$

$$f''(x) = -\sin x, \qquad\qquad f''(a) = -\sin \frac{\pi}{6} = -\frac{1}{2},$$

$$f'''(x) = -\cos x, \qquad\qquad f'''(a) = -\cos \frac{\pi}{6} = -\frac{\sqrt{3}}{2},$$

$$\begin{array}{ccc} \cdot & \cdot & \cdot \\ \cdot & \cdot & \cdot \\ \cdot & \cdot & \cdot \end{array}$$

Hence by (2), Art. 140,

$$\sin x = \frac{1}{2} + \frac{\sqrt{3}}{2}\left(x - \frac{\pi}{6}\right) - \frac{1}{4}\left(x - \frac{\pi}{6}\right)^2 - \frac{\sqrt{3}}{12}\left(x - \frac{\pi}{6}\right)^3 + \cdots;$$

This series converges and represents sin x for all values of x (see (19), Art. 143).

We now let

$$x = \frac{29\pi}{180}, \quad \text{so that} \quad x - \frac{\pi}{6} = -\frac{\pi}{180},$$

obtaining

$$\sin 29° = \frac{1}{2} - \frac{\sqrt{3}}{2}\left(\frac{\pi}{180}\right) - \frac{1}{4}\left(\frac{\pi}{180}\right)^2 + \frac{\sqrt{3}}{12}\left(\frac{\pi}{180}\right)^3 + \cdots$$

$$= 0.500000 - 0.015112 - 0.000076 + 0.000001 + \cdots$$

$$= 0.48481,$$

correct to five decimal places.

It should be noted that each term is carried to six decimal places in order to insure the required accuracy.

Solution by Maclaurin's Series. In general, Maclaurin's series is useful in evaluating a function $f(x)$ only for values of x near zero. Thus it would not be convenient to calculate sin 29° by Maclaurin's series for sin x. However, it may be computed to advantage by the series for $\sin\left(\dfrac{\pi}{6} - x\right)$; for if $x = \dfrac{\pi}{180}$, $\sin\left(\dfrac{\pi}{6} - x\right)$ becomes sin 29°. Accordingly we let

$$f(x) = \sin\left(\frac{\pi}{6} - x\right), \quad \text{whence} \quad f(0) = \sin\frac{\pi}{6} = \frac{1}{2};$$

then

$$f'(x) = -\cos\left(\frac{\pi}{6} - x\right), \qquad\qquad f'(0) = -\cos\frac{\pi}{6} = -\frac{\sqrt{3}}{2},$$

$$f''(x) = -\sin\left(\frac{\pi}{6} - x\right), \qquad\qquad f''(0) = -\sin\frac{\pi}{6} = -\frac{1}{2},$$

$$f'''(x) = \cos\left(\frac{\pi}{6} - x\right), \qquad\qquad f'''(0) = \cos\frac{\pi}{6} = \frac{\sqrt{3}}{2},$$

$$\cdots \qquad\qquad\qquad\qquad \cdots$$

Hence by (2), Art. 139,

$$\sin\left(\frac{\pi}{6} - x\right) = \frac{1}{2} - \frac{\sqrt{3}}{2}x - \frac{1}{4}x^2 + \frac{\sqrt{3}}{12}x^3 + \cdots;$$

This series converges and represents $\sin\left(\dfrac{\pi}{6} - x\right)$ for all values of x (see (21), Art. 143)

To evaluate sin 29° we let $x = \dfrac{\pi}{180}$. Thus

$$\sin 29° = \frac{1}{2} - \frac{\sqrt{3}}{2}\left(\frac{\pi}{180}\right) - \frac{1}{4}\left(\frac{\pi}{180}\right)^2 + \frac{\sqrt{3}}{12}\left(\frac{\pi}{180}\right)^3 + \cdots = 0.48481,$$

in agreement with the first solution.

Example 2. Evaluate ln 1.02 to five decimal places.
By (4), Art. 143,

$$\ln(1 + x) = x - \frac{x^2}{2} + \frac{x^3}{3} - \frac{x^4}{4} + \cdots;$$

This series represents ln $(1 + x)$ throughout the interval of convergence $-1 < x \leqq 1$. Therefore if $x = 0.02$, we have

$$\ln 1.02 = 0.02 - \frac{(0.02)^2}{2} + \frac{(0.02)^3}{3} - \frac{(0.02)^4}{4} + \cdots$$

$$= 0.020000 - 0.000200 + 0.000003 - \cdots.$$

This is an alternating series of the type discussed in Art. 132. Hence the error introduced by summing only the first two terms is numerically less than the third term 0.000003, which does not affect the fifth place. Hence to five decimal places ln 1.02 = 0.01980.

Example 3.   Evaluation of π.   From the relation

(1)
$$\frac{\pi}{4} = \tan^{-1}\frac{1}{7} + 2\tan^{-1}\frac{1}{3}$$

find the value of π to four decimal places.

By (7), Art. 143,

(2)
$$\tan^{-1} x = x - \frac{x^3}{3} + \frac{x^5}{5} - \frac{x^7}{7} + \cdots,$$

for all values of x in the interval $-1 \leqq x \leqq 1$.

Replacing x by $\frac{1}{7}$ and $\frac{1}{3}$ in (2) and substituing the resulting series in (1) we find that

$$\frac{\pi}{4} = \frac{1}{7} - \frac{1}{3}\left(\frac{1}{7}\right)^3 + \frac{1}{5}\left(\frac{1}{7}\right)^5 - \frac{1}{7}\left(\frac{1}{7}\right)^7 + \cdots$$

$$+ 2\left[\frac{1}{3} - \frac{1}{3}\left(\frac{1}{3}\right)^3 + \frac{1}{5}\left(\frac{1}{3}\right)^5 - \frac{1}{7}\left(\frac{1}{3}\right)^7 + \frac{1}{9}\left(\frac{1}{3}\right)^9 + \cdots\right]$$

$$= 0.14190 + 2(0.32175)$$

$$= 0.78540.$$

Hence to four decimal places $\pi = 3.1416$.

Example 4.   Evaluate

$$\int_{0.1}^{0.2} \frac{e^x - 1}{x}\,dx$$

to four decimal places.   (See Example 1, Art. 115, and Example 2, Art. 116.)
The indefinite integral

$$\int \frac{e^x - 1}{x}\,dx$$

cannot be expressed in finite form in terms of elementary functions.   We therefore replace e^x by the series in (1), Art. 143, obtaining for the integrand

$$\frac{e^x - 1}{x} = 1 + \frac{x}{2!} + \frac{x^2}{3!} + \frac{x^3}{4!} + \cdots.$$

The function in the left member is not defined for $x = 0$.   However, it may be shown that the series converges for all values of x, and represents the function except for $x = 0$.   Hence by Theorem 7, Art. 138, we have

$$\int_{0.1}^{0.2} \frac{e^x - 1}{x}\,dx = \int_{0.1}^{0.2}\left(1 + \frac{x}{2!} + \frac{x^2}{3!} + \frac{x^3}{4!} + \cdots\right)dx$$

$$= \left[x + \frac{x^2}{4} + \frac{x^3}{18} + \frac{x^4}{96} + \cdots\right]_{0.1}^{0.2}$$

$$= \left(0.2 + \frac{0.04000}{4} + \frac{0.00800}{18} + \frac{0.00160}{96} + \cdots\right)$$

$$- \left(0.10000 + \frac{0.01000}{4} + \frac{0.00100}{18} + \frac{0.00010}{96} + \cdots\right)$$

$$= 0.10000 + \frac{0.03000}{4} + \frac{0.00700}{18} + \frac{0.00150}{96} + \cdots$$
$$= 0.1079,$$

to four decimal places.

PROBLEMS

By the use of series, evaluate, to the degree of accuracy specified, the given quantity in each of the Problems 1 to 20 inclusive.

1. $\sin 31°$ to five places.
2. $\cos 28°$ to five places.
3. $\cos\ 2°$ to five places.
4. $\sin\ 3°$ to five places.
5. $\sin 62°$ to five places.
6. $\cos 58°$ to five places.
7. $\sin 89°$ to five places.
8. $\cos 88°$ to five places.

9. $\ln 0.98$ to five places.
10. $\ln 1.04$ to five places.
11. $\ln 2.04$ to four places ($\ln 2 = 0.69315$).
12. $\ln 1.97$ to four places.
13. $\ln 1.95$ to four places.
14. $e^{0.2}$ to five decimal places.
15. $e^{-0.2}$ to five decimal places.
16. $\sqrt{e}$ to four decimal places.

17. $\dfrac{1}{\sqrt{e}}$ to four decimal places.

18. $e^{2.1}$ to three decimal places ($e^2 = 7.3891$).

19. $e^{1.8}$ to three decimal places.

20. $e^{-1.7}$ to three decimal places.

21. From the Maclaurin expansion of $\sqrt{4+x}$ obtain $\sqrt{4.02}$ to five decimal places.

22. Solve Problem 21 by the use of a series for $\sqrt{x}$ in powers of $(x-4)$.

23. From the Maclaurin expansion of $\sqrt[3]{(8-x)^2}$ obtain $\sqrt[3]{(7.95)^2}$ to five decimal places.

24. Solve Problem 23 by means of a Taylor series for $\sqrt[3]{x^2}$.

25. Compute $\sqrt[4]{16.5}$ to five decimal places.

26. Compute $\sqrt[5]{31}$ to five decimal places.

27. Compute $\sqrt[3]{65}$ to three decimal places.

28. Compute $\sqrt[3]{999}$ to five decimal places.

29. Using the fact that $\sqrt{99} = 3\sqrt{11}$, obtain $\sqrt{11}$ to four decimal places from the series for $\sqrt{1-0.01}$.

30. Using the fact that $\sqrt{98} = 7\sqrt{2}$, obtain $\sqrt{2}$ to four decimal places from the series for $\sqrt{1-0.02}$.

31. Using the fact that $\sqrt[3]{1029} = 7\sqrt[3]{3}$, obtain $\sqrt[3]{3}$ to four decimal places from the series for $\sqrt[3]{1+0.029}$.

32. Using the fact that $\sqrt[3]{999} = 3\sqrt[3]{37}$, obtain $\sqrt[3]{37}$ to five decimal places from the series for $\sqrt[3]{1-0.001}$.

33. *Computation of logarithms.* From (6), Art. 143, it follows that

$$\ln \frac{1+x}{1-x} = 2\left(x + \frac{x^3}{3} + \frac{x^5}{5} + \cdots\right),$$

provided $-1 < x < 1$. Putting

$$\frac{1 + x}{1 - x} = \frac{y + 1}{y}, \quad \text{whence} \quad x = \frac{1}{2y + 1},$$

and noting that

$$\ln \frac{y + 1}{y} = \ln (y + 1) - \ln y,$$

show that

$$\ln (y + 1) = \ln y + 2 \left[\frac{1}{2y + 1} + \frac{1}{3} \left(\frac{1}{2y + 1} \right)^3 + \frac{1}{5} \left(\frac{1}{2y + 1} \right)^5 + \cdots \right],$$

provided $y > 0$.

Thus if $\ln y$ is known, $\ln (y + 1)$ can be found.

Hence, starting with $\ln 1 = 0$, calculate to four decimal places

(a) $\ln 2$,   (c) $\ln 4 = 2 \ln 2$,   (e) $\ln 6 = \ln 2 + \ln 3$.
(b) $\ln 3$,   (d) $\ln 5$,

Convert these results to logarithms to the base 10 by Formula $4(h)$, p. 507.

34. From the series for $\ln \dfrac{1 + x}{1 - x}$ in Problem 33, find $\ln 2$ to four decimal places. Now knowing $\ln 2$, let $x = 0.2$ and find $\ln 3$.

35. Find the area under the curve $y = \dfrac{\sin x}{x}$ from $x = 0$ to $x = 1$, correct to four decimal places.

36. Find the area under the curve $y = e^{-x^2}$ from $x = 0$ to $x = \frac{1}{2}$, correct to four decimal places.

37. Evaluate $\displaystyle\int_0^{\frac{1}{5}} e^{-\frac{x^2}{8}} \, dx$ to four decimal places.

38. Evaluate $\displaystyle\int_0^{\frac{1}{2}} \sqrt{1 - x^3} \, dx$ to four decimal places.

39. Evaluate $\displaystyle\int_0^{0.4} e^{-\frac{1}{2} x^2} \, dx$ to four decimal places (cf. Prob. 5, Art 118).

40. Find, correct to six decimal places, the volume generated by revolving about the x-axis the area bounded by the coördinate axes, the line $x = 0.1$, and the curve

$$y = \frac{1}{\sqrt[4]{1 - x^5}}.$$

41. Find, correct to four decimal places, the volume generated by revolving about the x-axis the area bounded by the coördinate axes, the line $x = 1$, and the curve

$$y = \frac{1}{x} \sin \frac{x}{2}.$$

HINT: See Problem 29, Art. 139.

Evaluate the following limits, using series:

42. $\displaystyle\lim_{\theta \to 0} \frac{\sin \theta}{\theta}$.

43. $\displaystyle\lim_{x \to 0} \frac{\sin ax}{x}$.

44. $\displaystyle\lim_{x \to 0} \frac{e^x - 1}{x}$.

45. $\displaystyle\lim_{x \to 0} \frac{\sin^{-1} x}{x}$.

46. $\displaystyle\lim_{x \to 0} \left[\frac{1}{x} \ln \left(1 + \frac{x}{a} \right) \right]$.

47. $\displaystyle\lim_{\theta \to 0} \frac{1 - \cos \theta}{\theta}$.

48. $\lim\limits_{x \to 0} \dfrac{1 - \cos ax}{ax}.$

49. $\lim\limits_{x \to 0} \dfrac{a^x - 1}{x}.$

50. $\lim\limits_{x \to 0} \dfrac{x - \tan^{-1} x}{x^3}.$

51. $\lim\limits_{x \to 0} \left[\dfrac{1}{x} \ln \dfrac{a + x}{a - x} \right].$

52. $\lim\limits_{x \to 0} \left[\dfrac{1}{2x} \left(e^x - e^{-x} \right) \right].$

146. The Remainder; Limit of Error. In the case of a function whose development is a convergent alternating series of the type discussed in Art. 132, it was mentioned in the last article that the error made in approximating the value of the function (for a given value of x) by summing the first n terms of the series is numerically less than the $(n + 1)$th term.

Clearly it is desirable to know such a limit of error for power series in general. This knowledge is gained from the remainder

$$(1) \qquad R_n = \frac{(x - a)^n}{n!} f^{(n)}[a + \theta(x - a)], \quad 0 < \theta < 1,$$

in Taylor's formula (Art. 141).

Now while $\bar{R}_n$ may be regarded as the actual error made in approximating the value of $f(x)$ by summing the first n terms of Taylor's series, it is not in general suitable for computation in its present form owing to the unknown value of $f^{(n)}[a + \theta(x - a)]$. However, (1) may be modified to give an upper limit of the error.* For if the largest numerical value of $f^{(n)}[a + \theta(x - a)]$ in the interval from a to x (including the end-points) does not exceed a certain positive number M, it follows from (1) that

$$(2) \qquad |R_n| \leq \left| \frac{(x - a)^n}{n!} \right| M.$$

In the case of Maclaurin's series, for which $a = 0$, this becomes

$$(3) \qquad |R_n| \leq \left| \frac{x^n}{n!} \right| M,$$

where here M is a positive number no less than the largest numerical value of $f^{(n)}(\theta x)$ in the interval from 0 to x (including the end-points).

These results enable one to find:

(a) How many terms of a series must be used to evaluate a function within a given limit of error.

(b) The maximum error made in using a given number of terms.

*A positive number which the error cannot exceed numerically.

(c) The interval within which the variable must lie in order that a specified number of terms shall give accuracy within a given limit of error.

Example 1. How many terms in Taylor's expansion of sin x in the neighborhood of $\dfrac{\pi}{6}$ must be used to find sin 29° within an error of 0.000001?

By Example 1, Art. 145,

$$\sin x = \frac{1}{2} + \frac{\sqrt{3}}{2}\left(x - \frac{\pi}{6}\right) - \frac{1}{4}\left(x - \frac{\pi}{6}\right)^2 - \frac{\sqrt{3}}{12}\left(x - \frac{\pi}{6}\right)^3 + \cdots,$$

for all values of x. By (5), Art. 142, with $a = \dfrac{\pi}{6}$, the remainder after n terms is

$$(4) \qquad R_n = \frac{1}{n!}\left(x - \frac{\pi}{6}\right)^n \sin\left[\frac{\pi}{6} + \theta\left(x - \frac{\pi}{6}\right) + \frac{n\pi}{2}\right], \qquad 0 < \theta < 1.$$

Since the sine of an angle cannot exceed 1 numerically, and the series represents sin 29° when $x = \dfrac{29\pi}{180}$ and $x - \dfrac{\pi}{6} = -\dfrac{\pi}{180}$, it follows from (4) * that

$$|R_n| \leqq \frac{1}{n!}\left(\frac{\pi}{180}\right)^n.$$

Hence $|R_n|$ will not exceed 0.000001 if

$$\frac{1}{n!}\left(\frac{\pi}{180}\right)^n \leqq 0.000001,$$

or if

$$(0.01745)^n \leqq 0.000001\, n!.$$

Our problem now becomes that of finding by trial the smallest positive integral value of n for which this condition is satisfied. The following table shows that the required value of n is 3.

n	$(0.01745)^n$	$0.000001\, n!$
2	0.000305	0.000002
3	0.0000053	0.000006
4	0.000000093	0.000024

Hence three terms of the series must be used to insure the required accuracy. The value of sin 29° was calculated to five decimal places in Example 1, Art. 145.

Example 2. Within what limit of error will the first three terms of the series of Example 1 give sin 27°?

* Or (2), with $M = 1$ and $a = \dfrac{\pi}{6}$.

Since $n = 3$ and $x = \dfrac{27\pi}{180}$ it follows from (4) that

$$|R_3| < \left| \frac{1}{3!} \left(\frac{27\pi}{180} - \frac{\pi}{6} \right)^3 \right|$$

$$= \frac{1}{3!} \left(\frac{\pi}{60} \right)^3$$

$$= 0.00002.$$

Example 3. For what interval of the variable x will the first two terms of Maclaurin's series for $\ln(2 + x)$ give an error not exceeding 0.005?

Here

$$f(x) = \ln(2 + x),$$

whence

$$f^{(n)}(x) = (-1)^{n-1} \frac{(n-1)!}{(2+x)^n}.$$

Therefore by (2), Art. 142,

(5) $$R_n = \frac{x^n}{n!} f^{(n)}(\theta x) = (-1)^{n-1} \frac{x^n}{n(2+\theta x)^n}, \qquad 0 < \theta < 1.$$

Two cases must be considered, according as x is positive or negative:

Case 1: $x > 0$. In this case, since x and θ are both positive,

$$(2 + \theta x)^n > 2^n,$$

so that

$$\frac{1}{(2 + \theta x)^n} < \frac{1}{2^n}.$$

Hence

$$|R_n| < \frac{x^n}{n \cdot 2^n} \quad \text{and} \quad |R_2| < \frac{x^2}{8}.$$

In order that the error shall not exceed 0.005, x must be so restricted that

$$\frac{x^2}{8} \leqq 0.005,$$

whence

$$x \leqq 0.2.$$

The same result may be obtained in another way. By (12), Art. 143,

$$\ln(2 + x) = \ln 2 + \frac{x}{2} - \frac{x^2}{2 \cdot 2^2} + \frac{x^3}{3 \cdot 2^3} - \cdots + (-1)^n \frac{x^{n-1}}{(n-1)2^{n-1}} + \cdots,$$

provided $-2 < x \leqq 2$. When $0 < x \leqq 2$ this is an alternating series of the type discussed in Art. 132. Hence the error made in approximating $\ln(2 + x)$ by summing only the first two terms of the series is numerically less than the third term $\dfrac{x^2}{8}$. Thus x must be so restricted that

$$\frac{x^2}{8} \leqq 0.005, \quad \text{whence} \quad x \leqq 0.2.$$

Case 2: $x < 0$. Concerning negative values of x, we are interested only in those which lie between 0 and -2; for if $x < -2$, $2 + x$ is negative and $\ln(2 + x)$ is not a real number, while if $x = -2$, $\ln(2 + x)$ does not exist.

Now since x is negative, and θ is a fraction lying between zero and unity,

$$\theta x > x,$$

so that

$$2 + \theta x > 2 + x.$$

Furthermore, since x and θx both exceed -2, it follows that $2 + \theta x$ and $2 + x$ are both positive. Hence

$$(2 + \theta x)^n > (2 + x)^n.$$

and

$$\frac{1}{(2 + \theta x)^n} < \frac{1}{(2 + x)^n}.$$

Therefore by (5)

$$|R_n| < \frac{|x^n|}{n(2 + x)^n},$$

whence

$$|R_2| < \frac{x^2}{2(2 + x)^2} = \frac{1}{2}\left(\frac{x}{2 + x}\right)^2.$$

In order that the error shall not exceed 0.005, x must be so restricted that

$$\frac{1}{2}\left(\frac{x}{2 + x}\right)^2 \leqq 0.005, \quad \text{or} \quad \left(\frac{x}{2 + x}\right)^2 \leqq 0.01,$$

whence

$$-0.1 \leqq \frac{x}{2 + x} \leqq 0.1.$$

As we are investigating the limitations on negative values of x between 0 and -2, we use only that part of the last inequality which states that

$$\frac{x}{2 + x} \geqq -0.1$$

whence

$$x \geqq -0.182.$$

We see, therefore, by combining the results of both cases, that the error caused by using only two terms of the series will not exceed 0.005, provided

$$-0.182 \leqq x \leqq 0.200.$$

PROBLEMS

1. How many terms of Taylor's series for $\sin x$ in the neighborhood of $\frac{\pi}{6}$ must be used to find $\sin 31°$ within an error of 0.000001?

2. Within what limit of error will the first three terms of the series used in Problem 1 give $\sin 33°$?

3. How many terms of Maclaurin's series for $\cos x$ must be used to evaluate $\cos 2°$ within an error of 0.0001?

4. Within what limit of error will the first five terms of the series used in Problem **3** give cos 5°?

5. Show that the remainder after n non-vanishing terms in Maclaurin's expansion of $\ln (1 - x)$ is such that

$$|R_n| < \frac{x^{n+1}}{(n + 1)(1 - x)^{n+1}}, \quad \text{when} \quad 0 < x < 1,$$

and

$$|R_n| < \frac{|x^{n+1}|}{n + 1}, \quad \text{when} \quad x < 0.$$

6. How many terms of the expansion referred to in Problem **5** must be used to find $\ln 0.98$ within an error of 0.000001?

7. Within what limit of error will the first three terms of the series used in Problem **5** give $\ln 0.95$?

8. For what interval of the variable x will the first term of the series used in Problem **5** give an error not exceeding 0.005?

9. Show that the error made by using only n terms of the series for $\tan^{-1} x$ is numerically less than

$$\frac{x^{2n+1}}{2n + 1},$$

when $-1 \leqq x \leqq 1$.

10. How many terms of the series mentioned in Problem **9** must be used to find $\tan^{-1} 0.2$ within an error of one minute?

11. Within what limit of error will the first two terms of the series referred to in Problem **9** give $\tan^{-1} 0.1$?

12. Within what range of values of x will $\sin x = x$ within an error of 0.0005? Express the result in degrees.

13. Show that the remainder after n non-vanishing terms in Taylor's expansion of $\ln x$ in powers of $(x - a)$ is such that

$$|R_n| < \frac{(x - a)^n}{n \cdot a^n}, \quad \text{when} \quad a < x \leqq a + 1,$$

and

$$|R_n| < \frac{(a - x)^n}{n \cdot x^n}, \quad \text{when} \quad a - 1 < x < a,$$

a being a positive number.

14. Using a result of the preceding problem find how many terms in Taylor's expansion of $\ln x$ in powers of $(x - 3)$ must be used to find $\ln 3.5$ within an error of 0.00005.

15. Within what limit of error will the first four terms of the series for $\ln x$ in powers of $(x - 3)$ give $\ln 3.5$?

16. For what range of values of x will two terms of the series for $\ln x$ in powers of $(x - 3)$ give an error not exceeding 0.000005?

17. Show that the error made by using only n terms of Maclaurin's series for e^x is less than $\dfrac{x^n e^x}{n!}$ if $x > 0$, and is less than $\dfrac{|x^n|}{n!}$ if $x < 0$.

18. How many terms of the series mentioned in Problem **17** will suffice to compute e within an error of 0.00005, if it is taken for granted that $e < 3$?

19. Within what limit of error will the first ten terms of Maclaurin's series for e^x give the value of e?   Of $\sqrt{e}$?

CHAPTER XV

HYPERBOLIC FUNCTIONS

147. Exponential Representation of Trigonometric Functions. By use of Maclaurin's series we shall now establish relations between the trigonometric and exponential functions. Aside from their intrinsic worth, as for example, in the study of differential equations, these relations lead naturally into the important field of *hyperbolic functions* to be treated in this chapter. We begin with a study of the exponential function for complex values of the exponent.

Not only does the series

$$1 + z + \frac{z^2}{2!} + \frac{z^3}{3!} + \cdots$$

converge and represent e^z for all real values of z (see (1), Art. 143), but also, as is shown in more advanced works, it converges for all finite values of the complex variable $z = x + iy$, where $i = \sqrt{-1}$ and x and y are real. Accordingly, when z is a complex number, the series is taken as the definition of e^z. Thus, whether z is real or complex, we have

$$e^z = 1 + z + \frac{z^2}{2!} + \frac{z^3}{3!} + \cdots.$$

Hence if $z = ix$,*

$$e^{ix} = 1 + (ix) + \frac{(ix)^2}{2!} + \frac{(ix)^3}{3!} + \frac{(ix)^4}{4!} + \frac{(ix)^5}{5!} + \cdots$$

$$= \left(1 - \frac{x^2}{2!} + \frac{x^4}{4!} - \cdots\right) + i\left(x - \frac{x^3}{3!} + \frac{x^5}{5!} - \cdots\right),$$

since $i^2 = -1$, $i^3 = -i$, $i^4 = 1$, $i^5 = i^4 \cdot i = i, \cdots$. But the series in parentheses are precisely those representing $\cos x$ and $\sin x$. Therefore

$$e^{ix} = \cos x + i \sin x.$$

Similarly we obtain

$$e^{-ix} = \cos x - i \sin x.$$

---

* When z is a pure imaginary number it is customary to express it as $z = ix$ rather than $z = iy$.

Hence by addition and subtraction we find that

$$(1) \qquad \sin x = \frac{e^{ix} - e^{-ix}}{2i},$$

and

$$(2) \qquad \cos x = \frac{e^{ix} + e^{-ix}}{2}.$$

Thus we have expressed the sine and cosine of any real angle x in terms of exponential functions of the pure imaginary number ix. The fundamental identities of trigonometry enable us to express the remaining trigonometric functions exponentially. For example,

$$\tan x = \frac{\sin x}{\cos x} = \frac{e^{ix} - e^{-ix}}{i(e^{ix} + e^{-ix})} = -i \frac{e^{ix} - e^{-ix}}{e^{ix} + e^{-ix}}.$$

As e^z has been defined for all complex values of z, the sine and cosine of any complex quantity $z = x + iy$ will be defined in accordance with (1) and (2) as

$$\sin z = \frac{e^{iz} - e^{-iz}}{2i}, \qquad \cos z = \frac{e^{iz} + e^{-iz}}{2}.$$

The other trigonometric functions of z may be defined in terms of $\sin z$ and $\cos z$. Thus $\tan z = \dfrac{\sin z}{\cos z}$, etc.

In particular, if $z = ix$, we have by definition

$$(3) \qquad \sin (ix) = i \frac{e^x - e^{-x}}{2}$$

and

$$(4) \qquad \cos (ix) = \frac{e^x + e^{-x}}{2}.$$

148. Definitions of the Hyperbolic Functions. The exponential functions

$$\frac{e^x - e^{-x}}{2} \quad \text{and} \quad \frac{e^x + e^{-x}}{2},$$

occurring in (3) and (4) of the preceding article, arise so frequently in technical investigations—as for example in connection with electrical transmission and with suspension cables—that a special study will be made of them. From the manner in which they arise they may be expected to bear some analogies with the trigonometric sine and cosine. Moreover, as will develop later, they are related to the equilateral hyperbola in much the same way that the trigonometric functions are related to the circle. Accordingly they are called, respectively, the **hyperbolic sine** and **hyperbolic cosine** of x and are denoted by the special functional symbols sinh x and cosh x. Thus for all real values of x we have by definition

$$\text{(1)} \qquad \sinh x = \frac{e^x - e^{-x}}{2},$$

$$\text{(2)} \qquad \cosh x = \frac{e^x + e^{-x}}{2}.$$

By setting up ratios involving sinh x and cosh x that are analogous to the ratios defining tan x, cot x, sec x, and csc x in terms of sin x and cos x, we define four other hyperbolic functions as follows:

$$\text{(3)} \qquad \tanh x = \frac{\sinh x}{\cosh x} = \frac{e^x - e^{-x}}{e^x + e^{-x}},$$

$$\text{(4)} \qquad \coth x = \frac{\cosh x}{\sinh x} = \frac{e^x + e^{-x}}{e^x - e^{-x}},$$

$$\text{(5)} \qquad \operatorname{sech} x = \frac{1}{\cosh x} = \frac{2}{e^x + e^{-x}},$$

$$\text{(6)} \qquad \operatorname{csch} x = \frac{1}{\sinh x} = \frac{2}{e^x - e^{-x}}.$$

These are read "hyperbolic tangent of x," etc.

Tabulated values and logarithms of sinh x, cosh x, and tanh x may be found in various tables.

149. Relations between Trigonometric and Hyperbolic Functions. From (3) and (4), Art. 147, and (1) and (2), Art. 148, it follows that

$$\text{(1)} \qquad \sin (ix) = i \sinh x,$$

$$\text{(2)} \qquad \cos (ix) = \cosh x.$$

Moreover, as the exponential function has been defined for all complex values of the exponent, the definitions of the six hyperbolic functions given in the preceding article may be extended so as to hold without change when x has any complex value. Thus from (1) and (2) we obtain

$$\sinh (ix) = i \sin x,$$

$$\cosh (ix) = \cos x.$$

Other similar relations are included among the problems of the next article.

150. Identities Involving Hyperbolic Functions. If the equations of Art. 148 are squared and appropriately combined, the following identities are obtained:

(1) $$\cosh^2 x - \sinh^2 x = 1,$$

(2) $$\tanh^2 x + \operatorname{sech}^2 x = 1,$$

(3) $$\coth^2 x - \operatorname{csch}^2 x = 1.$$

For example, the first of these is derived as follows:

$$\cosh^2 x - \sinh^2 x = \left(\frac{e^x + e^{-x}}{2}\right)^2 - \left(\frac{e^x - e^{-x}}{2}\right)^2$$

$$= \frac{e^{2x} + 2 + e^{-2x} - e^{2x} + 2 - e^{-2x}}{4}$$

$$= 1.$$

Two other important relations are found from (1) and (2), Art. 148, by addition and subtraction:

$$\cosh x + \sinh x = e^x,$$

$$\cosh x - \sinh x = e^{-x}.$$

With the help of these relations, formulas for the hyperbolic functions of the sum and difference of two quantities may be derived. For example,

$$\sinh (x + y) = \frac{e^{x+y} - e^{-x-y}}{2} \qquad \text{(by definition)}$$

$$= \frac{e^x \cdot e^y - e^{-x} \cdot e^{-y}}{2}$$

$$= \tfrac{1}{2}[(\cosh x + \sinh x)(\cosh y + \sinh y)$$

$$- (\cosh x - \sinh x)(\cosh y - \sinh y)],$$

whence by simple reduction we have

(4) $$\sinh (x + y) = \sinh x \cosh y + \cosh x \sinh y.$$

Replacing y by $-y$ and noting that $\cosh (-y) = \cosh y$ and $\sinh (-y) = -\sinh y$ (by (1) and (2), Art. 148), we have

(5) $$\sinh (x - y) = \sinh x \cosh y - \cosh x \sinh y.$$

Other important results are contained in the following problems.

PROBLEMS

1. Show that

$$\tan (ix) = i \tanh x,$$
$$\cot (ix) = - i \coth x,$$
$$\tanh (ix) = i \tan x,$$
$$\coth (ix) = - i \cot x.$$

2. Derive formulas (2) and (3) of this article.

3. Prove that

$$\sinh (-x) = - \sinh x,$$
$$\cosh (-x) = \cosh x,$$
$$\tanh (-x) = - \tanh x,$$
$$\coth (-x) = - \coth x,$$
$$\operatorname{sech} (-x) = \operatorname{sech} x,$$
$$\operatorname{csch} (-x) = - \operatorname{csch} x.$$

4. From the exponential definitions of the hyperbolic functions of $(x + y)$, and by use of the identities in Problem 3, prove that

$$\cosh (x \pm y) = \cosh x \cosh y \pm \sinh x \sinh y,$$

$$\tanh (x \pm y) = \frac{\tanh x \pm \tanh y}{1 \pm \tanh x \tanh y},$$

$$\coth (x \pm y) = \frac{1 \pm \coth x \coth y}{\coth x \pm \coth y}.$$

5. Using (4) or the formulas in Problem 4 prove that

$$\sinh 2x = 2 \sinh x \cosh x,$$
$$\cosh 2x = \cosh^2 x + \sinh^2 x$$
$$= 2 \cosh^2 x - 1$$
$$= 2 \sinh^2 x + 1,$$

$$\tanh 2x = \frac{2 \tanh x}{1 + \tanh^2 x},$$

$$\coth 2x = \frac{1 + \coth^2 x}{2 \coth x}.$$

6. Prove the identities of Problem 5 by the use of exponential functions.

7. Using the formulas for $\cosh 2x$ and replacing x by $\dfrac{x}{2}$ prove that

$$\sinh \frac{x}{2} = \pm \sqrt{\frac{\cosh x - 1}{2}},$$

$$\cosh \frac{x}{2} = \sqrt{\frac{\cosh x + 1}{2}}, \qquad (\cosh \frac{x}{2} \text{ is always positive})$$

$$\tanh \frac{x}{2} = \pm \sqrt{\frac{\cosh x - 1}{\cosh x + 1}},$$

$$\coth \frac{x}{2} = \pm \sqrt{\frac{\cosh x + 1}{\cosh x - 1}}.$$

8. Prove the identities of Problem 7 by the use of exponential functions.

9. Placing $u = x + y$ and $v = x - y$, and using the formulas for $\sinh (x + y)$, $\sinh (x - y)$, $\cosh (x + y)$, and $\cosh (x - y)$, deduce the following *factorization formulas*:

$$\sinh u + \sinh v = 2 \sinh \frac{u + v}{2} \cosh \frac{u - v}{2},$$

$$\cosh u + \cosh v = 2 \cosh \frac{u + v}{2} \cosh \frac{u - v}{2},$$

$$\sinh u - \sinh v = 2 \cosh \frac{u + v}{2} \sinh \frac{u - v}{2},$$

$$\cosh u - \cosh v = 2 \sinh \frac{u + v}{2} \sinh \frac{u - v}{2}.$$

10. Prove the identities of Problem 9 by the use of exponential functions.

11. From (3) and (4), Art. 147, show that

$$\cos (ix) - i \sin (ix) = e^x$$
$$\cos (ix) + i \sin (ix) = e^{-x}.$$

Verify these relations by the use of hyperbolic functions.

12. From the results of Problem 11, show that the trigonometric identities

(a) $$\sin^2 x + \cos^2 x = 1,$$

(b) $$\sin (x \pm y) = \sin x \cos y \pm \cos x \sin y,$$

in which x and y are real, hold likewise when x and y are replaced by ix and iy, respectively, and infer from the relations

$$\sin (ix) = i \sinh x,$$
$$\cos (ix) = \cosh x,$$

that to (a), to (b), and to every trigonometric identity deducible from them, there corresponds an analogous identity involving hyperbolic functions, which is obtainable from the trigonometric identity by replacing

$$\sin x \text{ by } i \sinh x,$$

and

$$\cos x \text{ by } \cosh x.$$

(Note that these quantities are not in reality equal.)

For example, from the identity
$$\cos^2 x + \sin^2 x = 1,$$
we obtain
$$\cosh^2 x + (i \sinh x)^2 = 1,$$
or
$$\cosh^2 x - \sinh^2 x = 1,$$

in accordance with (1) of this article.

13. Verify (2), (3), (4), and (5) in the text of this article by the replacements suggested in the preceding problem.

14. Similarly deduce sundry identities of Problems (4), (5), (7), and (9), noting that tan x and cot x may be replaced, where necessary, by $i \tanh x$ and $- i \coth x$, respectively, in the corresponding trigonometric identities.

15. From the definitions of sinh x and cosh x show that

$$\sinh x = x + \frac{x^3}{3!} + \frac{x^5}{5!} + \cdots$$

and

$$\cosh x = 1 + \frac{x^2}{2!} + \frac{x^4}{4!} + \cdots$$

for all values of x.

16. Obtain expansions of sin (ix) and cos (ix) in powers of x from the definitions of these functions, and thus verify the series of Problem 15.

151. Derivatives of the Hyperbolic Functions. It follows from the definitions of sinh u and cosh u (Art. 148) that

$$(1) \qquad \frac{d}{dx} \sinh u = \cosh u \, \frac{du}{dx},$$

$$(2) \qquad \frac{d}{dx} \cosh u = \sinh u \, \frac{du}{dx},$$

where u is any differentiable function of x.

The derivative of tanh u may now be found as follows:

$$\frac{d}{dx} \tanh u = \frac{d}{dx} \frac{\sinh u}{\cosh u}$$

$$= \frac{\cosh u \, \dfrac{d}{dx}\sinh u - \sinh u \, \dfrac{d}{dx}\cosh u}{\cosh^2 u}$$

$$= \frac{\cosh^2 u - \sinh^2 u}{\cosh^2 u} \frac{du}{dx}.$$

Hence by (1), Art. 150, and (5), Art. 148, we obtain

$$(3) \qquad \frac{d}{dx} \tanh u = \operatorname{sech}^2 u \, \frac{du}{dx}.$$

The same result may be obtained by starting with the exponential definition of tanh u. Thus

$$\frac{d}{dx} \tanh u = \frac{d}{dx} \frac{e^u - e^{-u}}{e^u + e^{-u}}$$

$$= \frac{(e^u + e^{-u})(e^u + e^{-u}) - (e^u - e^{-u})(e^u - e^{-u})}{(e^u + e^{-u})^2} \frac{du}{dx}$$

$$= \left(\frac{2}{e^u + e^{-u}}\right)^2 \frac{du}{dx}$$

$$= \operatorname{sech}^2 u \frac{du}{dx}.$$

It will be left to the student to show similarly that

(4) $$\frac{d}{dx} \operatorname{coth} u = - \operatorname{csch}^2 u \frac{du}{dx},$$

(5) $$\frac{d}{dx} \operatorname{sech} u = - \operatorname{sech} u \tanh u \frac{du}{dx},$$

(6) $$\frac{d}{dx} \operatorname{csch} u = - \operatorname{csch} u \operatorname{coth} u \frac{du}{dx}.$$

152. The Inverse Hyperbolic Functions. Just as the equation $x = \sin y$ may be written $y = \sin^{-1} x$, the equation $x = \sinh y$ may be written $y = \sinh^{-1} x$, the function $\sinh^{-1} x$ being called the **inverse hyperbolic sine of x.** Clearly there are five other inverse hyperbolic functions, the proper symbols for which should be evident.

As the hyperbolic functions are defined in terms of the exponential function, the inverse hyperbolic functions are expressible in terms of the inverse of the exponential function—that is, in terms of the logarithmic function.

For example, to show that $\sinh^{-1} x$ may be so expressed, we let

$$y = \sinh^{-1} x.$$

Then

$$x = \sinh y = \frac{e^y - e^{-y}}{2}$$

and

$$2x = e^y - e^{-y}.$$

Multiplying both sides of this equation by e^y and rearranging the terms, we have

$$(e^y)^2 - 2x(e^y) - 1 = 0,$$

whence, by the quadratic formula (2, p. 507), we obtain

$$e^y = \frac{2x \pm \sqrt{4x^2 + 4}}{2} = x \pm \sqrt{x^2 + 1}.$$

As $\sqrt{x^2 + 1} > x$ for all real values of x, and e^y is always positive, we reject the minus sign and have

$$e^y = x + \sqrt{x^2 + 1},$$

whence

$$y = \ln (x + \sqrt{x^2 + 1}).$$

Replacing y by its value, $\sinh^{-1} x$, we obtain (1) below. It is left to the student to verify formulas (2), $\cdots$, (6).

(1) $\qquad \sinh^{-1} x = \ln (x + \sqrt{x^2 + 1}), \qquad$ for any real x,

(2) $\qquad \cosh^{-1} x = \ln (x \pm \sqrt{x^2 - 1}), \quad x \geq 1,$

(3) $\qquad \tanh^{-1} x = \dfrac{1}{2} \ln \dfrac{1 + x}{1 - x}, \quad -1 < x < 1,$

(4) $\qquad \coth^{-1} x = \dfrac{1}{2} \ln \dfrac{x + 1}{x - 1}, \quad x < -1 \ \text{ or } \ x > 1.$

(5) $\qquad \operatorname{sech}^{-1} x = \ln \dfrac{1 \pm \sqrt{1 - x^2}}{x}, \quad 0 < x \leq 1,$

(6) $\qquad \begin{cases} \operatorname{csch}^{-1} x = \ln \dfrac{1 + \sqrt{x^2 + 1}}{x}, \quad x > 0, \\[3mm] \operatorname{csch}^{-1} x = \ln \dfrac{1 - \sqrt{x^2 + 1}}{x}, \quad x < 0. \end{cases}$

153. Derivatives of the Inverse Hyperbolic Functions. General formulas for the derivatives of the inverse hyperbolic functions of a real variable may be derived either from the numbered equations of the preceding article, or by a method analogous to that by which the derivatives of the inverse trigonometric functions were found in Art. 48.

For example, if u is any real function of x possessing a derivative, it follows from (1) of the preceding article that

$$\frac{d}{dx} \sinh^{-1} u = \frac{d}{dx} \ln (u + \sqrt{u^2 + 1})$$

$$= \frac{1}{u + \sqrt{u^2 + 1}} \left[1 + \frac{1}{2}(u^2 + 1)^{-\frac{1}{2}} \cdot 2u \right] \frac{du}{dx}$$

$$= \frac{1}{u + \sqrt{u^2 + 1}} \cdot \frac{\sqrt{u^2 + 1} + u}{\sqrt{u^2 + 1}} \cdot \frac{du}{dx},$$

whence

$$\frac{d}{dx} \sinh^{-1} u = \frac{1}{\sqrt{u^2 + 1}} \frac{du}{dx},$$

for all values of x for which u has a derivative.

In the second method let $y = \sinh^{-1} u$. Then since

$$u = \sinh y,$$

it follows from (1), Art. 151, that

$$\frac{du}{dx} = \cosh y \frac{dy}{dx},$$

whence

$$\frac{dy}{dx} = \frac{1}{\cosh y} \frac{du}{dx}.$$

But (1), Art. 150, shows that

$$\cosh y = \sqrt{1 + \sinh^2 y}$$
$$= \sqrt{1 + u^2},$$

the negative square root being impossible, since by definition $\cosh y$ is always positive. Hence

$$\frac{dy}{dx} = \frac{1}{\sqrt{u^2 + 1}} \frac{du}{dx},$$

for all values of x for which $\dfrac{du}{dx}$ exists. Replacing y by its value $\sinh^{-1} u$, we obtain (1) below. The derivations of formulas (2), $\cdots$, (6) are left to the student.

(1) $$\frac{d}{dx} \sinh^{-1} u = \frac{1}{\sqrt{u^2 + 1}} \frac{du}{dx}, \quad \text{for any real } u,$$

(2) $$\frac{d}{dx} \cosh^{-1} u = \pm \frac{1}{\sqrt{u^2 - 1}} \frac{du}{dx}, \quad u > 1,$$

(3) $$\frac{d}{dx} \tanh^{-1} u = \frac{1}{1 - u^2} \frac{du}{dx}, \quad -1 < u < 1,$$

(4) $$\frac{d}{dx} \coth^{-1} u = \frac{1}{1 - u^2} \frac{du}{dx}, \quad u < -1 \quad \text{or} \quad u > 1,$$

(5) $$\frac{d}{dx} \operatorname{sech}^{-1} u = \pm \frac{1}{u\sqrt{1 - u^2}} \frac{du}{dx}, \quad 0 < u < 1,$$

(6)
$$\begin{cases} \dfrac{d}{dx} \operatorname{csch}^{-1} u = -\dfrac{1}{u\sqrt{1+u^2}} \dfrac{du}{dx}, & u > 0, \\[3mm] \dfrac{d}{dx} \operatorname{csch}^{-1} u = \dfrac{1}{u\sqrt{1+u^2}} \dfrac{du}{dx}, & u < 0. \end{cases}$$

PROBLEMS

1. Derive formulas (1) and (2), Art. 151.

2. Verify formulas (4), (5), and (6), Art. 151, each by two methods.

3. Derive formulas (2), $\cdots$, (6), Art. 152.

4. By two methods derive each of the last five formulas of this article.

5. Show that $e^{\sinh^{-1}x} = x + \sqrt{x^2+1}$.

6. Show that $e^{2\tanh^{-1}x} = \dfrac{1+x}{1-x}$, provided $-1 < x < 1$.

7. Find $\dfrac{dy}{dx}$, and simplify:

(a) $y = \sinh \dfrac{1}{x}$,

(b) $y = \cosh(x^2 - 2)$,

(c) $y = \tanh(\ln x)$,

(d) $y = \coth(\cot x)$,

(e) $y = \operatorname{sech} \dfrac{3}{x^2}$,

(f) $y = \operatorname{csch}\left(\ln \dfrac{1}{x}\right)$,

(g) $y = \sinh^2 2x$,

(h) $y = \cosh^3(1-x)$,

(i) $y = \tanh x \sinh x$,

(j) $y = \dfrac{\coth 2x}{\sinh 2x}$,

(k) $y = x^2 \operatorname{sech} x^2$,

(l) $y = (\ln 3x)(\operatorname{csch} 3x)$.

8. Find $\dfrac{dy}{dx}$, and simplify:

(a) $y = \sinh^{-1} \dfrac{x}{2}$,

(b) $y = \cosh^{-1} 3x$,

(c) $y = \tanh^{-1} \dfrac{2}{x}$,

(d) $y = \coth^{-1} \dfrac{1}{2x}$,

(e) $y = e^{\coth^{-1} x}$,

(f) $y = \operatorname{sech}^{-1}(\sin x)$,

(g) $y = x^2 \operatorname{csch}^{-1} x$,

(h) $y = \dfrac{\sinh^{-1} x}{x}$.

9. Evaluate the following limits:

(a) $\lim\limits_{x \to 0} \dfrac{\sinh x}{x}$,

(b) $\lim\limits_{x \to 0} \dfrac{\cosh x - 1}{x}$,

(c) $\lim\limits_{x \to 0} \dfrac{\tanh x}{x}$,

(d) $\lim\limits_{x \to 0} \dfrac{\sinh^{-1} x}{x}$,

(e) $\lim_{x \to \frac{1}{2}} \dfrac{1 - \cosh (2x - 1)}{1 - 2x}$,   (h) $\lim_{x \to 0} \dfrac{\ln \cosh x}{x}$,

(f) $\lim_{x \to 0} \dfrac{\sinh^2 x}{2x}$,   (i) $\lim_{x \to \infty} \tanh x$,

(g) $\lim_{x \to 0} \dfrac{\sinh 2x}{\sinh x}$,   (j) $\lim_{x \to \infty} \coth x$.

10. Without making use of the series for e^x, obtain the Maclaurin series for $\sinh x$ and $\cosh x$.

11. Find the critical point of the curve $y = \cosh x$ and classify it. Discuss symmetry and concavity. Sketch the curve.

12. Find the point of inflection of the curve $y = \sinh x$. Sketch the curve, using information obtained from the first and second derivatives of y.

13. Find the point of inflection of the curve $y = \tanh x$. Show that the lines $y = 1$ and $y = -1$ are asymptotes. Discuss concavity. Sketch the curve.

14. Find the maximum point and points of inflection of the curve $y = \operatorname{sech} x$. Show that the x-axis is an asymptote. Sketch the curve.

15. Show that $\ln (x - \sqrt{x^2 - 1}) = -\ln (x + \sqrt{x^2 - 1})$ and hence infer from (2), Art. 152, that

$$\cosh^{-1} x = \pm \ln (x + \sqrt{x^2 - 1}), \qquad x \geqq 1.$$

16. Show that $\ln \dfrac{1 - \sqrt{1 - x^2}}{x} = -\ln \dfrac{1 + \sqrt{1 - x^2}}{x}$, and hence infer from (5), Art. 152, that

$$\operatorname{sech}^{-1} x = \pm \ln \dfrac{1 + \sqrt{1 - x^2}}{x}, \qquad 0 < x \leqq 1.$$

17. Express each of the inverse hyperbolic functions of $\dfrac{1}{x}$ as an inverse hyperbolic function of x.

18. Using the results of Problem 17, deduce the logarithmic expressions for $\operatorname{sech}^{-1} x$ and $\coth^{-1} x$, from those for $\cosh^{-1} x$ and $\tanh^{-1} x$.

154. Integration; Hyperbolic Substitution.
By means of the formulas of Art. 152, the secondary formulas of integration (XXI to XXIV, Art. 82) may be written as follows:

XXI $$\int \frac{du}{\sqrt{u^2 + a^2}} = \ln (u + \sqrt{u^2 + a^2}) + C_1$$

$$= \sinh^{-1} \frac{u}{a} + C,$$

XXII $$\int \frac{du}{\sqrt{u^2 - a^2}} = \ln (u + \sqrt{u^2 - a^2}) + C_1$$

$$= \cosh^{-1} \frac{u}{a} + C,$$

XXIII $$\int \frac{du}{a^2 - u^2} = \frac{1}{2a} \ln \frac{a + u}{a - u} + C$$

$$= \frac{1}{a} \tanh^{-1} \frac{u}{a} + C,$$

XXIV $$\int \frac{du}{u^2 - a^2} = \frac{1}{2a} \ln \frac{u - a}{u + a} + C_1$$

$$= -\frac{1}{a} \tanh^{-1} \frac{u}{a} + C.$$

Let us derive the first of these. From (1), Art. 152, it follows that

$$\sinh^{-1} \frac{u}{a} = \ln \left(\frac{u}{a} + \sqrt{\frac{u^2}{a^2} + 1} \right)$$

$$= \ln (u + \sqrt{u^2 + a^2}) - \ln a.$$

Hence if u and a are real, and a is constant,

$$d \left(\sinh^{-1} \frac{u}{a} \right) = d [\ln (u + \sqrt{u^2 + a^2})] = \frac{du}{\sqrt{u^2 + a^2}},$$

the final result being obtained either by direct differentiation or by the use of (1), Art. 153. Therefore

$$\int \frac{du}{\sqrt{u^2 + a^2}} = \ln (u + \sqrt{u^2 + a^2}) + C_1 = \sinh^{-1} \frac{u}{a} + C,$$

where $C_1 = C - \ln a$. Thus we have established XXI.

The second form of the result may be found alternatively as follows: Let $u = a \sinh \phi$; then

$$du = a \cosh \phi \, d\phi$$

and

$$\sqrt{u^2 + a^2} = \sqrt{a^2 \sinh^2 \phi + a^2} = a \sqrt{\sinh^2 \phi + 1} = a \cosh \phi.$$

Hence

$$\int \frac{du}{\sqrt{u^2 + a^2}} = \int d\phi = \phi + C = \sinh^{-1} \frac{u}{a} + C,$$

in agreement with the first derivation.

Formulas XXII to XXIV may be derived by methods analogous to the two just employed. The device used in the second method, namely, that of replacing the variable of integration by a hyperbolic function of a new variable, is called **hyperbolic substitution**. Clearly, it is quite analogous to trigonometric substitution (Art. 90).   Its use is explained more fully in the following discussion.

In general, hyperbolic substitution may be applied with the same facility as trigonometric substitution to the integration of expressions involving functions of $\sqrt{u^2 + a^2}$, $\sqrt{u^2 - a^2}$, or $\sqrt{a^2 - u^2}$.   Its purpose is primarily to render the integrand rational in terms of hyperbolic functions of a new variable, though in certain special instances it may be effective when the resulting integrand is irrational.   Various cases in which irrational integrands may always be expressed rationally in terms of hyperbolic functions will now be considered.

If the integrand is algebraic and involves no irrational function of u, aside from integral powers of

$$\sqrt{u^2 + a^2}, \quad \text{substitute} \quad u = a \sinh \phi,$$

$$\sqrt{u^2 - a^2}, \quad \text{substitute} \quad u = a \cosh \phi,$$

$$\sqrt{a^2 - u^2}, \quad \text{substitute} \quad u = a \tanh \phi,$$

where for simplicity in formal integration we restrict ϕ, without loss of generality, to positive values.   We implicitly adopted an analogous restriction in formal integration by trigonometric substitution (Art. 90), where, as was signified by our use of triangle constructions, θ was taken as an acute angle.

It is easily seen that these substitutions convert the respective radicals to rational expressions in terms of hyperbolic functions; for

$$\text{when } u = a \sinh \phi, \ \sqrt{u^2 + a^2} = \sqrt{a^2 \sinh^2 \phi + a^2} = a \cosh \phi,$$

$$\text{when } u = a \cosh \phi, \ \sqrt{u^2 - a^2} = \sqrt{a^2 \cosh^2 \phi - a^2} = a \sinh \phi,$$

$$\text{when } u = a \tanh \phi, \ \sqrt{a^2 - u^2} = \sqrt{a^2 - a^2 \tanh^2 \phi} = a \operatorname{sech} \phi.$$

In the problem list which follows, the student will be called upon to derive formulas XXII to XXIV by appropriate hyperbolic substitutions.

Example 1.   Evaluate $\int \dfrac{\sqrt{4x^2 - 9}}{x^2} \, dx$ by hyperbolic substitution.

Letting

$$2x = 3 \cosh \phi,$$

we have

$$\sqrt{4x^2 - 9} = \sqrt{9 \cosh^2 \phi - 9}$$

$$= 3 \sinh \phi$$

and

$$dx = \tfrac{3}{2} \sinh \phi \, d\phi.$$

Then

$$\int \frac{\sqrt{4x^2 - 9}}{x^2}\, dx = 2 \int \frac{\sinh^2 \phi}{\cosh^2 \phi}\, d\phi$$

$$= 2 \int \tanh^2 \phi\, d\phi$$

$$= 2 \int (1 - \operatorname{sech}^2 \phi)\, d\phi$$

$$= 2(\phi - \tanh \phi) + C \qquad \text{(cf. (3), Art. 151)}$$

$$= 2 \left(\phi - \frac{\sinh \phi}{\cosh \phi} \right) + C.$$

Since ϕ is restricted to positive values we have (Problem 15, Art. 153),

$$\phi = \cosh^{-1} \frac{2x}{3} = + \ln \left(\frac{2x}{3} + \sqrt{\frac{4x^2}{9} - 1} \right)$$

$$= \ln (2x + \sqrt{4x^2 - 9}) - \ln 3.$$

Therefore

$$\int \frac{\sqrt{4x^2 - 9}}{x^2}\, dx = 2 \left[\ln (2x + \sqrt{4x^2 - 9}) - \ln 3 - \frac{\sqrt{4x^2 - 9}}{2x} \right] + C$$

$$= 2 \ln (2x + \sqrt{4x^2 - 9}) - \frac{\sqrt{4x^2 - 9}}{x} + C_1,$$

where $C_1 = C - 2 \ln 3$.

Example 2. Evaluate $\int_0^3 \dfrac{dx}{(x^2 + 1)^{\frac{3}{2}}}$.

Letting

$$x = \sinh \phi,$$

we have

$$dx = \cosh \phi\, d\phi$$

and

$$(x^2 + 1)^{\frac{3}{2}} = \cosh^3 \phi.$$

To establish the limits on the transformed integral, we note that

$$\text{when } x = 0, \phi = \sinh^{-1} 0 = 0,$$

and

$$\text{when } x = 3, \phi = \sinh^{-1} 3.$$

Hence

$$\int_0^3 \frac{dx}{(x^2 + 1)^{\frac{3}{2}}} = \int_0^{\sinh^{-1} 3} \operatorname{sech}^2 \phi\, d\phi$$

$$= \left[\tanh \phi \right]_0^{\sinh^{-1} 3}$$

$$= \left[\frac{\sinh \phi}{\sqrt{1 + \sinh^2 \phi}} \right]_0^{\sinh^{-1} 3}$$

$$= \frac{3}{10} \sqrt{10}.$$

The integral may be evaluated approximately by the use of a table of hyperbolic functions, as follows:

$$\int_0^3 \frac{dx}{(x^2+1)^{\frac{3}{2}}} = \left[\tanh \phi \right]_0^{\sinh^{-1}3} = [\tanh \phi]_0^{1.8185}$$

$$= \tanh 1.8185 = 0.9487,$$

to four decimal places.

By (4), Art. 90, the given integral can be evaluated also by the substitution $x = \tan \theta$.

As illustrated by these examples, hyperbolic substitution leads in general to an integral involving one or more hyperbolic functions. Accordingly, the following formulas will be found useful. They are readily verified by differentiation.

(1) $$\int \sinh u \, du = \cosh u + C,$$

(2) $$\int \cosh u \, du = \sinh u + C,$$

(3) $$\int \tanh u \, du = \ln \cosh u + C,$$

(4) $$\int \coth u \, du = \ln \sinh u + C,$$

(5) $$\int \operatorname{sech}^2 u \, du = \tanh u + C,$$

(6) $$\int \operatorname{csch}^2 u \, du = -\coth u + C,$$

(7) $$\int \operatorname{sech} u \tanh u \, du = -\operatorname{sech} u + C,$$

(8) $$\int \operatorname{csch} u \coth u \, du = -\operatorname{csch} u + C.$$

PROBLEMS

Evaluate the integrals in Problems 1 to 16 inclusive.

1. $\displaystyle\int \sinh \frac{2x}{3} \, dx.$

2. $\displaystyle\int \cosh \frac{3-x}{4} \, dx.$

3. $\displaystyle\int x \tanh x^2 \, dx.$

4. $\displaystyle\int \frac{1}{x^2} \coth \frac{2}{x} \, dx.$

5. $\displaystyle\int \operatorname{sech}^2 \frac{3x}{4} \, dx.$

6. $\displaystyle\int x^2 \operatorname{csch}^2 (2x^3) \, dx.$

7. $\displaystyle\int \frac{1}{x} \operatorname{sech} (\ln x) \tanh (\ln x) \, dx.$

8. $\displaystyle\int \operatorname{csch} (2-x) \coth (2-x) \, dx.$

9. $\int \sinh^2 x \cosh x \, dx.$

13. $\int \sinh^2 x \, dx.$

10. $\int \cosh^3 2x \, dx.$

14. $\int \cosh^2 x \, dx.$

11. $\int \tanh^2 3x \, dx.$

15. $\int -\dfrac{\sinh x}{\sqrt{1 - \cosh x}} \, dx.$

12. $\int \coth^2 \dfrac{x}{2} \operatorname{csch}^2 \dfrac{x}{2} \, dx.$

16. $\int \dfrac{\cosh 2x}{1 + \sinh 2x} \, dx.$

17. Show by methods analogous to those used above in deriving Formula XXI that

$$\int \frac{du}{\sqrt{u^2 - a^2}} = \ln\left(\frac{u}{a} + \sqrt{\left(\frac{u}{a}\right)^2 - 1}\right) + C$$

$$= \cosh^{-1}\frac{u}{a} + C.$$

This amounts to a derivation of Formula XXII. Note that in order for

$$\ln\left(\frac{u}{a} + \sqrt{\left(\frac{u}{a}\right)^2 - 1}\right)$$

to be real, $\dfrac{u}{a}$ must exceed unity; and since this makes $\ln\left(\dfrac{u}{a} + \sqrt{\left(\dfrac{u}{a}\right)^2 - 1}\right)$ posi-

tive, $\cosh^{-1}\dfrac{u}{a}$ must be limited to positive values, in accordance with the restriction

made on ϕ in the discussion on hyperbolic substitution.

18. Derive Formula XXIII.

Perform the integrations in Problems 19 to 24 and verify the results by formula or by trigonometric substitution.

19. $\int \dfrac{dx}{\sqrt{9 + 4x^2}}.$

22. $\int \dfrac{dx}{(1 + x^2)^{\frac{5}{2}}}.$

20. $\int \dfrac{dx}{9 - x^2}.$

23. $\int \dfrac{x^2 dx}{\sqrt{x^2 + 4}}.$

21. $\int \dfrac{dx}{\sqrt{2x^2 - 3}}.$

24. $\int \dfrac{dx}{\sqrt{25 + 4x^2}}.$

25. Noting that

$$\operatorname{sech} u = \frac{\cosh u}{1 + \sinh^2 u}$$

show that

$$\int \operatorname{sech} u \, du = \tan^{-1} \sinh u + C.$$

By means of a right triangle whose legs are respectively unity and $\sinh u$, show that this integral may be represented also by any one of the following expressions: $\sin^{-1} \tanh u = \cos^{-1} \operatorname{sech} u = \cot^{-1} \operatorname{csch} u = \sec^{-1} \cosh u = \csc^{-1} \coth u.$ The function represented by these equivalent expressions is called the **gudermannian** of u, and is designated by the functional symbol gd u.

26. Noting that

$$\operatorname{csch} u = \frac{\sinh u}{\cosh^2 u - 1} = \frac{\operatorname{sech} u \tanh u}{1 - \operatorname{sech}^2 u}$$

show that

$$\int \operatorname{csch} u \, du = \frac{1}{2} \ln \frac{\cosh u - 1}{\cosh u + 1} + C = - \coth^{-1} \cosh u + C$$

$$= \frac{1}{2} \ln \frac{1 - \operatorname{sech} u}{1 + \operatorname{sech} u} + C = - \tanh^{-1} \operatorname{sech} u + C.$$

27. Derive Formula XXIV.

Evaluate the following definite integrals by hyperbolic substitution, using the results of Problems 25 and 26 where necessary:

28. $\displaystyle\int_0^{\sqrt{5}} \frac{x^2 dx}{(9 - x^2)^{\frac{3}{2}}}.$

29. $\displaystyle\int_1^2 \frac{dx}{(4x^2 + 9)^{\frac{3}{2}}}.$

30. $\displaystyle\int_0^1 \frac{dx}{\sqrt{x^2 + 4x + 8}}.$

31. $\displaystyle\int_3^5 \sqrt{x^2 - 9} \, dx.$

32. $\displaystyle\int_1^2 \frac{dx}{x\sqrt{9 - x^2}}.$

33. $\displaystyle\int_4^8 \frac{dx}{\sqrt{x^2 - 15}}.$

34. $\displaystyle\int_3^4 \frac{dx}{4x^2 - 4x - 15}.$

35. $\displaystyle\int_3^4 \frac{dx}{x^2 \sqrt{25 - x^2}}.$

155. Relation to the Equilateral Hyperbola. It was stated in Art. 148 that the hyperbolic functions owe their name to the fact that they are related to the equilateral hyperbola in much the same way that the trigonometric (or circular) functions are related to the circle. These analogies will now be demonstrated.

The equations

$$(1) \qquad \begin{cases} x = a \cos \theta, \\ y = a \sin \theta, \end{cases}$$

in the parameter θ, represent a circle with center at the origin and of radius a (Fig. 155a).

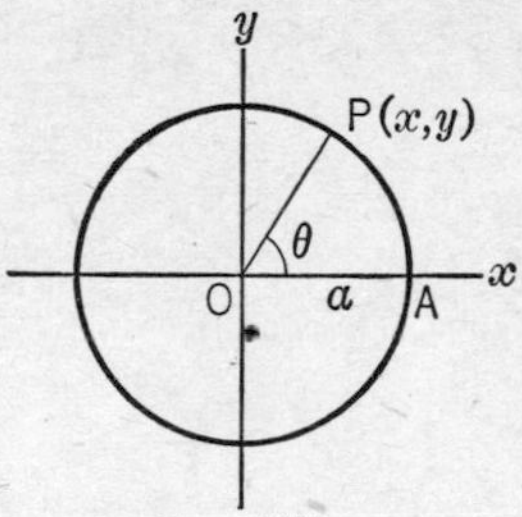

Similarly, the equations

$$(2) \qquad \begin{cases} x = a \cosh \phi, \\ y = a \sinh \phi, \end{cases}$$

Fig. 155a

in the parameter ϕ, represent an equilateral hyperbola with center at the origin and of semi-transverse axis a (Fig. 155b), for in the same way that the equation $x^2 + y^2 = a^2$, of the circle, may be found by eliminating θ from (1), by use of the relation $\cos^2 \theta + \sin^2 \theta = 1$, so also may the equation $x^2 - y^2 = a^2$, of the hyperbola, be found by eliminating ϕ from (2), by use of the relation $\cosh^2 \phi - \sinh^2 \phi = 1$.

While the parameter θ obviously represents an angle, the parameter ϕ has no such simple geometric meaning. However, θ and ϕ admit of certain analogous geometric interpretations.

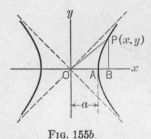

For instance, the area of the sector OAP of the circle (Fig. 155a) is

$$K = \tfrac{1}{2} a^2 \theta,$$

where θ is expressed in radians.

FIG. 155b

Similarly, as we shall now prove, the area of the sector OAP (Fig. 155b), bounded by the hyperbola, the x-axis, and the line through the origin and the point $P(x, y)$, is

$$K = \tfrac{1}{2} a^2 \phi,$$

where ϕ is the value of the parameter corresponding to the point $P(x, y)$.

$$K = \text{area } OBP - \text{area } ABP$$

$$= \tfrac{1}{2} xy - \int_a^x \sqrt{x^2 - a^2}\, dx$$

$$= \tfrac{1}{2} xy - a^2 \int_0^\phi \sinh^2 \phi\, d\phi \qquad \text{(by (2))}$$

$$= \tfrac{1}{2} xy - \frac{a^2}{2} \left[\tfrac{1}{2} \sinh 2\phi - \phi \right]_0^\phi$$

$$= \tfrac{1}{2} xy - \frac{a^2}{2} (\sinh \phi \cosh \phi - \phi)$$

$$= \tfrac{1}{2} xy - \frac{a^2}{2} \left(\frac{y}{a} \cdot \frac{x}{a} - \phi \right)$$
$$= \tfrac{1}{2} a^2 \phi.$$

Thus the parameters θ and ϕ in the parametric equations (1) and (2) of the circle and equilateral hyperbola admit of the following analogous geometric interpretations:

If K is the area of the circular sector OAP (Fig. 155a), and a is the radius of the circle, then

$$\theta = \cos^{-1}\frac{x}{a} = \sin^{-1}\frac{y}{a} = \frac{2K}{a^2},$$

while if K represents the area of the hyperbolic sector OAP (Fig. 155b), and a is the semi-transverse axis of the hyperbola, then

$$\phi = \cosh^{-1}\frac{x}{a} = \sinh^{-1}\frac{y}{a} = \frac{2K}{a^2}.$$

CHAPTER XVI

PARTIAL DIFFERENTIATION

156. Functions of More Than One Variable; Continuity. Hitherto we have devoted our attention to functions of a single variable. We shall now consider applications of calculus to functions of more than one independent variable. Such functions are of frequent occurrence, even in the most elementary branches of mathematics. For example, the volume, $V = xyz$, of a rectangular parallelepiped, is a function of the lengths x, y, z of the edges. Since V depends upon the values assigned to x, y, z, and these values may be chosen quite independently, we call V the dependent variable, and x, y, z the independent variables. In accordance with custom we shall adopt the symbols $f(x, y), f(x, y, z)$, $f(x_1, x_2, \ldots, x_n)$ to represent functions of two, three, and n variables, respectively.

In what follows we shall be concerned primarily with functions which are continuous. We already know what is meant by the continuity of a function of one variable (Art. 7). We now extend the conception of continuity to functions of two variables.

A function $f(x, y)$ of two independent variables is said to be **continuous** *for $x = a$, $y = b$, if it is defined for these values and for neighboring values, and if*

$$\lim_{\substack{x \to a \\ y \to b}} f(x, y) = f(a, b),$$

regardless of the manner in which x and y approach their respective limits a and b.

For a function of more than two variables we adopt a similar definition.

Let us consider the foregoing definition from a geometric standpoint. In analytic geometry it is shown that an equation of the form

$$(1) \qquad\qquad z = f(x, y)$$

in general represents a surface when x, y, and z are interpreted as rectangular space coördinates. Now if $P_1(a, b, c)$ is a point of the surface (1) which corresponds to the values $x = a$, $y = b$, for which $f(x, y)$

is continuous, and $P(x, y, z)$ is any other point of the surface (see Fig. 156), the definition of continuity assures us that $f(x, y)$, or z, approaches $f(a, b)$, or c, regardless of the manner in which x and y approach a and b—that is, regardless of the manner in which P approaches P_1 along the surface.

Thus the continuity of a function $f(x, y)$, for $x = a, y = b$, guarantees that there shall be no discontinuities or breaks in the surface $z = f(x, y)$, such as would make it impossible for a point moving on the surface to approach from any direction what-ever, or in any manner whatever, the fixed point of the surface corresponding to $x = a, y = b$.

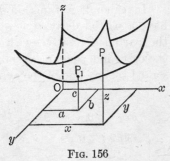

If a function $f(x, y)$ is continuous for $x = a, y = b$, we say in geometric language that it is continuous at the point (a, b) of the xy-plane.

FIG. 156

A function $f(x, y)$ is said to be con-tinuous in a *region* of the xy-plane when it is continuous at each point of the region.

157. Partial Derivatives. If z is a function of two independent variables,

$$z = f(x, y),$$

and y is held constant, while x is allowed to vary, z becomes a function of x alone. Accordingly, when y is held constant, we may find the deriva-tive of z with respect to x just as though z were a function of one variable. The derivative obtained in this way is called the **partial derivative** of z with respect to x, and is represented by the symbol $\dfrac{\partial z}{\partial x}$. Similarly, when x is held constant, we may find the partial derivative of z with respect to y, which we shall denote by the symbol $\dfrac{\partial z}{\partial y}$.

It follows, therefore, from the definition of a derivative (Art. 12) that

$$\frac{\partial z}{\partial x} = \frac{\partial}{\partial x} f(x, y) = \lim_{\Delta x \to 0} \frac{f(x + \Delta x, y) - f(x, y)}{\Delta x},$$

$$\frac{\partial z}{\partial y} = \frac{\partial}{\partial y} f(x, y) = \lim_{\Delta y \to 0} \frac{f(x, y + \Delta y) - f(x, y)}{\Delta y},$$

provided these limits exist.

The following symbols are commonly used to designate the partial derivatives of a function of two variables:

$$\frac{\partial z}{\partial x}, \quad \frac{\partial f}{\partial x}, \quad \frac{\partial}{\partial x} f(x, y), \quad f_x(x, y), \quad f_x, \quad z_x;$$

$$\frac{\partial z}{\partial y}, \quad \frac{\partial f}{\partial y}, \quad \frac{\partial}{\partial y} f(x, y), \quad f_y(x, y), \quad f_y, \quad z_y.$$

In general, a function $z = f(x_1, x_2, \cdots, x_n)$, of n variables, may have a partial derivative with respect to each variable. In obtaining the partial derivative with respect to x_2, for example, we regard all the other independent variables as constants. This derivative is represented by any one of the symbols

$$\frac{\partial z}{\partial x_2}, \quad \frac{\partial f}{\partial x_2}, \quad \frac{\partial}{\partial x_2} f(x_1, x_2, \cdots, x_n), \quad f_{x_2}(x_1, x_2, \cdots, x_n), \quad f_{x_2}, \quad z_{x_2}.$$

Example 1. If $z = x^2 + 5xy - 2y^2$ we obtain

$$\frac{\partial z}{\partial x} = 2x + 5y \quad \text{and} \quad \frac{\partial z}{\partial y} = 5x - 4y,$$

by treating y and x, respectively, as constants.

Example 2. Consider a perfect gas obeying the law

$$v = \frac{ct}{p},$$

where v is the volume of the gas (cubic inches), t is the absolute temperature (degrees), p is the pressure (pounds per square inch), and c is a constant. If the pressure is held constant and the temperature is varied, the rate at which the volume changes with respect to the temperature is

$$\frac{\partial v}{\partial t} = \frac{c}{p} \text{ cu. in. per degree;}$$

while if the temperature is held constant and the pressure is varied, the rate at which the volume changes with respect to pressure is

$$\frac{\partial v}{\partial p} = -\frac{ct}{p^2} \text{ cu. in. per lb./in.}^2$$

Example 3. If x and y are given parametrically by the equations

$$(1) \qquad x = e^{-t} \cos \theta, \qquad y = e^{-t} \sin \theta,$$

in terms of the two independent variables t and θ, find $\dfrac{\partial x}{\partial t}, \dfrac{\partial x}{\partial \theta}, \dfrac{\partial y}{\partial t}$, and $\dfrac{\partial y}{\partial \theta}$. Then regarding t and θ as the dependent and x and y as the independent variables, find $\dfrac{\partial t}{\partial x}, \dfrac{\partial t}{\partial y}, \dfrac{\partial \theta}{\partial x}$, and $\dfrac{\partial \theta}{\partial y}$.

We see at once that

$$\frac{\partial x}{\partial t} = - e^{-t} \cos \theta, \qquad \frac{\partial y}{\partial t} = - e^{-t} \sin \theta,$$

$$\frac{\partial x}{\partial \theta} = - e^{-t} \sin \theta, \qquad \frac{\partial y}{\partial \theta} = e^{-t} \cos \theta.$$

In order to find the required partial derivatives of t and θ, when x and y are regarded as the independent variables, we may solve the given equations for t and θ in terms of x and y. By squaring and adding these equations, and by dividing their corresponding members, we obtain, respectively,

$$(2) \qquad\qquad x^2 + y^2 = e^{-2t}, \qquad \tan \theta = \frac{y}{x},$$

whence

$$t = - \tfrac{1}{2} \ln (x^2 + y^2), \qquad \theta = \tan^{-1} \frac{y}{x}.$$

Therefore

$$(3) \qquad\qquad \frac{\partial t}{\partial x} = \frac{-x}{x^2 + y^2}, \qquad \frac{\partial \theta}{\partial x} = \frac{-y}{x^2 + y^2},$$

$$(4) \qquad\qquad \frac{\partial t}{\partial y} = \frac{-y}{x^2 + y^2}, \qquad \frac{\partial \theta}{\partial y} = \frac{x}{x^2 + y^2}.$$

These four partial derivatives may be found alternatively in modified but equivalent forms, without solving the given equations for t and θ. The method by which this is done will therefore be especially useful in those problems in which it is either inconvenient or impossible to express the original independent variables wholly in terms of the dependent ones.

We illustrate the procedure by finding $\dfrac{\partial t}{\partial x}$ and $\dfrac{\partial \theta}{\partial x}$.

Regarding t and θ as functions of the independent variables x and y and differentiating the given equations implicitly with respect to x, we obtain

$$1 = - e^{-t} \cos \theta \frac{\partial t}{\partial x} - e^{-t} \sin \theta \frac{\partial \theta}{\partial x},$$

$$0 = - e^{-t} \sin \theta \frac{\partial t}{\partial x} + e^{-t} \cos \theta \frac{\partial \theta}{\partial x},$$

where it is understood that y has been held constant. These equations involve the required derivatives linearly, as will always be the case in problems of this type. Hence, applying any of the methods for solving simultaneous linear equations, we obtain

$$\frac{\partial t}{\partial x} = - e^t \cos \theta, \qquad \frac{\partial \theta}{\partial x} = - e^t \sin \theta.$$

These results may be converted to the form of (3) as follows:

$$\frac{\partial t}{\partial x} = - \frac{\cos \theta}{e^{-t}} = - \frac{e^{-t} \cos \theta}{e^{-2t}} = \frac{-x}{x^2 + y^2},$$

$$\frac{\partial \theta}{\partial x} = - \frac{\sin \theta}{e^{-t}} = - \frac{e^{-t} \sin \theta}{e^{-2t}} = \frac{-y}{x^2 + y^2},$$

the last step in each case being a consequence of (1) and (2).

It is left to the student to find $\dfrac{\partial t}{\partial y}$ and $\dfrac{\partial \theta}{\partial y}$ similarly.

It is important to observe that the derivatives

$$\frac{\partial x}{\partial t} = - e^{-t} \cos \theta \quad \text{and} \quad \frac{\partial t}{\partial x} = - e^{t} \cos \theta$$

are not reciprocals. Nor is there any reason why they should be; for the former was obtained with θ held constant, and the latter with y held constant. Sometimes, when confusion or ambiguity is likely to arise in matters of this sort, it may be advisable to signify by means of a subscript the variable held constant in the process of differentiation. Thus the notation

$$\left(\frac{\partial x}{\partial t}\right)_{\theta} = - e^{-t} \cos \theta, \qquad \left(\frac{\partial t}{\partial x}\right)_{y} = - e^{t} \cos \theta$$

would indicate at once that there is no necessity for these functions to be reciprocals.

158. Geometric Interpretation of Partial Derivatives. Let $f(x, y)$ be a continuous function, and consider the surface $z = f(x, y)$ shown in

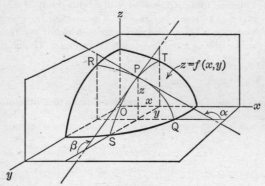

Fig. 158. Now if y is held constant and x is allowed to vary, the point $P(x, y, z)$ is constrained to move parallel to the xz-plane along a curve RPQ of the surface. It follows, therefore (Art. 13), that the partial derivative $\dfrac{\partial z}{\partial x}$, obtained with y held constant, is the slope of the curve cut from the surface by a plane parallel to the xz-plane.

Similarly, $\dfrac{\partial z}{\partial y}$ is the slope of the curve cut from the surface by a plane parallel to the yz-plane.

Accordingly, by reference to the figure, we see that

$$(1) \qquad \frac{\partial z}{\partial x} = \tan \alpha = \text{slope of } RPQ \text{ at } P,$$

$$(2) \qquad \frac{\partial z}{\partial y} = \tan \beta = \text{slope of } SPT \text{ at } P.$$

159. Higher Partial Derivatives. The partial derivatives $\dfrac{\partial z}{\partial x}$ and $\dfrac{\partial z}{\partial y}$ of a function $z = f(x, y)$ are usually functions of both x and y, though one or both of them may be either constant or dependent on only one of the variables. In any case, however, $\dfrac{\partial z}{\partial x}$ and $\dfrac{\partial z}{\partial y}$ may themselves possess partial derivatives, which are called the **second partial derivatives of z,** or its partial derivatives of the **second order,** and for each of which various equivalent symbols are in common use, namely,

$$\frac{\partial}{\partial x}\left(\frac{\partial z}{\partial x}\right) = \frac{\partial^2 z}{\partial x^2} = z_{xx} = \frac{\partial}{\partial x}\left(\frac{\partial f}{\partial x}\right) = \frac{\partial^2 f}{\partial x^2} = f_{xx}(x, y) = f_{xx},$$

$$\frac{\partial}{\partial y}\left(\frac{\partial z}{\partial x}\right) = \frac{\partial^2 z}{\partial y\,\partial x} = z_{yx} = \frac{\partial}{\partial y}\left(\frac{\partial f}{\partial x}\right) = \frac{\partial^2 f}{\partial y\,\partial x} = f_{yx}(x, y) = f_{yx},$$

$$\frac{\partial}{\partial x}\left(\frac{\partial z}{\partial y}\right) = \frac{\partial^2 z}{\partial x\,\partial y} = z_{xy} = \frac{\partial}{\partial x}\left(\frac{\partial f}{\partial y}\right) = \frac{\partial^2 f}{\partial x\,\partial y} = f_{xy}(x, y) = f_{xy},$$

$$\frac{\partial}{\partial y}\left(\frac{\partial z}{\partial y}\right) = \frac{\partial^2 z}{\partial y^2} = z_{yy} = \frac{\partial}{\partial y}\left(\frac{\partial f}{\partial y}\right) = \frac{\partial^2 f}{\partial y^2} = f_{yy}(x, y) = f_{yy}.$$

Thus it would appear that a function of two variables might have four partial derivatives of the second order. However, in general, it has only three which are distinct from one another; for it may be shown that the *mixed* partial derivatives $\dfrac{\partial^2 f}{\partial x\,\partial y}$ and $\dfrac{\partial^2 f}{\partial y\,\partial x}$ are identical at all points of the xy-plane at which these derivatives are continuous. Hence, barring consideration of possible exceptional points, we may write

$$(1) \qquad\qquad \frac{\partial^2 f}{\partial x\,\partial y} = \frac{\partial^2 f}{\partial y\,\partial x}.$$

That is, the order in which the differentiations are performed—whether first with respect to x and then with respect to y, or the reverse—is immaterial.

This result enables us to establish the equality of certain mixed partial derivatives of higher order. For example, it follows from (1) that

$$\frac{\partial^3 f}{\partial x^2\,\partial y} = \frac{\partial}{\partial x}\left(\frac{\partial^2 f}{\partial x\,\partial y}\right) = \frac{\partial}{\partial x}\left(\frac{\partial^2 f}{\partial y\,\partial x}\right) = \frac{\partial}{\partial x}\left[\frac{\partial}{\partial y}\left(\frac{\partial f}{\partial x}\right)\right]$$

$$= \frac{\partial}{\partial y}\left[\frac{\partial}{\partial x}\left(\frac{\partial f}{\partial x}\right)\right] = \frac{\partial}{\partial y}\left(\frac{\partial^2 f}{\partial x^2}\right) = \frac{\partial^3 f}{\partial y\,\partial x^2}.$$

Thus the three possible sequences of differentiating a function $f(x, y)$ twice with respect to x and once with respect to y, namely those signified by the symbols

$$\frac{\partial^3 f}{\partial x^2 \, \partial y}, \quad \frac{\partial^3 f}{\partial x \, \partial y \, \partial x} = \frac{\partial}{\partial x}\left[\frac{\partial}{\partial y}\left(\frac{\partial f}{\partial x}\right)\right], \quad \frac{\partial^3 f}{\partial y \, \partial x^2},$$

lead to identical results. Accordingly, save for possible exceptional points, a function of two variables has only four distinct partial derivatives of the third order, namely

$$\frac{\partial^3 f}{\partial x^3} \quad \frac{\partial^3 f}{\partial x^2 \, \partial y}, \quad \frac{\partial^3 f}{\partial x \, \partial y^2}, \quad \frac{\partial^3 f}{\partial y^3}.$$

Moreover, any higher partial derivative, such as $\dfrac{\partial^{m+n} f}{\partial x^m \, \partial y^n}$, in general may be obtained by differentiating $f(x, y)$ with respect to x and y in any order whatever, provided m differentiations are performed with respect to x and n with respect to y.

What has been said in this article about functions of two variables admits readily of extension to functions of any number of variables.

Example. Show that (1) holds if $z = \sqrt{x^2 + y^2}$.

$$\frac{\partial z}{\partial x} = x(x^2 + y^2)^{-\frac{1}{2}}, \qquad \frac{\partial z}{\partial y} = y(x^2 + y^2)^{-\frac{1}{2}},$$

$$\frac{\partial^2 z}{\partial y \, \partial x} = \frac{\partial}{\partial y}\left(\frac{\partial z}{\partial x}\right) = -\frac{1}{2}x(x^2 + y^2)^{-\frac{3}{2}}(2y) = \frac{-xy}{(x^2 + y^2)^{\frac{3}{2}}},$$

$$\frac{\partial^2 z}{\partial x \, \partial y} = \frac{\partial}{\partial x}\left(\frac{\partial z}{\partial y}\right) = -\frac{1}{2}y(x^2 + y^2)^{-\frac{3}{2}}(2x) = \frac{-xy}{(x^2 + y^2)^{\frac{3}{2}}}.$$

Hence

$$\frac{\partial^2 z}{\partial x \, \partial y} = \frac{\partial^2 z}{\partial y \, \partial x}$$

except for $x = y = 0$, in which case it may be shown that these derivatives do not exist.

PROBLEMS

In each of the first twenty of the following problems find $\dfrac{\partial z}{\partial x}$ and $\dfrac{\partial z}{\partial y}$.

1. $z = x^6 - 5x^5 y + 2x^2 y^3$.

2. $z = \sqrt{x^2 - y^2}$.

3. $z = \dfrac{x}{y} - \dfrac{y}{x}$.

4. $z = \dfrac{x^2 + y^2}{x - y}$.

5. $z = (x^2 - xy + y^2)^8$.

6. $z = (x - y)^4 (x + y)^5$.

7. $z = \sin (x - y)$.

8. $z = \cos^2 \dfrac{y}{x}$.

9. $z = \sin^{-1} (x - y)$.

10. $z = \cot (x^2 + y^2)$.

11. $z = \tan \dfrac{x + y}{y}$.

12. $z = \tan^{-1} \left(\dfrac{y}{x} - \dfrac{x}{y} \right)$.

13. $z = e^{x^2 + y^2}$.

14. $z = e^{x-y} \ln (x - y)$.

15. $z = \ln \sqrt{\dfrac{x - y}{x + y}}$.

16. $z = \ln \tan \dfrac{y}{x}$.

17. $z = \tan^{-1} \ln (xy)$.

18. $z = \sin^{-1} e^{x-y}$.

19. $z = \sin^2 \ln (xy^2)$.

20. $z = \cos^3 (e^y - e^x)$.

21. If $u = x^3 - x^2y + xy^2 - y^3 + y^2z - yz^2 + z^3$ show that $xu_x + yu_y + zu_z = 3u$.

22. Show that $xu_x + yu_y + zu_z = 0$, if $u = \dfrac{z}{x} \ln \dfrac{y}{x}$.

23. Show that $xz_x + yz_y = 0$, if $z = e^{\frac{y}{x}}$.

24. Show that $xz_x + yz_y + z = 0$, if $z = \dfrac{x + y}{xy}$.

25. Show that $3(xu_x + yu_y + zu_z) = u$, if $u = \dfrac{z}{\sqrt[3]{x^2 + y^2}}$.

26. Find the general expression for the slope of the curve of intersection of the ellipsoid

$$\frac{x^2}{16} + \frac{y^2}{9} + \frac{z^2}{4} = 1$$

and the plane $y = 1$. In particular find the slope of this curve at the point in the first octant where $x = 2$.

27. At what point of the surface $z = x^2 + y^2$ does a tangent line lying in the plane $y = 1$ have a slope 2?

28. Consider a sphere with center at the origin and of radius 13. A line drawn tangent to this sphere at a point in the first octant where $x = 3$ lies in a plane parallel to the xz-plane and has a slope of $-\frac{1}{4}$. Find the equation of the plane.

29. A tangent line to the conical surface $z = \sqrt{9x^2 + 4y^2}$ lies in the plane $x = 1$ and has a slope $\dfrac{\partial z}{\partial y}$ of $\dfrac{8}{5}$. Find the coördinates of the point of tangency (assumed in the first octant).

30. If $z = \sin^{-1} \dfrac{y}{x}$, find $\dfrac{\partial^2 z}{\partial x^2}$.

31. If $z = (x^2 + y^2) \tan^{-1} \dfrac{y}{x}$, find $\dfrac{\partial^2 z}{\partial y^2}$.

32. If $z = \sin (x - y) + \ln (x + y)$ show that $\dfrac{\partial^2 z}{\partial x^2} = \dfrac{\partial^2 z}{\partial y^2}$.

33. If $z = \tan^{-1} (x + 2y) + e^{x-2y}$, show that $\dfrac{\partial^2 z}{\partial y^2} = 4 \dfrac{\partial^2 z}{\partial x^2}$.

34. If $z = \sqrt{y + 3x} - (y - 3x)^2$, show that $\dfrac{\partial^2 z}{\partial x^2} = 9 \dfrac{\partial^2 z}{\partial y^2}$.

In Problems 35 to 40 inclusive show that $\dfrac{\partial^2 z}{\partial x\,\partial y} = \dfrac{\partial^2 z}{\partial y\,\partial x}$.

35. $z = \ln\left(\dfrac{y}{x} + \dfrac{x}{y}\right)$.   **38.** $z = \tan^{-1}\dfrac{y}{x}$.

36. $z = e^x \sqrt{x^2 + y^2}$.   **39.** $z = \sin^{-1}(x - y)$.

37. $z = \tan(x^2 - y^2)$.   **40.** $z = e^{xy} \ln xy$.

41. Show that $\dfrac{\partial^3 z}{\partial x^2\,\partial y} = \dfrac{\partial^3 z}{\partial x\,\partial y\,\partial x} = \dfrac{\partial^3 z}{\partial y\,\partial x^2}$ if $z = y \sin x + x \cos y$.

42. If $x = r \cos \theta$, $y = r \sin \theta$, find $\left(\dfrac{\partial x}{\partial \theta}\right)_r$, $\left(\dfrac{\partial x}{\partial r}\right)_\theta$, $\left(\dfrac{\partial y}{\partial \theta}\right)_r$, $\left(\dfrac{\partial y}{\partial r}\right)_\theta$, $\left(\dfrac{\partial \theta}{\partial x}\right)_y$, $\left(\dfrac{\partial \theta}{\partial y}\right)_x$, $\left(\dfrac{\partial r}{\partial x}\right)_y$, and $\left(\dfrac{\partial r}{\partial y}\right)_x$.

43. Find the same derivatives required in Problem 42, if $x = re^\theta$, $y = re^{-\theta}$.

160. The Increment of a Function of Two Variables. Let a function $z = f(x, y)$ and its partial derivatives of the first order be single-valued and continuous throughout a certain region Σ of the xy-plane, and let (x_0, y_0) be any fixed point within the region. Then if the independent variables, with x_0 and y_0 as their initial values, are assigned arbitrary increments Δx and Δy, the given function changes by an amount

$$\Delta z = f(x_0 + \Delta x, y_0 + \Delta y) - f(x_0, y_0).$$

It is our purpose here to express this increment in terms of Δx, Δy, and the first partial derivatives of z.

To accomplish this we transform Δz by adding and subtracting $f(x_0, y_0 + \Delta y)$. Thus we obtain

$$\Delta z = f(x_0 + \Delta x, y_0 + \Delta y) - f(x_0, y_0 + \Delta y) + f(x_0, y_0 + \Delta y) - f(x_0, y_0).$$

By virtue of the assumed single-valuedness and continuity of $f(x, y)$ and $f_x(x, y)$ in the neighborhood of the point (x_0, y_0), we may apply the law of the mean (Art. 121) to the first two terms of Δz, holding Δy constant, and thus obtain

$$f(x_0 + \Delta x,\, y_0 + \Delta y) - f(x_0,\, y_0 + \Delta y) = \Delta x\, f_x(x_0 + \theta \Delta x,\, y_0 + \Delta y),\ \ 0 < \theta < 1.$$

Similarly, the last two terms of Δz may be written

$$f(x_0, y_0 + \Delta y) - f(x_0, y_0) = \Delta y\, f_y(x_0, y_0 + \theta' \Delta y),\ \ \ \ 0 < \theta' < 1.$$

Hence

$$\Delta z = f_x(x_0 + \theta \Delta x, y_0 + \Delta y)\Delta x + f_y(x_0, y_0 + \theta' \Delta y)\Delta y.$$

Since by hypothesis the first partial derivatives of $f(x, y)$ are continuous in the neighborhood of the point (x_0, y_0), we may write

$$f_x(x_0 + \theta\Delta x, y_0 + \Delta y) = f_x(x_0, y_0) + \epsilon,$$

$$f_y(x_0, y_0 + \theta'\Delta y) = f_y(x_0, y_0) + \epsilon',$$

where ϵ and ϵ' are infinitesimals such that

(1) $$\lim_{\substack{\Delta x \to 0 \\ \Delta y \to 0}} \epsilon = 0, \qquad \lim_{\Delta y \to 0} \epsilon' = 0.$$

Therefore we have

$$\Delta z = f_x(x_0, y_0)\Delta x + f_y(x_0, y_0)\Delta y + \epsilon\Delta x + \epsilon'\Delta y.$$

Now since the point (x_0, y_0) was chosen at random in the region Σ, we may drop subscripts and write

(2) $$\Delta z = \frac{\partial z}{\partial x}\Delta x + \frac{\partial z}{\partial y}\Delta y + \epsilon\Delta x + \epsilon'\Delta y.$$

The increment of a function of more than two independent variables may be found similarly. For example, if $u = f(x, y, z)$,

(3) $$\Delta u = \frac{\partial u}{\partial x}\Delta x + \frac{\partial u}{\partial y}\Delta y + \frac{\partial u}{\partial z}\Delta z + \epsilon\Delta x + \epsilon'\Delta y + \epsilon''\Delta z,$$

where ϵ, ϵ', ϵ'', all approach zero with Δx, Δy, Δz.

161. Total Differential. From (2) of the preceding article it follows that

$$\frac{\partial z}{\partial x}\Delta x + \frac{\partial z}{\partial y}\Delta y$$

differs from Δz by an infinitesimal of higher order than Δx and Δy, since ϵ and ϵ' both approach zero simultaneously with Δx and Δy. Thus $\frac{\partial z}{\partial x}\Delta x + \frac{\partial z}{\partial y}\Delta y$ constitutes the principal part (cf. Art. 25) of the infinitesimal Δz, and accordingly is called the **differential** of z. Hence by definition we write

(1) $$dz = \frac{\partial z}{\partial x}\Delta x + \frac{\partial z}{\partial y}\Delta y.$$

In particular, if we place $z = x$, we obtain

$$dx = 1 \cdot \Delta x + 0 \cdot \Delta y,$$

or

$$dx = \Delta x.$$

Similarly, placing $z = y$, we find that

$$dy = \Delta y.$$

Thus, while the increment and the differential of the dependent variable z differ by an infinitesimal of higher order, the differential of each independent variable is identical with its increment.

In view of these results we may write (1) in the form

(2) $$dz = \frac{\partial z}{\partial x} dx + \frac{\partial z}{\partial y} dy.$$

It will be observed, by reference to Art. 24, that $\frac{\partial z}{\partial x} dx$ represents the differential of the function z corresponding to a prescribed variation in x alone, y being held constant. Similarly, $\frac{\partial z}{\partial y} dy$ represents the differential of z corresponding to a prescribed variation in y alone, x being held constant. These terms are therefore called the **partial differentials** of z, in contradistinction to which their sum dz is often called the **total differential** of z.

The differential of a function of more than two independent variables is defined similarly. For example, if $u = f(x, y, z)$, we define the differential (or total differential) of u as

(3) $$du = \frac{\partial u}{\partial x} dx + \frac{\partial u}{\partial y} dy + \frac{\partial u}{\partial z} dz,$$

by dropping the infinitesimals involving ϵ, ϵ', ϵ'' from (3) of the preceding article.

162. Geometric Interpretation of the Total Differential. In Art. 24 we found that the differential of a function $f(x)$, for given values of x and its increment Δx, equals the corresponding increment of y for the line drawn tangent to the curve $y = f(x)$ at the point (x, y). (See Fig. 24a).

Similarly, as we shall now see, *the total differential of a function $f(x, y)$, for given values of x and y and of their increments Δx and Δy, equals the corresponding increment of z for the plane drawn tangent to the surface $z = f(x, y)$ at the point (x, y, z).* (See Fig. 162.)

To prove this assume that the function $f(x, y)$ and its partial derivatives $\frac{\partial f}{\partial x}$ and $\frac{\partial f}{\partial y}$ are single-valued and continuous throughout a certain region Σ of the xy-plane, and construct within Σ a rectangle with vertices at the points $P'(x, y, 0)$, $R'(x, y + \Delta y, 0)$, $Q'(x + \Delta x, y + \Delta y, 0)$, $S'(x + \Delta x, y, 0)$, as shown in Fig. 162. Moreover, suppose that the four planes drawn parallel to the z-axis through the respective sides of this rectangle intersect the surface $z = f(x, y)$ in the curves PR, RQ, QS, SP, and that T, U, V are the points in which the projecting lines RR', QQ', SS' pierce the plane tangent to the surface * at $P(x, y, z)$. Finally, let A, B, C denote the points in which these projecting lines pierce the plane through P parallel to the xy-plane, and draw the auxiliary lines AW and VW parallel to PV and PA, respectively.

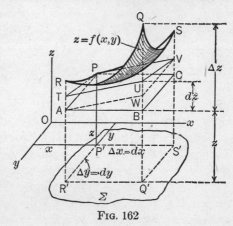

FIG. 162

Then, since $\Delta x = dx$ and $\Delta y = dy$, it follows from the equation

$$dz = \frac{\partial z}{\partial x} dx + \frac{\partial z}{\partial y} dy,$$

and from (1) and (2), Art. 158, that

$$dz = (\tan CPV)\, dx + (\tan APT)\, dy$$
$$= CV + AT$$
$$= BW + WU$$
$$= BU,$$

which is the increment of z for the tangent plane, corresponding to the values of x, y, Δx, Δy shown.

Thus it appears from the figure that the increment and the differential of $z = f(x, y)$ differ by an amount

$$\Delta z - dz = UQ.$$

It should be evident that dz will be negative if the surface and its tangent plane are so situated that U falls below B, and that $\Delta z - dz$ will be negative if Q lies beneath U.

* The tangent plane to a surface at a point will be formally defined and discussed in Art. 168.

163. Approximate Increments. In general, when Δx and Δy are sufficiently small numerically, the difference between the increment and the differential of a function $z = f(x, y)$ is for ordinary purposes negligible. For if $f(x, y)$ and its partial derivatives $\dfrac{\partial f}{\partial x}$ and $\dfrac{\partial f}{\partial y}$ are single-valued and continuous, it follows from (2), Art. 160, and (1), Art. 161, that

$$(1) \qquad\qquad \Delta z - dz = \epsilon \Delta x + \epsilon' \Delta y;$$

and this difference is an infinitesimal of higher order, since ϵ and ϵ' both approach zero simultaneously with Δx and Δy.

Thus we may say that *the increment Δz and the differential dz, of the function $z = f(x, y)$, are approximately equal when Δx and Δy (i.e., dx and dy) are sufficiently small numerically.*

Hence if we wish to approximate the increment of the function, corresponding to given values of x and y and specified small changes Δx and Δy, it will generally suffice—and indeed will usually be advantageous—to compute the differential of the function and use that rather than the increment.

It is evident graphically from Fig. 162 that in using this approximation we neglect the segment UQ included between the surface $z = f(x, y)$ and the tangent plane at the point $P(x, y, z)$, a segment whose length we have shown to be negligible in comparison with Δz when Q is sufficiently near P.

Analogously, under suitable conditions as to continuity, the increment and the differential of a function of any number of independent variables are approximately equal when the increments of these variables are sufficiently small numerically.

Example 1. Find and compare the increment and the differential of the function $x^2 + y^2 - xy$, corresponding to an increase in x from 1 to 1.02 and a decrease in y from 2 to 1.99.

Let $z = x^2 + y^2 - xy$. Then corresponding to the initial and final values of x and y we have, respectively,

$$z = 1^2 + 2^2 - 1 \cdot 2 = 3,$$

$$z + \Delta z = 3 + \Delta z = (1.02)^2 + (1.99)^2 - (1.02)(1.99) = 2.9707.$$

Hence for the increment of the function we have $\Delta z = 2.9707 - 3 = -0.0293$.

Alternatively Δz may be found as follows:

$$z + \Delta z = (x + \Delta x)^2 + (y + \Delta y)^2 - (x + \Delta x)(y + \Delta y),$$

whence, on expanding and making use of the equation $z = x^2 + y^2 - xy$, we obtain

$$(2) \qquad \Delta z = (2x - y)\Delta x + (2y - x)\Delta y + (\Delta x)^2 + (\Delta y)^2 - (\Delta x)(\Delta y).$$

Substituting $x = 1, y = 2, \Delta x = 0.02, \Delta y = -0.01$, we find as before $\Delta z = -0.0293$.

By (2), Art. 161, the differential of z is

$$(3) \qquad\qquad dz = (2x - y)dx + (2y - x)dy.$$

Therefore when $x = 1, y = 2, dx = 0.02, dy = -0.01$, we have $dz = -0.03$.

Owing to the small numerical values of Δx and Δy, the increment Δz and the differential dz are approximately equal; in fact $\Delta z - dz = 0.0007$.

On comparison of (2) and (3) with (1) it will be noted that the general expression for $\Delta z - dz$ may be written in the form

$$\epsilon\Delta x + \epsilon'\Delta y = (\Delta x)^2 + (\Delta y)^2 - (\Delta x)(\Delta y),$$

which, for the values of Δx and Δy given, becomes 0.0007, as previously found.

Example 2. Find the radius of the arc of a circular segment whose base and altitude are 8 in. and 2 in., respectively. Assuming that these dimensions may be in error at most by 0.020 in. and 0.010 in., respectively, find the greatest possible error in the computed value of the radius.

(a) *Solution by Increments.* Denoting by r, b, and h, the radius, base, and altitude, we have for the segment ABC shown in Fig. 163

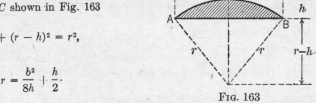

$$\left(\frac{b}{2}\right)^2 + (r - h)^2 = r^2,$$

whence

$$(4) \qquad\qquad r = \frac{b^2}{8h} + \frac{h}{2}.$$

FIG. 163

Substituting $b = 8$ and $h = 2$ we find that $r = 5$ in.

It will be clear from the figure that for a fixed altitude the radius will increase or decrease according as the base increases or decreases, and for a fixed base will increase or decrease according as the altitude decreases or increases, provided in each case that the segment is less than a semicircle. Hence the greatest possible positive error Δr in the computed value of the radius will be the result of a positive error $\Delta b = 0.020$ in. in the base and a negative error $\Delta h = -0.010$ in. in the altitude.

Now from (4) we find that a segment of base 8.020 in. and altitude 1.990 in. has a radius

$$r' = \frac{(8.020)^2}{8(1.990)} + \frac{1.990}{2} = 5.0352 \text{ in.,}$$

to four decimal places. Hence

$$\Delta r = r' - r = 5.0352 - 5 = 0.0352 \text{ in.}$$

Since it is futile to give the result to any greater degree of accuracy than that used to express the maximum errors in b and h, we say that the greatest possible error in the computed value of the radius is 0.035 in.

(b) *Solution by Differentials.* The errors in the base and altitude are sufficiently small numerically to justify the use of dr as an approximation to Δr.

From (4) we find that

$$dr = \frac{\partial r}{\partial b}\, db + \frac{\partial r}{\partial h}\, dh = \frac{b}{4h}\, db + \left(\frac{1}{2} - \frac{b^2}{8h^2}\right) dh.$$

Now for the given dimensions ($b = 8$, $h = 2$) the coefficients of db and dh are respectively positive and negative. Hence the approximate error dr will be greatest when $db = + 0.020$ and $dh = - 0.010$, for then the terms comprising dr are both positive. Therefore the required error is approximately

$$dr = \frac{8}{4 \cdot 2} (0.020) + \left(\frac{1}{2} - \frac{8^2}{8 \cdot 2^2} \right) (-0.010) = 0.035 \text{ in.}$$

It should be observed that, though dr and Δr are not equal, they differ by an amount which is small in comparison with the errors in r, b, and h.

164. Relative Error; Percentage Error. Frequently we are more interested in the percentage error in the determination of a quantity than in the error itself.

If a value z, found either by measurement or computation, is subject to an error Δz, the fraction $\dfrac{\Delta z}{z}$ is called the **relative error** in the determination of z. Clearly, this is the error per unit of z. The **percentage error**—that is, the corresponding error per hundred units of z—is obviously $100 \dfrac{\Delta z}{z}$ per cent.

It follows from the foregoing article that, for sufficiently small errors in the variables on which z depends, the relative error in z is approximately $\dfrac{dz}{z}$. The following example will show that logarithmic differentiation frequently expedites the calculation of a relative error.

Example. The area of a triangular plot is to be computed from data obtained by measuring two of its sides and the included angle. If the maximum relative error in the linear measurements is 1 part in 5000, and the angle, $58° 15'$, is measured with a transit graduated to minutes, find approximately the greatest possible percentage error in the computed area.

Let x and y denote the lengths of the measured sides, θ the included angle, and A the computed area. Then

$$\frac{dx}{x} = \frac{dy}{y} = \frac{\pm 1}{5000} \; , \; \theta = 58° 15'$$

$$d\theta = \pm 0° 00' 30'' = \frac{\pm \pi}{21600} \text{ radians,}$$

and we must find the approximate value $\dfrac{dA}{A}$ of the maximum relative error $\dfrac{\Delta A}{A}$.

Evidently, from the relation

(1) $$A = \tfrac{1}{2} xy \sin \theta,$$

connecting the variables subject to error, the general expression for the required quantity may be found in terms of those which are given by forming dA (by the method of Example 2 (b), Art. 163) and dividing it by A. However, the work is facilitated by taking the natural logarithm of both sides of (1). Thus we obtain

$$\ln A = \ln \tfrac{1}{2} + \ln x + \ln y + \ln \sin \theta,$$

whence

$$\frac{dA}{A} = \frac{dx}{x} + \frac{dy}{y} + \cot \theta \; d\theta.$$

Clearly $\dfrac{dA}{A}$ will be greatest when the terms which comprise it are all positive. Hence we restrict the given errors to their positive values and thus find that the corresponding maximum relative error in A is approximately

$$\frac{dA}{A} = \frac{1}{5000} + \frac{1}{5000} + \frac{\pi}{21,600} \cot 58° \; 15' = 0.00049,$$

or approximately 0.05 per cent.

PROBLEMS

1. Find the increment and the differential of each of the following functions corresponding to the given values of the independent variables and their increments, and explain why the two results are not approximately equal:

(a) $x^2 - y^2$, $x = 4$, $y = 2$, $\Delta x = 1.2$, $\Delta y = 0.8$;

(b) $x^3 - xy + y^2$, $x = 1$, $y = -1$, $\Delta x = -1$, $\Delta y = 2$;

(c) $\dfrac{x}{y} - \dfrac{y}{x}$, $x = 2$, $y = 1$, $\Delta x = 1$, $\Delta y = 2$;

(d) $\sqrt{x + y + z}$, $x = 1$, $y = 2$, $z = 6$, $\Delta x = 4$, $\Delta y = 5$, $\Delta z = -2$;

(e) $\sqrt{x^2 + y^2 + z^2}$, $x = 0$, $y = 3$, $z = 4$, $\Delta x = -6$, $\Delta y = 0$, $\Delta z = 2$;

(f) $\ln \sqrt{xy}$, $x = 1$, $y = e$, $\Delta x = e - 1$, $\Delta y = 1 - e$;

(g) $\tan (x + y)$, $x = \dfrac{\pi}{6}$, $y = \dfrac{\pi}{12}$, $\Delta x = \Delta y = \dfrac{\pi}{24}$;

(h) $\sin^2 (x - y)$, $x = \dfrac{\pi}{3}$, $y = \dfrac{\pi}{12}$, $\Delta x = \dfrac{\pi}{6}$, $\Delta y = \dfrac{\pi}{4}$;

(i) $e^{\cos(x-y)}$, $x = 90°$, $y = 30°$, $\Delta x = \dfrac{2\pi}{9}$, $\Delta y = \dfrac{\pi}{18}$;

(j) $\tan^{-1} \dfrac{y^2}{x}$, $x = 2$, $y = 2$, $\Delta x = 7$, $\Delta y = 1$;

(k) $\sin^{-1} \dfrac{x}{y}$, $x = 1$, $y = 2$, $\Delta x = \sqrt{2} - 1$, $\Delta y = 0$.

2. Find and compare the increment and the differential of each of the following functions for the given values of the independent variables and their increments:

(a) $x^3 - x^2 y + 2xy^2 + y^3$, $x = 1$, $y = 1$, $\Delta x = 0.01$, $\Delta y = -0.001$;

(b) $\ln \dfrac{x^2 - y^2}{xy}$, $x = 2$, $y = 1$, $\Delta x = 0.02$, $\Delta y = 0.01$;

(c) $e^{xy} \sin^{-1} x$, $x = 0$, $y = 1$, $\Delta x = 0.02$, $\Delta y = 0.1$;

(d) $\sqrt{\dfrac{x}{y} - \dfrac{y}{x}}$, $x = 4$, $y = 2$, $\Delta x = 0.04$, $\Delta y = 0.02$;

(e) $\sqrt{x^2 + y^2}$, $x = 7$, $y = 24$, $\Delta x = 0.04$, $\Delta y = -0.02$;

(f) $xy \ln xy$, $x = 1$, $y = 1$, $\Delta x = 0.02$, $\Delta y = 0.01$;

(g) $\dfrac{1}{x + y} \sin \dfrac{\pi}{y - x}$, $x = 1$, $y = 3$, $\Delta x = 0.02$, $\Delta y = 0.02$.

3. Find the approximate change in the volume of a right circular cylinder caused by changing the base-radius from 3 in. to 3.02 in. and the altitude from 6 in. to 5.99 in.

4. Approximately how much do the volume and the total surface of a right circular cone change when the radius of the base is increased from 2 in. to 2.01 in. and the altitude is decreased from 4 in. to 3.97 in.?

5. Find by the use of differentials the approximate volume of a rectangular parallelepiped the lengths of whose edges are 2.02 in., 3.03 in., and 4.95 in. Compare the result with the exact volume.

6. Compute by the use of differentials the approximate length of the base of a circular segment of radius 4.96 in. and altitude 2.01 in. (See Example 2, Art. 163.)

7. By means of a scale and a protractor the radius and the central angle of a circular sector are found to be 6 in. and 30°. If these measurements may be in error at most by $\frac{1}{50}$ in. and $\frac{1}{5}$ of a degree, respectively, find approximately the greatest possible error in the computed area of the sector.

8. A projectile is fired obliquely into the air at an angle α with the horizontal, and attains a maximum height h. If by measurement α and h are found to be 45° and 36 ft., and these values are subject to errors of $\frac{1}{8}$ degree and $\frac{1}{10}$ ft., respectively, find approximately the greatest possible error in the computed value of the initial speed $v_0 = \sqrt{2 gh} \csc \alpha$. Take $g = 32$ ft./sec.^{2}

9. The axial load causing failure of a slender square column with round ends is given by *Euler's Formula*

$$P = \frac{\pi^2 d^4 E}{12 L^2},$$

where L is the over-all length of the column, d is the length of one side of its square cross-section, and E is the modulus of elasticity of the material. For a certain timber column, $L = 216$ in., $d = 4$ in., and $E = 10^6$ lb./in.^{2} Compute the breaking load P, and find approximately how much it may be in error if L and E are subject to errors of 0.1 in. and 1000 lb./in.^{2}, respectively.

10. One angle of a triangular lot is 120°. The lengths of the sides adjacent to this angle are found to be 110 ft. and 240 ft. If each of these dimensions is subject to an error of 1 in., find approximately the greatest possible error in the computed length of the third side.

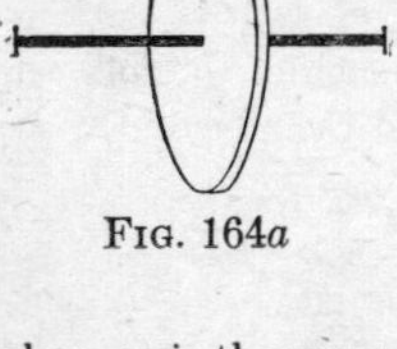

11. Find approximately the maximum error in the computed area of the triangular lot of Problem 10.

12. A circular disc is rigidly attached to a shaft as shown in Fig. 164a. The *critical speed*, or angular speed at which the shaft will fail, is given by the formula

FIG. 164a

$$\omega = \sqrt{\frac{\alpha}{m}},$$

where m is the mass of the disc and α is a quantity depending on the physical characteristics of the shaft and journals. If possible errors of 1 per cent and 2 per cent, are made in determining m and α, respectively, find approximately the greatest possible percentage error in the computed value of ω.

13. The angular speed of a ball-governor (Fig. 164b) is given by the formula

$$\omega = \sqrt{\frac{g}{h}} \text{ radians per second,}$$

where h is the distance shown in the figure and g is the acceleration of gravity. If, in a certain locality, the value of g is 32.16 ft./sec.² and this is taken as 32 ft./sec.², while the measurement of h is subject to an error of 1 per cent, find approximately the maximum percentage error in the computed value of ω.

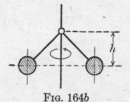

14. A swamp interferes with the direct measurement of a survey line AB. Hence an auxiliary point C is established and the distance AC is measured with an accuracy of 1 part in 1000. Then the angles BAC and ABC are found to be 45° and 30°, respectively, with a possible error of

Fig. 164b

2 minutes in each. Find approximately the greatest possible percentage error in the computed length of AB.

15. Errors in the measurements of the slant height and base-diameters of a frustum of a right circular cone do not exceed 1 per cent each. Find approximately the greatest possible percentage error in the computed area of the curved surface.

16. If a body's weight in air is A, and in water is W, its specific gravity is

$$s = \frac{A}{A - W}.$$

If for a certain body $A = 20$ lb. and $W = 10$ lb., and each of these values is subject to a possible error of 3 per cent, compute the specific gravity and find approximately the greatest possible percentage error in the result.

17. A sphere impinges on a rough plane and rebounds. If the angles of approach and departure, measured from a normal to the plane, are respectively α and β, then

$$\tan \beta = \frac{1}{\lambda} [\tan \alpha - \mu (1 + \lambda)],$$

where λ is the coefficient of restitution and μ the coefficient of friction. A sphere strikes a plane at an angle $\alpha = 45°$.

(a) If $\lambda = \frac{1}{2}$ and $\mu = \frac{1}{3}$, at what angle β will the sphere rebound?

(b) On the assumption that these values of λ and μ may be in error at most by 5 per cent, find approximately the maximum error and percentage error in the computed value of $\tan \beta$.

(c) Find the approximate limits between which β must lie.

18. In physics it is shown that the period (or time for one complete oscillation) of a simple pendulum of length l is $P = 2\pi\sqrt{\dfrac{l}{g}}$. The value of g, the acceleration of gravity, is to be found experimentally by means of a pendulum whose period is approximately 2 sec. If the error in the measurement of l can be limited to $\frac{3}{10}$ per cent and the allowable error in the experimental value of g is not to exceed $\frac{1}{10}$ per cent, what are the approximate maximum allowable error and percentage error in the measurement of P?

19. The area of the segment cut from a circle of radius r by a chord subtending an angle θ at the center of a circle is

$$A = \tfrac{1}{2}r^2(\theta - \sin \theta).$$

If, for a certain segment, r and θ are found to be 5 in. and $\dfrac{\pi}{3}$ radians, and the errors in these measurements do not exceed 0.1 in. and 0.01 radian, respectively, find approximately the greatest possible error in the computed value of A.

165. Rates; Total Derivative. Frequently we are confronted with the problem of finding the rate of change of a function $f(x, y)$ with respect to a variable, say t, on which both x and y depend. If

(1) $$z = f(x, y), \quad \text{and} \quad x = \phi(t), \quad y = \chi(t),$$

it is clear that, when the expressions for x and y are substituted in $f(x, y)$, z becomes a function of t alone. Therefore to find the derivative of this function with respect to t, we form

(2) $$\frac{\Delta z}{\Delta t} = \frac{\partial z}{\partial x}\frac{\Delta x}{\Delta t} + \frac{\partial z}{\partial y}\frac{\Delta y}{\Delta t} + \epsilon \frac{\Delta x}{\Delta t} + \epsilon' \frac{\Delta y}{\Delta t},$$

from (2), Art. 160, and let Δt approach zero. But as Δt approaches zero both Δx and Δy do likewise, since $\Delta x = \phi(t + \Delta t) - \phi(t)$ and $\Delta y = \chi(t + \Delta t) - \chi(t)$. It follows, therefore, from (1), Art. 160, that

$$\lim_{\Delta t \to 0} \epsilon = 0, \quad \lim_{\Delta t \to 0} \epsilon' = 0.$$

Hence in the limit (2) becomes

(3) $$\frac{dz}{dt} = \frac{\partial z}{\partial x}\frac{dx}{dt} + \frac{\partial z}{\partial y}\frac{dy}{dt},$$

provided the limits of the respective terms exist as Δt approaches zero.

Multiplying both sides of (3) by dt we obtain

$$dz = \frac{\partial z}{\partial x} dx + \frac{\partial z}{\partial y} dy,$$

a result which has been shown (Art. 161) to hold when x and y are independent of each other, and which we now see *holds also when x and y are related variables.*

What has been done here admits of extension to any number of variables. For example, if

(4) $$u = f(x, y, z) \quad \text{and} \quad x = \phi(t), \quad y = \chi(t), \quad z = \psi(t),$$

we find by a method analogous to that used in deriving (3) that

(5)
$$\frac{du}{dt} = \frac{\partial u}{\partial x}\frac{dx}{dt} + \frac{\partial u}{\partial y}\frac{dy}{dt} + \frac{\partial u}{\partial z}\frac{dz}{dt}.$$

Hence, even though x, y, z, are related variables, du has the same form as that given in (3), Art. 161, in which x, y, z were all independent of each other.

Suppose now that $t = x$. Then by (1) and (3) we have, respectively,

(6)
$$z = f(x, y), \quad y = \chi(x),$$

and

(7)
$$\frac{dz}{dx} = \frac{\partial z}{\partial x} + \frac{\partial z}{\partial y}\frac{dy}{dx}.$$

The distinction between $\frac{dz}{dx}$ and $\frac{\partial z}{\partial x}$ in (7) should be carefully noted. The partial derivative $\frac{\partial z}{\partial x}$ is obtained from the first of equations (6) on the supposition that y is a constant, despite the fact that the equation $y = \chi(x)$ shows that y depends on x. On the other hand

$$\frac{dz}{dx} = \lim_{\Delta x \to 0} \frac{\Delta z}{\Delta x},$$

where Δz is the increment of z caused by changing both x and y, x by the amount Δx, and y by the amount $\Delta y = \chi(x + \Delta x) - \chi(x)$. Since here both x and y vary, $\frac{dz}{dx}$ is called the **total derivative** of z with respect to x.

Similarly, if $t = x$, (4) and (5) yield, respectively,

(8)
$$u = f(x, y, z), \quad y = \chi(x), \quad z = \psi(x),$$

and

(9)
$$\frac{du}{dx} = \frac{\partial u}{\partial x} + \frac{\partial u}{\partial y}\frac{dy}{dx} + \frac{\partial u}{\partial z}\frac{dz}{dx}.$$

By analogy with the preceding paragraph the student should note carefully the distinction between the total derivative $\frac{du}{dx}$ and the partial derivative $\frac{\partial u}{\partial x}$.

Example 1. If $z = y \ln x - x \ln y$, and $x = e^t, y = e^{-t}$, evaluate $\frac{dz}{dt}$ for $t = 0$.

Since

$$\frac{\partial z}{\partial x} = \frac{y}{x} - \ln y, \qquad \frac{\partial z}{\partial y} = \ln x - \frac{x}{y}$$

and

$$\frac{dx}{dt} = e^t, \qquad \frac{dy}{dt} = -e^{-t},$$

we have by (3)

$$\frac{dz}{dt} = \left(\frac{y}{x} - \ln y\right) e^t - \left(\ln x - \frac{x}{y}\right) e^{-t}.$$

When $t = 0$, $x = y = 1$, and $\dfrac{dz}{dt} = 2$.

Alternatively, we may write z as a function of t alone by substituting in the given equation the expressions for x and y in terms of t, and then find $\dfrac{dz}{dt}$ directly. Thus we have

$$z = e^{-t} \ln e^t - e^t \ln e^{-t} = t(e^t + e^{-t}) = 2t \cosh t,$$

$$\frac{dz}{dt} = 2(t \sinh t + \cosh t),$$

so that, for $t = 0$, $\dfrac{dz}{dt} = 2$.

Example 2. The intensity of illumination on a plane surface at a point P due to light from a point-source at L is

$$I = \frac{k \cos \alpha}{x^2} \text{ foot-candles,}$$

where k is the candlepower of the source, α is the angle of incidence of the ray LP, and x is the length of LP in feet.

A 30-candlepower light is moved directly toward the center of a doorway 4 ft. wide (Fig. 165) at the constant rate of 1 ft./sec. Simultaneously the door is being opened at the constant angular rate of 1.5 radians/sec. If P denotes the moving point in which the line of motion of the light meets the door, how fast is the intensity of illumination at P changing at the instant when the light is 12 ft. from the doorway and the door has been opened 45°? Is the intensity increasing or decreasing?

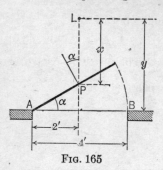

FIG. 165

Let y be the variable distance from the light to the doorway AB. Then, in order to express I in terms of the variables α and y whose rates of change are given, we note from the figure that $y = x + 2 \tan \alpha$, whence $x = y - 2 \tan \alpha$. Therefore

$$I = \frac{30 \cos \alpha}{(y - 2 \tan \alpha)^2}.$$

From this we obtain

$$\frac{\partial I}{\partial \alpha} = \frac{30}{(y - 2 \tan \alpha)^3} (4 \sec \alpha - y \sin \alpha + 2 \sin \alpha \tan \alpha),$$

$$\frac{\partial I}{\partial y} = \frac{30}{(y - 2 \tan \alpha)^3} (-2 \cos \alpha).$$

Hence (3) shows that

$$\frac{dI}{dt} = \frac{30}{(y - 2 \tan \alpha)^3} \left[(4 \sec \alpha - y \sin \alpha + 2 \sin \alpha \tan \alpha) \frac{d\alpha}{dt} - 2 \cos \alpha \frac{dy}{dt} \right].$$

Substituting $\alpha = \dfrac{\pi}{4}, \dfrac{d\alpha}{dt} = \dfrac{3}{2}, y = 12, \dfrac{dy}{dt} = -1$, we have, for the instant specified,

$$\frac{dI}{dt} = \frac{30}{(12 - 2)^3} [(4\sqrt{2} - 6\sqrt{2} + \sqrt{2}) \cdot \tfrac{3}{2} - \sqrt{2}(-1)]$$

$$= -0.021 \text{ foot-candle per second.}$$

The negative sign indicates that I is decreasing.

166. Directional Derivative. The concept of *directional derivative* will be introduced by means of an example.

A stationary point-source of light at L (Fig. 166a) illuminates a fixed plane MN. Let us find the rate at which I, the intensity of illum-

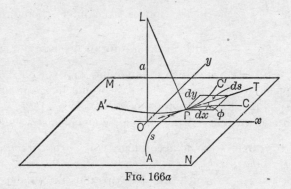

Fig. 166a

ination on MN at a point P, changes with respect to the variable arc AP of a fixed curve AC lying in MN, as P moves along the curve.

Let O be the projection of L on MN, and through O draw a pair of rectangular axes in the plane. Designate the moving point as $P(x, y)$, and denote by s the variable length of the arc AP, regarding A as an origin of arcs.

By Example 2 of the foregoing article we may write

$$(1) \qquad I = \frac{k \cos OLP}{LP^2} = \frac{ka}{(x^2 + y^2 + a^2)^{\frac{3}{2}}},$$

where $a = OL$, and x, y, a are expressed in feet. Thus the intensity of illumination on the plane at P depends only on x and y. But these coördinates refer to a point moving on AC and hence are both functions of s. Therefore by (3) of the preceding article we have

$$\frac{dI}{ds} = \frac{\partial I}{\partial x}\frac{dx}{ds} + \frac{\partial I}{\partial y}\frac{dy}{ds}.$$

By (4) and (5), Art. 59, if PT is the tangent line to AC at P, directed in the sense in which s increases, and ϕ is the counterclockwise angle from the positive x-axis to PT,

$$\frac{dx}{ds} = \cos\phi, \qquad \frac{dy}{ds} = \sin\phi.$$

Hence

(2) $$\frac{dI}{ds} = \frac{\partial I}{\partial x}\cos\phi + \frac{\partial I}{\partial y}\sin\phi.$$

We observe now that the only characteristic of the curve AC at P, which affects $\dfrac{dI}{ds}$, is the inclination ϕ. We infer, therefore, that the value of $\dfrac{dI}{ds}$ at P depends only on the instantaneous position of P and the instantaneous direction in which it is moving, and not on the particular curve it happens to be tracing. Thus we would have obtained exactly the same result (2), had we used some other curve $A'PC'$ having with AC the common tangent PT at P. For convenience we say that this tangent has the direction s and accordingly call $\dfrac{dI}{ds}$ the *directional derivative* of I at P in the direction s.

Any function $f(x, y)$ which, like I in this illustration, depends for its value only on the coördinates of the point (x, y) is frequently called a **point-function**. Its directional derivative at any point in a direction s making the counterclockwise angle ϕ with the positive x-axis, is, by analogy with (2),

$$\frac{df}{ds} = \frac{\partial f}{\partial x}\cos\phi + \frac{\partial f}{\partial y}\sin\phi.$$

Clearly this derivative is not a point-function, for it depends not only on x and y but also on ϕ. By taking $\phi = 0$ we see that $\dfrac{\partial f}{\partial x}$ may be regarded as the directional derivative of f in the direction of the x-axis at the point (x, y). A similar statement holds for $\dfrac{\partial f}{\partial y}$.

Returning now to (1) we have

$$\frac{\partial I}{\partial x} = \frac{-3kax}{(x^2 + y^2 + a^2)^{\frac{5}{2}}}, \qquad \frac{\partial I}{\partial y} = \frac{-3kay}{(x^2 + y^2 + a^2)^{\frac{5}{2}}}.$$

Hence by (2)

(3) $$\frac{dI}{ds} = \frac{-3ka}{(x^2 + y^2 + a^2)^{\frac{5}{2}}} (x \cos \phi + y \sin \phi).$$

In particular, if a 30-candlepower light (Fig. 166b) is situated at a distance $a = 2$ ft. above a table-top MN, the directional derivative of

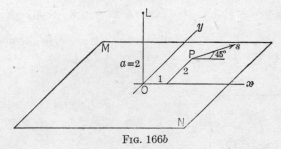

FIG. 166b

I at the point $(1, 2)$ in a direction s making an angle of $45°$ with the x-axis is

$$\frac{dI}{ds}\Bigg]_{\substack{(1,\,2) \\ \phi\,=\,45°}} = \frac{-3 \cdot 30 \cdot 2}{(1^2 + 2^2 + 2^2)^{\frac{5}{2}}} \left(1 \cdot \frac{\sqrt{2}}{2} + 2 \cdot \frac{\sqrt{2}}{2} \right)$$

$$= -1.57 \text{ foot-candles per foot.}$$

Let us now find the curves in the plane MN, along any one of which I remains constant. Equating the expression for I in (1) to an arbitrary constant K and simplifying, we obtain the equation

$$x^2 + y^2 = C$$

of a system of circles with centers at O, where $C = \left(\frac{ka}{K} \right)^{\frac{2}{3}} - a^2$. We readily justify this result intuitively, for clearly the intensity of illumination is the same for all points of any such circle.

Let us now regard P as any fixed point of MN and find in what directions from P the intensity of illumination experiences the greatest and least rates of change. In other words let us find the values of ϕ for which $\frac{dI}{ds}$ attains its maximum and minimum values at any fixed point P.

Regarding x and y as constants and equating to zero the result of differentiating (3) with respect to ϕ we obtain

$$- x \sin \phi + y \cos \phi = 0,$$

or

$$\tan \phi = \frac{y}{x}.$$

From the fact that this equation fixes the terminal side of ϕ along the line joining O and P, it follows that, if $\dfrac{dI}{ds}$ attains a maximum or minimum value at P, it must do so in one or the other of the two directions determined by this line. It should be clear physically that $\dfrac{dI}{ds}$ will be a maximum (and hence I will experience its greatest rate of change) in the direction from P toward O, and will be a minimum (corresponding to the numerically largest negative rate of change of I) in the opposite direction, namely along the line OP produced.

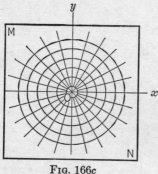

Fig. 166c

Summarizing, we see that along each of the circles of Fig. 166c the intensity of illumination remains constant, while along any one of the radial lines it changes most rapidly.

It is noteworthy that each of the lines cuts every circle **orthogonally**, or at right angles, and vice versa. This illustrates a characteristic property of point-functions in general, namely, that each of the curves along which a function $f(x, y)$ remains constant intersects orthogonally every curve along which the function experiences its maximum and minimum rates of change. The two families of curves thus defined are therefore called **orthogonal trajectories** of each other.

PROBLEMS

1. In each of the following problems find $\dfrac{dz}{dt}$ in two ways, and evaluate it for the given value of t:

(a) $z = e^x \cos \dfrac{y}{2}$, $x = \sqrt{\dfrac{t}{\pi}}$, $y = 3t$; $t = \pi$;

(b) $z = \ln (y^2 - x^2)$, $x = \sin t$, $y = \cos t$; $t = \dfrac{\pi}{8}$;

(c) $z = \tan^{-1} \dfrac{y}{x}$, $x = \sin t^2$, $y = \cos t^2$; $t = \tfrac{1}{2}$;

(d) $z = \sin^{-1}(x^2 - y^2)$, $x = \cos\dfrac{1}{t}$, $y = \sin\dfrac{1}{t}$; $t = 1$;

(e) $z = \ln(x^y y^x)$, $x = e^t$, $y = e^{-t}$; $t = 1$;

(f) $z = e^{4x^2 y^2}$, $x = \sin\dfrac{t}{2}$, $y = \cos\dfrac{t}{2}$; $t = \dfrac{\pi}{4}$;

(g) $z = \ln\dfrac{x + \sqrt{x^2 + y^2}}{y}$, $x = \cos t$, $y = \sin t$; $t = \dfrac{\pi}{2}$;

(h) $z = \dfrac{1}{2}\ln\dfrac{x+y}{x-y}$, $x = \sec t$, $y = 2\sin t$; $t = \pi$.

2. A batter knocks a ball obliquely into the air. After t seconds its horizontal distance from the batter is $x = 30t$ feet, and its height above his level is $y = 48t - 16t^2$ feet. How fast is the ball's distance from the batter changing at the end of 1 sec.?

3. In Problem 2 what is the angular speed of the line joining the batter and the ball when $t = 1$ sec.?

4. A particle moves in the xy-plane so that at any time t its abscissa and ordinate are respectively $x = 4t$, $y = 16t^2$. If x and y are expressed in feet and t in seconds, how fast is the particle's distance from the point $(5, 4)$ changing when $t = \frac{1}{4}$ sec.?

5. In Problem 4 find the angular speed of the line joining the particle and the point $(5, 4)$ when $t = \frac{1}{4}$ sec.

6. Two planes leave an airport simultaneously. One flies at 240 mi./hr. eastward and the other at 110 mi./hr. in a direction 30° west of north. Show that the distance between the planes increases at a constant rate, and find this rate.

7. The altitude of a right circular cone is 12 in. and is increasing at the rate of 4 in./sec. The radius of the base is 9 in. and is decreasing at the rate of 3 in./sec. How fast is the volume changing? The lateral surface?

8. The characteristic equation of a certain gas is $pv = 60T$. Suppose that at a certain instant the pressure p is 2400 lb./ft.² and is decreasing at the rate of 30 lb./ft.² per minute, and that the absolute temperature T is 648° and is increasing at the rate of 0.7° per minute. Find the rate at which the volume v is changing at this instant.

9. In each of the following problems find $\dfrac{dz}{dx}$ in two ways:

(a) $z = \ln(x^2 - y^2)$, $y = x \sin x$;

(b) $z = \tan^{-1}\dfrac{y}{x}$, $y = \sqrt{1 - x^2}$;

(c) $z = \ln(x^y y^x)$, $y = e^x$;

(d) $z = \ln\dfrac{x \mid y}{a}$, $y = \sqrt{a^2 + x^2}$;

(e) $z = \dfrac{x}{y} - \dfrac{y}{x}$, $y = \sqrt{4 - x^2}$;

(f) $z = e^{xy}y^e$, $y = e^x$.

10. The temperature in degrees of a heated circular plate varies thus with the distance r (inches) from its center:

$$T = \frac{343}{\sqrt{4 + r^2}}.$$

Choose rectangular axes through the center of the plate and find at the point (3, 6) the rate of change of the temperature in a direction making an angle of 30° with the x-axis.

11. Find in what directions from the point (3, 6) the temperature of the plate in Problem 10 experiences a zero rate of change. Find the general equation of that family of curves (**isothermal curves**) along each of which the temperature is constant.

12. Find in what direction from the point (3, 6) the temperature of the plate in Problem 10 increases fastest.

13. The electric potential at any point of the xy-plane is $V = \ln (x^2 + y^2)$. Find the directional derivative of V in any direction at the point (x_1, y_1). Show (a) that V is a constant along any circle with center at the origin, and (b) that V changes most rapidly along the system of radial lines passing through the origin.

14. Find in what direction from the point (x_1, y_1) the function $z = \tan^{-1} \dfrac{y}{x}$ increases most rapidly.

15. Show that the maximum value of the directional derivative of a function $f(x, y)$ at a fixed point (x, y) is

$$\sqrt{\left(\frac{\partial f}{\partial x}\right)^2 + \left(\frac{\partial f}{\partial y}\right)^2}.$$

167. Differentiation of Implicit Functions. If $z = f(x, y)$ and y is a function of x, it follows from (7), Art. 165, that

$$\frac{dz}{dx} = \frac{\partial f}{\partial x} + \frac{\partial f}{\partial y}\frac{dy}{dx}.$$

By taking $z = 0$, so that $\dfrac{dz}{dx} = 0$, we have $\dfrac{\partial f}{\partial x} + \dfrac{\partial f}{\partial y}\dfrac{dy}{dx} = 0$. Hence

From the equation $f(x, y) = 0$, defining y as an implicit function of x, $\dfrac{dy}{dx}$ may be found by the formula

(1) $$\frac{dy}{dx} = -\frac{\dfrac{\partial f}{\partial x}}{\dfrac{\partial f}{\partial y}}, \quad provided \quad \frac{\partial f}{\partial y} \neq 0.$$

The result of applying (1) is always identical with that found by the method of implicit differentiation (Art. 43).

Now let us regard the equation $F(x, y, z) = 0$ as defining z implicitly in terms of x and y, and find $\dfrac{\partial z}{\partial x}$ and $\dfrac{\partial z}{\partial y}$. First hold y constant. Then

$F(x, y, z)$ reduces to a function of x and z. Therefore, by analogy with (1), we may write

$$\frac{\partial z}{\partial x} = - \frac{\dfrac{\partial F}{\partial x}}{\dfrac{\partial F}{\partial z}}, \quad \text{provided} \quad \frac{\partial F}{\partial z} \neq 0,$$

where the symbol for partial differentiation is used in the left member because y is held constant. Similarly, by holding x constant, we may find $\dfrac{\partial z}{\partial y}$. Summarizing, we see that

From the equation $F(x, y, z) = 0$, defining z as an implicit function of x and y, the partial derivatives of z may be found by the formulas

$$(2) \qquad \frac{\partial z}{\partial x} = - \frac{\dfrac{\partial F}{\partial x}}{\dfrac{\partial F}{\partial z}}, \quad \frac{\partial z}{\partial y} = - \frac{\dfrac{\partial F}{\partial y}}{\dfrac{\partial F}{\partial z}}, \quad \text{provided} \quad \frac{\partial F}{\partial z} \neq \mathbf{0.}$$

Example 1.   Find $\dfrac{dy}{dx}$ if $\ln \dfrac{y}{x} + ye^x = 0$.

Let $f(x, y) = \ln \dfrac{y}{x} + ye^x = \ln y - \ln x + ye^x$. Then since

$$\frac{\partial f}{\partial x} = -\frac{1}{x} + ye^x, \qquad \frac{\partial f}{\partial y} = \frac{1}{y} + e^x,$$

we find from (1) that

$$\frac{dy}{dx} = \frac{\dfrac{1}{x} - ye^x}{\dfrac{1}{y} + e^x} = \frac{y(1 - xye^x)}{x(1 + ye^x)}.$$

It will be left as an exercise to show that the same result may be obtained by the method of Art. 43.

Example 2.   Find $\dfrac{\partial z}{\partial x}$ and $\dfrac{\partial z}{\partial y}$ if $z^{xy} - y^z x^y = 0$.

Writing the equation in the form $\dfrac{z^{xy}}{y^z x^y} = 1$, and denoting by $F(x, y, z)$ the natural logarithm of the left member, we obtain

$$(3) \qquad F(x, y, z) = xy \ln z - z \ln y - y \ln x = 0.$$

Therefore

$$\frac{\partial F}{\partial x} = y \ln z - \frac{y}{x},$$

$$\frac{\partial F}{\partial y} = x \ln z - \frac{z}{y} - \ln x = \frac{z}{y}(\ln y - 1),$$

$$\frac{\partial F}{\partial z} = \frac{xy}{z} - \ln y,$$

the final form of $\dfrac{\partial F}{\partial y}$ being a consequence of (3). Hence, applying (2) and simplifying, we have

$$\frac{\partial z}{\partial x} = \frac{yz(1 - x \ln z)}{x(xy - z \ln y)},$$

$$\frac{\partial z}{\partial y} = \frac{z^2(1 - \ln y)}{y(xy - z \ln y)}.$$

168. Tangent Plane and Normal Line to a Surface. In Fig. 168 let P_1RQS be a portion of the surface $z = f(x, y)$ included between the planes

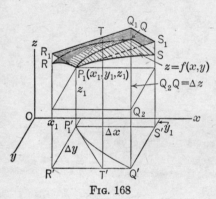

FIG. 168

$x = x_1$, $x = x_1 + \Delta x$, $y = y_1$, and $y = y_1 + \Delta y$, so that P_1 (a fixed point) and Q have the coördinates (x_1, y_1, z_1) and $(x_1 + \Delta x, y_1 + \Delta y, z_1 + \Delta z)$, respectively. Moreover, let $f(x, y)$, together with its partial derivatives $\dfrac{\partial f}{\partial x}$ and $\dfrac{\partial f}{\partial y}$, be single-valued and continuous in the neighborhood of $x = x_1$, $y = y_1$. Then, as we shall now prove, *all the tangent lines to the surface at the point $P_1(x_1, y_1, z_1)$ lie in a plane*, called the **tangent plane** to *the surface at P_1*.

Since Δx, Δy, Δz are the direction parameters of the straight line through P_1 and Q, it follows from Formula 28, p. 510, that the equations of this line are

$$\frac{x - x_1}{\Delta x} = \frac{y - y_1}{\Delta y} = \frac{z - z_1}{\Delta z},$$

or

(1)
$$\begin{cases} y - y_1 = \dfrac{\Delta y}{\Delta x}(x - x_1), \\[2mm] z - z_1 = \dfrac{\Delta z}{\Delta x}(x - x_1). \end{cases}$$

Now let Q approach P_1 along an arbitrary continuous curve QP_1 of the surface, and take $y = \chi(x)$ as the equation of the projection $(Q'P'_1)$

of this curve on the xy-plane. Then, for any point of the curve QP_1,

$$z = f(x, y) \quad \text{and} \quad y = \chi(x).$$

Hence by (7), Art. 165, we have

$$\frac{dz}{dx} = \frac{\partial z}{\partial x} + \frac{\partial z}{\partial y}\frac{dy}{dx}.$$

The values, for $x = x_1$, $y = y_1$, $z = z_1$, of the derivatives appearing in this equation will be denoted by $\left(\dfrac{dz}{dx}\right)_1$, $\left(\dfrac{\partial z}{\partial x}\right)_1$, $\left(\dfrac{\partial z}{\partial y}\right)_1$, $\left(\dfrac{dy}{dx}\right)_1$, so that

(2)
$$\left(\frac{dz}{dx}\right)_1 = \left(\frac{\partial z}{\partial x}\right)_1 + \left(\frac{\partial z}{\partial y}\right)_1 \left(\frac{dy}{dx}\right)_1.$$

Now as Q approaches P_1 along the curve QP_1, the straight line (1) through P_1 and Q approaches a line P_1T which is tangent to the curve and hence to the surface at P_1; and, since Δx, Δy, Δz all tend toward zero during the motion of Q, the equations of the tangent line P_1T are evidently

(3)
$$\begin{cases} y - y_1 = \left(\dfrac{dy}{dx}\right)_1 (x - x_1), \\[2mm] z - z_1 = \left(\dfrac{dz}{dx}\right)_1 (x - x_1). \end{cases}$$

Substituting in (2) the expressions for $\left(\dfrac{dy}{dx}\right)_1$ and $\left(\dfrac{dz}{dx}\right)_1$ given by (3), we find that the coördinates of any point (x, y, z) on the tangent line (3) satisfy the equation

(4)
$$z - z_1 = \left(\frac{\partial z}{\partial x}\right)_1 (x - x_1) + \left(\frac{\partial z}{\partial y}\right)_1 (y - y_1),$$

which, being of the first degree in x, y, z, represents a plane. Moreover, since Q approached P_1 along an arbitrary curve of the surface, the coördinates (x, y, z) of a point on any tangent line to the surface at P_1 satisfy (4). Hence (4) represents a plane containing all tangent lines to the surface at P_1 and may therefore properly be called the **equation of the tangent plane** to the surface $z = f(x, y)$ at the point P_1 (x_1, y_1, z_1).

If the equation of the surface is in the implicit form $F(x, y, z) = 0$, the equation of the tangent plane to the surface at the point (x_1, y_1, z_1) may be found (without solving for z explicitly) by the formula

(5)
$$\left(\frac{\partial F}{\partial x}\right)_1 (x - x_1) + \left(\frac{\partial F}{\partial y}\right)_1 (y - y_1) + \left(\frac{\partial F}{\partial z}\right)_1 (z - z_1) = 0,$$

where, as in (4), the subscripts affixed to the partial derivatives signify that the latter are to be evaluated for the point of tangency P_1. To prove this we need only to substitute in (4) the values of $\dfrac{\partial z}{\partial x}$ and $\dfrac{\partial z}{\partial y}$ given by (2), Art. 167, and simplify.

The line perpendicular to the tangent plane to a surface at the point of tangency is called the **normal line** to the surface at this point.

Since the coefficients A, B, C in the general equation $Ax + By + Cz + D = 0$ of a plane are direction parameters of any line perpendicular to the plane, it follows from (4), and from Formula 28, p. 510, that the equations of the normal line to the surface $z = f(x, y)$ at the point (x_1, y_1, z_1) are

$$(6) \qquad \frac{x - x_1}{\left(\dfrac{\partial z}{\partial x}\right)_1} = \frac{y - y_1}{\left(\dfrac{\partial z}{\partial y}\right)_1} = \frac{z - z_1}{-1}.$$

By (2), Art. 167, (6) becomes

$$(7) \qquad \frac{x - x_1}{\left(\dfrac{\partial F}{\partial x}\right)_1} = \frac{y - y_1}{\left(\dfrac{\partial F}{\partial y}\right)_1} = \frac{z - z_1}{\left(\dfrac{\partial F}{\partial z}\right)_1},$$

a formula which could have been obtained directly from (5) and which readily yields the normal line to a surface whose equation occurs in the implicit form $F(x, y, z) = 0$.

Example 1. Find the equation of the tangent plane and the equations of the normal line to the paraboloid $z = x^2 + y^2$ at the point $(1, 2, 5)$.

Since $x_1 = 1$, $y_1 = 2$, and $z_1 = 5$, we have

$$\left(\frac{\partial z}{\partial x}\right)_1 = 2x_1 = 2,$$

$$\left(\frac{\partial z}{\partial y}\right)_1 = 2y_1 = 4.$$

Hence by (4) the equation of the tangent plane is

$$z - 5 = 2(x - 1) + 4(y - 2),$$

or

$$2x + 4y - z - 5 = 0.$$

By (6) the equations of the normal line are

$$\frac{x - 1}{2} = \frac{y - 2}{4} = \frac{z - 5}{-1}.$$

Example 2. Find the equation of the tangent plane and the equations of the normal line to the ellipsoid

$$\frac{x^2}{a^2} + \frac{y^2}{b^2} + \frac{z^2}{c^2} = 1$$

at the point (x_1, y_1, z_1).

Write $F(x, y, z) = \dfrac{x^2}{a^2} + \dfrac{y^2}{b^2} + \dfrac{z^2}{c^2} - 1$. Then

$$\left(\frac{\partial F}{\partial x}\right)_1 = \frac{2x_1}{a^2}, \qquad \left(\frac{\partial F}{\partial y}\right)_1 = \frac{2y_1}{b^2}, \qquad \left(\frac{\partial F}{\partial z}\right)_1 = \frac{2z_1}{c^2}.$$

Hence by (5) the equation of the tangent plane is

$$\frac{2x_1}{a^2}(x - x_1) + \frac{2y_1}{b^2}(y - y_1) + \frac{2z_1}{c^2}(z - z_1) = 0,$$

which reduces to

$$\frac{x_1 x}{a^2} + \frac{y_1 y}{b^2} + \frac{z_1 z}{c^2} = 1,$$

since x_1, y_1, z_1 satisfy the equation of the ellipsoid.

By (7) the equations of the normal line are

$$\frac{x - x_1}{\dfrac{x_1}{a^2}} = \frac{y - y_1}{\dfrac{y_1}{b^2}} = \frac{z - z_1}{\dfrac{z_1}{c^2}}.$$

PROBLEMS

1. In each of the following problems find $\dfrac{dy}{dx}$ in two ways:

(a) $x^3 + x^2 y + xy^2 + y^3 = 0$;

(b) $\dfrac{x}{y} - \dfrac{y}{x} = 1$;

(c) $x \sin y = y \sin x$;

(d) $e^x \sin y + e^y \cos x = 0$;

(e) $\ln \dfrac{y}{x} = \tan^{-1} \dfrac{y}{x}$;

(f) $\sin^{-1} \dfrac{y}{x} = \sqrt{x^2 - y^2}$;

(g) $\cot x \cot y = e^{xy}$;

(h) $\ln \left(\dfrac{y}{x} - \dfrac{x}{y}\right) = xy$.

2. Find $\dfrac{\partial z}{\partial x}$ and $\dfrac{\partial z}{\partial y}$ in each of the following cases:

(a) $x^2 + y^2 + z^2 = a^2$;

(b) $(x - y)(y - z)(z - x) = c$;

(c) $\dfrac{x^2}{y + z} = z$;

(d) $e^z \sin xy = e^{xy} \sin z$;

(e) $\cos xz = yz$;

(f) $\tan^{-1} \dfrac{z}{x} = \sin^{-1} \dfrac{z}{y}$;

(g) $x^y y^z z^x = 1$;

(h) $e^{xy} + e^{xz} + e^{yz} = c$.

3. Find the equations of the tangent plane and the normal line to the elliptic paraboloid $z = 2x^2 + 3y^2$ at the point $(2, 1, 11)$.

4. Find the equations of the tangent plane and the normal line to the hyperbolic paraboloid $z = 3xy$ at the point $(1, 2, 6)$.

5. Find the equations of the tangent plane and the normal line to the ellipsoid $2x^2 + 3y^2 + z^2 = 12$ at the point $(2, 1, 1)$.

6. Find formulas for the tangent plane and the normal line to each of the following surfaces at the point (x_1, y_1, z_1):

(a) the elliptic paraboloid $z = ax^2 + by^2$, $ab > 0$;

(b) the hyperboloid of one sheet $\dfrac{x^2}{a^2} + \dfrac{y^2}{b^2} - \dfrac{z^2}{c^2} = 1$;

(c) the cone $\dfrac{x^2}{a^2} + \dfrac{y^2}{b^2} - \dfrac{z^2}{c^2} = 0$;

(d) the hyperboloid of two sheets $\dfrac{x^2}{a^2} - \dfrac{y^2}{b^2} - \dfrac{z^2}{c^2} = 1$;

(e) the hyperbolic paraboloid $z = ax^2 - by^2$, $ab > 0$;
(f) the hyperbolic paraboloid $z = kxy$.

7. Show that any tangent plane to the hyperbolic paraboloid in Problem 6(f) cuts the surface in two straight lines.

8. Find the intercepts on the coördinate axes of any tangent plane to the surface

$$x^{\frac{2}{3}} + y^{\frac{2}{3}} + z^{\frac{2}{3}} = a^{\frac{2}{3}},$$

and show that the sum of their squares is a constant.

9. Show that the tetrahedron bounded by the coördinate planes and any tangent plane to the surface $xyz = a^3$ is of constant volume.

10. Show that the equation of the tangent plane to any quadric surface

$$Ax^2 + By^2 + Cz^2 + Dxy + Exz + Fyz + Gx + Hy + Jz + K = 0,$$

at the point (x_1, y_1, z_1), may be obtained from the equation of the surface by replacing x^2 by x_1x, y^2 by y_1y, z^2 by z_1z, xy by $\frac{1}{2}(x_1y + y_1x)$, xz by $\frac{1}{2}(x_1z + z_1x)$, yz by $\frac{1}{2}(y_1z + z_1y)$, x by $\frac{1}{2}(x + x_1)$, y by $\frac{1}{2}(y + y_1)$, and z by $\frac{1}{2}(z + z_1)$.

Apply this device to Problems 3, 4, 5, 6.

11. Find the equations of the tangent lines P_1R_1 and P_1S_1 to the curves P_1R and P_1S in Fig. 168, and show that they are deducible from (4).

169. Maxima and Minima. A function $f(x, y)$,* of two independent variables, is said to have a **maximum** value for $x = x_1$, $y = y_1$, if $f(x_1, y_1)$ is greater than $f(x, y)$ for all values of x and y in the immediate neighborhood of x_1 and y_1. Similarly, $f(x, y)$ is said to have a **minimum** value for $x = x_1$, $y = y_1$, if $f(x_1, y_1)$ is less than $f(x, y)$ for all values of x and y in the immediate neighborhood of x_1 and y_1. Frequently it is convenient to call a maximum or a minimum value of a function an **extreme**.

The above definitions may be clarified by the following geometrical considerations.

* Throughout this article we assume that the function $f(x, y)$ and its partial derivatives of the first order are single-valued and continuous in the neighborhood of the point (x_1, y_1).

Let $z = f(x, y)$, and suppose that this equation represents the surface shown in Fig. 169. Then to each pair of values of x and y for which $f(x, y)$ is a maximum there corresponds on the surface a point (such as M) which, being higher than any other point of the surface in its immediate neighborhood, is called a **maximum point.** Similarly, to each pair of values of x and y for which $f(x, y)$ is a minimum there corresponds on the surface a point (such as N) which, being lower than any other point of the surface in its immediate neighborhood, is called a **minimum point.**

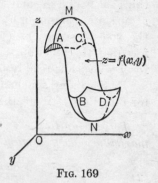

FIG. 169

Thus any vertical plane through M intersects the surface in a curve (such as AMC) having a maximum point at M, while any vertical plane through N intersects the surface in a curve (such as BND) having a minimum point at N.

Hence whether $z_1 = f(x_1, y_1)$ is a maximum or a minimum it is necessary (though not sufficient) that the tangent plane to the surface $z = f(x, y)$ at the point (x_1, y_1, z_1) be parallel to the xy-plane, and consequently that it have the equation $z = z_1$. Hence by (4), Art. 168,

$$\left(\frac{\partial z}{\partial x}\right)_1 (x - x_1) + \left(\frac{\partial z}{\partial y}\right)_1 (y - y_1) = 0.$$

Since this condition must be satisfied by the x- and y-coördinates of any point in the tangent plane, and these coördinates are quite independent of each other, we conclude that

For the function $z = f(x, y)$ of two independent variables to have a maximum or a minimum value $z_1 = f(x_1, y_1)$, it is necessary that

(1) $$\frac{\partial z}{\partial x} = 0, \quad \frac{\partial z}{\partial y} = 0,$$

for $x = x_1, y = y_1$.

The necessity of the conditions (1) assures us that each pair of values of x and y for which z is a maximum or a minimum is contained among the simultaneous solutions of (1). On the other hand, since the conditions are not sufficient, they may yield solutions which do not correspond to extremes of z. Moreover, the equations afford no analytical means of distinguishing between the two possible kinds of extremes, i.e., maxima and minima. Frequently, however, no such means are needed, for both the existence and nature of an extreme are often evident from the physical or geometrical aspects of the given problem. When such evidence is lacking, additional analytical conditions are needed, which are sufficient for classifying the solutions of (1) according as they give rise to maximum or minimum values of z, or neither. Such conditions will be discussed in the next article.

The equations (1) may be derived in another way. For if y maintains the value y_1, and x varies, the function $f(x, y_1)$, of one variable, attains a maximum or a minimum value for $x = x_1$, and hence (Art. 22) the first of equations (1) holds when $x = x_1$, $y = y_1$. Likewise, the fact that the function $f(x_1, y)$ attains a maximum or a minimum value for $y = y_1$ leads readily to the second equation.

By reasoning similar to this we arrive at conditions analogous to (1) for functions of more than two variables. Thus

For the function $u = f(x, y, z)$ of three independent variables to have a maximum or a minimum value $u_1 = f(x_1, y_1, z_1)$, it is necessary that

$$(2) \qquad \frac{\partial u}{\partial x} = 0, \quad \frac{\partial u}{\partial y} = 0, \quad \frac{\partial u}{\partial z} = 0,$$

for $x = x_1, y = y_1, z = z_1$; and so on for any number of independent variables.

Example. Show that, of all triangles having a given perimeter, the largest one is equilateral.

Let x, y, z denote the lengths of the sides of the triangle, A the area, and $2s$ the perimeter, so that $2s = x + y + z$. Then, from geometry,

$$(3) \qquad A = \sqrt{s(s - x)(s - y)(s - z)}.$$

We cannot here use the conditions $\dfrac{\partial A}{\partial x} = 0, \dfrac{\partial A}{\partial y} = 0, \dfrac{\partial A}{\partial z} = 0$, furnished by (2),

for x, y, z, are not all independent. Within certain limits two of the sides, say x and y, may be chosen at will, whereupon z is automatically determined by the relation

$$(4) \qquad z = 2s - x - y.$$

In view of (4), (3) becomes

$$(5) \qquad A = \sqrt{s(s - x)(s - y)(x + y - s)},$$

so that A is a function of only two independent variables.

The problem may now be simplified by finding the values of x and y for which the function

$$(6) \qquad \frac{A^2}{s} = (s - x)(s - y)(x + y - s)$$

is a maximum; for clearly A will be a maximum when $\dfrac{A^2}{s}$ is.

From (6) we obtain

$$\frac{\partial}{\partial x}\left(\frac{A^2}{s}\right) = (s - y)(2s - 2x - y),$$

$$\frac{\partial}{\partial y}\left(\frac{A^2}{s}\right) = (s - x)(2s - 2y - x).$$

Hence by (1) the values of x and y corresponding to a maximum area must satisfy the simultaneous equations

$$(s - y)(2s - 2x - y) = 0,$$

$$(s - x)(2s - 2y - x) = 0.$$

Obviously we are not interested in the solutions $x = s$, $y = 0$; $x = 0$, $y = s$; or $x = s$, $y = s$; for in all three of these cases $A = 0$. Hence, solving the equations

$$2s - 2x - y = 0, \qquad 2s - 2y - x = 0,$$

for x and y, and substituting these values in (4), we obtain $x = y = z = \dfrac{2s}{3}$.

From the nature of the problem it is clear that a maximum area exists and hence that these values correspond to this maximum. The largest triangle is therefore equilateral, and by (3) or (5) its area is $\dfrac{\sqrt{3}\, s^2}{9}$.

PROBLEMS

1. Find the minimum value of the function $x^2 + y^2 - 4x + 2y + 9$.

HINT: To show that the result is really a minimum complete the square in the terms in x and in y.

2. Find the maximum value of the function $12y - 12x - 2x^2 - 3y^2 - 21$.

3. Find the minimum value of the function $x^4 + 4x^2y^2 + 4y^4 - 2$.

4. Find the minimum value of the function $2x^2 + y^2 + 2xy + 6x + 6y + 3$.

HINT: To show that the result is really a minimum express the function as a constant plus the sum of the squares of a monomial and a trinomial.

5. Find the maximum value of the function $4 - x^2 - 2y^2 + 2xy + 2x - 2y$.

6. Find the maximum product of three numbers whose sum is the positive number a.

7. Assuming that $x \neq 0$, calculate the values of x and θ for which the function $x^2 + a^2 - 2ax \cos\theta$ is a minimum. Interpret the results geometrically.

8. A man has 48 sq. ft. of lumber with which to build a bin in the form of a rectangular parallelepiped open at the top. Making no allowance for thickness of material or waste in construction, find the dimensions he should choose to produce the greatest capacity. What is this capacity?

9. A chemical industry must construct a large number of expensively lined vats, each having the form of an open-top rectangular parallelepiped and a capacity of 256 cu. ft. What dimensions will make the cost of lining a minimum?

10. Find by calculus the shortest distance from the origin to the plane $3x - 4y + 12z = 26$.

11. Find by calculus the shortest distance from the origin to the plane $x + y + z = 3$.

12. A long strip of tin 18 in. wide is to be made into a gutter by bending up equal amounts along the sides of the strip so as to form a trapezoidal cross-section with sides of equal inclination. If the carrying capacity is to be a maximum what should be the width and inclination of each side?

13. Show that the largest rectangular parallelepiped that can be inscribed in a sphere is a cube.

14. Find the dimensions and volume of the largest rectangular parallelepiped that can be placed with three faces in the coördinate planes and with the vertex common to the other three faces in the plane $x + y + 2z = 6$.

15. For what point in the plane of a triangle is the sum of the squares of its distances from the vertices (x_1, y_1), (x_2, y_2), (x_3, y_3) a minimum?

16. Perpendiculars of lengths x, y, z are drawn from any point in the plane of a triangle to the three sides a, b, c, respectively. Show that the minimum value of the sum of the squares of x, y, and z is $\dfrac{4K^2}{a^2 + b^2 + c^2}$, where K is the area of the triangle.

17. Find the equation of the plane through the point $(2, 1, 3)$ which cuts the least volume from the first octant.

170. Sufficient Condition for an Extreme. Suppose now that for the function $z = f(x, y)$ we have found a pair of values x_1 and y_1 satisfying the conditions (1) of the preceding article, so that

$$(1) \qquad \frac{\partial z}{\partial x} = 0, \quad \frac{\partial z}{\partial y} = 0$$

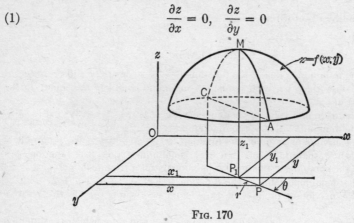

Fig. 170

for $x = x_1$, $y = y_1$. As these are only necessary conditions for an extreme of the function, we are naturally led to seek a criterion for ascertaining whether $z_1 = f(x_1, y_1)$ is actually an extreme, and if it is, whether it is a maximum or a minimum. To establish such a criterion it is necessary to assume that the first and second partial derivatives of z are single-valued and continuous for $x = x_1$, $y = y_1$.

Let Fig. 170 represent a portion of the surface $z = f(x, y)$ in the neighborhood of the point $M(x_1, y_1, z_1)$. Then if $P(x, y, 0)$ is any point in the xy-plane at distance r from the point $P_1(x_1, y_1, 0)$, and θ is the angle shown in the figure, we may write

$$x = x_1 + lr, \quad y = y_1 + mr,$$

where $l = \cos\theta$, $m = \sin\theta$. Thus the equation $z = f(x, y)$ becomes

$$z = f(x_1 + lr, y_1 + mr).$$

Allowing θ to have any constant value, and observing that z is then a function of the one variable r, we have by (3), Art. 165,

$$\frac{dz}{dr} = \frac{\partial z}{\partial x}\frac{dx}{dr} + \frac{\partial z}{\partial y}\frac{dy}{dr} = l\frac{\partial z}{\partial x} + m\frac{\partial z}{\partial y}.$$

Hence for $x = x_1$, $y = y_1$, we conclude from (1) that

$$\frac{dz}{dr} = 0,$$

regardless of the value of θ. Thus the slope of any curve (such as AMC) cut from the surface by a vertical plane through M is zero at M. But this in itself is not sufficient to insure the existence of either a maximum or a minimum point of the surface at M; in addition, every such curve must be concave downward if M is a maximum point, and concave upward if M is a minimum point.

Hence, if for $x = x_1$ and $y = y_1$, the second derivative,

$$(2) \qquad \frac{d^2z}{dr^2} = l^2\frac{\partial^2 z}{\partial x^2} + 2lm\frac{\partial^2 z}{\partial x\,\partial y} + m^2\frac{\partial^2 z}{\partial y^2},$$

is different from zero and is of the same sign for all values of θ, then according as that sign is minus or plus, $z_1 = f(x_1, y_1)$ will be a maximum or a minimum (Art. 22).

For brevity now let

$$\frac{\partial^2 z}{\partial x^2} = A, \quad \frac{\partial^2 z}{\partial x\,\partial y} = B, \quad \frac{\partial^2 z}{\partial y^2} = C,$$

when $x = x_1$, $y = y_1$. Then, for these values of x and y, (2) becomes

$$(3) \qquad \frac{d^2z}{dr^2} = Al^2 + 2Blm + Cm^2.$$

By completing the square, first in the terms involving A and B, and then in those involving B and C, we obtain

$$(4) \qquad \frac{d^2z}{dr^2} = \frac{1}{A}[(Al + Bm)^2 + m^2(AC - B^2)],$$

and

$$(5) \qquad \frac{d^2z}{dr^2} = \frac{1}{C}[(Bl + Cm)^2 + l^2(AC - B^2)],$$

when $x = x_1$, $y = y_1$.

The discussion may now be divided into three cases, according as $AC - B^2$ is positive, negative, or zero.

Case 1. If

$$AC - B^2 > 0,$$

so that neither A nor C is zero and both have the same sign, then the corresponding value of $\dfrac{d^2z}{dr^2}$ will differ from zero and will agree in sign with A and C for all values of θ. Therefore, when $AC - B^2 > 0$, $z_1 = f(x_1, y_1)$ will be a maximum or a minimum according as A (or C) is negative or positive.

Case 2. If

$$AC - B^2 < 0,$$

three sub-cases must be considered, according as

(a) $AC \neq 0,$

(b) $AC = 0$, but A and C are not both zero,

or

(c) $A = C = 0.$

(a) Suppose that $AC \neq 0$, so that neither A nor C is zero. Then if we place $m = 0$ (i.e., $\sin \theta = 0$) we find from (4) that

$$\frac{1}{A} \frac{d^2z}{dr^2} = l^2 = 1,$$

while if we choose θ so that $Al + Bm = 0$, we obtain

$$A \frac{d^2z}{dr^2} = m^2(AC - B^2) < 0.$$

Hence when $AC \neq 0$ the value of $\dfrac{d^2z}{dr^2}$ for $x = x_1$, $y = y_1$ fails to have the same sign for all values of θ, and therefore $z_1 = f(x_1, y_1)$ is neither a maximum nor a minimum.

Similarly, when $AC - B^2 < 0$ and $AC \neq 0$, the right member of (5) has opposite signs when $l = 0$ and $Bl + Cm = 0$, and we have a second proof that z_1 cannot be an extreme.

(b) Suppose that $AC = 0$, but that A and C are not both zero. Then, if $A \neq 0$, we may show exactly as in the first proof under (a) that z_1 is neither a maximum nor a minimum. Similarly, if $C \neq 0$, we arrive at the same conclusion, using the arguments presented in the second proof under (a).

(c) If $A = C = 0$, the right member of (3) reduces to

$$2Blm = 2B \sin \theta \cos \theta = B \sin 2\theta,$$

where $B \neq 0$.   Hence $\dfrac{d^2z}{dr^2}$ for $x = x_1$, $y = y_1$ fails to have the same sign

for all values of θ, and z_1 is neither a maximum nor a minimum.

Thus whenever $AC - B^2 < 0$, the function $f(x, y)$ can have **no** extreme for $x = x_1$, $y = y_1$.

Case 3.   If

(6) $$AC - B^2 = 0,$$

three sub-cases arise according as

(a) $AC \neq 0$,

(b) $AC = 0$, but A and C are not both zero,

or

(c) $A = C = 0$.

(a) Suppose that $AC \neq 0$, so that neither A nor C is zero and both have the same sign.   Then, since (4) and (5) become respectively

$$\frac{d^2z}{dr^2} = \frac{(Al + Bm)^2}{A}, \quad \frac{d^2z}{dr^2} = \frac{(Bl + Cm)^2}{C},$$

the right members of these equations being identical by virtue of (6), we conclude that $\dfrac{d^2z}{dr^2}$ for $x = x_1$, $y = y_1$, will vanish for those values of θ which render $Al + Bm = 0$ (and hence also $Bl + Cm = 0$).   We are therefore unable, without further analysis, to draw any conclusion regarding the existence of a maximum or minimum; for, by Art. 22, the second derivative test for classifying extremes fails if the second derivative vanishes.

(b) If $AC = 0$, then $B = 0$.   Hence (3) becomes

$$\frac{d^2z}{dr^2} = Al^2, \quad \text{or} \quad \frac{d^2z}{dr^2} = Cm^2,$$

according as $A \neq 0$, or $C \neq 0$.   As these expressions vanish respectively when $l = 0$ and $m = 0$, we are again unable to decide, without further examination, whether z_1 is an extreme.

(c) A similar situation arises when $A = C = 0$; for then $B = 0$, and by (3) $\dfrac{d^2z}{dr^2}$ is identically zero when $x = x_1$, $y = y_1$.

It thus appears that, when $AC - B^2 = 0$, the existence of an extreme is uncertain; further tests, which we shall omit, are then needed to determine whether there is an extreme, and if there is, to what class it belongs.

We now summarize our findings in the following theorem, in which, for convenience, we let $\Delta(x, y)$ be the function of x and y represented by

$$\frac{\partial^2 z}{\partial x^2} \frac{\partial^2 z}{\partial y^2} - \left(\frac{\partial^2 z}{\partial x \, \partial y}\right)^2,$$

so that $\Delta(x_1, y_1) = AC - B^2$.

THEOREM. *If, for $x = x_1, y = y_1$,*

$$(1) \qquad \frac{\partial z}{\partial x} = 0, \quad \frac{\partial z}{\partial y} = 0,$$

and

$$(7) \qquad \Delta(x, y) = \frac{\partial^2 z}{\partial x^2} \frac{\partial^2 z}{\partial y^2} - \left(\frac{\partial^2 z}{\partial x \, \partial y}\right)^2 > 0,$$

then the function $z = f(x, y)$ of two independent variables will have a maximum or a minimum value $z_1 = f(x_1, y_1)$ according as $\dfrac{\partial^2 z}{\partial x^2} \left(or \ \dfrac{\partial^2 z}{\partial y^2} \right)$ is negative or positive for $x = x_1, y = y_1$. If (1) holds and $\Delta(x_1, y_1) < 0$, z_1 is neither a maximum nor a minimum; if $\Delta(x_1, y_1) = 0$ the question is undecided.

It is possible for the function to have a maximum or minimum value even when $\Delta(x_1, y_1) = 0$. Therefore, when the necessary conditions (1) are fulfilled, (7) is only a sufficient condition for the existence of an extreme. Although the test furnished by the theorem fails if $\Delta(x_1, y_1) = 0$, it is adequate in many important cases.

The discussion of analogous questions concerning functions of more than two variables is left to more advanced works.

Example. Examine the function $(6 - x)(6 - y)(x + y - 6)$ for extremes.
Let $z = (6 - x)(6 - y)(x + y - 6)$. Then

$$\frac{\partial z}{\partial x} = (6 - y)(12 - 2x - y), \qquad \frac{\partial^2 z}{\partial x^2} = 2y - 12,$$

$$\frac{\partial z}{\partial y} = (6 - x)(12 - 2y - x), \qquad \frac{\partial^2 z}{\partial y^2} = 2x - 12,$$

$$\frac{\partial^2 z}{\partial x \, \partial y} = 2x + 2y - 18,$$

$$\Delta(x, y) = \frac{\partial^2 z}{\partial x^2} \frac{\partial^2 z}{\partial y^2} - \left(\frac{\partial^2 z}{\partial x \, \partial y}\right)^2 = (2y - 12)(2x - 12) - (2x + 2y - 18)^2.$$

Since the values of x and y corresponding to any extreme of z are contained among the solutions of the simultaneous equations $\dfrac{\partial z}{\partial x} = 0$, $\dfrac{\partial z}{\partial y} = 0$, we set

$$(6 - y)(12 - 2x - y) = 0,$$

$$(6 - x)(12 - 2y - x) = 0,$$

and find the following pairs of solutions:

(a) $x = 6$, $y = 6$,   (c) $x = 0$, $y = 6$,

(b) $x = 6$, $y = 0$,   (d) $x = 4$, $y = 4$.

Evidently $\Delta(6, 6) = -36$, $\Delta(6, 0) = -36$, $\Delta(0, 6) = -36$; thus $\Delta < 0$ in all these cases. Hence, by the preceding theorem, none of the pairs of values in (a), (b), (c), yields an extreme of z.

However, corresponding to the solution (d), we have

$$\Delta(4, 4) = 12, \qquad \frac{\partial^2 z}{\partial x^2} = -4.$$

Hence, for $x = 4$ and $y = 4$, z has a maximum value, which by the original equation is 8.

PROBLEMS

1. By the method of this article establish (except when the test fails) the nature of the extreme in

(a) Problem 1, Art. 169.   (d) Problem 4, Art. 169.

(b) Problem 2, Art. 169.   (e) Problem 5, Art. 169.

(c) Problem 3, Art. 169.   (f) Problem 7, Art. 169. Discuss the case $x = 0$.

2. Find and classify the extreme of the function $x^2 + y^2 + (3 - x - y)^2$.

3. Test the function $(s - x)(s - y)(x + y - s)$, in the example of Art. 169, for maxima and minima.

4. Show that the function $a^2xy + \dfrac{1}{x} + \dfrac{1}{y}$ has a maximum or a minimum value $3a$ according as $a \lessgtr 0$.

5. Show that the function $x + y + \dfrac{a^3}{xy}$ has a maximum or a minimum value $3a$ according as $a \lessgtr 0$.

6. Examine the function $3axy - x^3 - y^3$ for extremes.

7. Find and classify the extreme of the function $x^2 + xy + y^2 - 2ax - 2by$.

8. Find the four pairs of values for which the first partial derivatives of the function $xy(6 - x - y)$ vanish, and show that only one of these pairs corresponds to an extreme of the function. Find and classify this extreme.

9. Find and classify the extreme of the function $xy + \dfrac{8}{x} + \dfrac{8}{y}$.

10. Find a pair of values of x and y (both positive) for which the function $x^2y^2(27 - x^2 - y^2)$ has an extreme. Find and classify this extreme.

11. Examine the function $(x - 2)^2 - y^2$ for extremes.

CHAPTER XVII

MULTIPLE INTEGRALS

171. Successive or Multiple Integration. Just as $\int f(x)dx$ represents any function of x whose first derivative is $f(x)$, the symbol

$$\int \left[\int f(x)dx \right] dx, \text{ or more compactly, } \iint f(x)dx^2,$$

read "the **indefinite double integral** of $f(x)$ with respect to x," represents any function of x whose second derivative is $f(x)$. Accordingly the symbol indicates that $f(x)$ is to be integrated twice with respect to x.

Thus, for example, if $f(x) = 20x^3 - 12x^2$, then

$$\int f(x)dx = 5x^4 - 4x^3 + C,$$

and

$$\iint f(x)dx^2 = x^5 - x^4 + Cx + C',$$

where C and C' are arbitrary constants.

Evidently

$$\frac{d^2}{dx^2} \iint f(x)dx^2 = \frac{d}{dx} \int f(x)dx = 20x^3 - 12x^2 = f(x).$$

Analogously, if x and y are independent variables, the symbol

$$(1) \qquad \int \left[\int f(x, y)dx \right] dy, \text{ or } \iint f(x, y)dx \, dy,$$

read "the **indefinite double integral** of $f(x, y)$ with respect to x and y," indicates that the function $f(x, y)$ is to be integrated first with respect to x with y held constant, and that the result is then to be integrated with respect to y with x held constant. Each integration thus performed is called **partial integration,** and is clearly inverse to partial differentiation. To signify the opposite order of integration we reverse the positions of

dx and dy. Thus the integration of $f(x, y)$ first with respect to y and then with respect to x is denoted by

(2) $$\int\left[\int f(x, y)dy\right]dx, \quad \text{or} \quad \int\int f(x, y)dy \, dx.$$

From (1), Art. 159, and from the above definition of the symbol (1), it follows that

$$\frac{\partial^2}{\partial x \, \partial y}\int\int f(x, y)dx \, dy = \frac{\partial^2}{\partial y \, \partial x}\int\int f(x, y)dx \, dy = f(x, y).$$

Similarly, the definition of (2) implies that

$$\frac{\partial^2}{\partial x \, \partial y}\int\int f(x, y)dy \, dx = \frac{\partial^2}{\partial y \, \partial x}\int\int f(x, y)dy \, dx = f(x, y).$$

Therefore, *irrespective of the order of integration, the indefinite double integral of a function $f(x, y)$ with respect to x and y is another function whose mixed partial derivative of the second order is $f(x, y)$.*

As may be inferred from what precedes, the symbol

$$\int\int \cdots \int f(x_1, x_2, \cdots, x_n)dx_1 dx_2 \cdots dx_n$$

indicates that the function $f(x_1, x_2, \cdots, x_n)$ is to be integrated partially n successive times, once with respect to each of the independent variables in the order in which their differentials are written. Such an integral is called an **indefinite multiple integral,** and is further classified as **double, triple,** etc., according to the number of independent variables.

Example.   For the function $f(x, y) = x^3 + y^3$ we have

$$\int\int (x^3 + y^3)dx \, dy = \int\left[\int (x^3 + y^3)dx\right]dy$$

$$= \int\left[\frac{x^4}{4} + y^3x + \phi(y)\right]dy,$$

where the arbitrary function $\phi(y)$ was introduced in order to provide the most general function whose partial derivative with respect to x is $x^3 + y^3$. Now performing the remaining integration with respect to y, we obtain

$$\int\int (x^3 + y^3)dx \, dy = \frac{x^4y}{4} + \frac{y^4x}{4} + \int \phi(y)dy + \Psi(x)$$

$$= \tfrac{1}{4}xy(x^3 + y^3) + \Phi(y) + \Psi(x),$$

where $\Psi(x)$ and $\Phi(y)$ are arbitrary functions.

It will be left for the student to show that the same result may be obtained by reversing the order of integration.

The above integration is immediately verified by observing that

$$\frac{\partial^2}{\partial x\,\partial y}\left[\tfrac{1}{4}xy(x^3+y^3)+\Phi(y)+\Psi(x)\right]=x^3+y^3.$$

172. Definite Double Integral. Frequently we have found it necessary to evaluate definite integrals of functions of one variable. In what follows we shall have occasion to deal with definite integrals of functions of more than one variable.

In conformity with the definition of an indefinite double integral set forth in the preceding article, the symbol

$$(1) \qquad\qquad \int_c^d \int_{u_1}^{u_2} f(x,\,y)dx\,dy,$$

in which c and d are constants and u_1 and u_2 are either constants or functions of y, will indicate that two successive integrations are to be carried out as follows:

First, regarding y as a constant, we evaluate the integral

$$(2) \qquad\qquad \int_{u_1}^{u_2} f(x,\,y)dx$$

in the usual way. Since the limits of integration do not depend on x, the result will be a function of y, say $F(y)$.*

Next we evaluate

$$\int_c^d F(y)dy,$$

which is a definite integral of the familiar type.

Thus (1) may be defined by the equation

$$(3) \qquad\qquad \int_c^d \int_{u_1}^{u_2} f(x,\,y)dx\,dy = \int_c^d F(y)dy.$$

* In performing the partial integration symbolized by (2) we may omit the arbitrary additive function $\phi(y)$ which for generality would be necessary if there were no limits of integration; for, if $\phi(y)$ were incorporated in the function represented by $\int f(x,\,y)dx$, it would disappear when the limits in (2) were introduced, just as the constant of integration disappears in the evaluation of ordinary definite integrals of the type $\int_a^b f(x)dx$ (cf. Art. 33).

Similarly, if a and b are constants and v_1 and v_2 are either constants or functions of x, we shall mean by the symbol

$$(4) \qquad \int_a^b \int_{v_1}^{v_2} f(x, y)dy \, dx$$

that the first integration is to be carried out partially with respect to y between the limits v_1 and v_2, and that the result is then to be integrated between the limits a and b. Thus by definition we write

$$(5) \qquad \int_a^b \int_{v_1}^{v_2} f(x, y)dy \, dx = \int_a^b G(x)dx,$$

where

$$G(x) = \int_{v_1}^{v_2} f(x, y)dy,$$

x being regarded as a constant in obtaining $G(x)$.

Since the right members of (3) and (5) have definite numerical values, (1) and (4) are called **definite double integrals**, though for brevity they are frequently referred to merely as **double integrals**.

It is important to observe that the order of integration in (1) or (4) cannot in general be reversed. Thus, for example, if v_1 and v_2 are functions of x, and the order of integration signified by (4) is reversed, the resulting double integral

$$\int_{v_1}^{v_2} \int_a^b f(x, y)dx \, dy$$

would lead to a function of x, rather than to the definite value arising from the original order of integration.

Example 1. Evaluate $\int_0^1 \int_0^2 (x^3 + y^3)dx \, dy$.

From the definition of (1) we have

$$\int_0^1 \int_0^2 (x^3 + y^3)dx \, dy = \int_0^1 \left[\int_0^2 (x^3 + y^3)dx \right] dy$$

$$= \int_0^1 \left[\frac{x^4}{4} + xy^3 \right]_{x=0}^{x=2} dy$$

$$= \int_0^1 (4 + 2y^3)dy$$

$$= \left[4y + \frac{y^4}{2} \right]_0^1$$

$$= \tfrac{9}{2}.$$

Example 2.   Evaluate $\int_0^2 \int_0^{x^2} xy \, dy \, dx$.

From the definition of (4) we have

$$\int_0^2 \int_0^{x^2} xy \, dy \, dx = \int_0^2 \left[\int_0^{x^2} xy \, dy \right] dx$$

$$= \int_0^2 \left[\frac{xy^2}{2} \right]_{y=0}^{y=x^2} dx$$

$$= \int_0^2 \frac{x^5}{2} \, dx$$

$$= \left[\frac{x^6}{12} \right]_0^2$$

$$= \tfrac{16}{3}.$$

Example 3.   Evaluate $\int_0^{\frac{\pi}{6}} \int_0^{a \sin \theta} \frac{r \, dr \, d\theta}{\sqrt{a^2 - r^2}}$.

Since the first integration is to be carried out with respect to r between the limit 0 and $a \sin \theta$ we have

$$\int_0^{\frac{\pi}{6}} \int_0^{a \sin \theta} \frac{r \, dr \, d\theta}{\sqrt{a^2 - r^2}} = \int_0^{\frac{\pi}{6}} \left[\int_0^{a \sin \theta} \frac{r \, dr}{\sqrt{a^2 - r^2}} \right] d\theta$$

$$= \int_0^{\frac{\pi}{6}} \left[- \sqrt{a^2 - r^2} \right]_0^{a \sin \theta} d\theta$$

$$= \int_0^{\frac{\pi}{6}} a(1 - \cos \theta) d\theta$$

$$= a \left[\theta - \sin \theta \right]_0^{\frac{\pi}{6}}$$

$$= \frac{a}{6} (\pi - 3).$$

PROBLEMS

Evaluate the following double integrals:

1. $\int_0^4 \int_0^2 x \, dx \, dy$.

2. $\int_0^2 \int_0^4 x \, dy \, dx$.

3. $\int_0^4 \int_0^2 x^2 \, dx \, dy$.

4. $\int_0^2 \int_0^4 x^2 \, dy \, dx$.

5. $\int_0^3 \int_0^{2x} y \, dy \, dx$.

6. $\int_0^6 \int_{\frac{y}{2}}^3 y \, dx \, dy$.

7. $\int_0^3 \int_0^{\frac{4}{3}(3-x)} y^2 \, dy \, dx$.

8. $\int_0^4 \int_0^{\frac{3}{4}(4-y)} y^2 \, dx \, dy$.

9. $\displaystyle\int_0^4 \int_0^{\frac{3}{4}(4-y)} x^2\,dx\,dy.$

10. $\displaystyle\int_0^3 \int_0^{\frac{4}{3}(3-x)} x^2\,dy\,dx.$

11. $\displaystyle\int_0^6 \int_0^{\frac{2}{3}x} xy\,dy\,dx.$

12. $\displaystyle\int_0^4 \int_{\frac{3}{2}y}^6 xy\,dx\,dy.$

13. $\displaystyle\int_0^1 \int_0^y 2e^{x+y}\,dx\,dy.$

14. $\displaystyle\int_0^{\frac{\pi}{2}} \int_0^{\sin x} \left(1 + \frac{1}{\sqrt{1-y^2}}\right) dy\,dx.$

15. $\displaystyle\int_0^3 \int_1^{e^x} \frac{x}{y}\,dy\,dx.$

16. $\displaystyle\int_0^1 \int_1^{e^y} \frac{e^{2y}}{x}\,dx\,dy.$

17. $\displaystyle\int_1^2 \int_0^y \frac{dx\,dy}{x^2+y^2}.$

18. $\displaystyle\int_0^a \int_0^{\sqrt{a^2-x^2}} 3y\,dy\,dx.$

19. $\displaystyle\int_0^a \int_0^{\sqrt{a^2-x^2}} 3x\,dy\,dx.$

20. $\displaystyle\int_0^{\frac{\pi}{2}} \int_{-1}^{\cos 2\theta} \frac{dr\,d\theta}{\sqrt{2+2r}}.$

21. $\displaystyle\int_0^{\frac{\pi}{3}} \int_0^{a\sin 3\theta} r^2\,dr\,d\theta.$

22. $\displaystyle\int_0^{\frac{\pi}{4}} \int_0^{\tan\theta} r\,dr\,d\theta.$

23. $\displaystyle\int_0^{\frac{\pi}{4}} \int_0^{\tan\theta} r^2\,dr\,d\theta.$

24. $\displaystyle\int_0^{\frac{\pi}{4}} \int_0^{\tan\theta} \frac{r^2+2r-1}{r^2+2r+1}\,dr\,d\theta.$

25. $\displaystyle\int_1^2 \int_0^{\ln r} \frac{1-\theta}{e^\theta}\,d\theta\,dr.$

26. $\displaystyle\int_0^2 \int_0^{\frac{x}{2}} \sinh \frac{x}{2} \sinh y\,dy\,dx.$

27. $\displaystyle\int_0^1 \int_0^{\frac{x}{2}} \cosh \frac{x}{2} \cosh y\,dy\,dx.$

28. $\displaystyle\int_1^2 \int_0^{x^{-2}} \frac{\mathrm{sech}^2\,xy}{x}\,dy\,dx.$

173. Area as a Double Integral; Rectangular Coördinates.

In Art. 34 a method was given whereby a plane area, such as $BCDE$ (Fig. 173a), bounded by the vertical lines $x = a$ and $x = b$ and by the curves $y = f(x)$ and $y = g(x)$, can be found by a single integration. We shall now show that this area can be represented by a double integral.

Divide the interval along the x-axis from $x = a$ to $x = b$ into n portions of common length Δx. Through each point of division pass a line parallel to the y-axis; then draw a set of horizontal lines spaced

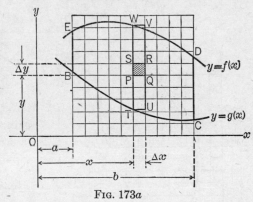

Fig. 173a

at equal intervals Δy. There is thus obtained a network of elementary rectangles each having as its area

$$\Delta A = \Delta y\,\Delta x.$$

and the area $BCDE$ is the limit, as Δy and Δx both approach zero, of the sum of a suitable approximating set of elementary rectangles. This limit will be formulated as a double integral.

Let x be the abscissa of one of the points of division on the x-axis, and let the vertical line through this point cut the curve $y = f(x)$ at W and $y = g(x)$ at T. Designating by V and U the points whose ordinates are respectively the same as those of W and T and whose common abscissa is $x + \Delta x$ we shall regard the area of the rectangular strip $TUVW$ as the limit, as Δy approaches zero, of the sum of the elementary areas (such as $PQRS$) contained within $TUVW$. Thus

$$(1) \qquad \text{area } TUVW = \left[\lim_{\Delta y \to 0} \Sigma \, \Delta y \right] \Delta x = \left[\int_{g(x)}^{f(x)} dy \right] \Delta x.$$

Observing that the area $BCDE$ is the limit, as n becomes infinite or Δx approaches zero, of the sum of the areas of n rectangular strips of which $TUVW$ is a typical one, we have by the Fundamental Theorem (Art. 35)

$$(2) \qquad \textbf{area } BCDE = \int_{a}^{b} \left[\int_{g(x)}^{f(x)} dy \right] dx = \int_{a}^{b} \int_{g(x)}^{f(x)} dy \, dx,$$

and this is the required representation.

It should be remarked that (2) provides no essentially new method of computing the area $BCDE$. For, performing the first integration and substituting the corresponding limits, we obtain

$$\int_{a}^{b} \int_{g(x)}^{f(x)} dy \, dx = \int_{a}^{b} [f(x) - g(x)] \, dx,$$

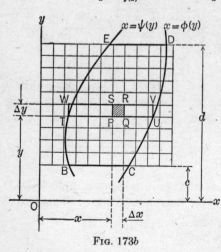

FIG. 173b

where the integral on the right is identical with that which would have been set up at once had the procedure of Art. 34 been followed. Thus no advantage is gained in finding plane areas by double integration. However, the practice of setting up double integrals for plane areas will prove helpful in important applications requiring multiple integration.

In finding by means of a double integral the area $BCDE$ (Fig. 173b), bounded by the horizontal lines $y = c$ and $y = d$ and the curves $x = \phi(y)$ and $x = \psi(y)$, it is convenient first to take the limit of the sum of the elementary rectangular areas contained within a horizontal strip $TUVW$ and then to take the limit of the sum of all such strips. Thus (cf. (1) and (2)) we obtain

$$\text{area } TUVW = \left[\int_{\psi(y)}^{\phi(y)} dx \right] \Delta y$$

and

(3) $$\text{area } BCDE = \int_c^d \int_{\psi(y)}^{\phi(y)} dx \, dy.$$

Example 1. Find by double integration the area bounded by the curves $y = \dfrac{16}{x^2 + 4}$ and $y = \dfrac{x^2}{4}$ and the lines $x = 0$ and $x = 2$.

From (2) we obtain for the required area (see Fig. 173c)

$$A = \int_0^2 \int_{\frac{x^2}{4}}^{\frac{16}{x^2+4}} dy \, dx$$

$$= \int_0^2 \left(\frac{16}{x^2 + 4} - \frac{x^2}{4} \right) dx$$

$$= \tfrac{2}{3}(3\pi - 1).$$

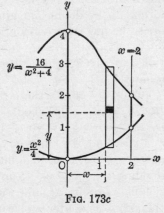

Fig. 173c

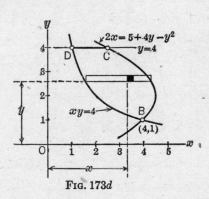

Fig. 173d

Example 2. Find by double integration the area BCD (Fig. 173d) bounded by the curves $xy = 4$ and $2x = 5 + 4y - y^2$ and the line $y = 4$.

The point B in the figure at which the given curves intersect is readily found to be $(4, 1)$; hence by (3) the required area is

$$A = \int_1^4 \int_{\frac{4}{y}}^{\frac{1}{2}(5+4y-y^2)} dx \, dy$$

$$= \int_1^4 \left(\frac{5}{2} + 2y - \frac{y^2}{2} - \frac{4}{y} \right) dy$$

$$= 12 - 8 \ln 2.$$

PROBLEMS

Find the following areas by double integration:

1. The area enclosed by the parabolas $3x^2 = 4y$ and $2y^2 = 9x$.

2. The area enclosed by the parabola $y = 4 - x^2$ and the line $y = x + 2$.

3. The area outside the parabola $y^2 = 4 - 4x$ and inside the circle $x^2 + y^2 = 4$.

4. The first-quadrant area outside the parabola $y^2 = 2x$ and inside the circle $x^2 + y^2 - 4x = 0$.

5. The area below the curve $y = \dfrac{4}{x^2 + 3}$ and inside the circle $x^2 + y^2 - 2y = 0$.

6. The area bounded by the hyperbola $xy = 2$, the parabola $y = 8 - x^2$, and the lines $x = 1$ and $x = 2$.

7. The first-quadrant area bounded by the curve $y = \dfrac{1}{\sqrt{25 - x^2}}$, the circle $x^2 + y^2 = 25$, and the lines $x = 3$ and $x = 4$.

8. The first-quadrant area bounded by the curve $x = \dfrac{4}{\sqrt{4 - y^2}}$, the circle $x^2 + y^2 = 4$, and the line $y = 1$.

9. The first-quadrant area between the circle $x^2 + y^2 = a^2$ and the hypocycloid $x^{\frac{2}{3}} + y^{\frac{2}{3}} = a^{\frac{2}{3}}$.

10. The area outside the circle $x^2 + y^2 = 16$ and inside the ellipse $16x^2 + 25y^2 = 400$.

174. Area as a Double Integral; Polar Coördinates.

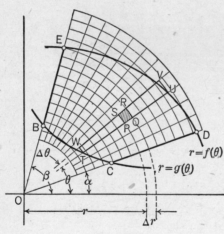

FIG. 174a

Let us next formulate as double integrals areas having for boundaries curves or lines whose equations are given in polar coördinates.

Consider first the area $BCDE$ (Fig. 174a) bounded by the curves $r = f(\theta)$ and $r = g(\theta)$ and the lines $\theta = \alpha$ and $\theta = \beta$. Draw radial lines dividing the angle $\beta - \alpha$ into n equal portions $\Delta\theta$, and with the origin as center and with successive radii differing by equal amounts Δr describe a set of circular arcs. There is thus obtained a network of elementary areas, of which a typical one, say $PQRS$, where P is the point (r, θ), is by (2), Art. 45,

$$(1) \qquad \Delta A = \tfrac{1}{2}(r + \Delta r)^2 \Delta\theta - \tfrac{1}{2}r^2 \Delta\theta$$

$$= r\, \Delta r\, \Delta\theta + \tfrac{1}{2}(\Delta r)^2 \Delta\theta,$$

provided that $\Delta\theta$ is expressed in radians. The area $BCDE$ is the limit, as Δr and $\Delta\theta$ both approach zero, of the sum of a suitable approximating set of elementary areas. Since the term $\frac{1}{2}(\Delta r)^2\Delta\theta$ in (1) is then an infinitesimal of higher order than the preceding term, we may in accordance with Duhamel's Theorem (Art. 35) neglect it without altering the limit, and proceed as though

$$(1')\qquad\qquad \Delta A = r\,\Delta r\,\Delta\theta.$$

Starting then with the element $PQRS$, designate by T and U the points where the radial line containing P and Q intersects the curves $r = g(\theta)$ and $r = f(\theta)$, respectively. Let W and V be the points at which circular arcs of radii OT and OU meet the radial line through S and R. We shall regard the area $TUVW$ as the limit, as Δr approaches zero, of the sum of the elementary areas (e.g., $PQRS$) within it. Using $(1')$ instead of (1), we thus have

$$\text{area } TUVW = \left[\lim_{\Delta r \to 0} \Sigma\, r\,\Delta r\right]\Delta\theta = \left[\int_{g(\theta)}^{f(\theta)} r\,dr\right]\Delta\theta.$$

Next we note that the area $BCDE$ is the limit, as n becomes infinite or $\Delta\theta$ approaches zero, of the sum of n areas of the same type as $TUVW$. Hence, by the Fundamental Theorem,

$$(2)\qquad \text{area } BCDE = \int_{\alpha}^{\beta}\left[\int_{g(\theta)}^{f(\theta)} r\,dr\right]d\theta = \int_{\alpha}^{\beta}\int_{g(\theta)}^{f(\theta)} r\,dr\,d\theta.$$

It will be left to the student to show that the area $BCDE$ (Fig. 174b)

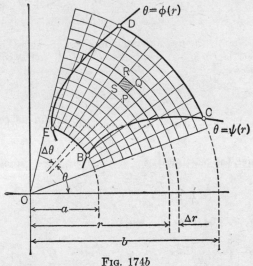

FIG. 174b

bounded by the curves $\theta = \phi(r)$ and $\theta = \psi(r)$ and the circles $r = a$ and $r = b$, is given by

$$(3) \qquad \text{area } BCDE = \int_a^b \int_{\psi(r)}^{\phi(r)} r \, d\theta \, dr.$$

Reference to the figure will suggest the necessary steps.

Example 1. Find by double integration the area OBC (Fig. 174c), bounded by the lemniscate $r^2 = 2a^2 \cos 2\theta$, the circle $r = 2a \sin \theta$, and the line $\theta = \dfrac{\pi}{4}$.

Noting that B is the point $\left(a, \dfrac{\pi}{6}\right)$, we obtain (cf. (2)) for the required area

$$A = \int_{\frac{\pi}{6}}^{\frac{\pi}{4}} \int_{a\sqrt{2 \cos 2\theta}}^{2a \sin \theta} r \, dr \, d\theta$$

$$= \int_{\frac{\pi}{6}}^{\frac{\pi}{4}} (2a^2 \sin^2 \theta - a^2 \cos 2\theta) \, d\theta = \frac{a^2}{12} (\pi + 6\sqrt{3} - 12).$$

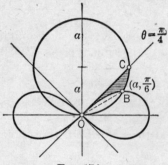

FIG. 174c

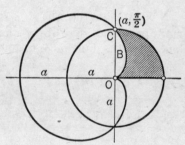

FIG. 174d

Example 2. Find by the use of (3) the first-quadrant area (Fig. 174d), bounded by the line $\theta = 0$, the circle $r = a$ and the cardioid $r = a(1 - \cos \theta)$.

By (3) this area is

$$A = \int_0^a \int_0^{\cos^{-1}\left(1 - \frac{r}{a}\right)} r \, d\theta \, dr$$

$$= \int_0^a r \cos^{-1} \left(1 - \frac{r}{a}\right) dr.$$

In the last integral, the substitution $t = 1 - \dfrac{r}{a}$ is suggested; applying this substitution, we obtain

$$A = a^2 \int_0^1 (1 - t) \cos^{-1} t \, dt.$$

Now we integrate by parts (Art. 88), with $u = \cos^{-1} t$, whence

$$A = a^2 \left[\left(t - \frac{t^2}{2}\right) \cos^{-1} t + \int \frac{t \, dt}{\sqrt{1 - t^2}} - \frac{1}{2} \int \frac{t^2 dt}{\sqrt{1 - t^2}}\right]_0^1.$$

Here $\int \dfrac{t^2 dt}{\sqrt{1-t^2}}$ is readily evaluated by the method of Art. 92.   The final result is

$$A = \frac{a^2}{8}(8 - \pi).$$

It should be remarked that the area under consideration is more easily computed by (2), or equivalently, and without double integration, by regarding it as the difference between the area of a quadrant of radius a and the area OBC.   Thus we obtain (cf. Art. 98)

$$A = \frac{\pi a^2}{4} - \frac{a^2}{2}\int_0^{\frac{\pi}{2}}(1 - \cos\theta)^2\,d\theta = \frac{a^2}{8}(8 - \pi).$$

PROBLEMS

Find the following areas by double integration:

1. The area bounded by the curves $r = a(3 - \cos\theta)$ and $r = a\cos 2\theta$, and the lines $\theta = 0$ and $\theta = \dfrac{\pi}{6}$.

2. The area between the circles $r = 2\cos\theta$ and $r = 4\cos\theta$.

3. The area inside the first-quadrant loop of the curve $r = a\sin 2\theta$ and outside the curve $r = a\cos 2\theta$.

4. The first-quadrant area bounded by the lemniscate $r^2 = a^2\cos 2\theta$, the circle $r = a\sqrt{2}\sin\theta$, and the line $\theta = \dfrac{\pi}{4}$.

5. The area outside the circle $r = a$ and inside the circle $r = 2a\sin\theta$.

6. The area outside the cardioid $r = 1 - \cos\theta$, bounded by this curve and the line $4r\cos\theta - 1 = 0$.

7. The area outside the parabola $r(1 - \cos\theta) = a$ and inside the cardioid $r = a(1 - \cos\theta)$.

8. The area bounded by the circle $r = a$, the line $\theta = \dfrac{\pi}{4}$, and the arc of the curve $r = a\cos 2\theta$ for which $0 \leqq \theta \leqq \dfrac{\pi}{4}$.

9. The first-quadrant area outside the curve $r^2 = a^2\sin 2\theta$ and inside the circle $r = a$.

10. The first-quadrant area outside the circle $r = a\sqrt{2}\sin\theta$ and inside the curve $r = a\sin 2\theta$.

175. Volume under a Surface; Rectangular Coördinates.   Let us now formulate as a double integral the volume V of a solid (Fig. 175a) bounded by the xy-plane, a surface $z = f(x, y)$, and a cylinder whose equation is known and whose elements are parallel to the z-axis.   For convenience we shall denote the regions of the xy-plane and of the surface $z = f(x, y)$ contained within the cylinder by Σ' and Σ, respectively.   Moreover, we shall briefly characterize V as *the volume under Σ*.

Designate by a and b the least and greatest values of x for the boundary of Σ'; then each of the two curves into which the corresponding points (A and B) divide the boundary has an equation identical with that of the portion of the cylinder containing the curve. The equations of these curves are therefore known; suppose that they are $y = \phi(x)$ and $y = \psi(x)$, as shown in the figure.

Divide the interval along the x-axis from $x = a$ to $x = b$ into n equal parts Δx, and through each point of division pass a line parallel to the y-axis. Then in the xy-plane draw a set of lines parallel to the x-axis and spaced at equal intervals Δy. A network of elementary rectangles each of area $\Delta y\, \Delta x$ is thus obtained as in Art. 173.

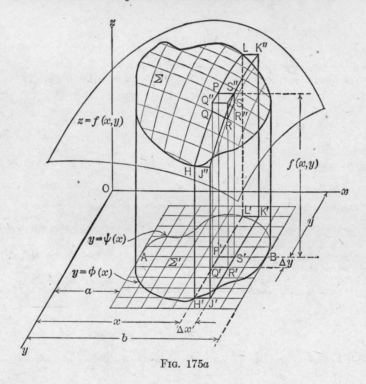

FIG. 175a

Through the vertices $P'(x, y, 0), Q'(x, y + \Delta y, 0), R'(x + \Delta x, y + \Delta y, 0)$, and $S'(x + \Delta x, y, 0)$ of an elementary rectangle within Σ', draw the line-segments $P'P$, $Q'Q''$, $R'R''$, and $S'S''$ parallel to the z-axis and all of equal length, P being the point (x, y, z) of the surface. These segments are the vertical edges of a parallelepiped PR' whose volume

(1)
$$\Delta V = z\, \Delta y\, \Delta x = f(x, y)\Delta y\, \Delta x$$

is, for sufficiently small Δy and Δx, an approximation to the volume under the portion $PQRS$ of Σ, where Q, R, and S are the points at which the edges $Q'Q''$, $R'R''$, and $S'S''$ (prolonged if necessary) cut the surface $z = f(x, y)$. The entire volume under Σ is then the limit, as Δx and Δy both approach zero, of the sum of the volumes of all the parallelepipeds which may be similarly constructed upon the elementary rectangles of a set which suitably approximates Σ'. It remains to represent this limit by a double integral.

Let the line through P' and Q' meet the boundary of Σ' at H' and L'; draw the lines $H'J'$ and $L'K'$, each parallel to the x-axis and of length Δx, thus forming the rectangular strip $H'J'K'L'$. Now pass planes parallel to the yz-plane through $H'L'$ and $J'K'$, and designate by HL the curve in which the first of these planes cuts the surface $z = f(x, y)$. Finally project the area $H'HLL'$ on the vertical plane through $J'K'$, thereby obtaining the area $J'J''K''K'$. For brevity, denote by $J'L$ the lamina of thickness Δx having these congruent areas as faces.

The volume of the lamina $J'L$ may be regarded as the limit, as Δy approaches zero, of the volumes, such as that given by (1), of the parallelepipeds whose bases are contained within $H'J'K'L'$. That is,

$$(2) \quad \text{volume } J'L = \lim_{\Delta y \to 0} \left[\Sigma f(x, y) \Delta y \right] \Delta x = \left[\int_{\psi(x)}^{\phi(x)} f(x, y) dy \right] \Delta x,$$

since the x- and y-coördinates of H' and L' satisfy, respectively, the equations $y = \phi(x)$ and $y = \psi(x)$.

It will be observed that in (2) $\int_{\psi(x)}^{\phi(x)} f(x, y) dy$, which is a function of x, represents the area $H'HLL'$ of cross-section of the volume V in a plane perpendicular to the x-axis. Then, by Art. 36, V is the limit, as n becomes infinite or Δx approaches zero, of the sum of the volumes of n laminas typified by $J'L$. Thus

$$(3) \quad V = \int_a^b \int_{\psi(x)}^{\phi(x)} f(x, y) \, dy \, dx.$$

Similarly, if c and d are the least and the greatest values of y for the boundary of Σ', and if a line in the xy-plane and parallel to the x-axis cuts this boundary at two points whose x-coördinates are given in terms of their y-coördinates by the equations $x = \Phi(y)$ and $x = \Psi(y)$, where, for $c < y < d$, $\Psi(y) < \Phi(y)$, we may also express the volume under consideration as

$$(3') \quad V = \int_c^d \int_{\Psi(y)}^{\Phi(y)} f(x, y) \, dx \, dy.$$

Example 1. Find the volume under the paraboloid $z = x^2 + y^2$ whose base is the triangle in the xy-plane bounded by the lines $x = 1$, $y = 1$, and $x + y = 3$.

Fig. 175b shows an elementary lamina corresponding to the required volume, which, in accordance with (3), is

$$V = \int_1^2 \int_1^{3-x} (x^2 + y^2) \, dy \, dx$$

$$= \int_1^2 \left[x^2 y + \frac{y^3}{3} \right]_{y=1}^{y=3-x} dx$$

$$= \int_1^2 \left[x^2(3 - x) + \tfrac{1}{3}(3 - x)^3 - x^2 - \tfrac{1}{3} \right] dx$$

$$= \tfrac{11}{6}.$$

The same result could have been obtained by integrating with respect to x from 1 to $3 - y$ and then integrating with respect to y from 1 to 2 (cf. (3′)).

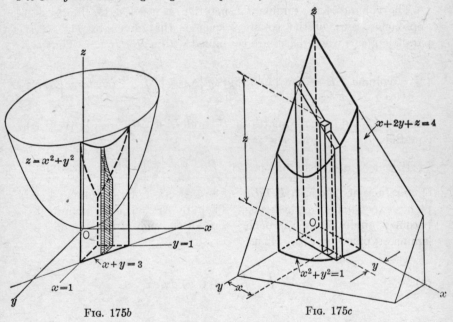

FIG. 175b FIG. 175c

Example 2. Find the volume (Fig. 175c) in the first octant under the plane $x + 2y + z = 4$ and within the cylinder $x^2 + y^2 = 1$.

Using (3′), we obtain for this volume

$$V = \int_0^1 \int_0^{\sqrt{1-y^2}} (4 - x - 2y) \, dx \, dy$$

$$= \int_0^1 \left[4\sqrt{1 - y^2} - \tfrac{1}{2}(1 - y^2) - 2y\sqrt{1 - y^2} \right] dy$$

$$= \pi - 1.$$

PROBLEMS

Find the following volumes by double integration:

1. The volume in the first octant between the cylinders $x^2 + y^2 = 9$ and $y^2 + z^2 = 9$.

2. The volume bounded by the paraboloid $z = x^2 + y^2$, the cylinder $x = 1 - y^2$, and the planes $x = 0$ and $z = 0$.

3. The volume in the first octant between the surface $z = x + y^2$ and the cylinder $x + y^2 = 4$.

4. The volume bounded by the paraboloid $z = x^2 + y^2$, the plane $x + y = 1$, and the coördinate planes.

5. The volume under the paraboloid $z = x^2 + y^2$ and inside the cylinder $x^2 + y^2 = a^2$.

6. The volume bounded by the xy-plane, the cylinder $x^2 + y^2 - 2x = 0$, and the plane $z = x$.

7. The volume in the first octant bounded by the cylinders $xz = 2$ and $xy = 2$, and the planes $x = 2$, $y = 2$, and $z = 0$.

8. The volume between the surface $z = 4 - 4x^2 - y^2$ and the xy-plane.

9. The volume under that portion of the surface $z = 8 + y - x^2$ whose projection on the xy-plane is the area common to the two parabolas $y = x^2$ and $x = y^2$.

10. The volume in the first octant bounded by the surface $z = (a^{\frac{2}{3}} - x^{\frac{2}{3}} - y^{\frac{2}{3}})^{\frac{3}{2}}$ and the coördinate planes.

176. Volume under a Surface; Cylindrical Coördinates.

In some three-dimensional problems it is convenient to introduce coördinate systems other than the rectangular coördinates hitherto used. For example, we may define the location of the point P (Fig. 176a) by stating its z-coördinate and the polar coördinates r and θ of its projection P' on the xy-plane. In this case r, θ, and z are said to be the **cylindrical coördinates** of the point P. The equation of a surface $z = F(x, y)$ may be transformed to cylindrical coördinates by making the substitutions (Art. 68) $x = r \cos \theta$,

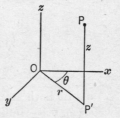

FIG. 176a

$y = r \sin \theta$; in this manner an equation of the form $z = f(r, \theta)$ is obtained for the surface.

We shall now formulate as a double integral the volume under such a portion Σ of a surface $z = f(r, \theta)$ as has for its projection on the xy-plane an area bounded by the curves $r = \phi(\theta)$ and $r = \psi(\theta)$, and the lines $\theta = \alpha$ and $\theta = \beta$ (Fig. 176b).

As in Fig. 174a construct a network of elementary areas in the xy-plane, of which a typical one, $P'Q'R'S'$, may be regarded as having the measure $r \, \Delta r \, \Delta \theta$, where r and θ are the polar coördinates of P', $\Delta r = P'Q' = S'R'$, and S' and R' are on the radial line specified by the polar angle $\theta + \Delta \theta$. Through P' pass a line parallel to the z-axis meeting the surface at $P(r, \theta, z)$, and through the remaining vertices of the elementary area draw $Q'Q''$, $R'R''$, and $S'S''$ parallel and equal to $P'P$. These four segments are the vertical edges of an elementary volume

$$\Delta V = zr \, \Delta r \, \Delta \theta = f(r, \theta) \, r \, \Delta r \, \Delta \theta,$$

which, for sufficiently small Δr and $\Delta \theta$, is an approximation to the volume under the portion $PQRS$ of Σ, where Q, R, and S are the points at which the edges $Q'Q''$, $R'R''$, and $S'S''$ (prolonged if necessary) cut the surface $z = f(r, \theta)$. The entire volume under Σ is then the limit, as

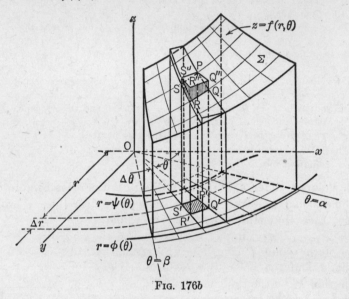

FIG. 176b

Δr and $\Delta \theta$ both approach zero, of the sum of all the elementary volumes which may be similarly constructed upon the elementary areas of a set which suitably approximates the projection of Σ. Hence, by an argument the steps of which will be suggested by a review of Arts. 174 and 175, it may be shown that the required volume is

(1)
$$V = \int_{\alpha}^{\beta} \int_{\psi(\theta)}^{\phi(\theta)} f(r, \theta) \, r \, dr \, d\theta.$$

Example 1. Using (1) find the volume of Example 2 of the preceding article.

In cylindrical coördinates the equation of the plane is $z = 4 - r \cos \theta - 2r \sin \theta$. Therefore, since r ranges from 0 to 1 (for the equation of the cylinder is $r = 1$), and θ ranges from 0 to $\dfrac{\pi}{2}$, we find by (1)

$$V = \int_{0}^{\frac{\pi}{2}} \int_{0}^{1} (4 - r \cos \theta - 2r \sin \theta) \, r \, dr \, d\theta$$

$$= \int_0^{\frac{\pi}{2}} (2 - \tfrac{1}{3} \cos\theta - \tfrac{2}{3} \sin\theta)\, d\theta$$

$$= \pi - 1,$$

in agreement with the result previously obtained.

Example 2. Find the volume (Fig. 176c) under the plane $z = x$ and above that loop of the curve $r = a \cos 2\theta$ for which $-\dfrac{\pi}{4} \leqq \theta \leqq \dfrac{\pi}{4}$.

In cylindrical coördinates the equation of the plane is $z = r \cos\theta$. Taking advantage of the symmetry of the required volume with respect to the xz-plane, we have by (1)

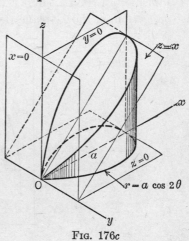

$$V = 2 \int_0^{\frac{\pi}{4}} \int_0^{a \cos 2\theta} r \cos\theta \cdot r \, dr \, d\theta$$

$$= 2 \int_0^{\frac{\pi}{4}} \left[\frac{r^3}{3} \right]_0^{a \cos 2\theta} \cos\theta \, d\theta$$

$$= \frac{2a^3}{3} \int_0^{\frac{\pi}{4}} \cos^3 2\theta \cos\theta \, d\theta$$

$$= \frac{2a^3}{3} \int_0^{\frac{\pi}{4}} (1 - 2\sin^2\theta)^3 \cos\theta \, d\theta = \frac{16a^3\sqrt{2}}{105}.$$

Fig. 176c

PROBLEMS

Using cylindrical coördinates, find the following volumes by double integration:

1. The volume of the sphere $x^2 + y^2 + z^2 = a^2$.

2. The volume of that segment of the sphere $x^2 + y^2 + z^2 + 6z = 16$ which is above the xy-plane.

3. The volume under that portion of the surface $z = e^{r^2}$ whose projection on the xy-plane is the circle $r = a$.

4. The volume between the paraboloid $x^2 + y^2 - 3z = 0$ and the plane $z = 3$.

5. The volume bounded by the cylinder $x^2 + y^2 = 25$ and the hyperboloid $x^2 + y^2 - z^2 = 16$.

6. The volume common to the sphere $x^2 + y^2 + z^2 = a^2$ and the cylinder $x^2 + y^2 = b^2$.

7. The volume under that portion of the paraboloid $z = x^2 + y^2$ whose projection on the xy-plane is the circle $x^2 + y^2 - 2y = 0$.

8. The volume in the first octant outside the cone $z = r$ and inside the cylinder $r = a \sin 2\theta$.

9. The volume common to the sphere $r^2 + z^2 = a^2$ and the cylinder $r^2 = a^2 \cos 2\theta$.

10. The volume in the first octant cut from the cylinder $r^2 = a^2 \sin 2\theta$ by that portion of the surface $z = a\theta$ for which $0 \leqq \theta \leqq \dfrac{\pi}{2}$.

11. The volume common to the sphere $r^2 + z^2 = a^2$ and the cylinder $r = a \sin\theta$.

12. The volume in the first octant bounded by the surface $z = \sqrt{r^2 + a^2}$, the cylinder $r = a \tan \theta$, and the plane $\theta = \dfrac{\pi}{4}$.

177. Areas of Curved Surfaces. In Art. 103 a method was given for computing the area of a surface of revolution. We shall now develop a general formula for finding the area of a curved surface whose projection on the xy-plane is bounded by given curves.

Consider a region Σ (Fig. 177a) of the surface $z = f(x, y)$ having for its projection on the xy-plane the area enclosed by the curves $y = \phi(x)$

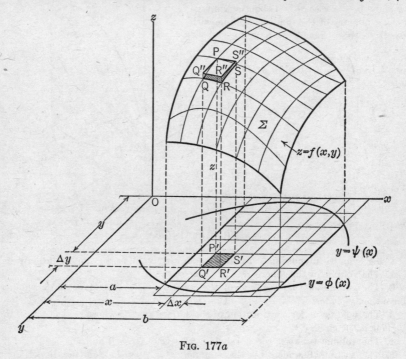

Fig. 177a

and $y = \psi(x)$ and the lines $x = a$ and $x = b$. Draw a network of elementary rectangles in the xy-plane, as in Fig. 173a, one of which has its vertices at the points $P'(x, y, 0), Q'(x, y + \Delta y, 0), R'(x + \Delta x, y + \Delta y, 0)$, and $S'(x + \Delta x, y, 0)$. Through P' pass a line parallel to the z-axis and cutting the surface at the point $P(x, y, z)$. Let Q'', R'', and S'' be the points at which lines through Q', R', and S', drawn parallel to the z-axis, meet the plane tangent to the surface at P.

The area of the parallelogram $PQ''R''S''$ on the tangent plane is equal to the quotient of the area of the elementary rectangle $P'Q'R'S'$ by the cosine of the angle the tangent plane makes with the xy-plane.

But this angle is equal to the direction angle γ between the z-axis and any line (e.g., the normal to the surface at P) which is perpendicular to the tangent plane. That is,

$$(1) \qquad \text{area } PQ''R''S'' = \frac{\text{area } P'Q'R'S'}{\cos \gamma} = \frac{\Delta y\, \Delta x}{\cos \gamma}.$$

Now by Art. 168 the direction parameters of the normal to the surface at $P(x, y, z)$ may be taken as $\dfrac{\partial z}{\partial x}$, $\dfrac{\partial z}{\partial y}$, and -1. Hence in accordance with 26(b), p. 510, we have

$$\cos \gamma = \frac{1}{\sqrt{1 + \left(\dfrac{\partial z}{\partial x}\right)^2 + \left(\dfrac{\partial z}{\partial y}\right)^2}},$$

and (1) may be rewritten as

$$(1') \qquad \text{area } PQ''R''S'' = \sqrt{1 + \left(\frac{\partial z}{\partial x}\right)^2 + \left(\frac{\partial z}{\partial y}\right)^2}\; \Delta y \Delta x.$$

The area $PQ''R''S''$, for sufficiently small Δy and Δx, is an approximation of the area $PQRS$ (Fig. 177a) of the portion of Σ which has $P'Q'R'S'$ for its projection on the xy-plane. Moreover, the limit as Δy and Δx both approach zero of the sum of expressions like the right member of (1'), one such expression being associated with every rectangular element of the projection of Σ, will give exactly the required area S; in fact this limit may be regarded as the definition of S. In taking the limit, we observe that y ranges from $\psi(x)$ to $\phi(x)$, and x from a to b. Thus

$$(2) \qquad S = \int_a^b \int_{\psi(x)}^{\phi(x)} \sqrt{1 + \left(\frac{\partial z}{\partial x}\right)^2 + \left(\frac{\partial z}{\partial y}\right)^2}\; dy\, dx,$$

where the radical in general involves x and y.

Obvious modifications of (2) will be required when the projection of Σ on the xy-plane is an area such as that shown in Fig. 173b, or when the projection of Σ on another coördinate plane is given.

Example 1. Find the area in the first octant cut from the cylindrical surface (Fig. 177b) $z = 4 - x^2$ by the plane $y = x$.

Since the boundaries of the projection of the required area S on the xy-plane are $y = 0$, $y = x$, and $x = 2$, we have by (2)

$$(3) \qquad S = \int_0^2 \int_0^x \sqrt{1 + 4x^2}\; dy\, dx$$

$$= \int_0^2 \sqrt{1 + 4x^2}\; x\, dx$$

$$= \tfrac{1}{12}\,(17\sqrt{17} - 1).$$

This result can also be found, though with considerable difficulty, from

$$S = \int_0^2 \int_y^2 \sqrt{1 + 4x^2} \, dx \, dy$$

in which the order of integration is the reverse of that given in (3) and the limits have been suitably altered. We thus have an illustration of the fact that the ease

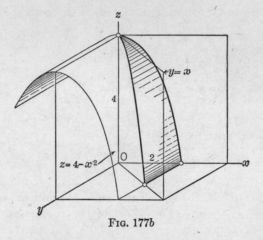

Fig. 177b

with which a quantity represented by a double integral may be computed often depends on the order of integration.

Example 2. Find the area above the xy-plane of the surface of the sphere $x^2 + y^2 + z^2 = a^2$ intercepted by the cylinder $x^2 - ax + y^2 = 0$ (Fig. 177c).

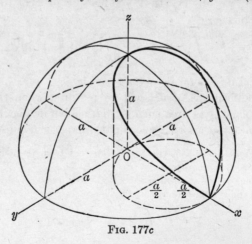

Fig. 177c

Taking advantage of symmetry with respect to the xz-plane, we have for the required area by (2)

$$S = 2 \int_0^a \int_0^{\sqrt{ax-x^2}} \sqrt{1 + \frac{x^2}{a^2 - x^2 - y^2} + \frac{y^2}{a^2 - x^2 - y^2}} \; dy \; dx$$

$$= 2a \int_0^a \int_0^{\sqrt{ax-x^2}} \frac{dy \; dx}{\sqrt{a^2 - x^2 - y^2}}$$

$$= 2a \int_0^a \sin^{-1} \sqrt{\frac{ax - x^2}{a^2 - x^2}} \; dx$$

$$= 2a \int_0^a \sin^{-1} \sqrt{\frac{x}{a + x}} \; dx$$

$$= 2a \left\{ \left[x \sin^{-1} \sqrt{\frac{x}{a + x}} \right]_0^a - \frac{\sqrt{a}}{2} \int_0^a \frac{\sqrt{x} \; dx}{a + x} \right\}$$

after an integration by parts and some algebraic reduction. Now

$$\int_0^a \frac{\sqrt{x} \; dx}{a + x} = 2 \int_0^{\sqrt{a}} \frac{t^2 dt}{a + t^2} = 2 \int_0^{\sqrt{a}} \left(1 - \frac{a}{a + t^2} \right) dt.$$

Thus we obtain

$$S = 2a \left[\frac{\pi a}{4} - \sqrt{a} \left(\sqrt{a} - \pi \frac{\sqrt{a}}{4} \right) \right] = (\pi - 2)a^2.$$

PROBLEMS

Find the areas of the following curved surfaces by double integration:

1. The area of the cylindrical surface $y^2 + z^2 = a^2$ lying between the planes $x = 0$ and $x = h$.

2. The area of the spherical surface $x^2 + y^2 + z^2 = a^2$.

3. The area of the surface of the cylinder $y^2 + z^2 = a^2$ intercepted by the cylinder $x^2 + y^2 = a^2$.

4. The area of the surface of the cylinder $y^2 + z^2 - az = 0$ intercepted by the sphere $x^2 + y^2 + z^2 = a^2$.

5. The area of the upper zone of the sphere $x^2 + y^2 + z^2 = 25$, contained within the paraboloid $z = 19 - x^2 - y^2$.

6. The area of the surface of the paraboloid $8z = x^2 + y^2$, contained within the sphere $x^2 + y^2 + z^2 = 20$.

7. The area of the surface $z = xy$ in the first octant and contained within the cylinder $x^2 + y^2 = a^2$.

8. The area of the spherical surface $x^2 + y^2 + z^2 - 2az = 0$ lying within the cone $z = \sqrt{x^2 + y^2}$.

9. The area of the surface of the cylinder $y^{\frac{2}{3}} + z^{\frac{2}{3}} = a^{\frac{2}{3}}$ in the first octant and contained within the cylinder $x^{\frac{2}{3}} + y^{\frac{2}{3}} = a^{\frac{2}{3}}$.

10. The area of the surface of the cone $z = \sqrt{x^2 + y^2}$ within the cylinder $x^2 + y^2 - 2x = 0$.

178. Centroid and Moment of Inertia of a Plane Area. It has previously been remarked (Arts. 107, 109, and 110) that the determination of centroids and moments of inertia in general requires multiple integration, although in the most important cases integration with respect to a single variable will suffice. For the sake of completeness we shall in this article give formulas involving double integrals for the coördinates of the centroid, and for the moments of inertia with respect to the axes, of a plane area A (Fig. 178a) bounded by the curves $y = f(x)$ and $y = g(x)$ and the lines $x = a$ and $x = b$. The notation employed is that of Chapter X.

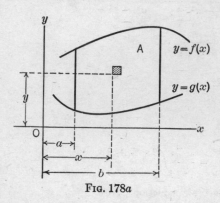

Fig. 178a

$$(1) \qquad A\bar{x} = \int_a^b \int_{g(x)}^{f(x)} x\, dy\, dx.$$

$$(2) \qquad A\bar{y} = \int_a^b \int_{g(x)}^{f(x)} y\, dy\, dx.$$

$$(3) \qquad I_x = \int_a^b \int_{g(x)}^{f(x)} y^2\, dy\, dx.$$

$$(4) \qquad I_y = \int_a^b \int_{g(x)}^{f(x)} x^2\, dy\, dx.$$

$$(5) \qquad I_z = \int_a^b \int_{g(x)}^{f(x)} (x^2 + y^2)\, dy\, dx.$$

Example 1. Find the centroid of the area (Fig. 178b) bounded by the parabola $y = 2x^2 - 8x + 5$ and the line $y = 2x - 3$.

By solving the given equations simultaneously, we find the points of intersection $(1, -1)$ and $(4, 5)$.

In accordance with (2), Art. 173, the area is

$$A = \int_1^4 \int_{2x^2-8x+5}^{2x-3} dy\, dx = 9.$$

By (1) we have

$$9\bar{x} = \int_1^4 \int_{2x^2-8x+5}^{2x-3} x\, dy\, dx$$

$$= \int_1^4 (10x^2 - 2x^3 - 8x)dx$$

$$= \tfrac{45}{2},$$

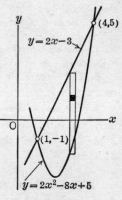

Fig. 178b

whence
$$\bar{x} = \tfrac{5}{2},$$

and, by (2),

$$9\bar{y} = \int_1^4 \int_{2x^2-8x+5}^{2x-3} y \, dy \, dx$$

$$= \tfrac{1}{2}\int_1^4 [(2x-3)^2 - (2x^2-8x+5)^2] \, dx$$

$$= \tfrac{9}{5},$$

whence
$$\bar{y} = \tfrac{1}{5}.$$

The centroid of the given area is therefore $(\tfrac{5}{2}, \tfrac{1}{5})$, a result which could have been found without double integration.

Example 2. Find the polar moment of inertia with respect to the origin of the area (Fig. 178c) bounded by the curve $y = \dfrac{2}{x^2+4}$, the coördinate axes, and the line $x = 2$.

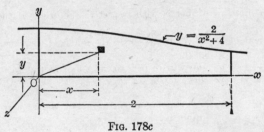

FIG. 178c

By (5) we have for the required moment of inertia

$$I_z = \int_0^2 \int_0^{\frac{2}{x^2+4}} (x^2 + y^2) \, dy \, dx$$

$$= \int_0^2 \left[\frac{2x^2}{x^2+4} + \frac{8}{3(x^2+4)^3} \right] dx$$

$$= \frac{1544 - 381\pi}{384}.$$

PROBLEMS

Find by double integration the centroids of the areas described in Problems 1–8.

1. The first-quadrant area outside the parabola $y^2 = 2x$ and inside the circle $y^2 = 4x - x^2$.

2. The first-quadrant area bounded by the curve $y = x^3$ and the line $y = 4x$.

3. The first-quadrant area bounded by the curve $y^2 = 5x^2 - x^4$ and the line $y = x$.

4. The entire area lying between the hyperbola $y = \dfrac{8}{4-x}$ and the parabola $y = x^2 - x + 2$.

5. The area bounded by the curve $r = a \tan \theta$, the first-quadrant arc of the circle $r = a$, and the line $\theta = 0$.

HINT: In (1) and (2), replace $dy\ dx$ by $r\ dr\ d\theta$ (cf. Art. 174), and x and y by $r \cos \theta$ and $r \sin \theta$, respectively.

6. The area enclosed by the cardioid $r = a\ (1 - \cos \theta)$.

7. The area enclosed by the first-quadrant loop of the curve $r = a \sin 3\theta$.

8. The area outside the circle $r = a$ and inside the circle $r = 2a \sin \theta$.

In Problems 9–16 find by double integration:

9. The moment of inertia with respect to the x-axis of the area described in Problem 1.

10. The polar moment of inertia with respect to the origin of the area described in Problem 2.

11. The moment of inertia with respect to the y-axis of the area described in Problem 3.

12. The moment of inertia with respect to the y-axis of the area described in Problem 4.

13. The polar moment of inertia with respect to the origin of the area described in Problem 5.

14. The polar moment of inertia with respect to the origin of the area described in Problem 6.

15. The moment of inertia with respect to the y-axis of the area enclosed by one loop of the curve $r^2 = a^2 \sin 2\theta$.

16. The moment of inertia with respect to the x-axis of the area enclosed by the first-quadrant loop of the curve $r = a \sin 2\theta$.

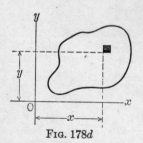

FIG. 178d

Product of Inertia. For the area of Fig. 178d, the quantity

$$H_{xy} = \iint xy\ dy\ dx,$$

where it is understood that suitable limits of integration must be supplied, is called the **product of inertia** of the area with respect to the x- and y-axes. The connection between product of inertia and moment of inertia, which will not be stated here, is of great importance in the theory of beams and columns whose cross-sections have no axes of symmetry.

17. Show that, for an area which is symmetrical with respect to either coördinate axis, $H_{xy} = 0$.

Find H_{xy} for each of the following areas:

18. The first-quadrant half of the area of the circle $x^2 + y^2 - 2ay = 0$.

19. The area bounded by the curve $y = e^x$, the coördinate axes, and the line $x = 1$.

20. The area under the curve $y = x^{-\frac{1}{2}}$, between $x = 4$ and $x = 9$.

21. The area of the right triangle with vertices at $(0, 0)$, $(6, 0)$, and $(0, 8)$.

22. The area bounded by the hyperbola $xy = 4$ and the line $x + y = 5$.

23. The area described in Problem 6.

24. The first-quadrant portion of the area enclosed by the lemniscate $r^2 = a^2 \cos 2\theta$.

179. Definite Triple Integrals.   The symbol

$$(1) \qquad \int_l^m \int_{v_1}^{v_2} \int_{u_1}^{u_2} f(x, y, z) \, dx \, dy \, dz,$$

in which l and m are constants, v_1 and v_2 are constants or functions of z, and u_1 and u_2 are constants or functions of either y or z or both, will indicate that three successive integrations are to be carried out as follows:

First, regarding y and z as constants, we evaluate

$$\int_{u_1}^{u_2} f(x, y, z) \, dx.$$

Since the limits of integration do not depend on x, the result in general will be a function of y and z, say $F(y, z)$.

Next, regarding z as constant, we evaluate

$$\int_{v_1}^{v_2} F(y, z) \, dy;$$

the result will be a function of z, say $G(z)$.

Finally, we evaluate

$$\int_l^m G(z) \, dz,$$

and this, being the ordinary type of definite integral, will yield a numerical result.

Similar sequences of operations are indicated by symbols analogous to (1), e.g.,

$$(2) \qquad \int_l^m \int_{u_1}^{u_2} \int_{v_1}^{v_2} f(x, y, z) \, dy \, dx \, dz,$$

in which u_1 and u_2 are constants or functions of z, and v_1 and v_2 are constants or functions of either x or z or both, and

$$(3) \qquad \int_a^b \int_{v_1}^{v_2} \int_{w_1}^{w_2} f(x, y, z) \, dz \, dy \, dx,$$

in which a and b are constants, v_1 and v_2 constants or functions of x, and w_1 and w_2 are constants or functions of either x or y or both.   In every case the function is to be integrated partially with respect to the variable whose differential is written first, and the limits affixed to the innermost integral sign applied; the result is then to be integrated partially with respect to the variable whose differential is written next, between limits designated on the middle integral sign; finally the remaining definite integral is to be evaluated.

Since (1), (2), and (3), as well as analogous symbols in which other permutations of the differentials occur and the functional dependence of the inner pairs of limits on the variables is suitably altered, indicate operations leading to definite numerical values, they are called **definite triple integrals,** though for brevity they are frequently referred to as **triple integrals.**

Example 1. Evaluate $\displaystyle\int_2^3 \int_{\frac{1}{z}}^1 \int_0^{\sqrt{yz}} xyz\, dx\, dy\, dz.$

From the definition of (1) we have

$$\int_2^3 \int_{\frac{1}{z}}^1 \int_0^{\sqrt{yz}} xyz\, dx\, dy\, dz = \int_2^3 \int_{\frac{1}{z}}^1 \left[\frac{x^2yz}{2}\right]_{x=0}^{x=\sqrt{yz}} dy\, dz$$

$$= \int_2^3 \int_{\frac{1}{z}}^1 \frac{y^2z^2}{2}\, dy\, dz$$

$$= \frac{1}{2}\int_2^3 \left[\frac{y^3z^2}{3}\right]_{y=\frac{1}{z}}^{y=1} dz$$

$$= \frac{1}{6}\int_2^3 \left(z^2 - \frac{1}{z}\right) dz$$

$$= \tfrac{1}{18}\left(19 - 3\ln\tfrac{3}{2}\right).$$

Example 2. Evaluate $\displaystyle\int_0^{\frac{1}{2}} \int_0^{(1-z^2)^{-\frac{1}{6}}} \int_0^x x\, dy\, dx\, dz.$

From the definition of (2) it follows that

$$\int_0^{\frac{1}{2}} \int_0^{(1-z^2)^{-\frac{1}{6}}} \int_0^x x\, dy\, dx\, dz = \int_0^{\frac{1}{2}} \int_0^{(1-z^2)^{-\frac{1}{6}}} [xy]_{y=0}^{y=x}\, dx\, dz$$

$$= \int_0^{\frac{1}{2}} \int_0^{(1-z^2)^{-\frac{1}{6}}} x^2\, dx\, dz$$

$$= \int_0^{\frac{1}{2}} \left[\frac{x^3}{3}\right]_0^{(1-z^2)^{-\frac{1}{6}}} dz$$

$$= \frac{1}{3}\int_0^{\frac{1}{2}} \frac{dz}{\sqrt{1-z^2}}$$

$$= \frac{1}{3}[\sin^{-1} z]_0^{\frac{1}{2}} = \frac{\pi}{18}.$$

PROBLEMS

Evaluate the following:

1. $\displaystyle\int_0^3 \int_0^{\sqrt{9-x^2}} \int_{x-y}^{x+y} z\, dz\, dy\, dx.$

2. $\displaystyle\int_1^2 \int_0^{2y} \int_0^{\frac{1}{\sqrt{xy}}} xyz\, dz\, dx\, dy.$

3. $\displaystyle\int_0^a \int_0^{\sqrt{a^2-x^2}} \int_0^{\sqrt{a^2-x^2-y^2}} \sqrt{a^2-x^2-y^2}\, dz\, dy\, dx.$

4. $\displaystyle\int_1^2 \int_x^{2x} \int_{\sqrt{1-x^2-y^2}}^{\sqrt{2xy}} \frac{z\, dz\, dy\, dx}{x^2+y^2+z^2}.$

5. $\displaystyle\int_1^4 \int_{\frac{1}{y}}^{e^y} \int_{\frac{1}{z^2}}^{\frac{y}{z}} z\, dx\, dz\, dy.$

6. $\displaystyle\int_1^3 \int_y^{2y} \int_{\sqrt{x^2-y^2}}^{\sqrt{x^2+y^2}} xyze^{-(x^2+y^2+z^2)}\, dz\, dx\, dy.$

7. $\displaystyle\int_{\frac{\pi}{6}}^{\frac{\pi}{2}} \int_1^{\frac{\pi}{2x}} \int_0^{y\sqrt{x}} \frac{xz}{y} \cos\frac{z^2}{y}\, dz\, dy\, dx.$

8. $\displaystyle\int_0^{\frac{\pi}{2}} \int_0^{9\cos x} \int_1^{y+9} \frac{dz\, dy\, dx}{z\sqrt{z}}.$

9. $\displaystyle\int_0^{\frac{\pi}{2}} \int_0^{\cos\theta} \int_0^{4+r\sin\theta} r\, dz\, dr\, d\theta.$

10. $\displaystyle\int_{\frac{\pi}{6}}^{\frac{\pi}{2}} \int_{\sqrt{1-\cos\theta}}^{\sqrt{1+\cos\theta}} \int_{a\sinh\frac{r}{a}}^{a\cosh\frac{r}{a}} rz\, dz\, dr\, d\theta.$

11. $\displaystyle\int_0^{\frac{\pi}{2}} \int_0^{\frac{\pi}{3}} \int_0^{a\sqrt{\cos\theta}} r^3 \sin\theta \cos\phi\, dr\, d\theta\, d\phi.$

12. $\displaystyle\int_0^{\frac{\pi}{2}} \int_0^{2\phi} \int_0^{a\sqrt{1-\cos\theta}} r^3 \sin\theta \cos\phi\, dr\, d\theta\, d\phi.$

180. Volume as a Triple Integral. In formulating volume as a triple integral, we shall for definiteness reconsider the volume V shown in Fig. 175a, and reproduced in Fig. 180a.

Suppose that two sets of lines parallel to the x- and y-axes and spaced at intervals Δy and Δx, respectively, have been drawn in the xy-plane, as in Art. 175. If now through the lines of both sets planes are passed parallel to the z-axis, then these planes, together with another set parallel to the xy-plane and Δz units apart, will subdivide space into elementary parallelepipeds each of volume $\Delta z\, \Delta y\, \Delta x$. The volume V is the limit of the sum of a suitable approximating set of elementary parallelepipeds as Δz, Δy, and Δx all approach zero.

In order to formulate V as a triple integral, consider the parallelepiped MN where the vertex M is at (x, y, z) and the diagonally opposite vertex N at $(x + \Delta x, y + \Delta y, z + \Delta z)$. The point $(x, y, 0)$ will be designated as P', the elementary rectangle in the xy-plane directly below MN as $P'Q'R'S'$, and the point $(x, y, f(x, y))$ on the surface $z = f(x, y)$

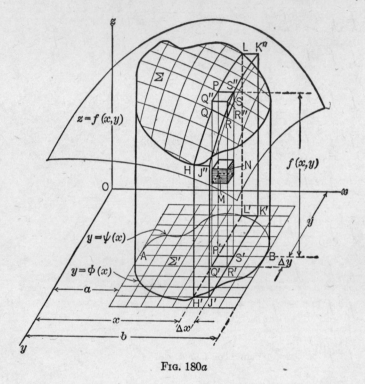

FIG. 180a

as P. The parallelepipeds which, including MN, form the largest possible column with $P'Q'R'S'$ as base and with an altitude not exceeding $P'P$ have a combined volume that, as Δz tends toward zero, approaches the volume of the column PR' as a limit. Hence

$$\text{volume } PR' = \left[\int_0^{f(x,y)} dz \right] \Delta y \, \Delta x.$$

Now the volume PR' is precisely the element from which we set out to give an integral formulation of V in Art. 175. We may therefore continue as in that article, obtaining by successive integrations, between limits there specified, first the laminar volume $J'L$ and then V itself. The result is

(1)
$$V = \int_a^b \int_{\psi(x)}^{\phi(x)} \int_0^{f(x,y)} dz\, dy\, dx.$$

It will be observed that the triple integral in (1) is of the same form as (3) of the preceding article, with $f(x, y, z) = 1$.

Volumes in general may be formulated as $\iiint dz\ dy\ dx$, $\iiint dy\ dx\ dz$, $\iiint dx\ dy\ dz$, etc., taken between integration limits satisfying the requirements laid down in the preceding article and corresponding in every case to the extent of the volume.

Example. Compute by triple integration the volume (Fig. 180b) bounded by the elliptic paraboloids $z = x^2 + 4y^2$ and $z = 8 - x^2 - 4y^2$.

The equations of the ellipse in which the two surfaces intersect are readily expressed in the form $x^2 + 4y^2 = 4$, $z = 4$. Moreover, the required volume V is symmetrical with respect to the plane $z = 4$, and hence is double the volume included between the surface $z = x^2 + 4y^2$ and the plane $z = 4$.

The latter volume may be obtained by integrating $dz\, dx\, dy$ partially with respect to z between the limits $x^2 + 4y^2$ and 4, then integrating this result partially with respect to x between the limits $-2\sqrt{1-y^2}$ and $+2\sqrt{1-y^2}$, and finally integrating the function of y thus found between the limits -1 and 1. The first two of these steps correspond to the determination of the volumes of a column and of a lamina such as those shown in the figure.

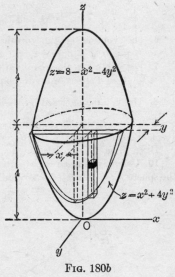

FIG. 180b

The work may, however, be further simplified by taking advantage of symmetry with respect to the xz- and yz-planes. Thus we have

$$V = 8 \int_0^1 \int_0^{2\sqrt{1-y^2}} \int_{x^2+4y^2}^4 dz\, dx\, dy$$

$$= 8 \int_0^1 \int_0^{2\sqrt{1-y^2}} (4 - x^2 - 4y^2)\, dx\, dy$$

$$= 8 \int_0^1 \left[8\sqrt{1-y^2} - \tfrac{8}{3}\sqrt{(1-y^2)^3} - 8y^2\sqrt{1-y^2} \right] dy$$

$$= 8\pi.$$

Evidently if the method of Art. 175 had been used, double integration would have sufficed. As a matter of fact, by choosing as elements elliptic laminas whose faces are perpendicular to the z-axis, the volume is easily found by a single integration.

PROBLEMS

In Problems 1–8, find the designated volumes by triple integration.

1. The volume in the first octant bounded by the paraboloid $z = x^2 + y^2$ and the planes $y = 0$, $z = 0$, $x = 1$, and $y = x$.

2. The volume in the first octant bounded by the cylindrical surface $z = \dfrac{1}{x^2}$ and the planes $x = 1$, $x = 2$, $y = 0$, $z = 0$, and $y = x$.

3. The volume in the first octant bounded by the cylindrical surface $z = \dfrac{8}{x^2 + 4}$ and the planes $y = 0$, $z = 0$, $x = 2$, and $y = x$.

4. The volume enclosed by the cylindrical surface $y = 4 - x^2$ and the planes $z = 0$ and $y = z$.

5. The volume in the first octant bounded by the cylindrical surfaces $z = \dfrac{1}{(x+1)^2}$, $y = 2x - x^2$, and the planes $y = 0$, $z = 0$.

6. The volume of the tetrahedron bounded by the planes $x + y + z = 4$, $x + y - z = 0$, $y = 0$, and $x = 0$.

7. The volume in the first octant bounded by the cylindrical surfaces $z = 4 - x^2$, $z = 4 - y^2$, and the coördinate planes.

8. The volume enclosed by the ellipsoid $\dfrac{x^2}{a^2} + \dfrac{y^2}{b^2} + \dfrac{z^2}{c^2} = 1$.

9. Using cylindrical coördinates, find by triple integration the volume above the xy-plane enclosed by the sphere $x^2 + y^2 + z^2 = 25$ and the cone $16z^2 = 9x^2 + 9y^2$.
HINT: The differential element of volume is $r\, dz\, dr\, d\theta$ (Fig. 180c).

10. Using cylindrical coördinates, find by triple integration the volume cut from the sphere $x^2 + y^2 + z^2 = 23$ by the upper sheet of the hyperboloid $z^2 - x^2 - y^2 = 9$.

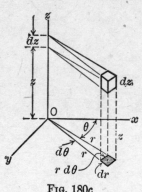

FIG. 180c

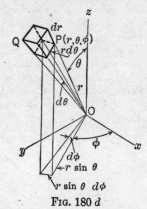

FIG. 180 d

Spherical Coördinates. The **spherical coördinates** of a point P (Fig. 180d) are the distance r of the point from the origin O, the angle θ the line OP makes with the z-axis, and the angle ϕ the plane through OP and the z-axis makes with the xz-plane.

It is evident that for any point in space θ may be restricted to lie between zero and π, and ϕ between zero and 2π.

An equation in rectangular coördinates may be transformed to spherical coördinates by means of the relations:

$$x = r \sin \theta \cos \phi, \qquad y = r \sin \theta \sin \phi, \qquad z = r \cos \theta.$$

An elementary volume PQ, with $P(r, \theta, \phi)$ as a vertex, is shown in the figure; the corresponding differential is

$$dV = r^2 \sin \theta \, dr \, d\theta \, d\phi.$$

11. Using spherical coördinates, find the volume of a sphere of radius a.
12. Using spherical coördinates, find the volume described in Problem 9.

181. Centroid and Moment of Inertia of a Mass or Volume. In Chapter X we considered centroids (or centers of gravity) and moments of inertia of volumes (or masses) in cases which can be treated by integration with respect to a single variable. We shall now give general formulas involving triple integrals for the coördinates $\bar{x}$, $\bar{y}$, $\bar{z}$ of a solid of mass m and density ρ (Fig. 181a) and for its moments of inertia with respect to the coördinate axes and planes. In applying these formulas to a particular solid, it will be necessary to know the equations of the boundaries and to supply corresponding integration limits which satisfy the requirements discussed and illustrated in the preceding two articles.

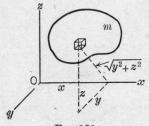

FIG. 181a

$$(1) \qquad m\bar{x} = \iiint \rho x \, dz \, dy \, dx.$$

$$(2) \qquad m\bar{y} = \iiint \rho y \, dz \, dy \, dx.$$

$$(3) \qquad m\bar{z} = \iiint \rho z \, dz \, dy \, dx.$$

$$(4) \qquad I_{xy} = \iiint \rho z^2 \, dz \, dy \, dx.$$

$$(5) \qquad I_{yz} = \iiint \rho x^2 \, dz \, dy \, dx.$$

$$(6) \qquad I_{xz} = \iiint \rho y^2 \, dz \, dy \, dx.$$

$$(7) \qquad I_x = \iiint \rho (y^2 + z^2) \, dz \, dy \, dx.$$

(8)
$$I_y = \iiint \rho(x^2 + z^2)\, dz\, dy\, dx.$$

(9)
$$I_z = \iiint \rho(x^2 + y^2)\, dz\, dy\, dx.$$

If in these formulas we replace $dz\, dy\, dx$ by the volume element dV, or $\rho\, dx\, dy\, dz$ by the mass element dm, we obtain results agreeing with the definitions laid down in Chapter X. Thus, for example, (4), (5), and (6) yield (5), (7), and (6) of Art. 110.

Formulas for the coördinates of the centroid of a volume V and for its various moments of inertia follow at once from (1) − (9) by setting $\rho = 1$, so that m becomes V.

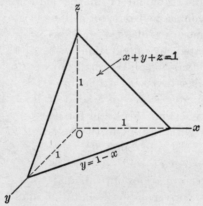

Fig. 181b

Example. Find the moment of inertia with respect to the x-axis of the volume of the tetrahedron (Fig. 181b) bounded by the coördinate planes and the plane $x + y + z = 1$.

We have in accordance with (7)

$$I_x = \int_0^1 \int_0^{1-x} \int_0^{1-x-y} (y^2 + z^2)\, dz\, dy\, dx$$

$$= \int_0^1 \int_0^{1-x} \left[y^2(1 - x - y) + \tfrac{1}{3}(1 - x - y)^3 \right] dy\, dx$$

$$= \tfrac{1}{6} \int_0^1 (1 - x)^4 dx$$

$$= \tfrac{1}{30}.$$

PROBLEMS

1. By triple integration, find the centroid of the tetrahedron bounded by the plane $2x + 3y + 4z = 12$ and the coördinate planes.

2. Find the center of gravity of the tetrahedron described in Problem 1, assuming that its density at any point is proportional to the distance of the point from the yz-plane.

3. For the same law of density as in Problem 2, find the moment of inertia of the mass of the tetrahedron with respect to (a) the xy-plane; (b) the xz-plane; (c) the x-axis.

4. Find the moments of inertia with respect to the coördinate planes of the solid in the first octant bounded by the surface $z = xy$ and the planes $z = 0$, $x = 2$ and $y = 2$.

5. Find the center of gravity of the solid described in Problem 4, assuming that its density at any point is proportional to the distance of the point from the xy-plane.

6. By triple integration, using cylindrical coördinates, find the centroid of the volume bounded by the sphere $x^2 + y^2 + z^2 = 4$, the paraboloid $4z = 8 - x^2 - y^2$ and the plane $z = 0$.

HINT: Perform the integration with respect to r first.

7. If the density at any point of the solid described in Problem 6 is proportional to the square of the distance of the point from the z-axis, find the center of gravity of the solid.

8. Find the moment of inertia with respect to the z-axis of the solid of Problem 7.

9. Find the moment of inertia with respect to the z-axis of the solid above the xy-plane and bounded by the surface $r = z(1 - \cos \theta)$, the cylinder $r = 4(1 - \cos \theta)$, and the plane $z = 0$.

10. Find the z-coördinate of the centroid of the solid described in Problem 9.

11. Using spherical coördinates, find the center of gravity of a hemisphere of radius a, assuming that its density at any point is proportional to the square of the distance of the point from the axis of symmetry.

12. Find the moment of inertia of the hemisphere described in Problem 11 with respect to the axis of symmetry.

CHAPTER XVIII

TABLE OF INTEGRALS

182. Use of a Table of Integrals. In many problems involving integration the applications of the formulas or methods of Chapter VIII would require much time and labor. The work may often be materially reduced by means of a table of integrals such as that given below. This table is not intended for indiscriminate use on the part of the beginning student, but rather to furnish a supplementary method of handling the more difficult types of integrals. The following examples illustrate its use.

Example 1. Evaluate $\int \dfrac{x^2 dx}{(9 - x^2)^{\frac{3}{2}}}$ (Example 4, Art. 90).

By Formula 35 of the table with $u = x$ and $a = 3$ we have

$$\int \frac{x^2 dx}{(9 - x^2)^{\frac{3}{2}}} = \frac{x}{\sqrt{9 - x^2}} - \sin^{-1} \frac{x}{3} + C.$$

Example 2. Evaluate $\int \dfrac{dx}{x^4 \sqrt{4x^2 + 9}}$.

By Formula 53 with $u = 2x$, $m = 4$, and $a = 3$ we have

$$\int \frac{dx}{x^4 \sqrt{4x^2 + 9}} = 8 \int \frac{2dx}{16x^4 \sqrt{4x^2 + 9}} = 8 \left[-\frac{\sqrt{4x^2 + 9}}{27(2x)^3} - \frac{2}{27} \int \frac{2\,dx}{4x^2 \sqrt{4x^2 + 9}} \right]$$

$$= 8 \left[-\frac{\sqrt{4x^2 + 9}}{216x^3} + \frac{2}{27} \frac{\sqrt{4x^2 + 9}}{18x} \right] + C \quad \text{(by 52)}$$

$$= \frac{1}{243x^3} \sqrt{4x^2 + 9}\,(8x^2 - 9) + C.$$

Example 3. Evaluate $\int \sin^4 x\, dx$.

By Formula 69 we have

$$\int \sin^4 x\, dx = -\tfrac{1}{4} \sin^3 x \cos x + \tfrac{3}{4} \int \sin^2 x\, dx$$

$$= -\frac{1}{4} \sin^3 x \cos x + \frac{3}{4} \left(\frac{x}{2} - \frac{1}{2} \sin x \cos x \right) + C \quad \text{(by 65)}$$

$$= \tfrac{3}{8}x - \tfrac{3}{8} \sin x \cos x - \tfrac{1}{4} \sin^3 x \cos x + C.$$

TABLE OF INTEGRALS

Some Basic Forms

1. $\displaystyle\int du = u + C.$

2. $\displaystyle\int c\,du = c\int du.$

3. $\displaystyle\int \left[f_1(u) + f_2(u) + \cdots + f_n(u) \right] du = \int f_1(u)du + \int f_2(u)du +$
$$\cdots + \int f_n(u)du.$$

4. $\displaystyle\int u\,dv = uv - \int v\,du.$

5. $\displaystyle\int u^n du = \frac{u^{n+1}}{n+1} + C, \quad n \neq -1.$

6. $\displaystyle\int \frac{du}{u} = \ln u + C.$

Forms Containing $a + bu$

7. $\displaystyle\int (a + bu)^n du = \frac{(a + bu)^{n+1}}{b(n+1)} + C, \quad n \neq -1.$

8. $\displaystyle\int \frac{du}{a + bu} = \frac{1}{b} \ln (a + bu) + C.$

9. $\displaystyle\int \frac{u\,du}{a + bu} = \frac{1}{b^2} \left[a + bu - a \ln (a + bu) \right] + C.$

10. $\displaystyle\int \frac{u^2\,du}{a + bu} = \frac{1}{b^3} \left[\tfrac{1}{2}(a + bu)^2 - 2a(a + bu) + a^2 \ln (a + bu) \right] + C.$

11. $\displaystyle\int \frac{u\,du}{(a + bu)^2} = \frac{1}{b^2} \left[\frac{a}{a + bu} + \ln (a + bu) \right] + C.$

12. $\displaystyle\int \frac{u^2\,du}{(a + bu)^2} = \frac{1}{b^3} \left[a + bu - \frac{a^2}{a + bu} - 2a \ln (a + bu) \right] + C.$

13. $\displaystyle\int \frac{du}{u(a + bu)} = -\frac{1}{a} \ln \frac{a + bu}{u} + C.$

14. $\displaystyle\int \frac{du}{u^2(a + bu)} = -\frac{1}{au} + \frac{b}{a^2} \ln \frac{a + bu}{u} + C.$

15. $\displaystyle\int \frac{du}{u(a+bu)^2} = \frac{1}{a(a+bu)} - \frac{1}{a^2}\ln\frac{a+bu}{u} + C.$

16. $\displaystyle\int u\sqrt{a+bu}\,du = -\frac{2(2a-3bu)(a+bu)^{\frac{3}{2}}}{15b^2} + C.$

17. $\displaystyle\int u^2\sqrt{a+bu}\,du = \frac{2(8a^2-12abu+15b^2u^2)(a+bu)^{\frac{3}{2}}}{105b^3} + C.$

18. $\displaystyle\int \frac{u\,du}{\sqrt{a+bu}} = -\frac{2(2a-bu)\sqrt{a+bu}}{3b^2} + C.$

19. $\displaystyle\int \frac{u^2\,du}{\sqrt{a+bu}} = \frac{2(8a^2-4abu+3b^2u^2)\sqrt{a+bu}}{15b^3} + C.$

20a. $\displaystyle\int \frac{du}{u\sqrt{a+bu}} = \frac{1}{\sqrt{a}}\ln\frac{\sqrt{a+bu}-\sqrt{a}}{\sqrt{a+bu}+\sqrt{a}} + C, \quad a>0.$

20b. $\displaystyle\int \frac{du}{u\sqrt{a+bu}} = \frac{2}{\sqrt{-a}}\tan^{-1}\sqrt{\frac{a+bu}{-a}} + C, \quad a<0.$

21. $\displaystyle\int \frac{du}{u^2\sqrt{a+bu}} = -\frac{\sqrt{a+bu}}{au} - \frac{b}{2a}\int\frac{du}{u\sqrt{a+bu}}.$

22. $\displaystyle\int \frac{\sqrt{a+bu}}{u}\,du = 2\sqrt{a+bu} + a\int\frac{du}{u\sqrt{a+bu}}.$

23. $\displaystyle\int \frac{\sqrt{a+bu}}{u^2}\,du = -\frac{(a+bu)^{\frac{3}{2}}}{au} + \frac{b}{2a}\int\frac{\sqrt{a+bu}}{u}\,du.$

Forms Containing $a^2 \pm u^2$ and $u^2 - a^2$

24. $\displaystyle\int \frac{du}{a^2+u^2} = \frac{1}{a}\tan^{-1}\frac{u}{a} + C.$

25. $\displaystyle\int \frac{du}{a^2-u^2} = \frac{1}{2a}\ln\frac{a+u}{a-u} + C$

$\displaystyle\qquad\qquad = \frac{1}{a}\tanh^{-1}\frac{u}{a} + C.$

26. $\displaystyle\int \frac{du}{u^2-a^2} = \frac{1}{2a}\ln\frac{u-a}{u+a} + C_1$

$\displaystyle\qquad\qquad = -\frac{1}{a}\tanh^{-1}\frac{u}{a} + C.$

$$\text{Forms Containing } \sqrt{a^2 - u^2}$$

27. $\displaystyle\int \frac{du}{\sqrt{a^2 - u^2}} = \sin^{-1}\frac{u}{a} + C.$

28. $\displaystyle\int \sqrt{a^2 - u^2}\, du = \frac{u}{2}\sqrt{a^2 - u^2} + \frac{a^2}{2}\sin^{-1}\frac{u}{a} + C.$

29. $\displaystyle\int (a^2 - u^2)^{\frac{n}{2}}\, du = \frac{u(a^2 - u^2)^{\frac{n}{2}}}{n + 1} + \frac{a^2 n}{n + 1}\int (a^2 - u^2)^{\frac{n}{2} - 1}\, du.$

30. $\displaystyle\int u^2\sqrt{a^2 - u^2}\, du = -\frac{u}{4}(a^2 - u^2)^{\frac{3}{2}} + \frac{a^2}{8}u\sqrt{a^2 - u^2}$

$$+ \frac{a^4}{8}\sin^{-1}\frac{u}{a} + C.$$

31. $\displaystyle\int u^m(a^2 - u^2)^{\frac{n}{2}}\, du = -\frac{u^{m-1}(a^2 - u^2)^{\frac{n}{2}+1}}{n + m + 1}$

$$+ \frac{a^2(m - 1)}{n + m + 1}\int u^{m-2}(a^2 - u^2)^{\frac{n}{2}}\, du.$$

32. $\displaystyle\int \frac{du}{(a^2 - u^2)^{\frac{3}{2}}} = \frac{u}{a^2\sqrt{a^2 - u^2}} + C.$

33. $\displaystyle\int \frac{u^2 du}{\sqrt{a^2 - u^2}} = -\frac{u}{2}\sqrt{a^2 - u^2} + \frac{a^2}{2}\sin^{-1}\frac{u}{a} + C.$

34. $\displaystyle\int \frac{u^m\, du}{\sqrt{a^2 - u^2}} = -\frac{u^{m-1}\sqrt{a^2 - u^2}}{m} + \frac{(m - 1)a^2}{m,}\int \frac{u^{m-2}\, du}{\sqrt{a^2 - u^2}}.$

35. $\displaystyle\int \frac{u^2\, du}{(a^2 - u^2)^{\frac{3}{2}}} = \frac{u}{\sqrt{a^2 - u^2}} - \sin^{-1}\frac{u}{a} + C.$

36. $\displaystyle\int \frac{u^m\, du}{(a^2 - u^2)^{\frac{n}{2}}} = -\frac{u^{m-1}}{(m - n + 1)(a^2 - u^2)^{\frac{n}{2} - 1}}$

$$+ \frac{a^2(m - 1)}{m - n + 1}\int \frac{u^{m-2}\, du}{(a^2 - u^2)^{\frac{n}{2}}}.$$

37. $\displaystyle\int \frac{du}{u\sqrt{a^2 - u^2}} = -\frac{1}{a}\ln\frac{a + \sqrt{a^2 - u^2}}{u} + C.$

38. $\displaystyle\int \frac{du}{u^2\sqrt{a^2 - u^2}} = -\frac{\sqrt{a^2 - u^2}}{a^2 u} + C.$

39. $\displaystyle\int \frac{du}{u^m(a^2 - u^2)^{\frac{n}{2}}} = - \frac{1}{a^2(m-1)u^{m-1}(a^2 - u^2)^{\frac{n}{2}-1}}$

$$+ \frac{m+n-3}{a^2(m-1)} \int \frac{du}{u^{m-2}(a^2 - u^2)^{\frac{n}{2}}}.$$

Forms Containing $\sqrt{u^2 \pm a^2}$

40. $\displaystyle\int \sqrt{u^2 \pm a^2}\, du = \frac{u}{2} \sqrt{u^2 \pm a^2} \pm \frac{a^2}{2} \ln\left(u + \sqrt{u^2 \pm a^2}\right) + C.$

41. $\displaystyle\int u^2 \sqrt{u^2 \pm a^2}\, du = \frac{u}{4}\left(u^2 \pm a^2\right)^{\frac{3}{2}} \mp \frac{a^2}{8} u\sqrt{u^2 \pm a^2}$

$$- \frac{a^4}{8} \ln\left(u + \sqrt{u^2 \pm a^2}\right) + C$$

42. $\displaystyle\int u^m(u^2 \pm a^2)^{\frac{n}{2}} du = \frac{u^{m-1}(u^2 \pm a^2)^{\frac{n}{2}+1}}{n+m+1}$

$$\mp \frac{a^2(m-1)}{n+m+1} \int u^{m-2}(u^2 \pm a^2)^{\frac{n}{2}}\, du$$

43. $\displaystyle\int \frac{du}{\sqrt{u^2 + a^2}} = \ln\left(u + \sqrt{u^2 + a^2}\right) + C_1$

$$= \sinh^{-1} \frac{u}{a} + C.$$

44. $\displaystyle\int \frac{du}{\sqrt{u^2 - a^2}} = \ln\left(u + \sqrt{u^2 - a^2}\right) + C_1$

$$= \cosh^{-1} \frac{u}{a} + C.$$

45. $\displaystyle\int \frac{u^2\, du}{\sqrt{u^2 \pm a^2}} = \frac{u}{2} \sqrt{u^2 \pm a^2} \mp \frac{a^2}{2} \ln\left(u + \sqrt{u^2 \pm a^2}\right) + C.$

46. $\displaystyle\int \frac{u^m\, du}{\sqrt{u^2 \pm a^2}} = \frac{u^{m-1}\sqrt{u^2 \pm a^2}}{m} \mp \frac{(m-1)a^2}{m} \int \frac{u^{m-2}\, du}{\sqrt{u^2 \pm a^2}}.$

47. $\displaystyle\int \frac{du}{(u^2 \pm a^2)^{\frac{3}{2}}} = \pm \frac{u}{a^2\sqrt{u^2 \pm a^2}} + C.$

48. $\displaystyle\int \frac{u^2\, du}{(u^2 \pm a^2)^{\frac{3}{2}}} = - \frac{u}{\sqrt{u^2 \pm a^2}} + \ln\left(u + \sqrt{u^2 \pm a^2}\right) + C.$

49. $\displaystyle \int \frac{u^m \, du}{(u^2 \pm a^2)^{\frac{n}{2}}} = \frac{u^{m-1}}{(m-n+1)(u^2 \pm a^2)^{\frac{n}{2}-1}}$

$$\mp \frac{a^2(m-1)}{m-n+1} \int \frac{u^{m-2} \, du}{(u^2 \pm a^2)^{\frac{n}{2}}}.$$

50. $\displaystyle \int \frac{du}{u \sqrt{u^2 + a^2}} = -\frac{1}{a} \ln \frac{a + \sqrt{u^2 + a^2}}{u} + C.$

51. $\displaystyle \int \frac{du}{u \sqrt{u^2 - a^2}} = \frac{1}{a} \sec^{-1} \frac{u}{a} + C.$

52. $\displaystyle \int \frac{du}{u^2 \sqrt{u^2 \pm a^2}} = \mp \frac{\sqrt{u^2 \pm a^2}}{a^2 u} + C.$

53. $\displaystyle \int \frac{du}{u^m \sqrt{u^2 \pm a^2}} = \mp \frac{\sqrt{u^2 \pm a^2}}{(m-1)a^2 u^{m-1}}$

$$\mp \frac{m-2}{a^2(m-1)} \int \frac{du}{u^{m-2} \sqrt{u^2 \pm a^2}}.$$

54. $\displaystyle \int \frac{du}{u^m (u^2 \pm a^2)^{\frac{n}{2}}} = \mp \frac{1}{a^2(m-1)u^{m-1}(u^2 \pm a^2)^{\frac{n}{2}-1}}$

$$\mp \frac{m+n-3}{a^2(m-1)} \int \frac{du}{u^{m-2}(u^2 \pm a^2)^{\frac{n}{2}}}.$$

TRIGONOMETRIC FORMS

55. $\displaystyle \int \sin u \, du = -\cos u + C.$

56. $\displaystyle \int \cos u \, du = \sin u + C.$

57. $\displaystyle \int \sec^2 u \, du = \tan u + C.$

58. $\displaystyle \int \csc^2 u \, du = -\cot u + C.$

59. $\displaystyle \int \sec u \tan u \, du = \sec u + C.$

60. $\displaystyle \int \csc u \cot u \, du = -\csc u + C.$

61. $\int \tan u \, du = \ln \sec u + C = -\ln \cos u + C.$

62. $\int \cot u \, du = \ln \sin u + C = -\ln \csc u + C.$

63. $\int \sec u \, du = \ln (\sec u + \tan u) + C.$

64. $\int \csc u \, du = -\ln (\csc u + \cot u) + C.$

65. $\int \sin^2 u \, du = \dfrac{u}{2} - \dfrac{1}{4} \sin 2u + C = \dfrac{u}{2} - \dfrac{1}{2} \sin u \cos u + C.$

66. $\int \cos^2 u \, du = \dfrac{u}{2} + \dfrac{1}{4} \sin 2u + C = \dfrac{u}{2} + \dfrac{1}{2} \sin u \cos u + C.$

67. $\int \sin^3 u \, du = -\cos u + \dfrac{1}{3} \cos^3 u + C.$

68. $\int \cos^3 u \, du = \sin u - \dfrac{1}{3} \sin^3 u + C.$

69. $\int \sin^n u \, du = -\dfrac{1}{n} \sin^{n-1} u \cos u + \dfrac{n-1}{n} \int \sin^{n-2} u \, du.$

70. $\int \cos^n u \, du = \dfrac{1}{n} \cos^{n-1} u \sin u + \dfrac{n-1}{n} \int \cos^{n-2} u \, du.$

71. $\int \tan^n u \, du = \dfrac{\tan^{n-1} u}{n-1} - \int \tan^{n-2} u \, du.$

72. $\int \cot^n u \, du = -\dfrac{\cot^{n-1} u}{n-1} - \int \cot^{n-2} u \, du.$

73. $\int \sec^n u \, du = \dfrac{1}{n-1} \sec^{n-2} u \tan u + \dfrac{n-2}{n-1} \int \sec^{n-2} u \, du.$

74. $\int \csc^n u \, du = -\dfrac{1}{n-1} \csc^{n-2} u \cot u + \dfrac{n-2}{n-1} \int \csc^{n-2} u \, du.$

75. $\int \sin mu \sin nu \, du = -\dfrac{\sin (m+n)u}{2(m+n)} + \dfrac{\sin (m-n)u}{2(m-n)} + C.$

76. $\int \sin mu \cos nu \, du = -\dfrac{\cos(m+n)u}{2(m+n)} - \dfrac{\cos(m-n)u}{2(m-n)} + C.$

77. $\displaystyle\int \cos mu \cos nu\, du = \frac{\sin (m+n)u}{2(m+n)} + \frac{\sin (m-n)u}{2(m-n)} + C.$

78a. $\displaystyle\int \sin^m u \cos^n u\, du = \frac{\sin^{m+1} u \cos^{n-1} u}{m+n}$
$$+ \frac{n-1}{m+n} \int \sin^m u \cos^{n-2} u\, du.$$

78b. $\displaystyle\int \sin^m u \cos^n u\, du = -\frac{\sin^{m-1} u \cos^{n+1} u}{m+n}$
$$+ \frac{m-1}{m+n} \int \sin^{m-2} u \cos^n u\, du.$$

79a. $\displaystyle\int \frac{du}{a + b \cos u} = \frac{2}{\sqrt{a^2 - b^2}} \tan^{-1}\left(\sqrt{\frac{a-b}{a+b}} \tan \frac{u}{2}\right) + C,$
$$a^2 > b^2.$$

79b. $\displaystyle\int \frac{du}{a + b \cos u} = \frac{1}{\sqrt{b^2 - a^2}} \ln \frac{b + a \cos u + \sqrt{b^2 - a^2}\, \sin u}{a + b \cos u}$
$$+ C, b^2 > a^2.$$

Miscellaneous Forms

80. $\displaystyle\int e^u\, du = e^u + C.$

81. $\displaystyle\int a^u\, du = \frac{a^u}{\ln a} + C.$

82. $\displaystyle\int u e^u\, du = e^u(u - 1) + C.$

83. $\displaystyle\int u^n e^u du = u^n e^u - n \int u^{n-1} e^u du.$

84. $\displaystyle\int \ln u\, du = u(\ln u - 1) + C.$

85. $\displaystyle\int u^n \ln u\, du = \frac{u^{n+1}}{(n+1)^2}\left[(n+1)\ln u - 1\right] + C.$

86. $\displaystyle\int u \sin u\, du = \sin u - u \cos u + C.$

87. $\displaystyle\int u \cos u\, du = \cos u + u \sin u + C.$

88. $\displaystyle\int u^n \sin u\, du = - u^n \cos u + n \int u^{n-1} \cos u\, du.$

89. $\displaystyle \int u^n \cos u\, du = u^n \sin u - n \int u^{n-1} \sin u\, du.$

90. $\displaystyle \int e^{au} \sin bu\, du = \frac{e^{au}(a \sin bu - b \cos bu)}{a^2 + b^2} + C.$

91. $\displaystyle \int e^{au} \cos bu\, du = \frac{e^{au}(a \cos bu + b \sin bu)}{a^2 + b^2} + C.$

92. $\displaystyle \int \sin^{-1} u\, du = u \sin^{-1} u + \sqrt{1 - u^2} + C.$

93. $\displaystyle \int \tan^{-1} u\, du = u \tan^{-1} u - \tfrac{1}{2} \ln (1 + u^2) + C.$

94. $\displaystyle \int u^n \sin^{-1} u\, du = \frac{1}{n+1} \left(u^{n+1} \sin^{-1} u - \int \frac{u^{n+1}\, du}{\sqrt{1 - u^2}} \right).$

95. $\displaystyle \int u^n \tan^{-1} u\, du = \frac{1}{n+1} \left(u^{n+1} \tan^{-1} u - \int \frac{u^{n+1}\, du}{1 + u^2} \right).$

WALLIS' FORMULAS

96. $\displaystyle \int_0^{\frac{\pi}{2}} \sin^n x\, dx = \int_0^{\frac{\pi}{2}} \cos^n x\, dx$

$$= \begin{cases} \dfrac{(n-1)(n-3)\cdots 4 \cdot 2}{n(n-2)\cdots 5 \cdot 3 \cdot 1}, \text{ if } n \text{ is an odd integer} > 1. \\[3mm] \dfrac{(n-1)(n-3)\cdots 3 \cdot 1}{n(n-2)\cdots 4 \cdot 2} \cdot \dfrac{\pi}{2}, \text{ if } n \text{ is an even integer.} \end{cases}$$

97. $\displaystyle \int_0^{\frac{\pi}{2}} \sin^m x \cos^n x\, dx$

$$= \begin{cases} \dfrac{(n-1)(n-3)\cdots 4 \cdot 2}{(m+n)(m+n-2)\cdots(m+5)(m+3)(m+1)}, \\ \qquad\qquad \text{if } n \text{ is an odd integer} > 1. \\[3mm] \dfrac{(m-1)(m-3)\cdots 4 \cdot 2}{(n+m)(n+m-2)\cdots(n+5)(n+3)(n+1)}, \\ \qquad\qquad \text{if } m \text{ is an odd integer} > 1. \\[3mm] \dfrac{(m-1)(m-3)\cdots 3 \cdot 1 \cdot (n-1)(n-3)\cdots 3 \cdot 1}{(m+n)(m+n-2)\cdots 4 \cdot 2} \cdot \dfrac{\pi}{2}, \\ \qquad\qquad \text{if } m \text{ and } n \text{ are both even integers.} \end{cases}$$

FORMULAS FOR REFERENCE

In calculus, one is constantly applying algebra, geometry, trigonometry, and analytic geometry. For convenience, we have assembled those formulas from more elementary mathematics which are used most frequently.

ALGEBRA

1. Binomial Theorem.

$$(a + b)^n = a^n + na^{n-1}b + \frac{n(n-1)}{2!} a^{n-2}b^2$$

$$+ \frac{n(n-1)(n-2)}{3!} a^{n-3}b^3 + \cdots + nab^{n-1} + b^n,$$

where n is a positive integer and $n!$ (read "n factorial") is defined by

$$n! = n(n-1)(n-2)\cdots 2 \cdot 1.$$

2. Quadratic Formula. The roots of the general quadratic equation $ax^2 + bx + c = 0$ are

$$x = \frac{-b \pm \sqrt{b^2 - 4ac}}{2a}.$$

(a) If $b^2 - 4ac < 0$, the roots are imaginary.
(b) If $b^2 - 4ac = 0$, the roots are real and equal.
(c) If $b^2 - 4ac > 0$, the roots are real and unequal.

3. Logarithm. If $N = a^L$, where a is a positive number other than 1, then $L = \log_a N$.

4. Logarithmic Formulas.

(a) $\log_a MN = \log_a M + \log_a N$.

(b) $\log_a \dfrac{M}{N} = \log_a M - \log_a N$.

(c) $\log_a N^n = n \log_a N$.

(d) $\log_a \sqrt[n]{N} = \dfrac{1}{n} \log_a N$.

(e) $\log_a \dfrac{1}{N} = -\log_a N$.

(f) $\log_a a = 1$.

(g) $\log_a 1 = 0$.

(h) $\log_b N = \log_a N \cdot \log_b a$.

(i) $\log_b a = \dfrac{1}{\log_a b}$.

Geometry

In the formulas listed below, the following notation is employed: b, length of base; h, altitude; r, radius; s, slant height; B, area of base.

5. Triangle: Area $= \frac{1}{2}bh$.

6. Trapezoid: Area $= \frac{1}{2}(b_1 + b_2)h$.

7. Circle: Circumference $= 2\pi r$.   Area $= \pi r^2$.

8. Prism: Volume $= Bh$.

9. Pyramid: Volume $= \frac{1}{3}Bh$.

10. Frustum of a Pyramid: Volume $= \frac{1}{3}(B_1 + B_2 + \sqrt{B_1 B_2})h$.

11. Right Circular Cone: Lateral surface $= \pi rs = \pi r\sqrt{r^2 + h^2}$. Volume $= \frac{1}{3}\pi r^2 h$.

12. Frustum of a Right Circular Cone: Lateral surface $= \pi(r_1 + r_2)s$. Volume $= \frac{1}{3}\pi(r_1^2 + r_2^2 + r_1 r_2)h$.

13. Right Circular Cylinder: Lateral surface $= 2\pi rh$.   Volume $= \pi r^2 h$.

14. Sphere: Surface $= 4\pi r^2$.   Volume $= \frac{4}{3}\pi r^3$.

Trigonometry

15. Fundamental Identities.

(a) $\csc \alpha = \dfrac{1}{\sin \alpha}$; $\sec \alpha = \dfrac{1}{\cos \alpha}$; $\cot \alpha = \dfrac{1}{\tan \alpha}$.

(b) $\tan \alpha = \dfrac{\sin \alpha}{\cos \alpha}$; $\cot \alpha = \dfrac{\cos \alpha}{\sin \alpha}$.

(c) $\sin^2 \alpha + \cos^2 \alpha = 1$; $1 + \tan^2 \alpha = \sec^2 \alpha$; $1 + \cot^2 \alpha = \csc^2 \alpha$.

16. Reduction Formulas.

(a) $\sin (90° - \alpha) = \cos \alpha$; $\tan (90° - \alpha) = \cot \alpha$; $\sec (90° - \alpha) = \csc \alpha$.

(b) $\sin (180° \pm \alpha) = \mp \sin \alpha$; $\cos (180° \pm \alpha) = - \cos \alpha$; $\tan (180° \pm \alpha) = \pm \tan \alpha$.

(c) $\sin (360° - \alpha) = \sin (-\alpha) = - \sin \alpha$; $\cos (360° - \alpha) = \cos (-\alpha) = \cos \alpha$.

17. Functions of the Sum and Difference of Two Angles.

(a) $\sin (\alpha \pm \beta) = \sin \alpha \cos \beta \pm \cos \alpha \sin \beta$.

(b) $\cos (\alpha \pm \beta) = \cos \alpha \cos \beta \mp \sin \alpha \sin \beta$.

(c) $\tan (\alpha \pm \beta) = \dfrac{\tan \alpha \pm \tan \beta}{1 \mp \tan \alpha \tan \beta}$.

18. Factorization Formulas.

(a) $\sin \alpha + \sin \beta = 2 \sin \frac{1}{2}(\alpha + \beta) \cos \frac{1}{2}(\alpha - \beta)$.

(b) $\sin \alpha - \sin \beta = 2 \cos \frac{1}{2}(\alpha + \beta) \sin \frac{1}{2}(\alpha - \beta)$.

(c) $\cos \alpha + \cos \beta = 2 \cos \frac{1}{2}(\alpha + \beta) \cos \frac{1}{2}(\alpha - \beta)$.

(d) $\cos \alpha - \cos \beta = - 2 \sin \frac{1}{2}(\alpha + \beta) \sin \frac{1}{2}(\alpha - \beta)$.

19. Relations between Functions of α and 2α.

(a) $\sin 2\alpha = 2 \sin \alpha \cos \alpha$.

(b) $\cos 2\alpha = \cos^2 \alpha - \sin^2 \alpha = 2 \cos^2 \alpha - 1 = 1 - 2 \sin^2 \alpha$.

(c) $\sin^2 \alpha = \frac{1}{2}(1 - \cos 2\alpha)$.

(d) $\cos^2 \alpha = \frac{1}{2}(1 + \cos 2\alpha)$.

(e) $\tan 2\alpha = \dfrac{2 \tan \alpha}{1 - \tan^2 \alpha}$.

20. Formulas for Any Triangle.

(a) $\dfrac{a}{\sin A} = \dfrac{b}{\sin B} = \dfrac{c}{\sin C}$.   (Sine law.)

(b) $a^2 = b^2 + c^2 - 2bc \cos A$.   (Cosine law.)

(c) Area $= \frac{1}{2} bc \sin A$.

(d) Area $= \sqrt{s(s-a)(s-b)(s-c)}$, where $2s = a + b + c$.

PLANE ANALYTIC GEOMETRY

21. Distance, Slope, Midpoint.

(a) $d = \sqrt{(x_2 - x_1)^2 + (y_2 - y_1)^2}$.   (Distance between $P_1(x_1, \ y_1)$ and $P_2(x_2, \ y_2)$.)

(b) $m = \dfrac{y_2 - y_1}{x_2 - x_1}$.   (Slope of the line through P_1 and P_2.)

(c) $x = \frac{1}{2}(x_1 + x_2); \ y = \frac{1}{2}(y_1 + y_2)$.   (Midpoint of P_1P_2.)

22. Angle (θ) between Two Lines of Slopes m_1 and m_2.

(a) $\tan \theta = \dfrac{m_1 - m_2}{1 + m_1 m_2}$.

(b) For parallel lines, $m_1 = m_2$.

(c) For perpendicular lines, $m_1 m_2 = -1$.

23. Four Forms of the Equation of a Straight Line.

(a) $Ax + By + C = 0$.   (General form.)

(b) $y - y_1 = m(x - x_1)$.   (Point-slope form.)

(c) $y = mx + b$.   (Slope-intercept form.)

(d) $\dfrac{x}{a} + \dfrac{y}{b} = 1$.   (Intercept form.)

24. Equations of Conics.

(a) *Circle:* $(x - h)^2 + (y - k)^2 = r^2$.   (Center at (h, k); radius r.)

(b) *Ellipse:* $\dfrac{(x - h)^2}{a^2} + \dfrac{(y - k)^2}{b^2} = 1$.   (Semi-axes a, b; major axis horizontal if $a > b$.)

(c) *Hyperbola:* $\dfrac{(x - h)^2}{a^2} - \dfrac{(y - k)^2}{b^2} = 1$.   (Transverse axis horizontal.)

(d) *Equilateral Hyperbola:* $xy = C$.   (Asymptotic to the coördinate axes; center at the origin.)

(e) *Parabola:* $(y - k)^2 = 4p(x - h)$.   (Vertex at (h, k); focus at $(h + p, k)$.)

SOLID ANALYTIC GEOMETRY

25. Distance between $P_1(x_1, y_1, z_1)$ and $P_2(x_2, y_2, z_2)$.

$$d = \sqrt{(x_2 - x_1)^2 + (y_2 - y_1)^2 + (z_2 - z_1)^2}.$$

26. Direction Parameters and Direction Cosines.

(a) Any numbers a, b, c, such that

$$\frac{x_2 - x_1}{a} = \frac{y_2 - y_1}{b} = \frac{z_2 - z_1}{c},$$

are called direction parameters of the line through $P_1(x_1, y_1, z_1)$ and $P_2(x_2, y_2, z_2)$.

(b) For a line whose direction parameters are a, b, and c, the direction cosines (i.e., cosines of the angles the line makes with the coördinate axes) are

$$\cos \alpha = \frac{a}{\pm \sqrt{a^2 + b^2 + c^2}},$$

$$\cos \beta = \frac{b}{\pm \sqrt{a^2 + b^2 + c^2}},$$

$$\cos \gamma = \frac{c}{\pm \sqrt{a^2 + b^2 + c^2}},$$

whence

$$\cos^2 \alpha + \cos^2 \beta + \cos^2 \gamma = 1.$$

27. Two Forms of the Equation of a Plane.

(a) $Ax + By + Cz + D = 0$.   (General form.)

(b) $A(x - x_1) + B(y - y_1) + C(z - z_1) = 0$.   (Plane through $P_1(x_1, y_1, z_1)$.)

In (a) and (b), the coefficients A, B, and C are direction parameters of a line perpendicular to the plane.

28. Equations of a Line through $P_1(x_1, y_1, z_1)$ and with Direction Parameters a, b, c.

$$\frac{x - x_1}{a} = \frac{y - y_1}{b} = \frac{z - z_1}{c}.$$

GREEK ALPHABET

A	α	Alpha	I	ι	Iota	P	ρ	Rho
B	β	Beta	K	κ	Kappa	Σ	σ	Sigma
Γ	γ	Gamma	Λ	λ	Lambda	T	τ	Tau
Δ	δ	Delta	M	μ	Mu	Υ	υ	Upsilon
E	ϵ	Epsilon	N	ν	Nu	Φ	ϕ	Phi
Z	ζ	Zeta	Ξ	ξ	Xi	X	χ	Chi
H	η	Eta	O	o	Omicron	Ψ	ψ	Psi
Θ	θ	Theta	Π	π	Pi	Ω	ω	Omega

ANSWERS TO PROBLEMS

Page 3. Art. 3

2. $2, 1, 1, \frac{1}{25}$.   **3.** 2.   **4.** 1.   **5.** 2, 1, 16.   **6.** $1, \frac{1}{4}, \frac{3}{4}\sqrt{6}$.

Pages 10–11. Art. 8

11. $-\dfrac{1}{2x^2}$.

12. $2 - 2x$.

13. 3.

14. 1.

15. 0.

21. -2.

22. 2, 3.

23. 0.

24. $0, \pm 1$.

25. ± 2.

26. $-3, 1$.

27. -2.

28. $(2n + 1)\dfrac{\pi}{4}$ radians $(n = 0, \pm 1, \pm 2, \cdots)$.

29. $(2n + 1)\dfrac{\pi}{6}$ radians $(n = 0, \pm 1, \pm 2, \cdots)$.

30. $2n\pi$ radians $(n = 0, \pm 1, \pm 2, \cdots)$.

31. $(2n + 1)\pi$ radians $(n = 0, \pm 1, \pm 2, \cdots)$.

32. $n\pi$ radians $(n = 0, \pm 1, \pm 2, \cdots)$.

Page 17. Art. 12

1. $-\dfrac{1}{x^2}$.

2. $\dfrac{1}{(1 - x)^2}$.

3. $-\dfrac{1}{x^2}$.

4. $6x^2$.

5. $2x + \dfrac{1}{x^2}$.

6. $\dfrac{-2}{x^3}$.

7. $\dfrac{2}{(1 - x)^3}$.

8. $\dfrac{1}{2\sqrt{x}}$.

9. $-\dfrac{1}{2x\sqrt{x}}$.

10. $\frac{3}{2}\sqrt{x}$.

11. $\dfrac{-x}{\sqrt{9 - x^2}}$.

12. $\dfrac{x + 2}{2(x + 1)^{\frac{3}{2}}}$.

13. $\dfrac{3\pi h}{\sqrt{9 + h^2}}$.

14. $-\frac{3}{5}$.

15. 16π.

Page 19. Art. 13

2. -4.

3. -4.

4. $\frac{1}{4}$.

5. 1.

6. 5.

7. $\frac{1}{2}$.

8. $\frac{1}{2}$.

9. $-\frac{1}{4}$.

10. $-\frac{1}{2}$.

11. $(3, 1)$.

12. $(2, 4)$.

13. $\tan^{-1}\frac{5}{3}$.

Pages 21–22. Art. 14

1. $32t$, 128 ft./sec.

2. (a) $2t - 4$,
   (b) 2 sec., 1 ft.

3. $-\frac{1}{2}$.

4. (a) $80 - 32t$,
   (b) 80 ft./sec.,
   (c) $\frac{5}{2}$ sec.,
   (d) 6 sec.,
   (e) -112 ft./sec.

5. 2 sec.; -3 ft./sec.,
   9 ft./sec.; 5 ft./sec.
   -7 ft./sec.

6. 0, 4.

7. -160 ft./sec.

Pages 23–24. Art. 15

1. $\dfrac{1}{2\sqrt{1+t}}$, $\dfrac{-1}{4(1+t)^{\frac{3}{2}}}$.

2. $-\frac{1}{2}$ ft./sec.^{2}

3. -6 ft./sec.^{2}, 6 ft./sec.^{2}

4. 2 sec., 8 ft./sec.

5. $s_1 = 18$ ft., $s_2 = 2$ ft., $v_1 = 32$ ft./sec., $v_2 = 14$ ft./sec.

Page 26. Art. 16

1. $2x + 5$.

2. $3t^2 - 12t + 5$.

3. $t - \frac{1}{4}$.

4. $-\frac{1}{2} + \frac{4}{3}x - 32x^3 + 5x^4$.

5. $3at^2 - 2bt + c$.

6. $\dfrac{3x^2}{a^3} + \dfrac{6x}{a^2} + \dfrac{9}{a}$.

7. $\dfrac{4x^3 - 2b^2x}{b^4} - c$.

8. $\dfrac{3x^2}{\sqrt{(a^2 - b^2)^3}} - \dfrac{2x}{\sqrt{b}} + 2\sqrt{a}$.

9. $t - 1$.

10. $(-2, -100)$, $(2, 28)$, $(3, 25)$.

Pages 27–28. Art. 17

1. $x - y + 4 = 0$, $x + y - 6 = 0$.

2. $2x - y - 11 = 0$, $x + 2y + 12 = 0$.

3. $7x - y - 32 = 0$, $7x + y - 3 = 0$.

4. $x + 20y + 42 = 0$, $x - 4y - 10 = 0$, $x + 5y + 7 = 0$.

5. $3x + y + 4 = 0$, $3x + y + 8 = 0$.

6. $(4, 0)$, $x + 2y - 4 = 0$.

7. $\tan^{-1}\frac{6}{17}$, $\tan^{-1}2$, $\tan^{-1}\frac{3}{11}$.

8. $\tan^{-1}\frac{12}{31}$.   **13.** $2\sqrt{2}$, $2\sqrt{2}$.   **14.** $\frac{4}{15}$, 540.

Page 29. Art. 18

1. $x < -2$, increases,
$-2 < x < 2$, decreases,
$x > 2$, increases.

2. $x < -2$, increases,
$-2 < x < 1$, decreases,
$x > 1$, increases.

3. $x < 0$, decreases,
$x > 0$, increases.

4. $x < -4$, decreases,
$-4 < x < -1$, increases,
$-1 < x < 4$, decreases,
$x > 4$, increases.

5. $x < -5$, decreases,
$-5 < x < -1$, decreases,
$x > -1$, increases

6. $t < 2$, $v < 0$; $t > 2$, $v > 0$.

7. $t < \frac{1}{3}$, $v > 0$;
$\frac{1}{3} < t < 2$, $v < 0$;
$t > 2$, $v > 0$.

8. $v > 0$, except when $t = 1$.

9. $t < 10$, $v < 0$;
$t > 10$, $v > 0$.

10. $t < 2$, $v < 0$;
$2 < t < 5$, $v < 0$;
$t > 5$, $v > 0$.

Page 31. Art. 20

1. $5x^4$, $20x^3$, $60x^2$, $120x$, 120.

2. $x < -3$, y' increases,
$-3 < x < 2$, y' decreases,
$x > 2$, y' increases.

3. $\dfrac{4}{(1+x)^3}$.

4. $6x - y + 2 = 0$.

5. $x < 2$, y' decreases,
$x > 2$, y' increases.

6. -60, decreasing algebraically,
increasing numerically.

Page 33. Art. 21

1. $(-1, \frac{1}{4})$, $(1, \frac{1}{4})$.   **2.** $21x - y - 17 = 0$.   **4.** $(0, 0)$, slope 0.

5. $(-1, -41)$, slope 32; $(1, 7)$, slope 16.
6. $(-2, -16)$, slope 4; $(0, -24)$, slope -12.
7. $(-3, -645)$, slope 294; $(4, -988)$, slope -392.
8. $(-3, -2262)$, slope 1964; $(3, -2142)$, slope -1924.
10. $(0, -20)$, slope -60.

Page 38. Art. 22

1. $(-2, -4)$, max. pt.;
    $(2, 4)$, min. pt.

2. $(\frac{2}{3}, \frac{32}{27})$, max. pt.;
    $(\frac{4}{3}, \frac{16}{27})$, pt. of infl.;
    $(2, 0)$, min. pt.

3. $(-1, 4)$, max. pt.;
    $(0, 2)$, pt. of infl.;
    $(1, 0)$, min. pt.

4. $(1, 0)$, H.P.I. (rising).

5. $(-3, 32)$, max. pt.;
    $(-1, 16)$, pt. of infl.;
    $(1, 0)$, min. pt.

6. $(0, 3)$, pt. of infl.;
    $(1, -6)$, pt. of infl.;
    $(2, -13)$, min. pt.

7. $(-3, 4)$, min. pt.

8. $(-3, -64\frac{4}{5})$, H.P.I.;
    $(0, 0)$, pt. of infl.;
    $(3, 64\frac{4}{5})$, H.P.I.

9. $(-6, 1568)$, min. pt.;
    $(-4, 1840)$, pt. of infl.;
    $(-\frac{3}{2}, 2160\frac{5}{16})$, max. pt.;
    $(3, 839)$, pt. of infl.;
    $(6, -160)$, min. pt.

10. $(-3, 242)$, max. pt.;
    $(-2, 148)$, pt. of infl.;
    $(1, -14)$, min. pt.

Pages 40–41. Art. 23

1. 6, 6.   **5.** 3, 9.   **9.** 432 cu. in.
2. 6, 6.   **6.** 60 yd., 120 yd.   **10.** 200 cu. in.
3. 6, 6.   **7.** 39 ft., 41 ft.   **11.** 2 in., 2 in.
4. 4, 8.   **8.** 6 in., 12 in., 8 in.

12. Diameter = side of square = $\dfrac{l}{4 + \pi}$.

13. Side of square = $\dfrac{\sqrt{3}\, l}{9 + 4\sqrt{3}}$; side of triangle = $\dfrac{3l}{9 + 4\sqrt{3}}$.

14. 32π cu. in.   **20.** 3456 cu. in.
15. 3 in.   **21.** 40 mi./hr.
16. Bases 3 in., 7 in., altitude 10 in.   **22.** 6 in., $6\sqrt{2}$ in.
17. 8 in.   **23.** 8 hr.
18. 2 in., 2 in.   **24.** 7000, $49.00.
19. $6 + \sqrt{3}$ in., $\frac{3}{2}(5 - \sqrt{3})$ in.

Pages 45–46. Art. 24

1. $(12x^2 - 18x + 7)dx$.

2. $(3x^4 - 7x^3 - 2x^2 + 5x)dx$.

3. $\dfrac{6dx}{(3 - x)^2}$.

4. $\dfrac{-dx}{\sqrt{1 - 2x}}$.

5. $\Delta y = 3x^2\Delta x + 3x(\Delta x)^2 + (\Delta x)^3$,
    $dy = 3x^2 dx$,
    $\Delta y - dy = 3x(\Delta x)^2 + (\Delta x)^3$.

6. $\Delta y = 2.002$, $dy = 1.9$.

7. $\Delta y = -7.688$, $dy = -8.2$.

8. 31.5, 28.5.

9. -821.8, -759.15.

10. $\frac{1}{4}$ sq. ft.

11. 5.4 cu. in.

12. $\dfrac{2}{\pi}$ sq. in., $\dfrac{5}{\pi^2}$ cu. in.

13. (a) 0.16π sq. in.,
   (b) 0.24π sq. in.,
   (c) 0.48π cu. in.

14. 0.48 sq. in.

15. 0.015, 1.5 per cent.

16. 0.01, 1 per cent.

18. 1 per cent.

Page 50. Art. 25

1. First.

2. Second.

3. (a) Second,
   (b) Third.

4. Fourth.

5. Second, $2\pi r^3$.

6. First, $\frac{1}{3}\pi r R^2$, where R is the radius of the larger base, and r is radius of smaller base.

7. First, First, Third, First.

8. First, Second, First, Second.

9. $(2 - 2x)\Delta x$.

10. $4(x - 1)^3 \Delta x$.

Page 53. Art. 28

1. $3x + C$.

2. $\dfrac{x^2}{2} - 2x + C$.

3. $3x - \dfrac{x^2}{2} + C$.

4. $\dfrac{5x^2}{2} - 2x + C$.

5. $ax + \dfrac{bx^2}{2} + C$.

6. $x^3 - \dfrac{3x^2}{2} + 2x + C$.

7. $\dfrac{4x^3}{3} + 6x^2 + 9x + C$.

8. $x^4 + 4x^3 + \dfrac{9x^2}{2} + C$.

9. $5(3x^3 + 3x^2 + x) + C$.

10. $\dfrac{x^5}{5} - \dfrac{4x^3}{3} + 4x + C$.

11. $\dfrac{x^8}{2} - \dfrac{4x^5}{5} + \dfrac{x^2}{2} + C$.

12. $x^3 - x^4 + C$.

13. $a^2 x - \dfrac{x^3}{3} + C$.

14. $2x - \dfrac{3x^2}{2} - \dfrac{2x^3}{3} + C$.

15. $16x - 112x^2 + 392x^3 - 686x^4 + \dfrac{2401}{5} x^5 + C$.

16. $\dfrac{a_0 x^4}{4} + \dfrac{a_1 x^3}{3} + \dfrac{a_2 x^2}{2} + a_3 x + C$.

17. $\sqrt{2}x^2 + C$.

18. $\dfrac{x^3}{3} - \dfrac{x^4}{2} + C$.

19. $\dfrac{9x^5}{5} - 6x^4 + \dfrac{16x^3}{3} + C$.

20. $\dfrac{2x^5}{5} - x^3 - \dfrac{x^2}{2} + 4x + C$.

21. $\dfrac{3x^{11}}{11} - \dfrac{x^8}{2} - \dfrac{3x^7}{7} - 3x^4 + 3x + C$.

22. $\dfrac{3x^5}{5} - x^3 + 2x^2 + 2x + C$.

23. $\dfrac{x^6}{2} - x^4 - \dfrac{7x^2}{2} + 2x + C$.

24. $x^4 - \dfrac{4x^3}{3} + \dfrac{x^2}{2} + C$.

Page 54. Art. 29

1. $y = x^2 + 2$.

2. $y = x^3 + x^2 - 3x - 5$.

3. $y = x^2 - 3x + 2$.

4. $s = \dfrac{t^2}{2} + 2$.

5. $y = \dfrac{3x^2}{2} + 2x - 7$.

Pages 59–61. Art. 31

1. 12.
2. $\frac{45}{2}$.
3. 9.
4. 2.
5. $\frac{39}{2}$.
6. 8.

7. $\frac{28}{3}$.
8. 15.
9. $\frac{34}{3}$.
10. $\frac{10}{3}$.
11. $\frac{32}{3}$.
12. $\frac{11}{3}$.

13. 36.
14. $\frac{34}{3}$.
15. $\frac{8}{3}$.
16. $\frac{255}{4}$.
17. 4.
18. 20.

19. 6.
20. $\frac{512}{15}$.
21. $\frac{1}{6}$.
22. $\frac{1}{12}$.
23. 9.
25. $\frac{15}{4}$.

26. 9.
27. 8.
28. $y = x^2 - 3x + 2$, $\frac{14}{3}$.
29. $y = x^3 - 6x^2 + 9x + 4$, $\frac{75}{4}$.
30. 768 ft., 1024 ft.
31. $\frac{500}{3}$ ft.

32. (a) 96 ft./sec., (b) 256 ft., (c) 128 ft./sec., (d) 112 ft.
33. (a) 200 ft./sec., (b) 216 ft., (c) 144 ft.
34. (a) $s = 96t - 16t^2$, (b) 128 ft., (c) 3 sec., (d) 144 ft., (e) 8 sec.
35. (a) $y = 256 + 96t - 16t^2$, (b) 384 ft., (c) 3 sec., (d) 400 ft., (e) 8 sec.

Page 66. Art. 33

1. 9.
2. 12.
3. 12.
4. $\frac{38}{15}$.
5. $\frac{14}{3}$.

6. 2.
7. $\frac{9}{4}$.
8. 1.
9. $\frac{28}{3}$.
10. 448.

11. $\frac{2240}{3}$.
12. $\frac{25}{3}$.
13. 21.
14. $\frac{32}{3}$.
15. $\frac{34}{3}$.

16. $-\frac{250}{3}$.
17. $\frac{5}{2}$.
18. 16.
19. 10.
20. $\frac{392}{3}$.

21. $\frac{665}{3}$.
22. 1.

Pages 72–73. Art. 34

1. $\frac{28}{3}$.
2. $\frac{23}{6}$.
3. $\frac{74}{3}$.
4. $\frac{32}{3}$.
5. $\frac{32}{3}$.

6. 36.
7. 2.
8. $\frac{38}{3}$.
9. $\frac{7}{2}$.
10. 8.

11. $\frac{32}{3}$.
12. 36.
13. 36.
14. $\frac{37}{6}$.
15. 9.

16. $\frac{124}{3}$.
17. $\frac{32}{3}$.
18. $\frac{125}{6}$.
19. 32.
20. $\frac{3}{4}$.

21. $\frac{1}{2}$.
22. $\frac{2770}{81}$.
23. $\frac{131}{4}$.
24. $\frac{131}{4}$.

Pages 82–83. Art. 36

1. (a) 2π,
   (b) $\frac{16}{15}\pi$,
   (c) $\frac{2}{5}\pi$,
   (d) $\frac{8}{5}\pi$.

2. $\dfrac{2059\pi}{7}$.

3. 40π.

4. $\dfrac{418\pi}{35}$.

5. 4π.

6. 16π.

7. $\dfrac{\pi}{105}$.

8. $\dfrac{16\pi}{15}$.

9. $\dfrac{64\pi}{3}$.

10. $\dfrac{3\pi}{10}$.

11. $\dfrac{16\pi}{15}$.

12. 128.

13. 144.

14. (a) 1152,
    (b) 288,
    (c) 576.

15. $\frac{64}{3}$.

Pages 88–89. Art. 38

1. 42 tons.
2. 7 ft.
3. $\frac{1}{3}$ ton, $\frac{2}{3}$ ton.

4. $421\frac{7}{8}$ lb.
5. 2250 lb.
6. 3250 lb.

7. 65 lb.
8. $933\frac{1}{3}$ tons.
9. 1 ton.

10. 80π tons.
11. 32,625 lb.
12. 3000 tons.
13. 6000 tons.

Page 93. Art. 39

1. 32 in-lb.

2. 5000 in-lb.

3. 30 in-lb.

4. 10,000 ft-lb.

5. 120,000 ft-lb.

6. 540,000 ft-lb.

7. $40,500\pi$ ft-lb.

8. $150,000\pi$ ft-lb.

9. $108,000\pi$ ft-lb.

10. $1,562,500\pi$ ft-lb.

11. $136,687.5\pi$ ft-lb.

12. $\dfrac{2000\pi}{3}$ ft-lb.

Pages 104–106. Art. 42

1. $-6(1 - 2x)^2$.

2. $10x(10x^4 - 11x^2 + 1)^4(20x^2 - 11)$.

3. $\dfrac{1}{5}\left(\dfrac{2}{\sqrt[5]{x^4}} + \dfrac{3}{x\sqrt[5]{x}}\right)$.

4. $\dfrac{5}{2}x^{\frac{1}{4}} - \dfrac{3}{4x^{\frac{1}{4}}} - \dfrac{3}{2x^{\frac{3}{4}}} - \dfrac{1}{2x^{\frac{5}{4}}} - \dfrac{15}{4x^{\frac{7}{4}}}$.

5. $\dfrac{2}{3\sqrt[3]{x}} + \dfrac{1}{3x\sqrt[3]{x}} - \dfrac{2}{x\sqrt[3]{x^2}} + \dfrac{16}{3x^2\sqrt[3]{x}}$.

6. $\dfrac{-2}{3(1 - 2x)^{\frac{2}{3}}}$.

7. $\dfrac{6}{5(1 - 2x)^{\frac{3}{5}}}$.

8. $\dfrac{-4x}{\sqrt{1 - 4x^2}}$.

9. $\dfrac{5 + 4x - 21x^2}{3\sqrt[3]{(8 + 5x + 2x^2 - 7x^3)^2}}$.

10. $\dfrac{3x + 1}{\sqrt{2x + 1}}$.

11. $\dfrac{2x(3 - 7x)}{3\sqrt[3]{(1 - 2x)^2}}$.

12. $\dfrac{4 + 9x^2}{(4 - 9x^2)^2}$.

13. $\dfrac{(x - 2)(27x^3 - 162x^2 + 16)}{(8 - 27x^3)^2}$.

14. $\dfrac{4}{(4 - 9x^2)\sqrt{4 - 9x^2}}$.

15. $-\dfrac{x^2 + 32}{x^3\sqrt{16 + x^2}}$.

16. $\dfrac{(2 - 3x)^3(15x^2 - 2x - 60)}{\sqrt{5 - x^2}}$.

17. $\dfrac{9x + 2}{2(2 - x)^3\sqrt{3x - 1}}$.

18. $\dfrac{2(2 + x^2)}{(4 - x^2)^{\frac{5}{2}}}$.

19. $\dfrac{24x^2 - 5x^5}{\sqrt[3]{8 - x^3}}$.

20. $-\dfrac{3x + 1}{(7x^2 - 6x - 1)\sqrt{7x^2 - 6x - 1}}$.

21. $\dfrac{3(x - 2)^2(15x^4 - 12x^3 + 1)}{\sqrt{9x^4 + 1}}$.

22. $\dfrac{-1}{(1 + x)\sqrt{1 - x^2}}$.

23. $\dfrac{2x}{(1 - x^2)\sqrt{1 - x^4}}$.

24. $\dfrac{-1}{\sqrt{4 + x^2}(x + \sqrt{4 + x^2})}$.

25. $\dfrac{-4}{\sqrt{4 - x^2}(x - \sqrt{4 - x^2})^2}$.

26. $\dfrac{2u - u^4}{1 - 2u^3}, \dfrac{2(1 + u^3)^4}{3(1 - 2u^3)^3}$.

27. $\dfrac{2t}{t^2 - 1}, \dfrac{(t^2 + 1)^3}{(t^2 - 1)^3}$.

28. $\dfrac{1}{2(t^2 - 1)\sqrt{1 - t^2}}$.

29. $\dfrac{2t^2 - t - 1}{(1 - 2t)\sqrt{1 - t^2}}$.

30. $\dfrac{-(1 + y^3)\sqrt{1 - y^6}}{3y^2}$.

31. $\dfrac{\sqrt{1 - 4y^2}}{2(\sqrt{1 - 4y^2} - 2y)}$.

32. $\sqrt{1 - y^2} + 1 - y^2$.

33. $4x + y - 8 = 0,\ x - 4y + 15 = 0$.

34. $\tan^{-1}\frac{7}{4}$.

35. $2x + y - 1 = 0,\ 2x + y - 5 = 0$.

36. $\tan^{-1}\frac{12}{11}$.

37. $\dfrac{5\sqrt{3}}{6},\ -\frac{1}{2}$.

38. $(-1, 1)$, slope $\frac{1}{2}$; $(1, 1)$, slope $-\frac{1}{2}$.

39. $(-2, 8)$, $(2, 8)$, min. pts.

40. (2, 1), max. pt.; (−2, −1) min. pt.; $\left(-2\sqrt{3}, -\dfrac{\sqrt{3}}{2}\right)$, (0, 0), $\left(2\sqrt{3}, \dfrac{\sqrt{3}}{2}\right)$, pts. of infl.

41. $(-\frac{2}{3}, -18)$, max. pt.; (2, −2), min. pt.

42. $\left(-1, -\dfrac{2}{9}\sqrt{3}\right)$, min. pt.; $\left(1, \dfrac{2}{9}\sqrt{3}\right)$, max. pt.; $\left(-\sqrt{3}, -\dfrac{2\sqrt{15}}{25}\right)$, (0, 0), $\left(\sqrt{3}, \dfrac{2\sqrt{15}}{25}\right)$, pts. of infl.

43. 8 in., 8 in., 4 in.   **45.** 4 in., 8 in.   **48.** 18π cu. in.   **50.** 1 mi.

44. 3 ft., 3 ft., 6 ft.   **47.** 96 sq. ft.   **49.** 2, 4.   **51.** 4 P.M., 150 mi.

Page 110. Art. 43

1. $-\dfrac{x}{y}, -\dfrac{16}{y^3}$.

2. $-\dfrac{4x}{9y}, -\dfrac{16}{9y^3}$.

3. $\dfrac{16x}{9y}, -\dfrac{256}{9y^3}$.

4. $\dfrac{ay - x^2}{y^2 - ax}, -\dfrac{2a^3xy}{(y^2 - ax)^3}$.

5. $\dfrac{4(xy^2 + 1)}{y(1 - 4x^2)}$.

6. $\dfrac{y^2 + 12x^2}{2y(2a - x)}$.

7. $-\dfrac{2x^2 + x^{\frac{1}{2}}y^{\frac{3}{2}}}{2y^2 + x^{\frac{3}{2}}y^{\frac{1}{2}}}$.

8. $\dfrac{3x - 2y - 2x\sqrt{y - x}}{x - 4y\sqrt{y - x}}$.

9. $\dfrac{y}{x}$.

10. $\dfrac{2x(x^2 - y^2) + a^2x}{2y(x^2 - y^2) - a^2y}$.

11. $\dfrac{4x^3 - 9x^2y + 10xy^2 - 6y^3}{3x^3 - 10x^2y + 18xy^2 - 12y^3}$.

12. $x + 2y - 6 = 0$, $2x - y - 7 = 0$.

13. $x + 5y + 8 = 0$, $5x - y - 12 = 0$.

14. $5x - 8y - 2a = 0$, $8x + 5y - 21a = 0$.

15. $6x - y - 4a = 0$, $x + 6y - 13a = 0$.

16. $2x - y - 2 = 0$, $x + 2y - 6 = 0$.

17. $45°$.

18. $\tan^{-1}\frac{7}{24}$.

19. $\tan^{-1}\frac{9}{13}$.

20. $\tan^{-1}\sqrt{2}$, $\tan^{-1}\frac{6}{13}$.

21. (1, 1), max. pt.

22. (0, 1), max. pt.; (0, −1), min. pt.

23. $4\sqrt{2}$ in., 8 in.

24. $\sqrt{2}$.

25. 128, $8\sqrt[4]{2}$.

26. 6 in., 18 in.

Pages 117–118. Art. 47

1. $3\cos(3x - 2)$.

2. $-\dfrac{1}{2}\sqrt{\dfrac{3}{x}}\sin(\sqrt{3x} - 2)$.

3. $-\dfrac{2}{x^3}\sec^2\dfrac{1}{x^2}$.

4. $\dfrac{2}{x^2}\csc^2\left(\dfrac{2}{x} - 1\right)$.

5. $\dfrac{-1}{2\sqrt{3-x}}\sec\sqrt{3 - x}\tan\sqrt{3 - x}$.

6. $\dfrac{3x-4}{2\sqrt{2-x}}\csc(x\sqrt{2-x})\cot(x\sqrt{2-x})$.

7. $\dfrac{8x}{(4 - x^2)^2}\cos\dfrac{x^2}{4 - x^2}$.

8. $2\sin(10 - 4x)$.

9. $-9\cot^2 3x \csc^2 3x$.

10. $4\sec^2 2x \tan 2x$.

11. $\sin^2\theta$.

12. $\cos^2\theta$.

13. $\sec^2 x + \csc^4 x$.

14. $\tan^2 \dfrac{x}{2}$.

15. $\cot 3x \, (\csc 3x - \cot 3x)$.

16. $\tan 2x \, (\sec 2x + \tan 2x)$.

17. $\frac{3}{4} \cos x \, (\cos x - 1)$.

18. $\sin^5 \dfrac{x}{5}$.

19. $\tan^4 x \sec^4 x$.

20. $\tan^3 3t \sec 3t$.

21. $\tan^4 4\theta$.

22. $\phi \sin 3\phi$.

23. $x \cos 2x$.

24. $x \sin^2 \dfrac{x}{2}$.

25. $8 \sin x \cos 3x$.

26. $\sec^2 x$.

27. $\dfrac{2 \sec 2\theta}{(\sec 2\theta + \tan 2\theta)^2}$.

28. $\dfrac{4}{1 - \sin 4x}$.

29. $\dfrac{3}{2} \sec^2 \dfrac{3x}{2}$.

30. $\dfrac{-2 \csc^2 4\phi}{\sqrt{\cot 4\phi}}$.

31. $\dfrac{2x \sin y - y^2 \cos x}{2y \sin x - x^2 \cos y}$

32. $\dfrac{y - y \cos x - \cos y - 2x}{\sin x - x \sin y - x}$.

33. $\dfrac{y - \tan y - y \sec x \tan x}{\sec x + x \sec^2 y - x}$.

34. $\dfrac{3 \sin (3x + y) - \cos (x + 3y)}{3 \cos (x + 3y) - \sin (3x + y)}$.

35. $\tan t \, (\tan^2 t + 3)$.

36. $\cot \dfrac{t}{2}$.

37. $\tan \dfrac{t}{2}$.

38. $-\tan t$.

39. $\dfrac{\sqrt{6}}{3} a, \; \dfrac{2\sqrt{3}}{3} a$.

40. $4a$.

41. $\frac{4}{3}a$.

42. $a(2 + \sqrt{2})$.

43. $4a$.

44. $\dfrac{a\sqrt{3}}{3}, \; \dfrac{a\sqrt{6}}{3}$.

45. 20 ft. 10 in.

46. $5\sqrt{5}$ ft.

47. $\tan^{-1} \mu$.

48. $(9 - 2\sqrt{3})$ mi.

49. 40 ft.

Page 123.   Art. 48

1. $\dfrac{1}{\sqrt{4 - x^2}}$.

2. $\dfrac{3}{1 + 9x^2}$.

3. $\dfrac{1}{x\sqrt{x^2 - 1}}$.

4. $\dfrac{-2x}{\sqrt{1 - x^4}}$.

5. $\dfrac{-1}{2x\sqrt{x - 1}}$.

6. $\dfrac{-1}{(x + 1)\sqrt{x^2 + 2x}}$.

7. $\dfrac{-1}{\sqrt{1 - x^2}}$.

8. $\dfrac{1}{\sqrt{1 - x^2}}$.

9. $\dfrac{1}{1 + x^2}$.

10. $\dfrac{1}{x^2 + 2x + 2}$.

11. $\dfrac{3x - 2x^2}{\sqrt{(1 - 2x^3 + x^4)(2x - x^2)}}$.

12. $\dfrac{1}{x\sqrt{x^2 - 1}}$.

13. $\dfrac{1}{x\sqrt{1 - x^2}} - \dfrac{1}{x^2} \sin^{-1} x$.

14. $\dfrac{2x}{1 + 4x^2} + \tan^{-1} 2x$.

15. $\dfrac{x^2}{\sqrt{4 - x^2}} + 2x \sin^{-1} \dfrac{x}{2}$.

16. $2 - \dfrac{4x \sin^{-1} 2x}{\sqrt{1 - 4x^2}}$

17. $\dfrac{8x \tan^{-1}\dfrac{2x}{3} - 6}{\left(\tan^{-1}\dfrac{2x}{3}\right)^2}.$

18. $\dfrac{1}{x\sqrt{2x-9}}.$

19. $\dfrac{\sqrt{x^2-4}}{x}.$

20. $4(9-x^2)^{\frac{3}{2}}.$

21. $2x^2\sqrt{4-x^2}.$

22. $\dfrac{18}{x^3\sqrt{x^2-9}}.$

23. $\dfrac{x^2}{\sqrt{16-x^2}}.$

24. $-\dfrac{\sqrt{4-x^2}}{x^2}.$

25. $\dfrac{x^2}{(4-x^2)^{\frac{3}{2}}}.$

26. $\sqrt{6x-x^2}.$

27. $\dfrac{1}{5+4\sin x}.$

28. $\dfrac{1}{5+4\cos x}.$

29. $2\sin^{-1}2x.$

30. $3\cos^{-1}3x.$

31. $\left(\sin^{-1}\dfrac{x}{2}\right)^2.$

32. $16x\sin^{-1}2x.$

33. $4x\sec^{-1}2x.$

34. $\dfrac{1}{4+x^2}$

35. 100 ft.

Page 130. Art. 49

14. $6\sqrt{3}x - 12y + 6 - \sqrt{3}\pi = 0,\ 12x + 6\sqrt{3}y - 3\sqrt{3} - 2\pi = 0.$

15. $8x - 2y + 2 - \pi = 0,\ 8x + 32y - 32 - \pi = 0.$

16. $24x - y + 4 - 2\pi = 0,\ 12x + 288y - 1152 - \pi = 0.$

17. $6\sqrt{3}x + 2y - 2 - \sqrt{3}\pi = 0,\ 6x - 18\sqrt{3}y + 18\sqrt{3} - \pi = 0.$

18. $y - \dfrac{\pi}{6} = \dfrac{3-\sqrt{3}\pi}{6}\left(x - \dfrac{\pi}{3}\right),\ y - \dfrac{\pi}{6} = \dfrac{6}{\sqrt{3}\pi - 3}\left(x - \dfrac{\pi}{3}\right).$

19. $y - \dfrac{3}{\pi} = \dfrac{6-\sqrt{3}\pi}{12}\left(x - \dfrac{6}{\pi}\right),\ y - \dfrac{3}{\pi} = \dfrac{12}{\sqrt{3}\pi - 6}\left(x - \dfrac{6}{\pi}\right).$

Pages 141–142. Art. 54

1. $-\dfrac{1}{x^2}e^{\frac{1}{x}}.$

2. $-2x10^{-x^2}\ln 10.$

3. $\dfrac{e^{\tan^{-1}x}}{1+x^2}.$

4. $a^{\sin x}\cos x \ln a.$

5. $xe^{3x}(3x+2).$

6. $\frac{1}{2}(e^{\frac{x}{a}} - e^{-\frac{x}{a}}).$

7. $-e^{-2x}(3\sin 3x + 2\cos 3x).$

8. $\dfrac{e^x - e^{-x}}{e^x + e^{-x}}\log_a e.$

9. $\dfrac{4}{2x+3}.$

10. $\dfrac{36x}{x^4-81}.$

11. $\dfrac{-4e^{2x}}{e^{4x}-1}.$

12. $\dfrac{x\cos x}{x\sin x + \cos x}.$

13. $\dfrac{e^x(e^x-3)}{e^{2x}-1}.$

14. $\csc x.$

15. $2e^{\sin^2 2x}\sin 4x.$

16. $\dfrac{-5x^2 - 16x + 3}{(x+2)(x^2+1)}.$

17. $\dfrac{-2}{x\sqrt{x+4}}.$

18. $\dfrac{3+4x^2}{x(1+x^2)}.$

19. $\dfrac{-xa^{\sqrt{4-x^2}}\ln a}{\sqrt{4-x^2}}.$

20. $\dfrac{(2-x)\ln(2-x) - 1}{e^{2-x}(2-x)}.$

21. $e^x e^{e^x}.$

22. $e^{ex+1}.$

23. $x^{e-1}e^{x^e+1}.$

30. $\dfrac{1}{e}.$

31. $0,\ \text{min.};\ \dfrac{e^{-2}}{4},\ \text{max.}$

32. $\frac{1}{8}e^{-\frac{3}{2}},\ \text{max.};\ -\frac{1}{8}e^{-\frac{3}{2}},\ \text{min.}$

Page 147.   Art. 56

2. $x^{x^2+1}(1 + 2 \ln x)$.

3. $x^{\frac{1-2x}{x}}(1 - \ln x)$.

4. $\frac{1}{3}x^{\sqrt{x}-\frac{2}{3}}(3 + \ln x)$.

5. $x^{\cos x-1}(\cos x - x \ln x \cdot \sin x)$.

6. $x^{\tan^{-1}e^x-1}\left(\tan^{-1}e^x + \dfrac{x\,e^x \ln x}{1 + e^{2x}}\right)$.

7. $e^{-x^2}x^{e^{-x^2}-1}(1 - 2x^2 \ln x)$.

8. $e^x(\sin x)^{e^x}(\cot x + \ln \sin x)$.

9. $2 \ln x \cdot x^{\ln x-1}$.

10. $(\tan x)^{\ln x-1}\left(\ln x \sec^2 x + \dfrac{\tan x}{x}\ln \tan x\right)$.

11. $\dfrac{4x^2 - 9x + 4}{2\sqrt{1-x}\,\sqrt{2-x}}$.

12. $\dfrac{-x(1+x)}{(1-x^3)^{\frac{2}{3}}(1+x^2)^{\frac{3}{2}}}$.

13. $\dfrac{x^4(8 - 3x^2 - 2x^7)}{(1-x^7)^{\frac{4}{7}}(1-2x^5)^{\frac{9}{5}}}$.

14. $\dfrac{x(4x^4 - 5x^2 + 2)}{(1-x^2)^{\frac{1}{2}}(1-2x^2)^{\frac{3}{2}}}$.

15. $\dfrac{-2 + 18x - 27x^2}{x^3(1-2x)^{\frac{1}{2}}(1-3x)^4}$.

16. $\dfrac{e^{-3x}(1 - 3x - 3x^3)}{(1+x^2)^{\frac{3}{2}}}$.

Pages 151–153.   Art. 58

1. -0.001 amp./sec.

2. 6 in./sec.

3. $\dfrac{3}{16\pi}$ ft./min.

4. $\frac{1}{16}$.

5. $\frac{1}{2}$ in./sec.

6. $\dfrac{4}{27\pi}$ in./sec.

7. 338π cu. ft./hr.

8. $-48\pi\sqrt{3}$ cu. in./sec.

9. $\dfrac{1}{\pi}$ ft./min.

10. $\frac{1}{5}$ cu. in./sec.

11. -0.0875 (lb./sq. in.) per sec.

12. $\frac{5}{4}$ ft./sec.

13. 5 ft./sec.

14. 3 mi./hr.

15. $\frac{7}{5}$ ft./sec.

16. 13 ft./sec.

17. $\dfrac{51}{\sqrt{13}}$ mi./hr.

18. $\frac{160}{13}$ ft./sec.

19. 10 ft./sec.

20. 0.9 ft./sec.

21. 240,000 ft./sec.^{2}

22. 7 sq. in./sec.

23. $-\frac{15}{2}(4\sqrt{2} + 1)$ ft./sec.

24. $\frac{801}{20}$ sq. in./sec.

25. $-\frac{1440}{17}$ ft./min.

26. $\frac{6}{5}$ rad./sec.

27. -1.24 (lb./sq. ft.) per sec.

Pages 162–163.   Art. 62

1. 5 ft./sec., 13 ft./sec.

2. 5 ft./sec., -10 ft./sec.

3. 30 ft./sec.^{2}, 15 ft./sec.^{2}

4. $\dfrac{-2}{e^3}$ ft./sec., $\dfrac{4}{e^3}$ ft./sec.^{2}

5. $3\sqrt{2}e^{-3t}$, $18e^{-3t}$.

6. $\dfrac{v^2}{r}$.

7. 6 ft./sec., 12 ft./sec.^{2}

8. 80 ft./sec., $8\sqrt{13}$ ft./sec.^{2}, $x^3 = 512(y - 5)^2$.

9. Max. of 9 ft./sec. at $(0, 0)$;   min. of $6\sqrt{2}$ ft./sec. at $(3, 8)$ and $(3, -8)$.

10. 6 ft./sec.^{2} and -12 ft./sec.^{2} at $t = 2$; 6 ft./sec.^{2} and 12 ft./sec.^{2} at $t = -2$.

11. $y = \dfrac{1}{2}\ln 8x$, $t = 2$, $\dfrac{\sqrt{2}}{2}$ ft./sec., $\dfrac{\sqrt{2}}{4}$ ft./sec.^{2}

12. $\frac{1}{2}\ln 2$ sec.　　　　13. 1, $6\sqrt{2}$.　　　　14. $\sqrt{3}, \dfrac{24}{\pi}$.

15. 2 ft./sec., -2 ft./sec.; -32 ft./sec.^{2}, -32 ft./sec.^{2}

16. 4 ft./sec., $-\frac{15}{2}$ ft./sec.; 0, $-\frac{289}{32}$ ft./sec.^{2}

17. $v_0\cos\theta$, $v_0\sin\theta - gt$; 0, $-g$.

Pages 168–169.　Art. 64

1. $\dfrac{\pi}{1800}$, $\left(\dfrac{\pi}{900}\right)^2$ ft./sec.^{2}

2. -12 ft./sec.^{2}, 12 ft./sec.^{2}; $\frac{9}{2}$ ft./sec.^{2}

3. ± 6 ft./sec.^{2}

5. $2\sqrt{14{,}677}$ ft./sec.^{2}

6. 80 ft./sec.^{2}, 0.

7. 10 ft./sec.^{2}

8. 12 ft./sec.^{2}

9. 4 ft./sec.^{2}, $-\dfrac{4}{e^2}$ ft./sec.^{2}

10. $-\frac{8}{17}$ radian per sec.

11. 0, -3 radians per sec.^{2}

Pages 172–173.　Art. 65

3. 5 ft., $\dfrac{5\pi}{2}$ sec.

4. 39 ft./sec., 13 ft.

5. $6\sqrt{3}$ ft./sec.^{2}

6. $\dfrac{2\pi}{\sqrt{3}}$ sec., 12 ft./sec.^{2}

7. π sec., 5 ft.

9. $\dfrac{\pi}{3}$ sec., 1 ft., 6 ft./sec.

10. $\frac{5}{2}$ sec.

11. (5, 0), 1 ft., 16 ft./sec.^{2}

12. $\dfrac{2\pi}{3}$ sec., 234 ft./sec.^{2}

13. $\dfrac{8}{\pi}$ oscillations per sec.

14. 1 in., 256 in./sec.^{2}

15. About 85 min.

Pages 178–179.　Art. 67

1. $5\sqrt{5}$.

2. $\sqrt{2}$.

3. $\sqrt{2}$.

4. $16\sqrt{3}$.

5. $-\frac{125}{24}$.

6. $-8\sqrt{10}$.

7. $6\sqrt{2}$.

8. $\frac{250}{7}$.

9. $\dfrac{(x^4 + a^4)^{\frac{3}{2}}}{2a^2x^3}$.

10. $-\dfrac{17\sqrt{17}}{2}$.

11. $-\dfrac{(x^2 + 1)^{\frac{3}{2}}}{x}$.

12. $-\dfrac{7\sqrt{7}}{4}$.

13. $-\csc x$.

14. $\dfrac{37\sqrt{37}}{36}$.

15. $-\dfrac{17\sqrt{17}}{16}$.

16. $-\frac{1}{2}$.

17. $-\dfrac{\sqrt{e}}{2}$.

18. a.

19. $-2\sqrt{2}$.

20. $\sec x$.

22. $-\frac{8}{5}$.

23. $\pm 3\sin 2t$.

24. $-\dfrac{v_0{}^2\cos^2\theta}{g}$.

25. (3, -4).

27. (0, 0).

28. (3, $\frac{15}{2}$).

29. $(a_t)^2 = \dfrac{[f'(t)f''(t) + g'(t)g''(t)]^2}{[f'(t)]^2 + [g'(t)]^2}$,

$(a_n)^2 = \dfrac{[f'(t)g''(t) - f''(t)g'(t)]^2}{[f'(t)]^2 + [g'(t)]^2}$.

30. $\dfrac{32EI}{3WL}$.

Page 182.   Art. 68

1. $r = a$.
2. $r = 2a \cos \theta$.
3. $r^2 = a^2 \sec 2\theta$.
4. $r^2 = 12 \csc 2\theta$.
5. $r = \dfrac{ea}{1 - e \cos \theta}$.
6. $r^2 = a^2 \cos 2\theta$.
7. $r = \dfrac{2a}{1 + \cos \theta}$.
8. $r = a \sin \theta \tan \theta$.
9. $r^2 = a^2 \cot^2 \theta \sec 2\theta$.

10. $\theta = \frac{1}{2} \tan^{-1} 2, \ \theta = \frac{1}{2} \tan^{-1} 2 + \dfrac{\pi}{2}$.
11. $x^2 + y^2 - 2ay = 0$.
12. $y^2(x^2 + y^2) - a^2 x^2 = 0$.
13. $(x^2 + y^2)^3 - a^2(x - y)^4 = 0$.
14. $y^2 - 2ax - a^2 = 0$.
15. $y = 2\sqrt{2}$.
16. $y = 2$.
17. $y^2(x^2 + y^2) - 4x^2 = 0$.
18. $(x^2 + y^2 - 2y)^2(x^2 + y^2) - x^2 = 0$.
19. $x^3 + xy^2 - x - 2y = 0$.
20. $(x^2 - 1)^2(x^2 + y^2) - 4x^4 = 0$.

Page 186.   Art. 70

1. $\pm a\, d\theta$.
2. $\pm a \sin \dfrac{\theta}{2}\, d\theta$.
3. $\pm a \cos^2 \dfrac{\theta}{3}\, d\theta$.
4. $\pm 2a \sin \dfrac{\theta}{2}\, d\theta$.
5. $\pm \dfrac{a}{2} \sec^3 \dfrac{\theta}{2}\, d\theta$.
6. $\pm 5\, d\theta$.
7. $\pm a \sec^2 \theta\, d\theta$.
8. $\pm a \sec^3 \dfrac{\theta}{2}\, d\theta$

9. $\pm a \csc^4 \dfrac{\theta}{3}\, d\theta$.
10. $\pm a (\tan \theta + \sec \theta)\sqrt{1 + \sec^2 \theta}\, d\theta$.
11. $2\sqrt{3}$ ft./sec., 1 ft./sec.
12. Each $2a$ ft./sec.
13. $\dfrac{4k^2 \sin^2 \dfrac{\theta}{2}}{a^2}$.
15. $\dfrac{-k^2}{ar^2}$.
16. $-\sqrt{3}$ ft./sec.

Pages 189–191.   Art. 72

1. $\cot^{-1} a$.
2. $\frac{1}{3}$.
3. $45°$.
4. $\tan^{-1}\left(-\frac{7}{48}\right)$.
5. $\frac{3}{4}\pi$.
6. $\dfrac{\pi}{6}$.
7. $\tan^{-1} \frac{1}{4}$.
8. 0.

9. $\dfrac{-9}{13}$.
10. $5x - 4y - 9 = 0$.
13. $\tan^{-1} \frac{4}{3}$.
14. $\tan^{-1} \dfrac{3\sqrt{3}}{5}$.
15. $\tan^{-1} \dfrac{5\sqrt{3} + 8}{11}$.

16. $\dfrac{\pi}{2}$.
17. 4.
18. $\frac{1}{5}$.
19. $-a (\csc 2\theta)^{\frac{2}{3}}$.
20. $8a$.
21. $\frac{2}{3}a$.

Pages 194–195.   Art. 73

1. 1.213.
2. 1.429.
3. -0.339.
4. 1.48.
5. 2.76 cu. cm./gm.
6. 1.02 ft.

7. 2.66 ft.
8. $(3.146, 1.146)$.
9. 2.996.
10. 0.860.
11. 0.3047 radian.
12. 2.84.

13. 4.965.
14. 3.712 lb.
15. 0.102 sec.
16. 1.303.

Pages 206–207. Art. 75

1. $2x \pm 3y = 0$.
2. $4x + 3y + 4 = 0$, $3x - 4y + 3 = 0$.
3. $x + y = 0$, $x = 0$.
4. $x = 0$, $y = 4$, $x - y - 4 = 0$.
5. $x = 0$, $x - 3y = 0$, $x + y = 0$.
6. $3x + 4 = 0$, $x + y - 1 = 0$, $3x - 9y - 1 = 0$
7. $x + y + a = 0$.
8. $x - y = 0$, $\dfrac{-1 \pm \sqrt{5}}{2} x - y = 0$.
9. $\dfrac{1 \pm \sqrt{5}}{2} x - y = 0$, $x - y = 0$.
10. $y = 0$, $x - y - 2 = 0$, $x + 2 = 0$.
11. $x = 0$, $x - y + 1 = 0$, $x - 2y - 1 = 0$.
12. $y = 0$, $2y \pm 2x - 1 = 0$.
13. $x = 0$, $2x - y + 2 = 0$, $x - y - 1 = 0$.
14. $x - 1 = 0$, $x - y + 1 = 0$, $x + y + 1 = 0$.
15. $x + y + 1 = 0$.
16. $x - y - 1 = 0$, $x + y - 1 = 0$, $x - 2y + 4 = 0$, $x + 2y + 4 = 0$.
17. $x - y = 0$, $x = 0$.
18. $x - y + 5 = 0$, $x + y + 5 = 0$.
19. $x = 0$, $x - y = 0$.
20. $y = 0$, $2x - y - 2 = 0$.
21. $y = 0$, $x = 3$, $x - y + 6 = 0$.

Page 213. Art. 76

1. $(0, 0)$, isolated point.   2. $(0, 0)$, cusp, slope 1.   3. $(0, 0)$, cusp, slope 1.
4. $(-3, 0)$, isolated point; $(-1, 0)$, node, slopes ± 2.
5. $(0, 0)$, tacnode, slope 0.   7. $(-3, 0)$, isolated point.
6. $(0, 0)$, cusp, slope infinite.   8. $(0, 0)$, cusp, slope 0.
9. $(\pm a, 0)$, cusps, slope 0; $(0, \pm a)$, cusps, slope infinite.
10. $(0, 0)$, node, slopes ± 1.   14. $(0, 0)$, triple point, slopes 0, $\pm \sqrt{3}$.
11. $(0, 2)$, node, slopes ± 2.   15. $(0, 0)$, triple point, slopes 0, 0, 1.
12. $(0, 0)$, cusp, slope 0.   16. $(0, 0)$, triple point, slopes -2, 0, 1.
13. $(0, 0)$, tacnode, slope 0.

Pages 217–218. Art. 78

2. $2a\omega$, at highest points of cycloid.   8. Two.
3. On cycloid, $\dfrac{a}{2}$ units from x-axis.   10. $x = a \cos^3 \phi$, $y = a \sin^3 \phi$; $x^{\frac{2}{3}} + y^{\frac{2}{3}} = a^{\frac{2}{3}}$.
5. -2 and 3.276.   12. $x^2 y + y^3 + 2ax^2 = 0$.

Page 224. Art. 80

1. $y^2 = \frac{4}{27}(x - 2)^3$.
2. $(x + y)^{\frac{2}{3}} - (x - y)^{\frac{2}{3}} = 4$.
3. $(3x)^{\frac{2}{3}} + (2y)^{\frac{2}{3}} = 5^{\frac{2}{3}}$.
4. $(3x)^{\frac{2}{3}} - (2y)^{\frac{2}{3}} = 13^{\frac{2}{3}}$.
5. $(x + y)^{\frac{2}{3}} + (x - y)^{\frac{2}{3}} = 2a^{\frac{2}{3}}$.
6. $x = \ln \dfrac{y \pm \sqrt{y^2 - 4}}{2} - \dfrac{y}{4}\sqrt{y^2 - 4}$.
7. $x = \dfrac{t}{2}(1 - 9t^4)$, $y = \dfrac{1 + 15t^4}{6t}$.

8. $x = -\dfrac{t^2}{2}(2 + 9t^2),\ y = \dfrac{4t}{3}(1 + 3t^2).$ **9.** $x = a(\phi + \sin\phi),\ y = -a(1 - \cos\phi).$

10. $x = t - \tan t\,(1 + \sin^2 t),\ y = -2\sin t\tan t.$

Pages 231–233.   Art. 83

1. $\dfrac{x^5}{5} + C.$

2. $-\dfrac{2}{x} + C.$

3. $4\sqrt{x} + C.$

4. $-\dfrac{3}{4x^4} + C.$

5. $-\dfrac{1}{6x^3} + C.$

6. $\dfrac{x^5}{5} - \dfrac{5x^4}{4} - x^2 + 8x + C.$

7. $\dfrac{7t^2}{2} + C.$

8. $\frac{2}{3}s\sqrt{6s} + C.$

9. $2\theta^3 - \frac{5}{2}\theta^2 + 2\theta + C.$

10. $\frac{4}{5}x^2\sqrt{x} + C.$

11. $\dfrac{t^4}{4} + \dfrac{1}{t} + C.$

12. $\dfrac{t^2}{2} - 4\ln t - \dfrac{2}{t^2} + C.$

13. $\frac{1}{6}(t^2 - 2)^3 + C.$

14. $x^3 + \dfrac{x^2}{2} - 2x + C.$

15. $\dfrac{2}{5}x^5 - \dfrac{x^7}{7} + C.$

16. $2x^2 - 6\sqrt{x} + C.$

17. $\dfrac{x^3}{3} - 10\ln x + \dfrac{5}{x} + C.$

18. $2\sqrt{\dfrac{s}{15}} + C.$

19. $2\sqrt{x} - \dfrac{2}{\sqrt{x}} + C.$

20. $\frac{1}{3}\ln(x^3 - 6x) + C.$

21. $\ln(x + 1) + C.$

22. $x - \ln(x + 1) + C.$

23. $\frac{1}{2}\ln(x^2 + 1) + C.$

24. $\frac{2}{9}(1 + 3x)^{\frac{3}{2}} + C.$

25. $-\frac{1}{9}(1 - 3x^2)^{\frac{3}{2}} + C.$

26. $-\frac{2}{5}\sqrt{3 - 5x} + C.$

27. $\dfrac{-1}{2(x^2 + 1)} + C.$

28. $-\dfrac{1}{2(x + 1)^2} + C.$

29. $\sqrt{x^2 - 9} + C.$

30. $\frac{1}{3}\ln(x^3 + 1) + C.$

31. $\frac{2}{3}\sqrt{x^3 + 1} + C.$

32. $\dfrac{-1}{6(x^3 + 1)^2} + C.$

33. $\ln(ax^2 + bx + c) + C.$

34. $\frac{1}{2}(\ln x)^2 + C.$

35. $\ln(e^x + e^{-x}) + C.$

36. $\frac{1}{2}\ln(e^{2x} + 9) + C.$

37. $\frac{1}{6}\sin^3 2x + C.$

38. $-\dfrac{1}{2x^2} + \dfrac{1}{x} + 2x + C.$

39. $\dfrac{x^3}{3} + \dfrac{x^2}{2} + x + \ln(x - 1) + C.$

40. $\frac{1}{3}\ln(3x - \sin 3x) + C.$

41. $\dfrac{-1}{3(3x - \sin 3x)} + C.$

42. $-\frac{1}{12}\cos^4 3x + C.$

43. $\frac{1}{3}\ln(2 + 3x) + C.$

44. $-\ln(1 - x) + C.$

45. $\dfrac{1}{1 - x} + C.$

46. $-\frac{1}{2}\ln(1 - x^2) + C.$

47. $\frac{1}{12}\tan^6 2x + C.$

48. $\ln(x^2 + x) + C.$

49. $\ln(x^2 + 5x) + C.$

50. $\ln(x^2 + 5x - 8) + C.$

51. $\frac{1}{3}\ln(e^{3x} + \tan 3x) + C.$

52. $\frac{1}{2}\ln(1 + \tan 2x) + C.$

53. $\frac{1}{6}(3 + e^{2x})^3 + C.$

54. $x + 3\ln(x - 1) + C.$

55. $x^2 - 4x + 2\ln x + C.$

56. $\sin^3\dfrac{x}{3} + C.$

57. $\frac{1}{2}(x + 2)^2 + 8\ln(x - 2) + C.$

58. $\frac{1}{10}\ln(5x^2 + 9) + C.$

59. $\frac{1}{5}\sqrt{5x^2 + 9} + C.$

60. $\frac{1}{30}(5x^2 + 9)^3 + C.$

Pages 233–234. Art. 84

1. $\frac{5}{3}e^{3x} + C.$

2. $4e^{\frac{x}{2}} + C.$

3. $\frac{10^x e^x}{1 + \ln 10} + C.$

4. $\frac{a^{3y}}{3 \ln a} + C.$

5. $\frac{1}{2}e^{x^2} + C.$

6. $\frac{-1}{e^x} + C.$

7. $\frac{1}{2}e^{\sin 2x} + C.$

8. $-e^{3-x} + C.$

9. $20e^{\frac{x}{5}} + C.$

10. $\frac{1}{2}(e^{2x} - e^{-2x} + 4x) + C.$

11. $\frac{1}{2}e^{2x} + \frac{x^{2e+1}}{2e+1} + \frac{x^3}{3} + e^2x + C.$

12. $e^x - e^{-x} + C.$

13. $\frac{a^{2x}e^{2x}}{2(1 + \ln a)} + C.$

14. $x + \frac{3}{2}e^{-2x} + C.$

15. $-\frac{1}{2}e^{-t^2} + C.$

16. $e^{\tan \theta} + C.$

17. $\frac{8^x}{\ln 8} + C.$

18. $\frac{1}{2}e^{\,2x-1} + C.$

19. $-\frac{1}{3e^{x^3}} + C.$

20. $2(e^{\frac{x}{2}} - e^{-\frac{x}{2}}) + C.$

21. $e^3 + C.$

22. $2\sqrt{e^3} + C.$

23. $\frac{1}{8}e^{8x} + C.$

24. $\ln(e^x - e^{-x}) + C.$

25. $\ln(e^x + 1) + C.$

26. $\frac{x^2}{2} + C.$

Pages 238–239. Art. 86

1. $-\frac{1}{3}\cos 3x + C.$

2. $-3\cos \frac{x}{3} + C.$

3. $\frac{1}{2}\sin 2x + C.$

4. $-\frac{1}{3}\cos(3x + 2) + C.$

5. $\frac{1}{3}\sin(3x - 2) + C.$

6. $\sin x + C.$

7. $\frac{1}{2}\cos(3 - 2x) + \mathbf{C}.$

8. $-\frac{1}{6}(3\cos 2x + 2\sin 3x) + C.$

9. $\frac{1}{3}\sec 3x + C.$

10. $\frac{1}{2}\tan 2x + C.$

11. $\frac{1}{2}\tan 2x - x + C.$

12. $-\frac{1}{8}\cos 4x + C.$

13. $-\frac{1}{6}\cos^3 2x + C.$

14. $\cos \frac{x}{3}(\cos^2 \frac{x}{3} - 3) + C.$

15. $-\frac{1}{5}\cot 5x + C.$

16. $2\ln \sec \frac{x}{2} + C.$

17. $\frac{1}{3}\ln \sin 3x + C.$

18. $-\frac{1}{2}\ln(\csc 2x + \cot 2x) + C.$

19. $3\ln\left(\sec \frac{x}{3} + \tan \frac{x}{3}\right) + C$

20. $2\sec \frac{x}{2} + C.$

21. $-\frac{1}{5}\csc 5x + C.$

22. $\frac{1}{3}\cos x(\cos^2 x - 3) + C.$

23. $\frac{2}{9}\sin \frac{3x}{2}\left(3 - \sin^2 \frac{3x}{2}\right) + C.$

24. $-\ln(\csc x + \cot x) + 2\cos x + C.$

25. $\frac{1}{4}\tan^2 2x + C.$

26. $\frac{1}{6}\sec^3 2x + C.$

27. $-\frac{1}{12}\csc^4 3x + C.$

28. $\frac{1}{6}\tan^2 3x + C.$

29. $\frac{2}{15}\sin \frac{x}{2}\left(15 - 10\sin^2 \frac{x}{2} + 3\sin^4 \frac{x}{2}\right) + C.$

30. $\frac{1}{15}\cos^3 x(3\cos^2 x - 5) + C.$

31. $\frac{1}{2}\ln \sin 2x + C.$

32. $-\frac{1}{210}\cos^3 2x(35 - 42\cos^2 2x + 15\cos^4 2x) + C.$

33. $\frac{1}{70} \sin^5 2x \, (7 - 5 \sin^2 2x) + C.$

34. $\frac{1}{40} \cos^8 \theta \, (4 \cos^2 \theta - 5) + C.$

35. $\frac{2}{21} (\sin x)^{\frac{3}{2}} \, (7 - 3 \sin^2 x) + C.$

36. $\frac{2}{45} \tan^3 3x \, (5 + 3 \tan^2 3x) + C.$

37. $\frac{1}{4} \tan^2 2x - \frac{1}{2} \ln \sec 2x + C.$

38. $\frac{1}{6} \tan 2x \, (3 + \tan^2 2x) + C.$

39. $\frac{1}{24} \tan^4 2x \, (3 + 2 \tan^2 2x) + C.$

40. $-\dfrac{1}{2} \cot^4 \dfrac{x}{2} + \cot^2 \dfrac{x}{2} + 2 \ln \sin \dfrac{x}{2} + C.$

41. $- \frac{1}{6} \csc^3 2x + C.$

42. $x - \dfrac{3}{2} \cos \dfrac{2x}{3} + C.$

43. $\dfrac{4\sqrt{2}}{3} \sin \dfrac{3x}{4} + C.$

44. $- \cos \theta + C.$

45. $\ln (\sin x - \cos x) + C.$

46. $\frac{1}{2} (\tan 2x - \cot 2x) + C.$

47. $\ln (x + \sin x) + C.$

48. $\dfrac{-1}{2(x + \sin x)^2} + C.$

49. $- \frac{2}{3} \cos 3x + C.$

50. $\tan x - x + C.$

51. $\frac{1}{12} \tan^3 4x - \frac{1}{4} \tan 4x + x + C.$

52. $- \frac{1}{10} \cot^5 2x + \frac{1}{6} \cot^3 2x - \frac{1}{2} \cot 2x - x + C.$

Page 242. Art. 87

1. $-\dfrac{1}{4(3 + 2x)^2} + C.$

2. $\sqrt{3 + 2x} + C.$

3. $\frac{1}{2} \ln (3 + 2x) + C.$

4. $\frac{1}{3} \tan^{-1} \dfrac{x}{3} + C.$

5. $\sin^{-1} \dfrac{x}{3} + C.$

6. $\dfrac{1}{15} \tan^{-1} \dfrac{3x}{5} + C.$

7. $\frac{1}{18} \ln (25 + 9x^2) + C.$

8. $\dfrac{-1}{18(25 + 9x^2)} + C.$

9. $\frac{1}{9} \sqrt{25 + 9x^2} + C.$

10. $-\frac{1}{9} \sqrt{25 - 9x^2} + C.$

11. $\frac{1}{3} \sin^{-1} \dfrac{3x}{5} + C.$

12. $\dfrac{1}{2\sqrt{3}} \tan^{-1} \dfrac{2x}{\sqrt{3}} + C.$

13. $\frac{1}{2} \sin^{-1} \dfrac{x}{2} + C.$

14. $\frac{1}{2} \sin^{-1} \dfrac{2x - 3}{4} + C.$

15. $\frac{1}{2} \tan^{-1} \dfrac{x + 3}{2} + C.$

16. $\frac{1}{2} \tan^{-1} x^2 + C.$

17. $\frac{1}{4} \ln (1 + x^4) + C.$

18. $\frac{1}{2} \sin^{-1} x^2 + C.$

19. $-\frac{1}{2} \sqrt{1 - x^4} + C.$

20. $\dfrac{1}{8} \ln (4x^2 + 9) - \dfrac{5}{6} \tan^{-1} \dfrac{2x}{3} + C.$

21. $\dfrac{1}{3} \tan^{-1} \dfrac{x - 4}{3} + C.$

22. $\dfrac{1}{4} \tan^{-1} \dfrac{x + 1}{4} + C.$

23. $\frac{1}{2} \tan^{-1} e^{2x} + C.$

24. $-\dfrac{1}{4} \sqrt{9 - 16x^2} - \dfrac{3}{4} \sin^{-1} \dfrac{4x}{3} + C.$

25. $2 \tan^{-1} \sqrt{x} + C.$

26. $\frac{1}{2} \ln (3x^2 - 2x + 5) + C.$

27. $\dfrac{1}{2} \tan^{-1} \dfrac{x - 1}{2} + C.$

28. $\sin^{-1} \dfrac{x - 1}{2} + C.$

29. $\sqrt{3 + 2x - x^2} + C.$

30. $\dfrac{1}{2} \ln (x^2 - 2x + 5) + \dfrac{1}{2} \tan^{-1} \dfrac{x-1}{2} + C.$

31. $\dfrac{1}{18} \ln (9x^2 + 16) + \dfrac{1}{6} \tan^{-1} \dfrac{3x}{4} + C.$

32. $\tan^{-1} e^x + C.$

33. $\dfrac{1}{5} \tan^{-1} \dfrac{\sin x}{5} + C.$

34. $\dfrac{3}{2} \ln (x^2 - 2x + 5) + 2 \tan^{-1} \dfrac{x-1}{2} + C.$

Pages 245–246.   Art. 88

1. $e^x(x - 1) + C.$
2. $\frac{1}{4}e^{2x}(2x - 1) + C.$
3. $e^x(x^2 - 2x + 2) + C.$
4. $-\frac{1}{2}x \cos 2x + \frac{1}{4}\sin 2x + C.$
5. $x^2 \sin x + 2x \cos x - 2 \sin x + C.$
6. $x \sin^{-1} x + \sqrt{1 - x^2} + C.$
7. $x \tan^{-1} 2x - \frac{1}{4}\ln (4x^2 + 1) + C.$
8. $\frac{1}{4}e^{2x} (\sin 2x + \cos 2x) + C.$
9. $\frac{1}{2}x \tan 2x + \frac{1}{4}\ln \cos 2x + C.$
10. $x \tan^{-1}\dfrac{x}{3} - \dfrac{3}{2}\ln (x^2 + 9) + C.$

11. $\dfrac{x^2}{4} - \dfrac{x}{4}\sin 2x - \dfrac{1}{8}\cos 2x + C.$
12. $\dfrac{x^4}{16} (4 \ln x - 1) + C.$
13. $\dfrac{e^{-x}}{2} (\sin x - \cos x) + C.$
14. $\dfrac{e^x}{5} (\sin 2x - 2 \cos 2x) + C.$
15. $\dfrac{x^3}{3} \tan^{-1} x - \dfrac{1}{6}x^2 + \dfrac{1}{6}\ln (x^2 + 1) + C.$
16. $\frac{1}{2}x + \frac{1}{4}\sin 2x + C.$

17. $-\frac{1}{10}[\csc 5x \cot 5x + \ln (\csc 5x + \cot 5x)] + C.$
18. $\frac{1}{8}\sec^3 2x \tan 2x + \frac{3}{16}\sec 2x \tan 2x + \frac{3}{16}\ln (\sec 2x + \tan 2x) + C.$
19. $\cos x(1 - \ln \cos x) + C.$

Pages 251–252.   Art. 90

1. $-\frac{2}{15}(2 - x)^{\frac{3}{2}}(4 + 3x) + C.$
2. $\frac{2}{15}\sqrt{x - 4}(3x^2 + 16x + 128) + C.$
3. $\frac{2}{3}x\sqrt{5x} + C.$
4. $\frac{2}{105}(x + 2)^{\frac{3}{2}}(15x^2 - 24x + 32) + C.$
5. $-\frac{3}{4}(8 - x)^{\frac{4}{3}} + C.$
6. $-\frac{2}{15}\sqrt{4 - x}(3x^2 + 16x + 128) + C.$
7. $-\frac{2}{3}\sqrt{4 - x^3} + C.$
8. $-\frac{1}{3}\ln (4 - x^3) + C.$
9. $\frac{1}{4}\tan^{-1}\dfrac{x^2}{2} + C.$
10. $-\frac{3}{28}(1 - s)^{\frac{4}{3}}(4s + 3) + C.$
11. $\dfrac{1}{9(4 - 3x)^3} + C.$
12. $\frac{2}{15}(16 + x)^{\frac{3}{2}}(3x - 32) + C.$
13. $\frac{1}{3}(16 + x^2)^{\frac{3}{2}} + C.$
14. $\frac{2}{3}\sqrt{1 + x}(x - 2) + C.$
15. $\frac{3}{14}x^{\frac{4}{3}}(7 - 2x) + C.$
16. $\frac{1}{6}\tan^{-1}\dfrac{2x}{3} + C.$
17. $\frac{1}{8}\ln (9 + 4x^2) + C.$

18. $\dfrac{-1}{2(x^2 + 2)} + C.$
19. $\frac{2}{5}\sqrt{x - 9}(x^2 + 12x + 216) + C.$
20. $\frac{2}{9}\sqrt{x^3 + 1}(x^3 - 2) + C.$
21. $\frac{2}{45}(4 + x^3)^{\frac{3}{2}}(3x^3 - 8) + C.$
22. $\frac{2}{15}(x^2 + 4)^{\frac{5}{4}}(5x^2 - 16) + C.$
23. $\frac{3}{10}(4 + x^2)^{\frac{5}{3}} + C.$
24. $\frac{1}{10}(1 + x^3)^{\frac{2}{3}}(2x^3 - 3) + C.$
25. $\dfrac{x^2}{4} - \dfrac{1}{4}x + \dfrac{1}{8}\ln (2x + 1) + C.$
26. $\frac{1}{15}\sqrt{2x + 1}(3x^2 - 2x + 2) + C.$
27. $-\frac{1}{4}\sqrt{9 - 4x^2} + C.$
28. $\frac{1}{2}\sin^{-1}\dfrac{2x}{3} + C.$
29. $\dfrac{-1}{24}\sqrt{9 - 4x^2}(9 + 2x^2) + C.$
30. $\dfrac{5(3x^2 + 1)^{\frac{4}{5}}}{13,608}(162x^4 - 60x^2 + 25) + C$
31. $\sqrt{x^2 - 1} - \sec^{-1} x + C.$
32. $\dfrac{(8 + x^2)^{\frac{5}{2}}}{35}(5x^2 - 16) + C.$

33. $\frac{1}{2}\left[x\sqrt{x^2 + 25} + 25 \ln (x + \sqrt{x^2 + 25})\right] + C.$
34. $\frac{1}{2}\left[x\sqrt{x^2 - 9} - 9 \ln (x + \sqrt{x^2 - 9})\right] + C.$

35. $\frac{1}{2}\left(x\sqrt{4-x^2}+4\sin^{-1}\frac{x}{2}\right)+C.$

36. $\frac{x}{2}\sqrt{x^2+9}-\frac{9}{2}\ln(x+\sqrt{x^2+9})+C.$

37. $\sqrt{x^2+9}+C.$

38. $-\frac{x}{2}\sqrt{4-x^2}+2\sin^{-1}\frac{x}{2}+C.$

39. $\frac{1}{3}\sqrt{x^2+9}(x^2-18)+C.$

40. $-\frac{1}{3}\sqrt{4-x^2}(x^2+8)+C.$

41. $\frac{x^2+8}{\sqrt{x^2+4}}+C.$

42. $-\frac{\sqrt{9x^2+1}}{x}+C.$

43. $\frac{2}{135}(3x-5)^{\frac{3}{2}}(9x+10)+C.$

44. $\frac{x}{4}\sqrt{4-x^2}(x^2-2)+2\sin^{-1}\frac{x}{2}+C.$

45. $-\frac{1}{3}(4-x^2)^{\frac{3}{2}}+C.$

46. $\frac{x}{4\sqrt{x^2+4}}+C.$

47. $\tan^{-1}(x+4)+C.$

48. $\sin^{-1}\frac{x-4}{4}+C.$

49. $3\sin^{-1}\frac{x}{6}-2\sqrt{36-x^2}+C.$

50. $3\sqrt{x^2+9}+13\ln(x+\sqrt{x^2+9})+C.$

51. $\frac{13}{3}\tan^{-1}\frac{x}{3}+\frac{3}{2}\ln(x^2+9)+C.$

52. $\frac{1}{2}\sec^{-1}\frac{3x}{2}+C.$

53. $\frac{x}{18}\sqrt{9x^2-4}+\frac{2}{27}\ln(3x+\sqrt{9x^2-4})+C.$

54. $\frac{1}{20}\ln\frac{2x-5}{2x+5}+C.$

55. $\ln(x+\sqrt{x^2+1})+C.$

56. $\frac{1}{6}\ln\frac{3+x}{3-x}+C.$

Pages 257–258. Art. 91

1. $\ln\frac{x^2(x-2)}{(x+2)^2}+C.$

2. $\frac{1}{5}\ln[(x-3)^2(x+2)^3]+C.$

3. $x+\frac{3}{5}\ln\frac{x-2}{x+3}+C.$

4. $\frac{1}{4}\ln\frac{(x-3)^5}{x+1}+C.$

5. $\frac{1}{2}\ln\frac{(x-1)^3}{x+3}+C.$

6. $\ln(x-1)+\frac{2}{3}\ln\frac{x+3}{x}+C.$

7. $\frac{5}{6}\ln x-\frac{8}{15}\ln(x+3)-\frac{3}{10}\ln(x-2)+C.$

8. $\ln\frac{x}{1-x^2}+C.$

9. $\frac{x^2}{2}-2x+\frac{1}{6}\ln(x-1)-\frac{1}{2}\ln(x+1)+\frac{16}{3}\ln(x+2)+C.$

10. $\ln\frac{(x-1)^2}{x}-\frac{x}{(x-1)^2}+C.$

11. $\frac{3}{x-2}+\ln\frac{(x-2)^2}{x^2}+C.$

12. $\ln\frac{(x-1)(x-2)^2}{(x-3)^3}+C.$

13. $\frac{x^2+2x-5}{x+2}-4\ln(x+2)+C.$

14. $\ln\frac{(x-1)^3}{x^2}+\frac{4x+1}{x(x-1)}+C.$

15. $\frac{12x+19}{(x+2)^2}+3\ln(x+2)+C.$

16. $\frac{1}{4}\ln\frac{x^2+1}{(x+1)^2}+\frac{1}{2}\tan^{-1}x+C.$

17. $\frac{1}{3} \ln (1 + x) - \frac{1}{6} \ln (1 - x + x^2) + \frac{1}{\sqrt{3}} \tan^{-1} \frac{2x - 1}{\sqrt{3}} + C.$

18. $\frac{1}{32} \ln \frac{x - 2}{x + 2} - \frac{1}{16} \tan^{-1} \frac{x}{2} + C.$

25. $\frac{1}{10} \ln [(2x - 3)^3 (x + 1)^2] + C.$

26. $\frac{1}{12} \ln \frac{(3x + 5)^7}{(x - 1)^3} + C.$

19. $\ln \frac{x^2 - 1}{(x + 2)^2} + C.$

27. $\frac{1}{2} \ln (3x^2 + 4x + 1) + C.$

20. $\ln \frac{2x^2 + x}{x - 1} + C.$

28. $\frac{1}{8} \ln \frac{(x + 2)^{10}}{x^3(x + 4)^7} + C.$

21. $\frac{1}{16} \ln [(2x - 1)(2x + 3)^3] + C.$

22. $\ln \frac{x^2 \sqrt{x - 3}}{\sqrt{(x + 3)^3}} + C.$

29. $\frac{x^3}{3} + 4x + 4 \ln \frac{x - 2}{x + 2} + C.$

23. $\ln \frac{x^2 \sqrt{x}}{x^2 - 9} + C.$

30. $2x + \frac{1}{6} \ln \frac{x - 3}{(x + 3)^{25}} + C.$

24. $\ln \frac{(x + 2)^3}{(x + 4)^2} + C.$

31. $x^2 - x + \frac{1}{2} \tan^{-1} \frac{x}{2} + C.$

32. $x + \frac{1}{2} \ln (x + 1) - \frac{3}{4} \ln (x^2 + 1) + \frac{1}{2} \tan^{-1} x + C.$

33. $\frac{1}{10} \ln [(2x + 3)(x^2 + 9)^2] - \frac{1}{5} \tan^{-1} \frac{x}{3} + C.$

34. $\frac{1}{36} \ln [(x + 3)^{41}(x - 3)^{67}] - \frac{23}{6(x - 3)} + C.$

35. $3 \ln \frac{x}{\sqrt{x^2 + 4}} + \frac{5}{2} \tan^{-1} \frac{x}{2} + C.$

36. $x + \frac{1}{6} \ln \frac{x^2 + 3}{x^2} - \sqrt{3} \tan^{-1} \frac{x}{\sqrt{3}} + C.$

37. $\frac{1}{4} \ln \frac{x^4}{(x + 1)^2(x^2 + 1)} - \frac{1}{2} \tan^{-1} x + C.$

38. $\frac{2 - x}{4(x^2 + 2)} + \ln \sqrt{x^2 + 2} - \frac{\sqrt{2}}{8} \tan^{-1} \frac{x}{\sqrt{2}} + C.$

39. $\ln (x + 1) + \frac{18x^2 + 27x + 11}{6(x + 1)^3} + C.$

40. $\frac{1}{2} \ln \frac{(2x + 3)^5}{x^2 + 1} + 3 \tan^{-1} x + C.$

41. $\frac{-1}{4(x - 1)^4} + C.$

42. $\frac{\sqrt{2}}{8} \left[\ln \frac{x^2 + \sqrt{2}x + 1}{x^2 - \sqrt{2}x + 1} + 2 \tan^{-1} (\sqrt{2}x + 1) + 2 \tan^{-1} (\sqrt{2}x - 1) \right] + C.$

43. $\frac{1}{384} \ln \frac{(x - 2)^2(x^2 - 2x + 4)}{(x + 2)^2(x^2 + 2x + 4)} - \frac{\sqrt{3}}{192} \left(\tan^{-1} \frac{x + 1}{\sqrt{3}} + \tan^{-1} \frac{x - 1}{\sqrt{3}} \right) + C.$

44. $\frac{1}{24} \tan^{-1} \frac{x^3}{8} + C.$

Páges 261–262. Art. 93

1. $\dfrac{x^4}{4} + \dfrac{x^3}{3} + \dfrac{x^2}{2} + x + C.$

2. $-\frac{2}{3}(1-x)^{\frac{3}{2}} + C.$

3. $-\dfrac{1}{x} + \ln x^2 + 2x + C.$

4. $-\frac{2}{3}\sqrt{1-3x} + C.$

5. $-\frac{2}{3}\sqrt{1-y^3} + C.$

6. $\dfrac{2}{5k}(1+kt)^{\frac{5}{2}} + C.$

7. $\frac{1}{4}(x^2-4)^2 + C.$

8. $\frac{1}{3}(x^2-4)^{\frac{3}{2}} + C.$

9. $-\frac{1}{8}\ln(9-4x^2) + C.$

10. $\dfrac{1}{12}\ln\dfrac{3+2x}{3-2x} + C.$

11. $\dfrac{1}{6}\tan^{-1}\dfrac{2x}{3} + C.$

12. $\frac{1}{8}\ln(9+4x^2) + C.$

13. $\dfrac{1}{2}\sin^{-1}\dfrac{2x}{3} + C.$

14. $-\frac{1}{4}\sqrt{9-4x^2} + C.$

15. $\dfrac{x^2}{2} - \dfrac{1}{2}\ln(x^2+1) + C.$

16. $\frac{1}{2}(1+6x+x^3)^{\frac{2}{3}} + C.$

17. $\dfrac{-2}{3\sqrt{3x+x^3}} + C.$

18. $a^{\frac{4}{3}}x - \frac{6}{5}a^{\frac{2}{3}}x^{\frac{5}{3}} + \frac{3}{7}x^{\frac{7}{3}} + C.$

19. $-\frac{1}{2}(a^{\frac{2}{3}} - x^{\frac{2}{3}})^3 + C.$

20. $\frac{1}{3}(\ln x)^3 + C.$

21. $\frac{1}{4}(\sin^{-1}x)^4 + C.$

22. $e^{\sin^2 x} + C.$

23. $\frac{1}{2}(\tan^{-1}x)^2 + C.$

24. $\frac{1}{45}\tan 3x(15 + 10\tan^2 3x + 3\tan^4 3x) + C.$

25. $\frac{1}{10}\sec^5 2x + C.$

26. $-\frac{1}{8}\cos^8 x + C.$

27. $\frac{1}{2}\theta - \frac{1}{8}\sin 4\theta + C.$

28. $\frac{1}{15}\sin 5x(3 - \sin^2 5x) + C.$

29. $-\frac{1}{30}\cot^3 2x(5 + 3\cot^2 2x) + C.$

30. $-\frac{1}{45}\cos 3x(15 - 10\cos^2 3x + 3\cos^4 3x) + C.$

31. $\dfrac{x}{8} - \dfrac{1}{64}\sin 8x + C.$

32. $\frac{2}{3}(\sin x)^{\frac{3}{2}} + C.$

33. $\frac{1}{9}(1+3\tan 2x)^{\frac{3}{2}} + C.$

34. $\frac{1}{3}\ln(\sec 3\theta + \tan 3\theta) - \frac{1}{3}\sin 3\theta + C.$

35. $\frac{1}{4}\tan 4\theta - \theta + C.$

36. $\frac{1}{10}\sec 5\theta \tan 5\theta + \frac{1}{10}\ln(\sec 5\theta + \tan 5\theta) + C.$

37. $\frac{1}{2}\ln(3x^2+4x+1) + C.$

38. $\ln \ln x + C.$

39. $\ln \tan^{-1}x + C.$

40. $\frac{1}{2}\ln(e^{2x}+e^{-2x}) + C.$

41. $\ln(e^x+e^{-x}) + C.$

42. $x + C.$

43. $-\cos 2\theta + C.$

44. $2x + C.$

45. $\frac{1}{4}\tan^4\theta + C.$

46. $\frac{2}{3}\sqrt{x-3}(x+6) + C.$

47. $\dfrac{1}{3}\ln\dfrac{\sqrt{x+9}-3}{\sqrt{x+9}+3} + C.$

48. $\dfrac{1}{6}\ln\dfrac{\sqrt{x^2+9}-3}{\sqrt{x^2+9}+3} + C.$

49. $\dfrac{1}{6}\tan^{-1}\dfrac{x^2}{3} + C.$

50. $-\frac{1}{2}(\cot^{-1}x)^2 + C.$

51. $\frac{1}{3}(\tan^{-1}x)^3 + C.$

52. $\tan^{-1}(x+2) + C.$

53. $\dfrac{3}{2}\ln(x^2+9) + \dfrac{7}{3}\tan^{-1}\dfrac{x}{3} + C.$

54. $\dfrac{1}{2}\ln(x^2+6x+18) + \dfrac{1}{3}\tan^{-1}\dfrac{x+3}{3} + C.$

55. $\sin^{-1}\dfrac{x-3}{3} + C.$

57. $\dfrac{2}{3}\sqrt{1+x^3} + \dfrac{1}{3}\ln\dfrac{\sqrt{1+x^3}-1}{\sqrt{1+x^3}+1} + C.$

56. $\dfrac{1}{6}\ln\dfrac{x-5}{x+1} + C.$

58. $\dfrac{1}{3}\sec^{-1}\dfrac{2x}{3} + C.$

59. $\frac{1}{2}x\sqrt{x^2-4} - 2\ln(x+\sqrt{x^2-4}) + C.$

60. $\dfrac{1}{2}x\sqrt{4-x^2} + 2\sin^{-1}\dfrac{x}{2} + C.$

61. $\ln(x+\sqrt{x^2-4}) + C.$

62. $\frac{1}{2}x\sqrt{x^2-4} + 2\ln(x+\sqrt{x^2-4}) + C.$

63. $\sqrt{x^2-4} + C.$

64. $-\frac{1}{15}(4-x^2)^{\frac{3}{2}}(8+3x^2) + C.$

65. $-x^3\cos x + 3x^2\sin x + 6x\cos x - 6\sin x + C.$

66. $\dfrac{e^{3x}}{27}(9x^2 - 6x + 2) + C.$

69. $\dfrac{x^3}{3}\sin^{-1}x + \dfrac{1}{9}\sqrt{1-x^2}(x^2+2) + C$

67. $x\tan^{-1}2x - \frac{1}{4}\ln(1+4x^2) + C.$

68. $\dfrac{x^3}{9}(\ln x^3 - 1) + C.$

70. $\dfrac{x^4}{32}[8(\ln x)^2 - \ln x^4 + 1] + C.$

71. $\frac{1}{2}x^2\sin^{-1}x + \frac{1}{4}x\sqrt{1-x^2} - \frac{1}{4}\sin^{-1}x + C.$

72. $\dfrac{1}{25}\ln\dfrac{x^2+4}{(x-1)^2} - \dfrac{1}{5(x-1)} - \dfrac{3}{50}\tan^{-1}\dfrac{x}{2} + C.$

73. $2\ln\dfrac{x+4}{x+2} - \dfrac{5x+12}{x^2+6x+8} + C.$

74. $\ln(x-2) + \dfrac{3}{2}\ln(x^2+2x+5) + \dfrac{1}{2}\tan^{-1}\dfrac{x+1}{2} + C.$

Pages 266–267. Art. 94

1. $\dfrac{\pi}{6}.$

2. $\dfrac{\pi}{3}.$

3. $\dfrac{\pi}{6}.$

4. $\dfrac{\pi}{6}.$

5. $\dfrac{\pi}{3} + \sqrt{3} - 1.$

6. $2\pi - 4.$

7. $\ln 2 - \frac{1}{2}.$

8. $124\ln 2 - 15.$

9. $\dfrac{1}{e}(e-2).$

10. $\frac{1}{2}(\ln 2 - 1).$

11. $\dfrac{e^{-\frac{\pi}{6}}(2\sqrt{3}-1)+2}{10}.$

12. $\frac{1}{64}(\pi^2+4).$

13. $\frac{1}{4}(\pi - \ln 4).$

14. $\frac{1}{24}(\pi + 6\sqrt{3} - 12).$

15. $\frac{1}{24}(3\sqrt{3} - \pi).$

16. $2 + \ln\frac{25}{9}.$

17. $40.8.$

18. $\frac{32}{3}.$

19. $\frac{9909}{40}.$

20. $5\ln 3 - 4.$

21. $\frac{1}{100}.$

22. $\frac{1}{8}(12 + 25\sin^{-1}\frac{4}{5}).$

23. $\frac{3}{4}(2\pi - 3\sqrt{3}).$

24. $\frac{15}{2} + 8\ln 2.$

Page 270. Art. 95

1. $\frac{1}{5}$.

2. $\frac{1}{24}$.

3. $\frac{1}{e}$.

4. No meaning.

5. No meaning.

6. No meaning.

7. $\frac{\pi}{4}$.

8. $4\pi a^2$.

9. $\frac{\pi}{2}$.

10. 2.

11. No meaning.

12. 3.

13. No meaning.

14. No meaning.

15. No meaning.

16. No meaning.

17. $\frac{9}{2}$.

18. $\frac{75}{4}$.

Pages 273–274. Art. 97

1. 16π.

2. 12π.

3. $\frac{2}{3}(20 - 9\ln 3)$.

4. πa^2.

5. $\frac{25}{4}(\pi - 2)$.

6. $\frac{1}{2}(25 \sin^{-1} \frac{7}{25} - 24 \ln \frac{4}{3}) = 0.095$.

7. $5 \tan^{-1} \frac{1}{2} - 2 + \frac{\pi}{2} = 1.889$.

8. $\frac{15}{2} \tan^{-1}(-7) - 3 \ln 8 = 6.606$.

9. $\frac{1}{2}(49 - 12\pi)$.

10. $6 \ln 2 - 2$.

11. $\frac{1}{e}(e^3 - 1)$.

12. 1.

13. $\frac{a^2}{e}(e^2 - 1)$.

14. 2.

15. $\sqrt{2} - 1$.

16. $\ln(3 + 2\sqrt{2})$.

17. $3\pi a^2$.

18. $\frac{3}{8}\pi a^2$.

19. $\frac{a^2}{6}$.

20. $\frac{32\sqrt{2}}{15}$.

21. $\frac{288\sqrt{3}}{35}$.

22. $\frac{2}{3}(3\pi - 2)$.

23. 4π.

24. $3\pi a^2$.

25. 9.

26. $\frac{1}{e}(e - 2)$.

27. $10 \ln 2 - 6$.

28. $10 \ln 4$.

29. $\frac{1}{e}(e - 2)$.

30. $\frac{n}{2}$.

Page 277. Art. 98

1. π.

2. $\frac{9\pi}{8}$.

3. $\frac{\pi}{2}$.

4. $\frac{3}{2}\pi a^2$.

5. a^2.

6. $\frac{19\pi}{2}$.

7. $\frac{3}{2}(3\sqrt{3} + 2\pi)$.

8. $\frac{4}{3}(8\pi + 3\sqrt{3})$.

9. $\frac{1}{3}(4\pi - 3\sqrt{3})$

10. $2\pi - 4$.

11. $\frac{3}{2}$.

Pages 281–282. Art. 99

1. π^2.

2. $12\pi(\sqrt{6} - \sqrt{3})$.

3. $12\sqrt{3}\pi[1 - \sqrt{2} + \ln(1 + \sqrt{2})]$.

4. $40\pi^2$.

5. $\frac{\pi}{2}(\ln \frac{8}{5} - \tan^{-1} \frac{1}{3}) = 0.2329$.

6. $3\pi(\pi - 2)$.

7. $\frac{128\pi}{15}$.

8. $\frac{\pi}{2}(e^4 - 1)$.

9. $2\pi(e^2 + 1)$.

10. $2\pi(e^2 - 3)$.

11. $\frac{\pi}{2}$.

12. $\pi[3(\ln 3)^2 - 6 \ln 3 + 4]$.

13. $\pi(9 \ln 3 - 4)$.

14. $\pi(9 \ln 3 - 8)$.

15. $\frac{\pi^2}{2}$.

16. $2\pi^2$.

17. π.

18. $\frac{\pi}{2}(\pi - 2)$.

19. $\frac{16}{3}a^3$.

20. $\frac{27}{2}(4\pi - 3\sqrt{3})$ cu. ft.

21. $48(8\pi + 3\sqrt{3})$ cu. in.

22. $32(18 \sin^{-1} \frac{1}{3} + 4\sqrt{2} + 9\pi) = 1281.5$ cu. in.

23. $\frac{1948\pi}{3} + 1000 \sin^{-1} \frac{3}{5} + 480 = 3163.4$ cu. in.

Pages 282–283. Art. 100

1. 900 lb.
2. $\frac{43}{54}$ lb.
3. $\frac{43}{72}$ lb.
4. 3770 lb.
5. 12,000π lb.
6. $\dfrac{ak\pi}{4}$ ft-lb.
7. 1 ft-lb.

8. $\dfrac{q}{r_0}$.

9. $k \ln \dfrac{v_2}{v_1}$.

10. $\dfrac{k}{0.41} \left(\dfrac{1}{v_1^{0.41}} - \dfrac{1}{v_2^{0.41}} \right)$.

11. $72,900\pi(1 + \ln 4)$ in-lb.

Page 286. Art. 102

1. $\frac{14}{3}$.
2. $\frac{2}{27}(10\sqrt{10} - 1)$.
3. $\frac{218}{9}$.
4. 21.
5. $\frac{335}{9}$.
6. $2\pi a$.
7. $6a$.
8. $6a$.

9. $\frac{14}{3}$.
10. 4π.
11. 1.

12. $\dfrac{a}{2e} (e^2 - 1)$.

13. $2 + 12 \ln \frac{5}{3}$.
14. $\ln (2 + \sqrt{3})$.

15. $\sqrt{e^2 + 1} - \sqrt{2} + \ln \dfrac{\sqrt{e^2 + 1} - 1}{\sqrt{2} - 1} - 1$.

16. $8a$.

17. $a\pi\sqrt{4\pi^2 + 1} + \frac{1}{2} a \ln (2\pi + \sqrt{4\pi^2 + 1})$.

18. πa. 　　19. $\dfrac{1}{a} (r_2 - r_1) \sqrt{a^2 + 1}$. 　　20. $4\sqrt{2}$.

Pages 289–290. Art. 103

1. 15π.
2. $33\pi \sqrt{5}$.
3. $3\pi \sqrt{17}$.
4. $16\pi \sqrt{10}$.

5. $\dfrac{\pi}{27} (10 \sqrt{10} - 1)$.

6. $\dfrac{\pi}{6} \left[3 \sqrt{10} + \ln (3 + \sqrt{10}) \right]$.

7. $\dfrac{8\pi}{3} (5\sqrt{5} - 1)$.

8. $\dfrac{\pi}{3} \left[52 \sqrt{5} - 8 + 6 \ln (2 + \sqrt{5}) \right]$.

9. $\frac{12}{5}\pi a^2$.

10. $\dfrac{35\sqrt{5}\pi}{3}$.

11. $\dfrac{\pi a^2}{4e^2} (e^4 + 4e^2 - 1)$.

12. $\dfrac{2\pi a^2}{e} (e - 1)$.

13. $\dfrac{47\pi}{16}$.

14. $\dfrac{\pi}{4} (15 + \ln 16)$.

15. $\dfrac{277\pi}{48}$.

16. $\frac{64}{3}\pi a^2$.

17. $\dfrac{232\pi}{15}$.

18. $2\pi(35 + 72 \ln \frac{4}{3})$.

19. $\pi \left(e \sqrt{e^2 + 1} - \sqrt{2} + \ln \dfrac{e + \sqrt{e^2 + 1}}{\sqrt{2} + 1} \right)$.

20. $\pi\left[\sqrt{2} + \ln(1 + \sqrt{2})\right].$

21. $4\pi a^2.$

22. $\frac{32}{5}\pi a^2.$

23. $\dfrac{2\pi\sqrt{a^2 + 1}(e^{a\pi} - 2a)}{4a^2 + 1}.$

24. $4\pi a^2(2 - \sqrt{2}).$

25. $4\pi a^2\sqrt{2}.$

Pages 302–306.   Art. 109

1. $(\frac{7}{5}, \frac{17}{5})$, origin at O.

2. $(\frac{11}{7}, 5)$, origin at O.

3. $(\frac{17}{11}, \frac{61}{11})$, origin at O.

4. $\left(0, \dfrac{h(a + 2b)}{3(a + b)}\right).$

5. $\left(0, \dfrac{4a}{3\pi}\right).$

6. $\left(-\dfrac{4a}{3\pi}, \dfrac{4a}{3\pi}\right).$

7. $\dfrac{200 + 24\pi}{3(16 + \pi)}$ in. above base.

8. $\left(0, \dfrac{4(18\pi + 107)}{3(60 + 13\pi)}\right)$, origin at O.

9. $\left(0, \dfrac{4(18\pi + 107)}{3(60 + 11\pi)}\right)$, origin at O.

10. $\left(0, \dfrac{4(15\pi + 107)}{3(11\pi + 60)}\right)$, origin at O.

11. $\left(\dfrac{272}{3(24 - \pi)}, \dfrac{416}{3(24 - \pi)}\right)$, origin at O.

12. $(\frac{3}{2}, \frac{3}{10}).$

13. $(\frac{3}{2}, \frac{12}{5}).$

14. $(\frac{10}{3}, \frac{1}{2}\ln\frac{3}{2}).$

15. $\left(1, \dfrac{\pi}{8}\right).$

16. $\left(\dfrac{1}{e - 1}, \dfrac{e + 1}{4}\right).$

17. $\left(\dfrac{3}{\ln 4}, \dfrac{3}{\ln 16}\right).$

18. $\left(\dfrac{\ln 16}{\pi}, \dfrac{\pi + 2}{2\pi}\right).$

19. $\left(\dfrac{3(\ln 16 - 1)}{3\pi - 2}, \dfrac{3(5\pi + 8)}{10(3\pi - 2)}\right).$

20. $(\frac{9}{5}, \frac{9}{5}).$

21. $\bar{x} = \bar{y} = \dfrac{9}{15 - 16\ln 2}.$

26. $\bar{x} = \bar{y} = \dfrac{128a}{105\pi}.$

27. $\left(\dfrac{128\sqrt{2}a}{105\pi}, \dfrac{16(8\sqrt{2} - 9)}{105\pi}\right).$

28. $\left(\dfrac{a}{2}, \dfrac{2a}{3\pi}\right).$

29. $\left(\dfrac{(16 - 5\pi)a}{2(3\pi - 8)}, \dfrac{2a}{3(3\pi - 8)}\right).$

30. $\frac{10}{31}$ ft. above center of parallelepiped

31. $\dfrac{h}{4}$ from base.

32. $\frac{33}{19}$ ft. from base.

33. $\frac{24}{31}$ ft. above center of cylinder.

34. $\frac{9}{16}$ ft. above center of cylinder.

35. $\frac{3}{8}h$ from base.

36. $\frac{587}{288}$ in. above apex.

37. $(\frac{8}{3}, 0, 0).$

38. $(0, \frac{10}{3}, 0).$

39. $(0, \frac{5}{3}, 0).$

40. $(\frac{8}{3}\ln 2, 0, 0).$

41. $\left(\dfrac{5}{\ln\frac{9}{4}}, 0, 0\right).$

42. $\left(\dfrac{e^2 + 1}{2(e^2 - 1)}, 0, 0\right).$

43. $\frac{8}{15}a$ from base.

44. $\frac{3}{5}h$ from apex.

45. $\left(\dfrac{2a}{\pi}, 0\right).$

46. $\left(\dfrac{2a}{\pi}, \dfrac{2a}{\pi}\right).$

47. $(\frac{2}{5}a, \frac{2}{5}a).$

48. $\dfrac{a}{2}$ from plane of base circle.

49. $\left(\dfrac{2a}{3}, 0, 0\right).$

52. $4\pi a^2.$

53. $\pi b\sqrt{a^2 + \delta^2}.$

54. $\frac{1}{3}\pi ab^2.$

55. $4\pi^2 ab.$

56. $2\pi^2 a^2 b.$

Pages 318–320. Art. 113

1. (a) 736, $\frac{92}{3}$; (b) 136, $\frac{17}{3}$.

2. (a) 352, $\frac{44}{3}$; (b) 136, $\frac{17}{3}$.

3. (a) $\frac{2992}{3}$, $\frac{748}{21}$; (b) $\frac{892}{3}$, $\frac{223}{21}$.

4. (a) $\frac{6400}{3}$, $\frac{160}{3}$; (b) $\frac{2080}{3}$, $\frac{52}{3}$.

5. (a) $\frac{bh^3}{12}, \frac{h^2}{6}$; (b) $\frac{bh^3}{36}, \frac{h^2}{18}$.

6. (a) 460, $\frac{46}{3}$; (b) $\frac{764}{5}$, $\frac{382}{75}$.

7. (a) 1948, $\frac{487}{9}$; (b) 652, $\frac{163}{9}$.

8. (a) 232, $\frac{29}{3}$; (b) 82, $\frac{41}{12}$.

9. (a) $\frac{512}{15}$; (b) $\frac{512}{7}$; (c) $\frac{11264}{105}$.

10. (a) $\frac{\pi ab^3}{4}$; (b) $\frac{5\pi ab^3}{4}$.

11. (a) $\frac{64}{27}$; (b) 64; (c) $\frac{1792}{27}$.

12. (a) $\frac{512}{15}$; (b) $\frac{32}{3}$; (c) $\frac{224}{5}$.

13. (a) $\frac{e^6 - 1}{9e^3}$; (b) $\frac{e^2 - 5}{e}$;

   (c) $\frac{e^6 + 9e^4 - 45e^2 - 1}{9e^3}$

14. (a) $\frac{4}{9}$; (b) $\pi^2 - 4$; (c) $\frac{9\pi^2 - 32}{9}$.

15. $4(4 - \pi)$, $\sqrt{\dfrac{4(4 - \pi)}{\pi}}$.

16. $\frac{768}{35}$.

17. (a) $\frac{4}{5}$; (b) $\frac{5}{21}$; (c) $\frac{109}{105}$.

18. $11\frac{1}{4}$.

19. $\frac{\pi a^4}{2}$, $\frac{\pi a^4}{4}$.

20. (a) $\frac{\pi a^4 h}{4}$; (b) $\frac{\pi a^2 h^3}{3}$;

   (c) $\frac{\pi a^2 h(3a^2 + 4h^2)}{12}$.

21. (a) $\frac{4\pi a^5}{15}$; (b) $\frac{8\pi a^5}{15}$; (c) $\frac{8\pi a^5}{5}$;

   (d) $\frac{28\pi a^5}{15}$.

22. $\frac{512\pi}{3}$.

23. $\frac{4096\pi}{9}$.

24. $\frac{416\pi}{81}$.

25. $\frac{1664\pi}{3}$.

26. $\frac{\pi}{8}(e^4 - e^{-4})$.

27. $\frac{603\pi}{10}$.

28. $\frac{l^3}{3}$.

29. $\frac{531}{5}$.

30. πa^3.

31. $\frac{3}{8}a^3$.

32. $I_x = \dfrac{a^3}{24e^3}(e^6 + 9e^4 - 9e^2 - 1)$,

   $I_y = \dfrac{a^3}{2e}(e^2 - 5)$.

33. $\frac{1178}{3}$.

34. $\frac{1}{3}\left[(1 + e^2)^{\frac{3}{2}} - 2^{\frac{3}{2}}\right]$.

35. $\frac{2}{5}\pi kha^5$.

36. (a) $\frac{\pi ka^6}{12}$, (b) $\frac{\pi ka^6}{12}$.

Pages 330–331. Art. 118

2. 0.0650, 0.0645, 0.06445.

3. 0.694, 0.693.

4. 2.13.

5. 0.39.

6. 65, $\frac{194}{3}$.

7. 2.05.

9. $\frac{4\pi a^3}{3}$.

10. $\frac{\pi}{3} a^2 h$.

11. $\frac{1}{3}ha^2$.

12. $\frac{1}{3}\pi h(a^2 + ab + b^2)$.

13. $\frac{1}{3}h(a^2 + ab + b^2)$.

14. $\frac{4}{3}\pi abc$.

15. 0.69315.

16. 3.14159.

Pages 341–342.   Art. 124

1. 0.
2. 2.
3. 2.
4. $\frac{1}{4}$
5. -1.
6. 1.
7. $\frac{1}{3}$.
8. 0.
9. $-\frac{2}{9}$.

10. $\frac{1}{4}$.
11. 1.
12. 2.
13. -3.
14. 1.
15. No limit.
16. $\ln a$.
17. 0.
18. -1.

19. 0.
20. 0.
21. -1.
22. 0.
23. 1.
24. 1.
25. No limit.
26. 0.
27. 0.

28. 0.
29. a.
30. No limit.
31. 0.
32. 1.
33. $-\frac{1}{4}$.

Page 344.   Art. 125

1. $\dfrac{1}{(n-1)!}$.

2. $(-1)^{n-1}\dfrac{x^{2n-2}}{(2n-2)!}$.

3. $(-1)^{n-1}\dfrac{x^{2n-1}}{(2n-1)!}$.

4. $\dfrac{2n-1}{(2n-2)!}$.

5. $\dfrac{n}{(n-1)!}$.

6. $\dfrac{n}{(2n-1)!}$.

7. $(-1)^{n-1}\dfrac{n}{(n+1)(n+2)(n+3)\cdots(2n)}$.

8. $(-1)^{n-1}\dfrac{n}{n^3+1}$.

9. $(-1)^{n-1}\dfrac{n^2+1}{n!+(n+1)}$.

10. $\dfrac{n^2}{(n+2)(n+3)\cdots(3n)}$.

11. $\dfrac{k(k-1)(k-2)\cdots(k-n+2)}{(n-1)!}x^{n-1}$.

12. $\dfrac{1\cdot3\cdot5\cdots(2n-3)}{2\cdot4\cdot6\cdots(2n-2)}\dfrac{x^{2n-1}}{2n-1}$.

13. $(-1)^{n-1}\dfrac{n+2}{n(n+1)!}$.

14. $(-1)^{n-1}\dfrac{n^3}{n(n+1)(n+2)\cdots(3n)}x^{2n-1}$.

Pages 350–351.   Art. 129

1. Converges.
2. Converges.
3. Diverges.
4. Diverges.
5. Converges.
6. Converges.
7. Converges.
8. Diverges.

9. Diverges.
10. Diverges.
11. Diverges.
12. Diverges.
13. Diverges.
14. Converges.
15. Converges.
16. Diverges.

17. Converges.
18. Diverges.
19. Diverges.
20. Diverges.
21. Converges.
22. Diverges.
23. Diverges.
24. Diverges.

25. Diverges.
26. Converges.
27. Diverges.
28. Converges.
29. Converges.
30. Converges.

Pages 353–354.   Art. 130

1. Converges.
2. Converges.
3. Converges.
4. Diverges.
5. Diverges.
6. Diverges.

7. Diverges.
8. Converges.
9. Diverges.
10. Diverges.
11. Diverges.
12. Converges.

13. Diverges.
14. Converges.
15. Converges.
16. Converges.
17. Converges.
18. Converges.

19. Converges.
20. Converges.
21. Converges.
22. Converges.
23. Converges.

Page 357. Art. 131

1. Converges.
2. Converges.
3. Diverges.
4. Converges.
5. Converges.
6. Converges.
7. Converges.
8. Converges.
9. Converges.
10. Converges.
11. Converges.
12. Diverges.
13. Diverges.
14. Converges.
15. Diverges.
16. Converges.
17. Converges.
18. Converges.
19. Diverges.
20. Converges.

Pages 366–367. Art. 137

1. $-1 < x < 1$.
2. All values of x.
3. All values of x.
4. All values of x.
5. All values of x.
6. $-1 \leqq x \leqq 1$.
7. $4 < x < 6$.
8. $-1 < x < 1$.
9. $x = 0$.
10. $-1 < x \leqq 1$.
11. $-3 < x < 3$.
12. $-2 \leqq x \leqq 2$.
13. $-3 < x \leqq -1$.
14. All values of x.
15. All values of x.
16. $-1 \leqq x \leqq 1$.
17. $x = 0$.
18. $-1 \leqq x < 1$.
19. $1 < x \leqq 3$.
20. $-\frac{1}{2} \leqq x \leqq \frac{1}{2}$.
21. $-\frac{4}{3} \leqq x \leqq -\frac{2}{3}$.

Pages 370–371. Art. 138

1. $$\sqrt{1 + x} = 1 + \frac{x}{2} - \frac{x^2}{2^3} + \frac{x^3}{2^4} - \frac{5x^4}{2^7} + \frac{7x^5}{2^8} - \frac{21x^6}{2^{10}} + \cdots,$$

$$\frac{1}{\sqrt{1 + x}} = 1 - \frac{x}{2} + \frac{3x^2}{2^3} - \frac{5x^3}{2^4} + \frac{35x^4}{2^7} - \frac{63x^5}{2^8} + \cdots.$$

2. $$\sqrt{1 - x^2} = 1 - \frac{x^2}{2} - \frac{x^4}{2^3} - \frac{x^6}{2^4} - \frac{5x^8}{2^7} - \frac{7x^{10}}{2^8} - \frac{21x^{12}}{2^{10}} - \cdots,$$

$$\frac{x}{\sqrt{1 - x^2}} = x + \frac{x^3}{2} + \frac{3x^5}{2^3} + \frac{5x^7}{2^4} + \frac{35x^9}{2^7} + \frac{63x^{11}}{2^8} + \cdots.$$

3. e^x.

4. $$x - \frac{1}{3} x^3 + \frac{1}{5} \frac{x^5}{2!} - \frac{1}{7} \frac{x^7}{3!} + \frac{1}{9} \frac{x^9}{4!} - \frac{1}{11} \frac{x^{11}}{5!} + \cdots.$$

5. $$(1 - x^2)^{-\frac{1}{2}} = 1 + \frac{x^2}{2} + \frac{3x^4}{2^3} + \frac{5x^6}{2^4} + \frac{35x^8}{2^7} + \frac{63x^{10}}{2^8} + \cdots,$$

$$\sin^{-1} x = x + \frac{1}{3} \frac{x^3}{2} + \frac{3}{5} \frac{x^5}{2^3} + \frac{5}{7} \frac{x^7}{2^4} + \frac{35}{9} \frac{x^9}{2^7} + \cdots.$$

6. $2 \left(x + \frac{x^3}{3} + \frac{x^5}{5} + \frac{x^7}{7} + \cdots \right).$ 8. 0.0198.   9. 0.4055.

Pages 374–375. Art. 139

3. $$\frac{1}{\sqrt{2}} \left[1 + x - \frac{x^2}{2!} - \frac{x^3}{3!} + \frac{x^4}{4!} + \cdots \pm \frac{x^{n-1}}{(n-1)!} + \cdots \right].$$

4. $$\frac{1}{\sqrt{2}} \left[1 + x - \frac{x^2}{2!} - \frac{x^3}{3!} + \frac{x^4}{4!} + \cdots \pm \frac{x^{n-1}}{(n-1)!} + \cdots \right].$$

5. $$-x - \frac{x^2}{2} - \frac{x^3}{3} - \frac{x^4}{4} - \frac{x^5}{5} - \cdots - \frac{x^n}{n} - \cdots.$$

6. $1 - x + \dfrac{x^2}{2!} - \dfrac{x^3}{3!} + \dfrac{x^4}{4!} - \dfrac{x^5}{5!} + \cdots + (-1)^{n-1} \dfrac{x^{n-1}}{(n-1)!} + \cdots$.

7. $ax - \dfrac{a^3}{3!} x^3 + \dfrac{a^5}{5!} x^5 - \dfrac{a^7}{7!} x^7 + \cdots + (-1)^{n-1} \dfrac{a^{2n-1}}{(2n-1)!} x^{2n-1} + \cdots$.

8. $1 - \dfrac{a^2}{2!} x^2 + \dfrac{a^4}{4!} x^4 - \dfrac{a^6}{6!} x^6 + \cdots + (-1)^{n-1} \dfrac{a^{2n-2}}{(2n-2)!} x^{2n-2} + \cdots$.

9. $1 + x \ln a + \dfrac{x^2}{2!} (\ln a)^2 + \dfrac{x^3}{3!} (\ln a)^3 + \cdots + \dfrac{x^{n-1}}{(n-1)!} (\ln a)^{n-1} + \cdots$.

10. $1 + \dfrac{x^2}{2!} + \dfrac{x^4}{4!} + \dfrac{x^6}{6!} + \cdots + \dfrac{x^{2n-2}}{(2n-2)!} + \cdots$.

11. $x + \dfrac{x^3}{3!} + \dfrac{x^5}{5!} + \dfrac{x^7}{7!} + \cdots + \dfrac{x^{2n-1}}{(2n-1)!} + \cdots$.

12. $x + \frac{1}{3} x^3 + \frac{2}{15} x^5 + \cdots$.   15. $-\dfrac{x^2}{2} - \dfrac{x^4}{12} - \dfrac{x^6}{45} - \cdots$.

13. $1 + \dfrac{x^2}{2!} + \dfrac{5x^4}{4!} + \cdots$.   16. $1 + x + \dfrac{x^2}{2} + \cdots$.

14. $1 + 2x + 2x^2 + \cdots$.   17. $x - \dfrac{x^3}{3!} + \dfrac{9x^5}{5!} - \cdots$.

18. $\left(x - \dfrac{x^3}{3!} + \dfrac{x^5}{5!} - \cdots \right) \cdot \dfrac{1}{2} - \left(1 - \dfrac{x^2}{2!} + \dfrac{x^4}{4!} - \cdots \right) \cdot \dfrac{\sqrt{3}}{2}$.

19. $\left(1 - \dfrac{x^2}{2!} + \dfrac{x^4}{4!} - \cdots \right) \cdot \dfrac{\sqrt{3}}{2} + \left(x - \dfrac{x^3}{3!} + \dfrac{x^5}{5!} - \cdots \right) \cdot \dfrac{1}{2}$.

20. $\dfrac{1}{2} \cdot \left(1 - \dfrac{x^2}{2!} + \dfrac{x^4}{4!} - \cdots \right) - \dfrac{\sqrt{3}}{2} \cdot \left(x - \dfrac{x^3}{3!} + \dfrac{x^5}{5!} - \cdots \right)$.

22. $2 + \dfrac{1}{2^2} x - \dfrac{1}{2^5} \dfrac{x^2}{2!} + \dfrac{3}{2^8} \dfrac{x^3}{3!} + \cdots$.

23. $1 - \dfrac{2}{3} x - \dfrac{1}{3^2} x^2 - \dfrac{8}{3^3} \dfrac{x^3}{3!} - \cdots$.

24. $\dfrac{1}{3} + \dfrac{1}{2 \cdot 3^3} x + \dfrac{1}{2^2 \cdot 3^4} \dfrac{x^2}{2!} + \dfrac{5}{2^3 \cdot 3^6} \dfrac{x^3}{3!} + \cdots$.

25. $1 - kx^2 + \dfrac{k^2 x^4}{2!} - \dfrac{k^3 x^6}{3!} + \cdots$.   28. $\ln (1-x) = -x - \dfrac{x^2}{2} - \dfrac{x^3}{3} - \dfrac{x^4}{4} - \cdots$.

26. $1 + \dfrac{1}{3} x^2 + \dfrac{2}{3^2} x^4 + \dfrac{14}{3^4} x^6 + \cdots$. $\ln \dfrac{1+x}{1-x} = 2 \left(x + \dfrac{x^3}{3} + \dfrac{x^5}{5} + \cdots \right)$.

27. $\sin x^2 = x^2 - \dfrac{x^6}{3!} + \dfrac{x^{10}}{5!} - \cdots$,   29. $\sin^2 \theta = \theta^2 - \dfrac{2^3 \theta^4}{4!} + \dfrac{2^5 \theta^6}{6!} + \cdots$,

$\cos x^2 = 1 - \dfrac{x^4}{2!} + \dfrac{x^8}{4!} - \cdots$. $\cos^2 \theta = 1 - \theta^2 + \dfrac{2^3 \theta^4}{4!} - \dfrac{2^5 \theta^6}{6!} + \cdots$.

Page 378. Art. 140

1. $e^x = e\left[1 + (x-1) + \dfrac{(x-1)^2}{2!} + \dfrac{(x-1)^3}{3!} + \cdots + \dfrac{(x-1)^{n-1}}{(n-1)!} + \cdots\right],$

$e^{1+h} = e\left[1 + h + \dfrac{h^2}{2!} + \dfrac{h^3}{3!} + \cdots + \dfrac{h^{n-1}}{(n-1)!} + \cdots\right].$

2. $k^x = k^2\left[1 + (\ln k)(x-2) + \dfrac{(\ln k)^2}{2!}(x-2)^2 + \dfrac{(\ln k)^3}{3!}(x-2)^3 + \cdots\right.$

$\left. + \dfrac{(\ln k)^{n-1}}{(n-1)!}(x-2)^{n-1} + \cdots\right],$

$k^{2+h} = k^2\left[1 + h(\ln k) + \dfrac{h^2}{2!}(\ln k)^2 + \dfrac{h^3}{3!}(\ln k)^3 + \cdots\right.$

$\left. + \dfrac{h^{n-1}}{(n-1)!}(\ln k)^{n-1} + \cdots\right].$

3. $\ln x = \ln k + \dfrac{1}{k}(x-k) - \dfrac{1}{2k^2}(x-k)^2 + \dfrac{1}{3k^3}(x-k)^3 - \cdots$

$+ \dfrac{(-1)^n(x-k)^{n-1}}{(n-1)k^{n-1}} + \cdots,$

$\ln(k+h) = \ln k + \dfrac{h}{k} - \dfrac{h^2}{2k^2} + \dfrac{h^3}{3k^3} - \cdots + \dfrac{(-1)^n h^{n-1}}{(n-1)k^{n-1}} + \cdots.$

4. $\sin x = 1 - \dfrac{1}{2!}\left(x - \dfrac{\pi}{2}\right)^2 + \dfrac{1}{4!}\left(x - \dfrac{\pi}{2}\right)^4 - \dfrac{1}{6!}\left(x - \dfrac{\pi}{2}\right)^6 + \cdots$

$+ (-1)^{n-1}\dfrac{\left(x - \dfrac{\pi}{2}\right)^{2n-2}}{(2n-2)!} + \cdots,$

$\sin\left(\dfrac{\pi}{2} + h\right) = 1 - \dfrac{h^2}{2!} + \dfrac{h^4}{4!} - \dfrac{h^6}{6!} + \cdots + (-1)^{n-1}\dfrac{h^{2n-2}}{(2n-2)!} + \cdots.$

5. $\cos x = -\left(x - \dfrac{\pi}{2}\right) + \dfrac{\left(x - \dfrac{\pi}{2}\right)^3}{3!} - \dfrac{\left(x - \dfrac{\pi}{2}\right)^5}{5!} + \cdots$

$+ (-1)^n\dfrac{\left(x - \dfrac{\pi}{2}\right)^{2n-1}}{(2n-1)!} + \cdots,$

$\cos\left(\dfrac{\pi}{2} + h\right) = -h + \dfrac{h^3}{3!} - \dfrac{h^5}{5!} + \cdots + (-1)^n\dfrac{h^{2n-1}}{(2n-1)!} + \cdots.$

6. $\sin x = \dfrac{1}{2} + \dfrac{\sqrt{3}}{2}\left(x - \dfrac{\pi}{6}\right) - \dfrac{1}{2(2!)}\left(x - \dfrac{\pi}{6}\right)^2 - \dfrac{\sqrt{3}}{2(3!)}\left(x - \dfrac{\pi}{6}\right)^3 + \cdots,$

$\sin\left(\dfrac{\pi}{6} + h\right) = \dfrac{1}{2} + \dfrac{\sqrt{3}}{2}h - \dfrac{1}{2(2!)}h^2 - \dfrac{\sqrt{3}}{2(3!)}h^3 + \cdots.$

7. $\cos x = \dfrac{1}{2} - \dfrac{\sqrt{3}}{2}\left(x - \dfrac{\pi}{3}\right) - \dfrac{1}{2(2!)}\left(x - \dfrac{\pi}{3}\right)^2 + \dfrac{\sqrt{3}}{2(3!)}\left(x - \dfrac{\pi}{3}\right)^3 + \cdots,$

$\cos\left(\dfrac{\pi}{3} + h\right) = \dfrac{1}{2} - \dfrac{\sqrt{3}}{2}h - \dfrac{1}{2(2!)}h^2 + \dfrac{\sqrt{3}}{2(3!)}h^3 + \cdots.$

8. $x^{\frac{3}{2}} = 8 + 3(x-4) + \dfrac{3}{2^4}(x-4)^2 - \dfrac{1}{2^7}(x-4)^3 + \cdots,$

$(4+h)^{\frac{3}{2}} = 8 + 3h + \dfrac{3h^2}{2^4} - \dfrac{h^3}{2^7} + \cdots.$

9. $\tan x = 1 + 2\left(x - \dfrac{\pi}{4}\right) + 2\left(x - \dfrac{\pi}{4}\right)^2 + \cdots,$

$\tan\left(\dfrac{\pi}{4} + h\right) = 1 + 2h + 2h^2 + \cdots.$

10. $\sqrt{x} = 3 + \dfrac{1}{6}(x-9) - \dfrac{1}{108(2!)}(x-9)^2 + \dfrac{1}{648(3!)}(x-9)^3 - \cdots,$

$\sqrt{9+h} = 3 + \dfrac{h}{6} - \dfrac{h^2}{108(2!)} + \dfrac{h^3}{648(3!)} - \cdots.$

11. $\sqrt[3]{x} = 2 + \dfrac{1}{12}(x-8) - \dfrac{1}{144(2!)}(x-8)^2 + \dfrac{5}{3456(3!)}(x-8)^3 - \cdots,$

$\sqrt[3]{8+h} = 2 + \dfrac{h}{12} - \dfrac{h}{144(2!)} + \dfrac{h^3}{3456(3!)} - \cdots.$

13. $x^3 - 2x^2 + 3x - 1 = 1 + 2(x-1) + (x-1)^2 + (x-1)^3,$

$\displaystyle\int \dfrac{x^3 - 2x^2 + 3x - 1}{(x-1)^4}\, dx = \dfrac{-3x^2 + 3x - 1}{3(x-1)^3} + \ln(x-1) + C.$

14. $x^4 - 3x^3 - x - 5 = -8 + 26(x-3) + 27(x-3)^2 + 9(x-3)^3 + (x-3)^4,$

$\displaystyle\int_0^1 \dfrac{x^4 - 3x^3 - x - 5}{(x-3)^5}\, dx = \dfrac{79}{162} + \ln\dfrac{2}{3}.$

Pages 390–391. Art. 144

1. 119 sq. in.
2. 59,200 cu. ft.
3. 2200 ft-lb.
4. 610.
5. 5100 ft.
6. 66.

7. 32.2 ft./sec.²
8. 0.83333.
9. 29.6 cu. in. < volume < 29.9 cu. in.
   57.5 sq. in. < total surface
   < 57.8 sq. in.
10. 9.90 < R < 10.1.

Pages 395–397. Art. 145

1. 0.51504.
2. 0.88295.
3. 0.99939.
4. 0.05234.
5. 0.88295.
6. 0.52992.
7. 0.99985.
8. 0.03490.
9. 9.97980 − 10.
10. 0.03922.
11. 0.7130.
12. 0.6780.
13. 0.6678.
14. 1.22140.

15. 0.81873.
16. 1.6487.
17. 0.6065.
18. 8.166.
19. 6.050.
20. 0.183.
21. 2.00499.
23. 3.98330.
25. 2.01545.
26. 1.98734.
27. 4.021.
28. 9.99667.
29. 3.3166.
30. 1.4142.

31. 1.4422.
32. 3.33222.
33. (a) ln 2 = 0.6931,
    log 2 = 0.3010,
    (b) ln 3 = 1.0986,
    log 3 = 0.4771,
    (c) ln 4 = 1.3863,
    log 4 = 0.6021,
    (d) ln 5 = 1.6094,
    log 5 = 0.6990,
    (e) ln 6 = 1.7918,
    log 6 = 0.7782
35. 0.9461.
36. 0.4613.

37. 0.1997.
38. 0.4920.
39. 0.3896.
40. 0.314160.
41. 0.7640.
42. 1.
43. a.

44. 1.
45. 1.
46. $\dfrac{1}{a}$.
47. 0.
48. 0.

49. $\ln a$.
50. $\frac{1}{3}$.
51. $\dfrac{2}{a}$.
52. 1.

Pages 400–401. Art. 146

1. Three.
2. 0.00002.
3. Two.
4. 7×10^{-18}.
6. Three.
7. 0.000002.
8. $-0.1 < x < 0.091$.
10. Two.

11. 0.000002.
12. $8.26°$.
14. Five.
15. 0.0002.
16. $2.99684 < x < 3.00949$.
18. Nine.
19. 0.0000008; 0.0000000004.

Pages 412–413. Art. 153

7. (a) $-\dfrac{1}{x^2}\cosh\dfrac{1}{x}$; (b) $2x\sinh(x^2 - 2)$; (c) $\dfrac{1}{x}\operatorname{sech}^2(\ln x)$;

(d) $\csc^2 x\operatorname{csch}^2(\cot x)$; (e) $\dfrac{6}{x^3}\operatorname{sech}\left(\dfrac{3}{x^2}\right)\tanh\left(\dfrac{3}{x^2}\right)$;

(f) $\dfrac{1}{x}\operatorname{csch}(\ln x)\coth(\ln x)$; (g) $2\sinh 4x$;

(h) $3\sinh(x-1)\cosh^2(x-1)$; (i) $\sinh x(1 + \operatorname{sech}^2 x)$;

(j) $-2\operatorname{csch}^3 2x(1 + \cosh^2 2x)$; (k) $2x\operatorname{sech} x^2(1 - x^2\tanh x^2)$;

(l) $\dfrac{1}{x}\operatorname{csch} 3x(1 - 3x\ln 3x\coth 3x)$.

8. (a) $\dfrac{1}{\sqrt{x^2 + 4}}$; (b) $\pm\dfrac{3}{\sqrt{9x^2 - 1}}$; (c) $\dfrac{2}{4 - x^2}$; (d) $\dfrac{2}{1 - 4x^2}$;

(e) $\dfrac{1}{(1 - x)\sqrt{x^2 - 1}}$; (f) $\pm\csc x$; (g) $2x\operatorname{csch}^{-1} x - \dfrac{x}{\sqrt{1 + x^2}}$;

(h) $\dfrac{1}{x\sqrt{x^2 + 1}} - \dfrac{1}{x^2}\sinh^{-1} x$.

9. (a) 1; (b) 0; (c) 1; (d) 1; (e) 0; (f) 0; (g) 2; (h) 0; (i) 1; (j) 1.

11. (0, 1), minimum point.

12. (0, 0).

13. (0, 0).

14. (0, 1); $\left(\pm\ln(\sqrt{2} + 1), \dfrac{\sqrt{2}}{2}\right)$.

17. $\sinh^{-1}\dfrac{1}{x} = \operatorname{csch}^{-1} x$,

$\cosh^{-1}\dfrac{1}{x} = \operatorname{sech}^{-1} x$,

$\tanh^{-1}\dfrac{1}{x} = \coth^{-1} x$,

$\coth^{-1}\dfrac{1}{x} = \tanh^{-1} x$,

$\operatorname{sech}^{-1}\dfrac{1}{x} = \cosh^{-1} x$,

$\operatorname{csch}^{-1}\dfrac{1}{x} = \sinh^{-1} x$.

Pages 417–419. Art. 154

1. $\dfrac{3}{2}\cosh\dfrac{2x}{3}+C.$

2. $-4\sinh\left(\dfrac{3-x}{4}\right)+C.$

3. $\frac{1}{2}\ln\cosh x^2+C.$

4. $-\dfrac{1}{2}\ln\sinh\dfrac{2}{x}+C.$

5. $\dfrac{4}{3}\tanh\dfrac{3x}{4}+C.$

6. $-\frac{1}{6}\coth(2x^3)+C.$

7. $-\operatorname{sech}(\ln x)+C.$

8. $\operatorname{csch}(2-x)+C.$

9. $\frac{1}{3}\sinh^3 x+C.$

10. $\frac{1}{2}\sinh 2x+\frac{1}{6}\sinh^3 2x+C.$

11. $x-\frac{1}{3}\tanh 3x+C.$

12. $-\dfrac{2}{3}\coth^3\dfrac{x}{2}+C.$

13. $\dfrac{1}{4}\sinh 2x-\dfrac{x}{2}+C.$

14. $\dfrac{1}{4}\sinh 2x+\dfrac{x}{2}+C.$

15. $-2\sqrt{1-\cosh x}+C.$

16. $\frac{1}{2}\ln(1+\sinh 2x)+C.$

19. $\dfrac{1}{2}\sinh^{-1}\dfrac{2x}{3}+C,$ or

$\frac{1}{2}\ln(2x+\sqrt{4x^2+9})+C_1.$

20. $\dfrac{1}{3}\tanh^{-1}\dfrac{x}{3}+C,$ or

$\dfrac{1}{6}\ln\dfrac{3+x}{3-x}+C.$

21. $\dfrac{1}{\sqrt{2}}\cosh^{-1}\dfrac{x\sqrt{6}}{3}+C,$ or

$\dfrac{1}{\sqrt{2}}\ln(\sqrt{2}\,x+\sqrt{2x^2-3})+C_1.$

22. $\dfrac{x(3+2x^2)}{3(1+x^2)^{\frac{3}{2}}}+C.$

23. $\dfrac{1}{2}x\sqrt{x^2+4}-2\sinh^{-1}\dfrac{x}{2}+C.$

24. $\dfrac{1}{2}\sinh^{-1}\dfrac{2x}{5}+C,$ or

$\frac{1}{2}\ln(2x+\sqrt{4x^2+25})+C_1.$

28. $\dfrac{\sqrt{5}}{2}-\sin^{-1}\dfrac{\sqrt{5}}{3}.$

29. $\frac{1}{585}(26-5\sqrt{13}).$

30. $\ln\dfrac{(3+\sqrt{13})(\sqrt{2}-1)}{2}.$

31. $10-\frac{9}{2}\ln 3.$

32. $\dfrac{1}{3}\ln\dfrac{(3+2\sqrt{2})(3-\sqrt{5})}{2}.$

33. $\ln 3.$

34. $\frac{1}{16}\ln\frac{27}{11}.$

35. $\frac{7}{300}.$

Pages 428–430. Art. 159

1. $6x^5-25x^4y+4xy^3,\; -5x^5+6x^2y^2.$

2. $\dfrac{x}{\sqrt{x^2-y^2}},\; \dfrac{-y}{\sqrt{x^2-y^2}}.$

3. $\dfrac{x^2+y^2}{x^2y},\; -\dfrac{x^2+y^2}{xy^2}.$

4. $\dfrac{x^2-2xy-y^2}{(x-y)^2}\quad \dfrac{x^2+2xy-y^2}{(x-y)^2}.$

5. $8(x^2-xy+y^2)^7(2x-y),\; 8(x^2-xy+y^2)^7(2y-x).$

6. $(x-y)^3(x+y)^4(9x-y),\; (x-y)^3(x+y)^4(x-9y).$

7. $\cos(x-y),\; -\cos(x-y).$

8. $\dfrac{y}{x^2}\sin\dfrac{2y}{x},\; -\dfrac{1}{x}\sin\dfrac{2y}{x}.$

9. $\dfrac{1}{\sqrt{1-(x-y)^2}},\; \dfrac{-1}{\sqrt{1-(x-y)^2}}.$

10. $-2x\csc^2(x^2+y^2),\; -2y\csc^2(x^2+y^2).$

11. $\dfrac{1}{y}\sec^2\dfrac{x+y}{y},\; -\dfrac{x}{y^2}\sec^2\dfrac{x+y}{y}.$

12. $\dfrac{-y(x^2+y^2)}{x^4-x^2y^2+y^4},\; \dfrac{x(x^2+y^2)}{x^4-x^2y^2+y^4}.$

13. $2xe^{x^2+y^2},\; 2ye^{x^2+y^2}.$

14. $\dfrac{e^{x-y}}{x-y}[1 + (x-y)\ln(x-y)], \dfrac{e^{x-y}}{y-x}[1 - (y-x)\ln(x-y)].$

15. $\dfrac{y}{x^2 - y^2}, \dfrac{-x}{x^2 - y^2}.$

20. $3e^x \sin(e^y - e^x)\cos^2(e^y - e^x),$
$\qquad -3e^y \sin(e^y - e^x)\cos^2(e^y - e^x).$

16. $-\dfrac{y}{x^2}\sec\dfrac{y}{x}\csc\dfrac{y}{x}, \dfrac{1}{x}\sec\dfrac{y}{x}\csc\dfrac{y}{x}.$

26. $\dfrac{\pm 3x}{2\sqrt{128 - 9x^2}}, \dfrac{-3}{2\sqrt{23}}.$

27. $(1, 1, 2).$

17. $\dfrac{1}{x[1 + (\ln xy)^2]}, \dfrac{1}{y[1 + (\ln xy)^2]}.$

28. $y = 4.$

29. $(1, 2, 5).$

18. $\dfrac{e^{x-y}}{\sqrt{1 - e^{2x-2y}}}, \dfrac{-e^{x-y}}{\sqrt{1 - e^{2x-2y}}}.$

30. $\dfrac{y(2x^2 - y^2)}{x^2(x^2 - y^2)^{\frac{3}{2}}}.$

19. $\dfrac{1}{x}\sin\ln(x^2 y^4), \dfrac{2}{y}\sin\ln(x^2 y^4).$

31. $\dfrac{2xy}{x^2 + y^2} + 2\tan^{-1}\dfrac{y}{x}.$

42. $-r\sin\theta, \cos\theta, r\cos\theta, \sin\theta, \dfrac{-y}{x^2 + y^2}, \dfrac{x}{x^2 + y^2}, \dfrac{x}{\sqrt{x^2 + y^2}}, \dfrac{y}{\sqrt{x^2 + y^2}}.$

43. $re^\theta, e^\theta, -re^{-\theta}, e^{-\theta}, \dfrac{1}{2x}, \dfrac{-1}{2y}, \dfrac{1}{2}\sqrt{\dfrac{y}{x}}, \dfrac{1}{2}\sqrt{\dfrac{x}{y}}.$

Pages 437–440. Art. 164

1. (a) $7.2, 6.4$; (b) $-2, -10$; (c) $-\frac{3}{2}, -\frac{15}{4}$; (d) $1, \frac{7}{6}$; (e) $4, \frac{9}{8}$; (f) $0, \dfrac{(e-1)^2}{2e}$;

(g) $\sqrt{3}-1, \dfrac{\pi}{6}$; (h) $-\dfrac{1}{4}, -\dfrac{\pi}{12}$; (i) $1-\sqrt{e}, -\dfrac{\pi\sqrt{3e}}{12}$; (j) $\dfrac{\pi}{4} - \tan^{-1}2, -1$;

(k) $\dfrac{\pi}{12}, \dfrac{1}{3}(\sqrt{6} - \sqrt{3}).$

2. (a) $0.024186119, 0.024$; (b) $0, 0$; (c) 0.02044 approx., 0.02; (d) $0,0$;
(e) -0.00796 approx., -0.008; (f) 0.03065 approx., 0.03; (g) -0.00248
approx., -0.0025.

3. 0.63π cu. in.

4. 0.013π cu. in., 0.04π sq. in.

5. 30.3 cu. in.

6. 7.975 in.

7. $\dfrac{\pi}{25}$ sq. in.

8. 0.24 ft./sec.

9. 4513 lb.; 9 lb., approx.

10. 1.7 in.

11. 12.63 sq. ft.

12. 1.5 per cent.

13. 0.75 per cent.

14. 0.2 per cent.

15. 2 per cent.

16. 2, 6 per cent.

17. (a) $45°$; (b) $\frac{7}{60}$, $11\frac{2}{3}$ per cent;
(c) $41\frac{1}{2}°$ and $48°$.

18. $\frac{1}{250}$ sec., 0.2 per cent.

19. 0.153 sq. in.

Pages 446–448. Art. 166

1. (a) $\dfrac{e^{\sqrt{\frac{t}{\pi}}}}{2\sqrt{\pi t}}\left(\cos\dfrac{3t}{2} - 3\sqrt{\pi t}\sin\dfrac{3t}{2}\right), \dfrac{3e}{2}$; (b) $-2\tan 2t, -2$; (c) $-2t, -1$;

(d) $\dfrac{2}{t^2}, 2$; (e) $e^{-t}(1 - t) - e^t(1 + t), -2e$; (f) $e^{\sin 2t}\sin 2t, \sqrt{e}$;

(g) $-\csc t, -1$; (h) $2\sec 2t, 2.$

2. 32.2 ft./sec.

3. $-\frac{120}{481}$ rad./sec.

4. -8 ft./sec.

5. $\frac{4}{5}$ rad./sec., clockwise.

6. 310 mi./hr.

7. -108π cu. in./sec., $-\dfrac{162\pi}{5}$ sq. in./sec.

8. 0.22 cu. ft./min.

9. (a) $\dfrac{2}{x}-2\tan x$; (b) $\dfrac{-1}{y}$;

   (c) $\dfrac{y}{x}+y\ln x+2x$; (d) $\dfrac{1}{y}$;

   (e) $\dfrac{16}{x^2y^3}$; (f) $z(xy+y+e)$.

10. $-\frac{3}{2}(\sqrt{3}+2)$ degrees per inch.

11. $\tan^{-1}\left(\dfrac{-1}{2}\right)$ with x-axis; $x^2+y^2=C$.

12. Toward origin.

13. $\dfrac{2(x_1\cos\phi+y_1\sin\phi)}{x_1{}^2+y_1{}^2}$.

14. $\dfrac{\pi}{2}+\tan^{-1}\dfrac{y_1}{x_1}$.

Pages 453–454. Art. 168

1. (a) $-\dfrac{3x^2+2xy+y^2}{x^2+2xy+3y^2}$; (b) $\dfrac{y}{x}$; (c) $\dfrac{y\cos x-\sin y}{x\cos y-\sin x}$; (d) $\dfrac{1+\tan x}{1-\cot y}$; (e) $\dfrac{y}{x}$;

   (f) $\dfrac{x^2+y}{x(1+y)}$; (g) $-\dfrac{y+\tan x\csc^2 x}{x+\tan y\csc^2 y}$; (h) $\dfrac{y(x^2+y^2+xy^3-x^3y)}{x(x^2+y^2-xy^3+x^3y)}$.

2. (a) $-\dfrac{x}{z}, -\dfrac{y}{z}$; (b) $\dfrac{(z-y)(y+z-2x)}{(x-y)(x+y-2z)}, \dfrac{(x-z)(z+x-2y)}{(x-y)(x+y-2z)}$;

   (c) $\dfrac{2x}{y+2z}, \dfrac{-z}{y+2z}$; (d) $\dfrac{ye^z(\sin xy-\cos xy)}{e^{xy}(\sin z-\cos z)}, \dfrac{xe^z(\sin xy-\cos xy)}{e^{xy}(\sin z-\cos z)}$;

   (e) $\dfrac{-z\sin xz}{y+x\sin xz}, \dfrac{-z}{y+x\sin xz}$;

   (f) $\dfrac{z\sqrt{y^2-z^2}}{x\sqrt{y^2-z^2}-x^2-z^2}, \dfrac{z(x^2+z^2)}{y(x^2+z^2-x\sqrt{y^2-z^2})}$;

   (g) $-\dfrac{z(x\ln z+y)}{x(z\ln y+x)}, -\dfrac{z(y\ln x+z)}{y(z\ln y+x)}$;

   (h) $-\dfrac{ye^{xy}+ze^{xz}}{xe^{xz}+ye^{yz}}, -\dfrac{xe^{xy}+ze^{yz}}{xe^{xz}+ye^{yz}}$.

3. $8x+6y-z=11, \dfrac{x-2}{8}=\dfrac{y-1}{6}=\dfrac{z-11}{-1}$.

4. $6x+3y-z=6, \dfrac{x-1}{6}=\dfrac{y-2}{3}=\dfrac{z-6}{-1}$.

5. $4x+3y+z=12, \dfrac{x-2}{4}=\dfrac{y-1}{3}=\dfrac{z-1}{1}$.

6. (a) $z+z_1=2ax_1x+2by_1y, \dfrac{x-x_1}{2ax_1}=\dfrac{y-y_1}{2by_1}=\dfrac{z-z_1}{-1}$;

   (b) $\dfrac{x_1x}{a^2}+\dfrac{y_1y}{b^2}-\dfrac{z_1z}{c^2}=1, \dfrac{x-x_1}{\dfrac{x_1}{a^2}}=\dfrac{y-y_1}{\dfrac{y_1}{b^2}}=\dfrac{z-z_1}{-\dfrac{z_1}{c^2}}$;

(c) $\dfrac{x_1x}{a^2} + \dfrac{y_1y}{b^2} - \dfrac{z_1z}{c^2} = 0,\quad \dfrac{x - x_1}{\dfrac{x_1}{a^2}} = \dfrac{y - y_1}{\dfrac{y_1}{b^2}} = \dfrac{z - z_1}{-\dfrac{z_1}{c^2}}$;

(d) $\dfrac{x_1x}{a^2} - \dfrac{y_1y}{b^2} - \dfrac{z_1z}{c^2} = 1,\quad \dfrac{x - x_1}{\dfrac{x_1}{a^2}} = \dfrac{y - y_1}{-\dfrac{y_1}{b^2}} = \dfrac{z - z_1}{-\dfrac{z_1}{c^2}}$;

(e) $z + z_1 = 2ax_1x - 2by_1y,\quad \dfrac{x - x_1}{-2ax_1} = \dfrac{y - y_1}{2by_1} = z - z_1$;

(f) $z + z_1 = k(y_1x + x_1y),\quad \dfrac{x - x_1}{ky_1} = \dfrac{y - y_1}{kx_1} = \dfrac{z - z_1}{-1}$.

8. The constant is a^2.   **9.** Vol. $= \frac{9}{2}a^3$.

11. $x = x_1,\ z - z_1 = \left(\dfrac{\partial z}{\partial y}\right)_1 (y - y_1);\qquad y = y_1,\ z - z_1 = \left(\dfrac{\partial z}{\partial x}\right)_1 (x - x_1).$

Pages 457–458.   Art. 169

1. 4.

2. 9.

3. −2.

4. −6.

5. 5.

6. $\dfrac{a^3}{27}$.

7. $x = a,\ \theta = 0$.

8. 4 ft., 4 ft., 2 ft.; 32 cu. ft.

9. 8 ft., 8 ft., 4 ft.

10. 2.

11. $\sqrt{3}$.

12. 6 in., 60°.

14. 2, 2, 1; 4 cubic units.

15. Intersection of medians.

17. $3x + 6y + 2z = 18$.

Page 463.   Art. 170

1. (c) Test fails; (f) no extreme for $x = 0,\ \theta = \dfrac{\pi}{2},\ \dfrac{3\pi}{2}$, etc.

2. Min. val. $= 3$ for $x = y = 1$.   **3.** Max. val. $= \dfrac{s^3}{27}$ for $x = y = \dfrac{2s}{3}$.

6. $x = y = a$ gives max. or min. $= a^3$, according as $a \gtrless 0$.

7. Min. val. $= \frac{4}{3}(ab - a^2 - b^2)$ for $x = \frac{2}{3}(2a - b),\ y = \frac{2}{3}(2b - a)$.

8. Max. val. $= 8$ for $x = y = 2$.   **10.** Max. val. $= 729$ for $x = y = 3$.

9. Min. val. $= 12$ for $x = y = 2$.   **11.** No extremes.

Pages 468–469.   Art. 172

1. 8.

2. 8.

3. $\frac{32}{3}$.

4. $\frac{32}{3}$.

5. 18.

6. 18.

7. 16.

8. 16.

9. 9.

10. 9.

11. 72.

12. 72.

13. $(e - 1)^2$.

14. $\frac{1}{8}(8 + \pi^2)$.

15. 9.

16. $\frac{1}{4}(e^2 + 1)$.

17. $\dfrac{\pi}{4}\ln 2$.

18. a^3.

19. a^3.

20. 2.

21. $\dfrac{4a^3}{27}$.

22. $\dfrac{4 - \pi}{8}$.

23. $\frac{1}{6}(1 - \ln 2)$.

24. $\frac{1}{4}(\ln 16 - \pi)$.

25. $\frac{1}{2}(\ln 2)^2$.

26. $(\cosh 1 - 1)^2$.

27. $\frac{1}{2}(\cosh 1 - 1)$.

28. $\ln \dfrac{\cosh 1}{\cosh \frac{1}{2}}$.

Page 472. Art. 173

1. 2.
2. $\frac{9}{2}$.
3. $\frac{6\pi - 8}{3}$.
4. $\frac{3\pi - 8}{3}$.

5. $\frac{\pi}{18}(9 + 8\sqrt{3}) - 2$.
6. $\frac{17 - 6\ln 2}{3}$.
7. 3.2636.

8. $\frac{2\pi - 3\sqrt{3}}{6}$.
9. $\frac{5\pi a^2}{32}$.
10. 4π.

Page 475. Art. 174

1. $\frac{a^2}{32}(24\pi - 48 + \sqrt{3})$.
2. 3π.
3. $\frac{a^2}{4}$.
4. $\frac{a^2}{24}(\pi + 6\sqrt{3} - 12)$.

5. $\frac{a^2}{6}(2\pi + 3\sqrt{3})$.
6. $\frac{1}{16}(15\sqrt{3} - 8\pi)$.
7. $\frac{a^2}{12}(9\pi + 16)$.

8. $\frac{\pi a^2}{16}$.
9. $\frac{a^2(\pi - 2)}{4}$.
10. $\frac{a^2(4 - \pi)}{16}$.

Page 479. Art. 175

1. 18.
2. $\frac{4}{7}$.
3. $\frac{64}{5}$.

4. $\frac{1}{6}$.
5. $\frac{\pi a^4}{2}$.

6. π.
7. $4\ln 2 - 2$.
8. 4π.

9. $\frac{1147}{420}$.
10. $\frac{\pi a^3}{70}$.

Pages 481–482. Art. 176

1. $\frac{4}{3}\pi a^3$.
2. $\frac{52\pi}{3}$.
3. $\pi(e^{a^2} - 1)$.
4. $\frac{27\pi}{2}$.
5. 36π.
6. $\frac{4\pi}{3}\left[a^3 - (a^2 - b^2)^{\frac{3}{2}}\right]$.
7. $\frac{3\pi}{2}$.

8. $\frac{2a^3}{9}$.
9. $\frac{2a^3}{9}(3\pi + 20 - 16\sqrt{2})$.
10. $\frac{\pi a^3}{8}$.
11. $\frac{2a^3}{9}(3\pi - 4)$.
12. $\frac{a^3}{12}[2\sqrt{2} + 2\ln(1 + \sqrt{2}) - \pi]$.

Page 485. Art. 177

1. $2\pi ah$.
2. $4\pi a^2$.
3. $8a^2$.
4. $4a^2$

5. 20π.
6. $\frac{32\pi}{3}(2\sqrt{2} - 1)$.

7. $\frac{\pi}{6}[(1 + a^2)^{\frac{3}{2}} - 1]$.
8. $2\pi a^2$.

9. $\frac{2}{5}a^2$.
10. $\pi\sqrt{2}$.

Pages 487–488. Art. 178

1. $\left(\dfrac{30\pi - 88}{5(3\pi - 8)},\ \dfrac{2}{3\pi - 8}\right).$

3. $\left(\dfrac{75\sin^{-1}\dfrac{2}{\sqrt{5}} - 46}{8(5\sqrt{5} - 7)},\ \dfrac{32}{5(5\sqrt{5}-7)}\right).$

2. $(\frac{16}{15},\ \frac{64}{21}).$

4. $(\frac{19}{14},\ \frac{229}{70}).$

5. $\left(\dfrac{4\sqrt{2}a(\sqrt{2} - 1)}{3(\pi - 2)},\ \dfrac{2a\big[3\ln(\sqrt{2} + 1) + 2 - 3\sqrt{2}\big]}{3(\pi - 2)}\right).$

6. $\left(-\dfrac{5a}{6},\ 0\right).$

11. $\dfrac{50\sqrt{5} - 82}{15}.$

16. $\dfrac{3\pi a^4}{128}.$

18. $\frac{2}{3}a^4.$

7. $\left(\dfrac{243a}{160\pi},\ \dfrac{81a\sqrt{3}}{160\pi}\right).$

12. $\frac{173}{60}.$

19. $\frac{1}{8}(e^2 + 1).$

20. $\frac{5}{2}.$

13. $\dfrac{a^4}{6}.$

21. 96.

8. $\left(0,\ \dfrac{a(8\pi + 3\sqrt{3})}{2(2\pi + 3\sqrt{3})}\right).$

14. $\dfrac{35\pi a^4}{16}.$

22. $\dfrac{165 - 64\ln 4}{8}.$

9. $\dfrac{15\pi - 32}{15}.$

23. 0.

15. $\dfrac{\pi a^4}{32}.$

24. $\dfrac{a^4}{48}.$

10. $\frac{848}{15}.$

Page 491. Art. 179

1. $\frac{81}{4}.$ 2. $\frac{3}{2}.$ 3. $\dfrac{\pi a^4}{8}.$ 4. $\ln\dfrac{81\sqrt{3}}{2} - \dfrac{9}{4}.$ 5. $3e^4 - 4\ln 4 - \frac{15}{2}.$

6. $\frac{1}{640}(20e^{-2} - 10e^{-4} - 5e^{-8} + 4e^{-10} - 20e^{-18} + 10e^{-36} + 5e^{-72} - 4e^{-90}).$

7. $\frac{1}{4}.$ 8. $6(\pi - 1).$ 9. $\frac{1}{12}(6\pi + 1).$ 10. $\dfrac{a^2}{4}.$ 11. $\dfrac{7a^4}{96}.$ 12. $\dfrac{2a^4}{21}.$

Pages 494–495. Art. 180

1. $\frac{1}{3}.$

6. $\frac{8}{3}.$

10. $\dfrac{2\pi}{3}(23\sqrt{23} - 101).$

2. $\ln 2.$

7. 8.

3. $4\ln 2.$

8. $\frac{4}{3}\pi abc.$

11. $\frac{4}{3}\pi a^3.$

4. $\frac{256}{15}.$

9. $\dfrac{100\pi}{3}.$

12. $\dfrac{100\pi}{3}.$

5. $4(\ln 3 - 1).$

Pages 496–497. Art. 181

1. $(\frac{9}{2},\ 1,\ \frac{3}{4}).$

2. $(\frac{12}{5},\ \frac{4}{5},\ \frac{3}{5}).$

3. (a) $\frac{54}{5}k$; (b) $\frac{96}{5}k$; (c) $30k.$

4. $I_{xy} = \frac{16}{3},\ I_{yz} = 8,\ I_{xz} = 8.$

5. $(\frac{3}{2},\ \frac{3}{2},\ \frac{3}{2}).$

6. $(0,\ 0,\ \frac{1}{2}).$

7. $(0,\ 0,\ \frac{5}{12}).$

8. $\dfrac{2304\pi k}{35}.$

9. $1792\pi.$

10. $\frac{3}{2}.$

11. $(0,\ 0,\ \frac{5}{16}a).$

12. $\dfrac{16\pi a^7 k}{105}.$

INDEX

The numbers refer to pages.

A

Absolute constant, 1
Absolute value, 3
Absolutely convergent series, 359
Acceleration, 22, 158
  angular, 167
  average, 22
  components of, 159
    in circular motion, 164
  in harmonic motion, 170
  instantaneous, 22
  radial and transverse components of, 186
  sign of, 31
Accuracy in computations, 387
Addition of infinite series, 367
Adiabatic expansion, 152, 283
Algebraic curves, 203
Algebraic equations, 203
Algebraic functions, 94, 203
  differentiation of, 94
Algebraic substitution, integration by, 246, 265
Alternating series, 358
Amplitude, of simple harmonic motion, 169
  of trigonometric functions, 125
Angle, between curves, 27, 105, 110, 190
  between line and curve, 19, 27, 105
  between radius vector and tangent, 187
  polar, 180
  radian measure of, 111
Angular acceleration, 167
Angular velocity, 167
Approximation, 321
  by differentials, 42, 434
  of arc length, 330

Approximation, of area under a curve, 63, 322, 327, 328, 396
  of definite integrals, 323, 327, 329, 394, 396
  of roots by Newton's Method, 191
  of volume, 327, 329, 331, 396
Arbitrary constant, 1
Arbitrary function, 465
Arc, centroid of, 305
  differential of, 154, 160, 283
    in polar coördinates, 183, 285
  length of, 283, 285, 330
Arc and chord, limit of ratio between, 154
Archimedes, spiral of, 182, 286
Area, as a double integral, 469, 472
  by integration, 56, 66, 271, 274, 469, 472
  by summation, 61
  derivative of, 56
  element of, 61, 275, 319, 469, 473
  in polar coördinates, 274, 472
  increment of, 61
  of a curved surface, 482
  of a surface of revolution, 286
Asymptotes, methods of determining, 200, 203
  oblique, 199
  of a hyperbola, 201
  vertical or horizontal, 126, 131, 142, 198, 413
Atmospheric pressure, 153
Attraction, 186, 195, 282
Average acceleration, 22
Average curvature, 174
Average density, 293
Average rate of change, 13
Average speed, 20
Axis of symmetry, 70, 79, 196, 296